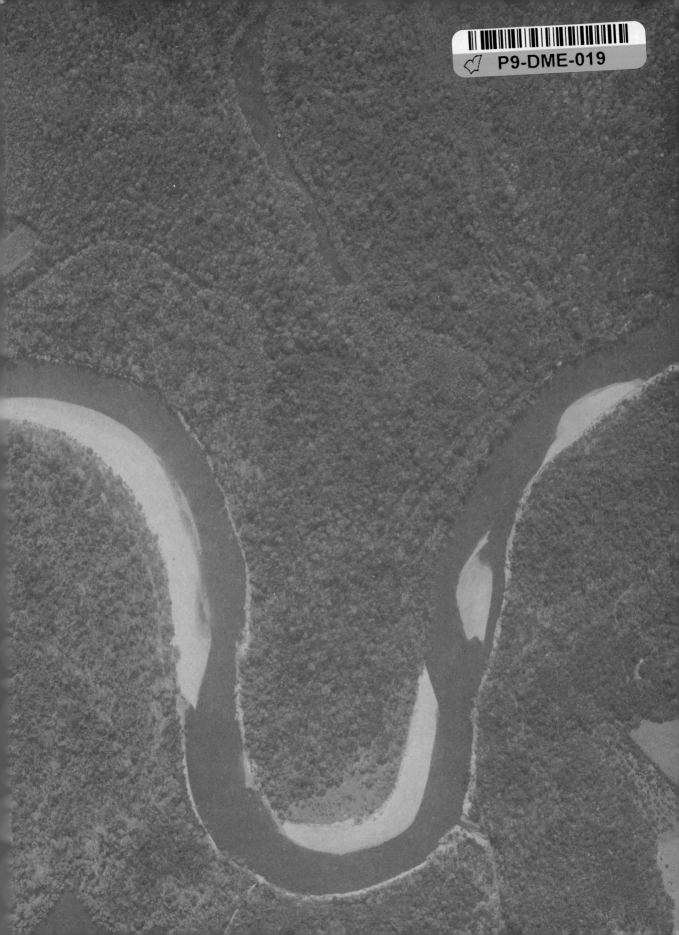

Principles of Geology

A Series of Books in Geology
Editors: JAMES GILLULY, A. O. WOODFORD

Third Edition **Principles of Geology**

JAMES GILLULY
Formerly of the U.S. Geological Survey

AARON C. WATERS
University of California, Santa Cruz

A. O. WOODFORD
Pomona College

W. H. FREEMAN AND COMPANY
San Francisco

Endsheet photograph by Edward J. Blood.

Preface

This is the third edition of a textbook first published in 1951 and revised in 1959. Further revision is necessary because of great forward steps in geology since 1958 when our second edition went to press. Advances have been particularly great in such widely different fields as quantitative studies of erosional processes and rates (especially in stream dynamics), sedimentology, geochronology, seismology, paleomagnetism, geochemistry, oceanography, and space geology. While attempting to incorporate some of the more salient aspects of these advances, we have also taken the opportunity to correct the errors—a few large and many small—that seem to creep into our work. We have had the kind advice and help of many colleagues and friends in reducing the number of errors, but any that remain are our responsibility.

We wish to express our appreciation for criticism of various sections of this revision to the following friends and colleagues: Paul Averitt, Allan Cox, Paul Damon, Jerry Eaton, Henry Faul, Clifford Hopson, Arthur Lachenbruch, Stanley Lohman, Don Mabey, John Obradovich, L. C. Pakiser, G. D. Robinson, Meyer Rubin, John Sass, Stanley Schumm, Tom Stern, and Frank Swenson. For illustrations and help in their selection we are grateful to Clarence R. Allen, Elso S. Barghoorn, William A. Cobban, Arturo Corte, Hollis Dole, Erling Dorf, Arthur Grantz, Warren Hamilton, N. King Huber, Kenneth E. Lohman, Robert F. Legget, James G. Moore, Tad Nichols, Garald G. Parker, George Plafker, Austin E. Post, A. S. Romer, R. J. Ross, Jr., Parke D. Snavely, Jr., Patsy Smith, Robert Tschudy, the Oregon State Highway Commission, the Oregon State Department of Mines and Geology, the National Aeronautics and Space Administration, and the United States Geological Survey.

To the first edition Professor Woodford contributed much original material until forced by illness to withdraw. He has limited his participation in later editions to valuable counsel. We wish to emphasize our sincere appreciation for his continued help as critic and advisor, and to absolve him from any continuing responsibilities for shortcomings of this text.

James Gilluly
Aaron C. Waters

January 1968

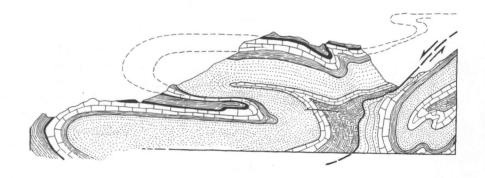

Contents

The Science, Geology

Geology is the science of the earth—man's systematic attempt to understand the planet on which he dwells: its origin and development through the past; its size, shape, and composition; the processes that are now or have formerly been at work upon its surface and in its interior; and the origin and evolution of the life upon it. Geology thus involves systematic observations and measurements of the soils, rocks, and fossils *; of the streams and oceans; of glaciers, earthquakes, hill slopes, mountains, plains, shores, and volcanoes.

The beginnings of geology are lost in antiquity. The Greeks, Egyptians, and Arabs made some progress, but few of their ideas influenced modern developments. The science as we know it has nearly all developed since the Renaissance—the word geology is less than 200 years old.

Despite its youth, geology has profoundly influenced men's thinking. Geology brought new concepts of time, just as astronomy revolutionized ideas of space and of the position and motions of the earth among the stars. The demonstration that sea shells and many other fossils entombed in the rocks are the remains of animals and plants that lived millions of years ago gradually overturned the ideas of the western world about the span of time involved in the history of the earth and of man's existence on it. Comparisons of the biological relations between living and fossil organisms, together with the geologic demonstration of a definite sequence of changing fossil assemblages in time, led to the doctrine of evolution—a concept that seriously challenged man's ideas of his place in nature, and thereby profoundly affected modern philosophical and scientific concepts that might seem remote from the study of geology.

Geology also has had a most pronounced impact on the economics of nations. Our

---

* Fossils are the remains or imprints of animals and plants of the geologic past, naturally preserved by burial in sediments.

interest in the minerals and rocks of the earth's crust is more than intellectual curiosity; it has its practical side as well. Modern civilization is a mineral civilization, wholly dependent on materials mined from the earth. Minerals are the source of the iron, copper, aluminum, and other metals upon which our economy is based. Our chief sources of power are the mineral fuels—natural gas, petroleum, and coal. They drive our ships, aircraft, railroads, and automobiles, and all of these are made chiefly of metals. Most industrial gas flows from wells and is pumped great distances through metal pipes. Our electric power has its source in the energy of flowing streams or of burning coal; it is generated by metal dynamos and distributed by metal wires. We have recently learned how to release stupendous amounts of nuclear energy. Its ultimate source is, again, minerals mined from the earth. The bricks in our houses, the salt that seasons our food, the asphalt and concrete that pave our highways, the ornaments and precious stones with which man has adorned himself through the ages, the gold reserves that conventionally stabilize most of the world's monetary systems—all these have been won from mineral deposits in the crust of the earth. Men have sought to refine, improve, and discover new uses for minerals as improved mining techniques made them easily available. Thus from primitive arts and crafts based on metal and stone have evolved the vast industries of the present.

On the international scene, the power and wealth of a nation is largely determined by its endowment of useful minerals, its skill in finding and utilizing them, or in obtaining needed supplies from other lands. In this age of political unrest and readjustment among nations, the vast accumulation of petroleum in such little-industrialized nations as Iran, Saudi Arabia, Iraq, and Kuwait is a potent force in world politics. We shall be wiser in world affairs if we know where and why petroleum occurs, how it is discovered, and how its quantity underground may be estimated. Without the economic urge for finding mineral wealth, many of the great advances in geology would have been long delayed, for geology is the science of the mine and quarry, of the oil field and the placer.

Geology is an eclectic science. It has its own techniques of geologic mapping (Chapter 6) and for reconstruction of past events, but it also borrows from chemistry, biology, physics, and engineering many methods, data, and theories that apply to earth problems. Geology, in turn, has contributed to the other sciences; progress in one advances all the others. Because of the complexity of its problems, geology has not advanced as far as physics and chemistry. Although some of its problems have been quantified in recent years, many are not susceptible of laboratory measurement in the way in which physical and chemical problems can be studied. Like the life sciences, geology has now and always will have problems that can never be meaningfully stated mathematically—they will always remain in the domain of "natural history." This is, indeed, one of the most challenging features of the science. Like a detective, a geologist generally needs to reconstruct the environments and causes of events of the past, most of them difficult or impossible to reproduce in the laboratory. Where is the calorimeter that will measure the thermal energy of a volcano? How can the geologist accurately predict where oil lies beneath the ground, or the nature of the moon's surface prior to the landing of the first astronaut?

chapter 2

Minerals and Matter

Of what is the earth's crust made? Certainly it is not homogeneous, for in the course of a walk in the country we seldom fail to find a wide variety of rocks and soils that differ in color, coherence, density, and other characteristics. Moreover, almost any fragment of rock or handful of soil we pick up is a mixture of different substances (Fig. 2–1). The individual grains that make up the rocks and soils, however, are not mixtures. Each is a distinct mineral—a homogeneous substance with definite physical characteristics. One mineral, present as hard, transparent particles, may resemble bits of broken glass; another may be in dull, earthy grains; and still another may consist of tiny, elastic flakes that flash brilliantly in the sun. *Rocks and soils are aggregates of minerals.* Hence, if we are to understand either soils or rocks, we must learn something about the various minerals that compose them.

DEFINITION OF MINERAL

First, let us define the real nature of minerals precisely: *A* **mineral** *is a naturally occurring substance with a characteristic internal structure determined by a regular arrangement of the atoms or ions within it; and with a chemical composition and physical properties that are either fixed or that vary within a definite range.*

Minerals, then, are *natural substances,* found ready-made out of doors. Synthetic laboratory products are not true minerals. A druggist who claims that a certain pharmaceutical preparation is "rich in vitamins and minerals" uses the word mineral differently than does a geologist.

To say that minerals have *definite chemical and physical properties,* or properties that vary within certain definite limits, is to point out that all particles of any single mineral are alike physically and chemically. They are alike whether one particle comes from Brazil and another from Canada, or whether

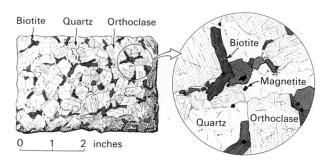

FIGURE 2–1
The mineral constituents of the common rock granite. Note that the mineral magnetite is visible only when the rock is greatly magnified (right).

one crystallized in the shell of a snail and another from the water of a hillside spring.

The most definitive characteristic of a mineral is its internal structure, the core of our definition. To show what we mean by internal structure, and hence the true nature of minerals, we must review what was first learned about the external form of crystals, and then digress into a brief summary of some things chemists and physicists have since learned about the fundamental structure of all matter.

FORM AND STRUCTURE OF CRYSTALS

Geometric form

Everyone is familiar with crystals of certain minerals, for example, those of garnet, quartz (also called rock crystal), and ice. Perfect crystals have strikingly regular geometric forms bounded by glistening planes called **crystal faces** (Fig. 2–2), but such well-formed crystals are rare. Most snowflakes fall as beautiful, six-sided, perfect crystals (Fig. 13–3), but frost on a windowpane shows less well-formed crystals, and the granules of ice on the surface of a freezing pond show few, if any, crystal faces. Few rock-forming minerals show perfect crystal faces, and many show none at all. Nevertheless, study of the common imperfect crystals, together with the relatively rare perfect ones, enabled **mineralogists** (as geologists who

specialize in minerals are called) to make sound deductions about the internal structure of minerals long before physicists and chemists proved that all matter is made up of atoms.

FIGURE 2–2
Common minerals showing good crystal form. A: epidote; B: orthoclase; C: garnet; D: pyrite. (Photos by Alexander Tihonravov.)

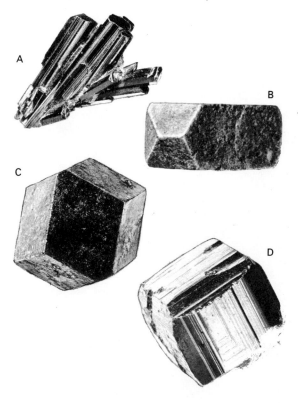

Constancy of interfacial angles

The first important step in the analysis of mineral form was made by Nicolaus Steno (1631–1687), a Danish physician who lived in Florence, Italy. Steno, an outstanding figure in the history of geology, also made fundamental observations of the origin and structural relations of rocks.

Steno showed, with the crude instruments at his disposal, that if a specimen of quartz shows crystal faces, these always meet at characteristic angles, regardless of the size and gross shape of the crystal (Fig. 2–3). An Italian student, Guglielmini, showed in 1688 and 1705 that similar relations held for other minerals, though the angles characterizing one mineral species differ from those of another. In halite (Fig. 2–7) for example, all angles between principal adjacent surfaces are right angles; this means the crystal may be a cube or some other rectangular boxlike figure. In quartz, as Steno had found, the

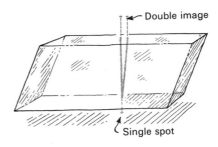

FIGURE 2–4
A fragment of clear calcite showing double refraction.

angles between the long crystal faces that form the sides of the crystal are always 120°.

Steno's and Guglielmini's methods were refined and extended by later workers. Thousands of consistent measurements made on many kinds of crystals convinced mineralogists that the internal structure of each mineral species is unique. They reasoned that the constancy of the interfacial angles in different specimens of the same mineral, regardless of the size and shape of the crystals, must mean that each crystal is built up of minute particles packed together in a definite geometric pattern. The pattern of packing determines the angles between faces and is identical in all specimens of a particular mineral. The size of the specimen depends merely on the number of such particles it contains.

FIGURE 2–3
Outlines of crystals to show various forms with constant angles.

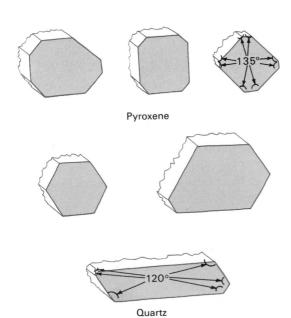

Pyroxene

Quartz

Optical properties

Other studies from a different viewpoint fortified this conclusion. The first studies concerned the way that crystals affect light transmitted through them. The Dutch physicist Christian Huygens (1629–1695) discovered the phenomenon of "double refraction" (Fig. 2–4) while studying the mineral calcite. One can easily observe this phenomenon by placing a fragment of transparent calcite on top of a dot on a sheet of paper. Instead of one dot, two are seen. If the calcite is revolved slowly, one dot traces a circle about the other. More than 100 years later physicists showed that this effect could be explained in terms of a theory of light: the light ray that penetrates the calcite is broken into two rays by the internal structure of the crystal. Our eyes register the points of emergence of the two rays; we see two dots instead of one. Furthermore, in contrast to ordinary light, which vibrates in all directions at right angles to the line of propagation, each of the two rays that pass through the crystal vibrates in only one plane. Light so modified that it vibrates in only one plane is said to be polarized.

This discovery opened the way for an important new technique in studying and identifying minerals. William Nicol, a worker in natural philosophy (today we call it physics) at Edinburgh, showed in 1829 that transparent fragments of calcite could be cut and glued together in such a way as to eliminate one of the two polarized rays by diverting it to the side. Others adapted these Nicol prisms to microscopes, making it possible to study the effects that thin slices of minerals produce on polarized light as it passes through them. Discussion of these effects demands detailed knowledge of the physics of light and is beyond the scope of this book, but it should be emphasized that the optical properties of minerals, determined by means of the petrographic microscope (a microscope equipped with two Nicol prisms), are precise and diagnostic. By them most minerals can be quickly identified. The petrographic microscope is the geologist's most efficient instrument for mineral and rock study.

The petrographic microscope also gave fundamental clues to the nature of matter and light. Polarized light passing through minerals behaves in ways definitely related to the interfacial angles of the individual minerals. This suggests that the light is influenced by very minute, systematically arranged rows and planes of invisible particles within the crystal, and strengthens the inference from the constancy of interfacial angles that minerals are made up of submicroscopic particles packed together in definite geometric patterns.

THE ATOMIC THEORY

In 1805, the English chemist John Dalton advanced the hypothesis that all matter is composed of tiny individual particles, which he called atoms. Dalton conceived this idea to explain constant ratios between the weights of different substances when they react chemically with one another. This was an entirely different basis from the studies of interfacial angles and optical properties which had led mineralogists to the same conclusion. Further work in chemistry, physics, and mineralogy verified the atomic hypothesis completely. Some of the best evidence came from X-ray studies of minerals, but before we discuss these, we must first review a few of the things chemists and physicists have learned about atoms.

Atoms are extremely minute. If a crystal the size of a walnut were enlarged to the size of the earth, the atoms composing it would average about the size of baseballs. One hundred million atoms placed side by side make a row only an inch long. Yet by ingenious experimental and theoretical work chemists and physicists have been able to show that the atom, small as it is, is composed of particles still smaller. Three of the many subatomic particles now recognized are important in explaining the chemical behavior of minerals: the proton, the neutron and the electron.

Subatomic particles

Electrons, protons, and neutrons differ in electrical properties and in other important respects. The electron carries a definite charge of negative electricity—a charge whose amount has been chosen as the international unit of electrical measurement. The proton has a positive charge of exactly the same amount. The neutron, as the name implies, is electrically neutral. Despite these differences, all three are nearly the same size, about one millionth of an inch in diameter. They differ in weight, however, with the proton and neutron each weighing nearly 1845 times as much as the electron. The neutron weighs slightly less than the combined weight of an electron and proton. These properties are unchanging—for example, all protons weigh exactly the same amount no matter whether one forms part of an atom of oxygen, another of iron, or a third of sulfur. In any atom, the subatomic particles composing it are always present in amounts that add up to electrical neutrality—that is, the number of protons always equals the number of electrons.

Structure of the atom

Every atom has a small, dense nucleus that contains one or more protons, and, except in hydrogen, the simplest atom, one or more neutrons. The nucleus holds over 99.9 percent of the mass of an atom but occupies only about one-billionth of its volume: the outer parts of atoms are mostly empty space. An **element** is a substance that consists of atoms of only one kind—another way of saying that each atom of a particular element has exactly the same electrical charge on its nucleus, and hence exactly the same number of protons. Atoms behave chemically as though their electrons circle about the nucleus in concentric shells. Hydrogen consists of one proton around which an electron revolves in orbit. Helium, the next simplest element, has a nucleus composed of two protons and two neutrons. Two electrons trace separate orbits at variable distances from this nucleus (Fig. 2–5). More complex

atoms with larger nuclei retain an inner orbital shell like the helium shell, and the additional electrons lie in one or more shells farther out. The chemical characteristics of an element seem to depend entirely on the number of positive electrical charges—and thus on the number of protons—in its nucleus. This number is the **atomic number** of the element. About ninety different elements have been found in nature, and scientists have made several others.

Each element has been assigned a definite symbol, such as H for hydrogen and Pb (from *plumbum*, Latin) for lead. This is merely a convenient shorthand that scientists use in writing chemical formulas and equations. The elements, together with their symbols, atomic numbers, and atomic weights are listed in Appendix IV.

For some reason, *those elements whose outermost electron shell contains eight electrons are chemically the most stable.* Such elements—for example, argon, neon, and xenon—are never found in nature combined with each other or with any other elements

FIGURE 2–5
Schematic drawing of hydrogen and helium atoms.

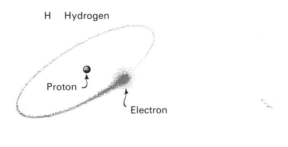

H   Hydrogen

Proton

Electron

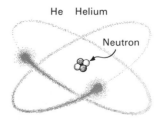

He   Helium

Neutron

and hence are called the **inert gases.** Helium, with only two electrons, is also an inert gas. (Chemists have recently been able, under rigorous laboratory conditions, to make some of the inert gases combine with other elements, but no natural compounds of any of them appear in rocks formed in earth.)

An atom having fewer than eight electrons in its outer shell readily combines with others. The most chemically active atoms are those with outermost shells containing either one or seven electrons. For example, sodium (Na) has only one electron in its outer shell; chlorine (Cl) has seven. Both are very active chemically. Sodium has only to lose, and chlorine to gain, a single electron for each to attain the stable number of eight. Thus combined, they form the **chemical compound,** sodium chloride (NaCl), common table salt. An electron is transferred from the sodium atom to the chlorine atom. The properties of this compound differ greatly from those of its component elements. After losing an electron the sodium atom is no longer neutral; it has one more proton in the nucleus than it has electrons in its orbital shells, giving it one unbalanced positive charge. Similarly the chlorine atom, by gaining an electron, acquires one unbalanced negative charge. A charged atom, in which the number of protons is either more or less than the number of electrons, is called an **ion.** Because unlike charges of electricity attract and like charges repel, the positively charged sodium ion is drawn to the negatively charged chlorine ion, and the two join to form a molecule of sodium chloride. **Molecules** are distinct groups of two or more atoms tightly bound together.

X-RAY STUDY OF CRYSTALS

Conclusive proof both of Dalton's atomic theory, and that crystals are composed of atoms arranged in a geometric latticework, came in 1912, when Max von Laue, of Munich, a specialist in the physics of light, proposed that X-rays are like light but of shorter wavelength. Laue reasoned that if crystals are composed of atoms geometrically packed in parallel planes, the surface of a crystal might diffract the short X-ray waves much as a closely ruled mirror surface diffracts light. When a series of closely spaced parallel lines is scratched on the surface of a mirror, light reflected from the mirror is broken into the colors of the spectrum.

In order to test this idea, two of von Laue's students, W. Friedrich and P. Knipping, using a crystal of copper sulfate in an apparatus much like that of Figure 2–6, developed the first "Laue X-radiogram," which conclusively confirmed Laue's reasoning on the wave properties of X-rays. Further experiments showed a definite internal structural pattern for each mineral tested, thus confirming the inference already made by mineralogists that the constancy of interfacial angles of crystals demands a regular packing of the submicroscopic particles in a pattern which is distinctive of each mineral. Thus X-ray studies enable the geometric arrangement of the atoms (or ions) within a crystal, the **internal structure,** to be worked out. This developed into a most useful diagnostic

FIGURE 2–6

Sketch of apparatus used in obtaining a refraction pattern. The crystal is calcite.

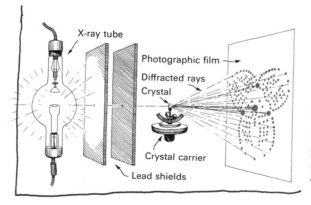

X-ray tube

Photographic film

Diffracted rays

Crystal

Crystal carrier

Lead shields

FIGURE 2–7

The cubic form, right, *and internal structure of halite. The lattice diagram,* left, *shows the relative positions of the Na and Cl nuclei, and the packing arrangement of the ions is depicted in the center.* (*Smithsonian Institution photo.*)

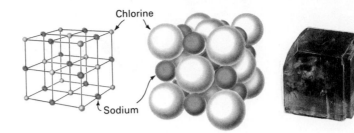

Chlorine

Sodium

technique for recognizing different minerals, for it can be applied to grains so small that they can hardly be seen microscopically.

Internal structure of crystals

X-ray studies show, for example, that crystals of halite (NaCl) have the structure illustrated in Figure 2–7. We have already seen that by the transfer of the one lone electron in the outer shell of a sodium atom to the almost-filled outer shell of a chlorine atom, each atom achieves the stable arrangement of eight electrons in its outer shell. In acquiring this arrangement, each atom loses its electrical neutrality and acquires a charge—it becomes an ion. In a liquid or gas, the sodium and chlorine ions might be drawn together to form a molecule, but in a crystal, the close packing of the particles necessitates a fixed geometric arrangement of the ions. Moreover, in this geometrical packing the electrical forces set up by the attraction of ions of unlike sign and the repulsion of those with the same sign must be satisfied. Figure 2–7 shows how this is accomplished in halite. Each positively charged sodium ion is equidistant from, and at the center of, six symmetrically placed chlorine ions. Each negatively charged chlorine ion is similarly surrounded by six symmetrically placed sodium ions. Most minerals are held together by similar **ionic bonds,** although most of their internal structures are far more complex and less easily visualized than that of halite.

Some minerals, diamond, for example, are held together by the sharing of their electrons. Diamond is composed entirely of carbon; it is one of the two common crystalline forms of this element. Carbon atoms have four electrons in the outer shell. In crystals of diamond (Fig. 2–8), each carbon atom is linked with four others. This linking allows each of the four outer electrons in a carbon atom to be "shared" with an adjacent carbon atom. Thus the carbon atoms in diamond achieve stability; each may be considered to have a complete outer shell of eight electrons, though each electron is actually shared with a neighboring carbon atom. Every electron may be thought of as oscillating within the orbits of the two neighboring carbon nuclei. Such bonds are called **covalent bonds;** there are no ions. Covalent bonding of the atoms in diamond is very strong; hence diamond is the hardest natural substance known.

Diamond and graphite illustrate strikingly that the fundamental difference between minerals lies not in their chemical composition, but in their internal structure. Both are pure carbon of identical chemical composition, but their crystal structures differ fundamentally (Fig. 2–8). The contrast in internal structures accounts for their dramatically contrasting physical properties. Diamond is the hardest natural substance; graphite is soft and greasy. Most diamonds are transparent; graphite is opaque. Diamond is used as an abrasive and cutting tool;

→ Electrical charge holds them together

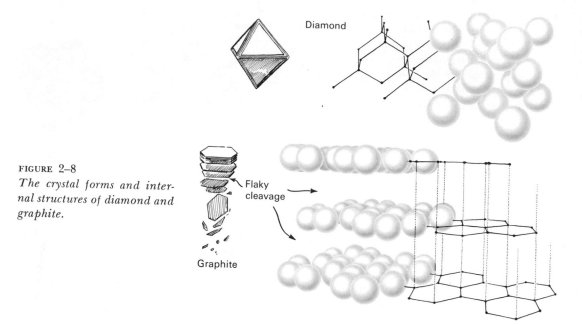

FIGURE 2–8

The crystal forms and internal structures of diamond and graphite.

graphite is used as a lubricant because it cleaves into fine flakes that glide smoothly one over another.

Even this brief discussion of internal structure of minerals shows that the chemist's concept of molecules, though applicable to gases and liquids, fails to apply to most minerals. Both in crystals bound together by electron exchange, such as halite, and in crystals with shared electrons, such as diamond, there is no particular part of the crystal that can be considered a molecule. Instead the ions and atoms behave as if they were solid spheres of different size packed together to form a geometric pattern, just as we might pack a mixture of grapefruit, oranges, and tangerines together to form a fruit display.

Ionic radii

Each ion in a crystal tends to surround itself with ions of opposite electrical charge, as in halite. The number of such oppositely charged ions that can be packed around it is determined partly by the charges on the

various ions but a more important limitation is placed by the *sizes* of the ions involved.

In the most general way, the size of an atom depends upon the number of electron shells surrounding its nucleus, and upon the charge on the nucleus. When an atom loses or gains electrons, transforming it into an ion, the electrical balance is upset and there is a corresponding change in radius. If the atom loses an electron and becomes a positive ion, for example, the excess positive charge on the nucleus pulls the orbital shells of electrons a little closer; if an electron is gained, the electron shells are less closely held, and the radius expands. Changes in size may also occur during ionization through a change in the number of electron shells. For example, the sodium atom has three electron shells, but there is only one electron in the outermost shell. If this outermost electron is lost, the resulting sodium ion has two electron shells, the outermost of which has the stable configuration of eight electrons. The sodium ion thus formed, how-

Table 2–1 **Most abundant elements in the earth's crust**

Atomic number	Element	Atomic and ionic radii (size in Ångstroms)				Abundance in earth's crust	
		Atom		Ion		Weight percent	Volume percent
8	Oxygen	O	0.60	O^{--}	1.32	46.60	91.97
14	Silicon	Si	1.17	Si^{++++}	0.44	27.72	0.80
13	Aluminum	Al	1.43	Al^{+++}	0.51	8.13	0.77
26	Iron	Fe	1.24	Fe^{++}	0.74	5.00	0.68
				Fe^{+++}	0.64		
20	Calcium	Ca	1.96	Ca^{++}	0.99	3.63	1.48
11	Sodium	Na	1.86	Na^{+}	0.97	2.83	1.60
19	Potassium	K	2.31	K^{+}	1.33	2.59	2.14
12	Magnesium	Mg	1.60	Mg^{++}	0.66	2.09	0.56
22	Titanium	Ti	1.46	Ti^{+++}	0.76	0.44	0.03
				Ti^{++++}	0.68		

SOURCE: Data on abundance from Brian Mason, *Principles of Geochemistry*, John Wiley and Sons, New York, 1952, p. 42.
Data on atomic and ionic radii from Jack Green, *Geochemical Table of the Elements for 1953*, Geological Society of America, Bull., v. 64, 1953, p. 1001–1012.

ever, is somewhat smaller than the atom of neon, which has exactly the same number of electrons distributed in the same shells. The excess positive charge on the nucleus of the sodium ion shrinks the electron cloud to slightly smaller dimensions than that of the electrically neutral neon atom.

Table 2–1 gives the atomic and ionic radii in Ångstrom units of the nine most abundant elements in the earth's crust. An Ångstrom is one-hundred-millionth of a centimeter (0.000,000,01 centimeter, or 10^{-8} centimeter, about 4 billionths of an inch). Sizes of atoms and ions are measured by determining the distances between successive rows of atoms or ions in crystals by X-ray and similar methods. Note the consistent relationship: negatively charged ions are larger, and positively charged ions smaller, than the corresponding atoms. The abundance of the elements given in the table has been arrived at indirectly as follows: Thousands of chemical analyses have been made of the different kinds of rock that compose the earth's crust. From geologic maps (Chapter 6), we can determine the areas occupied by, and hence the relative abundance of, the different rocks. From these data, the percentages of the different elements that compose the crust of the earth have been calculated. Table 2–1 makes it clear that investigation of the chemical relations between oxygen and silicon is of the greatest importance in our study of minerals. These two elements constitute nearly 75 percent by weight of the crust, because the most abundant minerals are **silicates,** minerals composed of oxygen, silicon, and one or more of the abundant metals, aluminum, iron, calcium, sodium, potassium, and magnesium.

The volume relations are even more striking; so large is the oxygen ion (O^{--}, 1.32 Ångstroms) that, although oxygen forms only 47 percent by weight of the rocks of the crust, it accounts for 92 percent of their volume. Thus by far the largest part of the earth's solid crust is composed of the same element that we are accustomed to think of only as a gas in the atmosphere!

Although over 2000 different minerals are

known, most are rare. Twenty common ones compose almost all of the visible rocks, and of these nearly all are silicates.

THE SILICON TETRAHEDRON

The silicon ion (Si^{4+}) has a radius of 0.44 Ångstroms; that of the oxygen ion (O^{2-}) is 1.32 Ångstroms. In silicates four oxygen ions and one silicon ion fit together into a compact pyramidal figure called the **silicon tetrahedron** (Fig. 2–9). The nucleus of the silicon ion lies at the center of the tetrahedron, and the nucleus of each of the four oxygen ions is located at a corner. (See A of Fig. 2–9). The silicon tetrahedron is an ion (not a crystal or a molecule) because the packing of *four* oxygen ions, each with *two* negative charges, and of *one* silicon ion with *four* positive charges leaves the resultant tetrahedral figure with four unsatisfied negative charges. To form an electrically neutral unit within a crystal this tetrahedral ion must be bonded with one or more additional positive ions, for example, with two ions of magnesium (Mg^{2+}) or of iron (Fe^{2+}) as in the mineral olivine (Fig. 2–11).

Because nearly all the common minerals are silicates, and because silicates are formed by combinations of this fundamental tetrahedral ion (SiO_4)$^{4-}$ with one or more additional elements, *the silicon tetrahedron is the most important "building block" in the architecture of the earth's crust.* In different minerals silicon tetrahedra are linked with one another and with various positive ions in characteristic geometric patterns. One classification of silicate minerals is based on the kind of linkage. In the common mineral pyroxene, the tetrahedra are strung together in long chains (Fig. 2–10,A); in micas they form double sheets (Fig. 2–10,B); and in the olivine and monticellite crystals sketched in Figure 2–11 they form a framework tied together by magnesium, iron, and calcium atoms.

VARIATION IN CHEMICAL COMPOSITION OF MINERALS

Some minerals, including diamond (C), sulfur (S), copper (Cu), and gold (Au), are elements. Others, such as ice (H_2O), quartz (SiO_2), calcite ($CaCO_3$), and kaolinite ($H_4Al_2Si_2O_9$), are compounds whose composition can be expressed by simple chemical formulas. Still others, as is indicated in the definition of mineral, vary within certain limits in the percentage of the various elements they contain: their compositions cannot be expressed by simple formulas. This is because one element may substitute for another although the crystal structure remains virtually unchanged. Such replacement is called **solid solution.** One of the simplest examples of solid solution is the olivine group of minerals. The formula of this group is written $(Mg,Fe)_2SiO_4$, meaning that different specimens of olivine may have chemical compositions intermediate between the two "**end members**"; that is, they range from pure Mg_2SiO_4 (called forsterite) to pure Fe_2SiO_4 (called fayalite). It is only the proportions of the magnesium (Mg) and the iron (Fe) that vary; those of silicon and oxygen remain constant. The intermediate members of the olivine series are regarded as solid solutions of the two end members. It

FIGURE 2–9

Three representations of the silicon tetrahedron. A: lattice diagram; B: tetrahedron with atoms drawn to scale; C: the mathematical figures called tetrahedra.

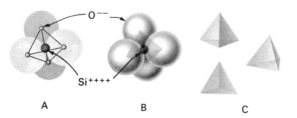

O^{--}

Si^{++++}

A   B   C

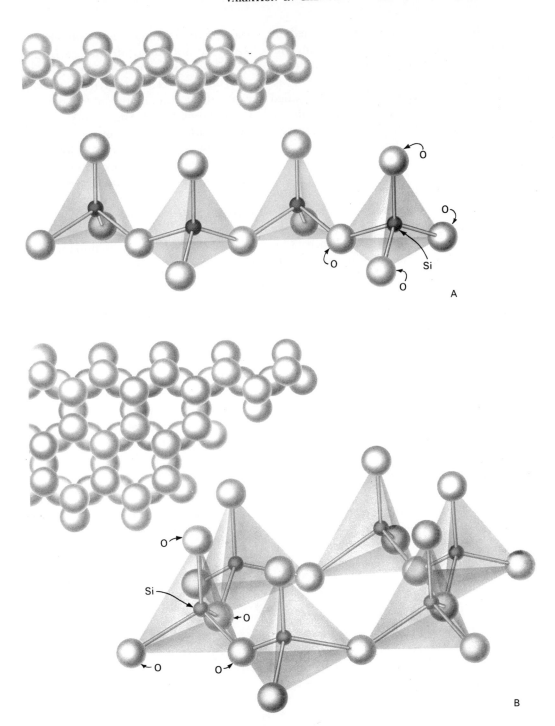

FIGURE 2–10   *Structural diagrams showing how the silicon tetrahedra are strung out in chains in one mineral, and are oriented in double plates in the other. A: pyroxene (side view) ; B: mica (top view).*

should be noted that these intermediate members are homogeneous crystals and not merely mixed aggregates of two different crystals.

Solid solution series cannot be explained by the molecular concept, applicable to gases and liquids, but require the ionic structure, as we shall now show.

Mechanism of substitution in solid solution

Chemical and X-ray studies of minerals show how the substitution of one element for another in crystals is accomplished. The major controlling factor in solid solution is not the number of electrons in the outer shells of the atoms of the two elements concerned, as might have been thought, but their ionic radii. In olivine, Fe and Mg can readily substitute for one another, for not only does each contain two electrons in its outer shell, but more important, the ionic radii are very nearly the same.

In many mineral groups, sodium (one electron in the outer shell) readily substitutes for calcium (two electrons in the outer shell) because their ionic radii are almost identical (0.97 and 0.99 Ångstroms) al-though their charges are different. But so-dium cannot substitute to nearly the same extent for potassium, despite the fact that each has one electron in its outer shell, be-cause the radius of the potassium ion is so much larger (1.33 Ångstroms) than that of the sodium ion. The importance of ionic radius in controlling substitution is particu-larly striking in this example because so-dium and potassium are so very similar in chemical properties. In plagioclase feldspar crystals, a little potassium may indeed sub-stitute for sodium—the internal structure is warped to take care of the difference in ionic diameters—but when the substitution ex-ceeds a certain amount, the warping is evi-dently too great for the structure to remain stable; it breaks up into many tiny interlock-ing crystals of two distinct minerals—potash feldspar and plagioclase feldspar. Warping of the internal structure of a mineral is il-lustrated in Figure 2–11, which shows the result of substituting calcium ions for about half of the iron and magnesium ions in the internal structure of olivine, giving the slightly different structure of monticellite, a mineral of closely related chemical composi-tion.

FIGURE 2–11   *Olivine and monticellite, showing how substitution of the larger calcium ion for an iron or a magnesium ion requires an expansion of the crystal structure. (After W. H. Bragg, 1928.)*

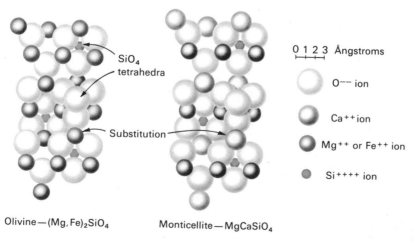

Olivine — $(Mg, Fe)_2SiO_4$ Monticellite — $MgCaSiO_4$

Clearly, an element that has only one electron in its outer shell cannot be substituted for another that has two without destroying the electrical neutrality of the structure; therefore, a second, concurrent substitution is required to maintain stability.

For example, in the plagioclase series of solid solutions, the change from pure albite ($NaAl Si_3O_8$) to pure anorthite ($CaAl_2Si_2O_8$) takes place by the simultaneous substitution of both Ca (two electrons in outer shell) and Al (three electrons) for Na (one electron) plus Si (four electrons). Chemical neutrality is thus retained, since $3 + 2 = 4 + 1$. The ionic radius of sodium is almost the same as that of calcium; the ionic radius of aluminum is close enough to that of silicon (Table 2–1) that the ionic arrangement is not so warped as to become unstable. These slight changes in structure and composition, however, produce easily measureable variations in the optical properties of plagioclase crystals of different compositions.

MINERALOIDS

Some natural substances that do not fulfill all the conditions in the definition of a mineral are nevertheless commonly grouped with them as **mineraloids.** Perhaps the commonest of these is opal—a constituent of many rocks but one that is almost completely without orderly internal structure.

IDENTIFICATION OF MINERALS

Of the more than 2000 minerals that have been recognized and described, only about twenty are abundant constituents of the earth's crust. Most of these common minerals may be readily identified at sight by anyone who will carefully study their ordinary physical properties. Appendix II describes the methods used in simple sight identification and lists the properties of twenty common minerals, and of ten others worth study because of their economic importance.

Facts, concepts, terms

Mineral, rock
The atomic theory
Atom, molecule
Proton, neutron, electron
Ions, complex ions, silicon tetrahedron
Elements, compounds, aggregates
Internal structure of minerals
Crystal form
Constancy of interfacial angles
X-ray and optical studies
Exchange and sharing of electrons
Solid solution
Role of ionic radii

BASED ON APPENDIX II
Methods of identifying minerals
Physical properties
Cleavage and fracture; crystal form
Relation to internal structure

Color and streak; luster
Hardness; scale of hardness
Specific gravity
Other properties

Questions

BASED IN PART ON APPENDIX II

1. What is the essential difference between a mineral and an animal? Between a mineral and a rock? Between a mineral and a chemical element?
2. What controls the external geometric form of crystals? Explain how we know this to be true.
3. Name three subatomic particles and outline briefly their chief characteristics.
4. State the characteristics that distinguish the following forms of matter: elements, ions, atoms.
5. What is the basic difference between a crystal and a molecule? Why does the idea of molecules fail to apply to most minerals?
6. What factors control the substitution of one element for another in a solid solution mineral series?
7. Explain how the difference in internal structure of diamond and graphite accounts for their differences in such physical properties as cleavage, hardness, and specific gravity.
8. Why is the specific gravity of quartz definite (2.65), whereas that of pyroxene is variable (3.2 to 3.6) ?
9. Why is the streak of some minerals more useful in identifying them than the color of a large piece of the same mineral.

Suggested readings

Bragg, W. L., *The Atomic Structure of Minerals.* Ithaca: Cornell University Press, 1937.

English, G. L., *Getting Acquainted with Minerals.* New York: McGraw-Hill, 1934.

Mason. Brian, *Principles of Geochemistry.* New York: Wiley, 1952.

Scientific American offprints

The *Scientific American* Offprints listed below and after the other Suggested Readings in this book are available from your bookstore or from W. H. Freeman and Company, 660 Market Street, San Francisco, California, 94104, and Warner House, Folkestone, Kent. Please order by the number preceding the author's name. The month and year in parentheses following the title of an article is the issue of the magazine in which the article was originally published.

249. Gregory H. Wannier, *The Nature of Solids* (December 1952)

260. Robert L. Fullman, *The Growth of Crystals* (March 1955)

262. Arthur M. Buswell and Worth H. Rodebush, *Water* (April 1956)

chapter 5

The Record
of the Rocks

Rocks are all about us—on mountain peaks, in the walls of cliffs, on the banks of rushing streams. Even where soil completely masks them at the surface, deep roadcuts and well borings reveal solid rocks beneath. The wide variations in appearance and physical properties of rocks depend on the relative amounts and kinds of different minerals they contain, and upon how the constituent mineral grains are held together. So far our study of minerals has focused upon their chemical composition and physical properties. Were this the only aim, **mineralogy** (the science of minerals) and **petrology,** (the study of rocks) would be little more than the chemistry and physics of earth materials. To a geologist, however, the chief interest of rocks is the record of physical conditions of long ago that they reveal. Imprinted upon nearly every rock is tell-tale evidence of the environment in which it was formed. The reading of the rock record becomes a fascinating exploration into many episodes of earth history, for later events have also left their traces. A geologist, therefore, is concerned not only with physical and chemical measurement; he becomes a detective who ferrets out clues and pieces together evidence—some perhaps seemingly unrelated—into a logical picture of events of the past.

How does a geologist reconstruct these events? For example, what is the evidence that the site of Glasgow, Scotland, did not always have a dour wet climate as it does today, but once shimmered under a brilliant desert sun? Or that the cold Alberta plains were formerly on the floor of a shallow tropical sea such as bathes northeastern Australian shores today? To lay the groundwork for answers to questions such as these, we introduce one of the great geologic generalizations—the Uniformitarian Principle—which began to unlock the dimension of time in early investigations of the earth.

As do all sciences, geology systematizes the data collected by observation and experiment into certain broad generalizations.

The inquiring student should look critically into the validity of each generalization.

The Uniformitarian Principle, proposed by James Hutton of Edinburgh in 1785, was popularized in a textbook by the great Scottish geologist Charles Lyell in 1830. It may be stated as follows:

"The present is the key to the past." Applied specifically, this means that *rocks formed long ago at the earth's surface may be understood and explained in accordance with physical processes now operating.*

The Uniformitarian Principle assumes that the physical laws now operating have always operated throughout the geologic past. It assumes, for example, that in the geologic past, just as today, water always flowed downhill, collected into streams, and carried loads of mud and silt to the sea. It assumes that rocks similar in every way to the lavas erupting from modern volcanoes are indeed the products of ancient volcanoes; and that clam shells embedded in rocks that resemble hardened sandy mud are the remains of former living clams similar to their descendants now living in sandy mud flats. Thus, basically, we take it for granted that features in ancient rocks identical to features we can watch forming today were indeed formed by the same process. In short, the origin of ancient rocks can be interpreted in the light of today's processes.

The Uniformitarian Principle, like any other scientific generalization, rests on the circumstance that no known facts contradict it; all can be interpreted in accordance with presently operating physical, chemical, and biological processes. Geologic study through generations has failed to find evidence of ancient processes totally unlike those existing today. Yet, the principle must be interpreted carefully and rather broadly. Although there is good evidence to believe that geologic processes have always operated in the same way, they did not always operate at their present rates or intensities. In Chapter 13 we give evidence that the climate was colder and glaciers far more widespread some 15,000 years ago than now; but we reason that the glaciers of that time formed, moved, eroded, and deposited precisely as glaciers do today.

It is not easy to judge the rate of a process operating in the geologic past. To early geologic observers the enormous thickness of rocks composed of consolidated sand and mud deposited by ancient streams and seas seemed to demand agencies of deposition far more powerful than those we see at work today. But a slow process can achieve in millions of years what a rapid operation could do more quickly. Now that several independent kinds of investigations show that more than 4½ billion years is available in the geologic record (see Chapter 7), the great thickness of the sediments need not be explained by mysterious catastrophic floods, but as the inevitable result of the long-continued operation of the slow erosion that we observe today.

Let us attempt some applications of the Uniformitarian Principle.

SEDIMENTARY ROCKS

Everyone has observed rills forming on a hillside during a downpour of rain, and noted the sheets of mud, sand, and gravel they spread at the base of steep slopes. Each tiny rill and every great river sweeps debris downstream, but soon drop most of it in sand and gravel bars, or in beds of silt and mud in the slack-water parts of the channel. Each flood carries it a little farther, and eventually most of it reaches the sea.

So commonplace are these processes that more than 2000 years ago the Greeks learned to recognize water-borne deposits. Some of them also recognized that beds of gravel and sand high above the reach of present-day floods must have been deposited by former streams, and they saw in the clam and oyster shells protruding from weakly coherent sandstones—far above high tide—the evidence of former higher standing seas.

It was a more difficult step—and one probably not made by the ancients—to conclude that a firm, well-consolidated sandstone containing only a few scattered fossil shells, and exposed on the peaks of a mountain range far from salt water, is actually the *cemented, shell-strewn* sand of an ancient sea floor. Yet fossil shells are common enough in rocks hundreds of miles from the nearest ocean that many centuries ago they became the subject of much philosophical and theological controversy. Medieval churchmen ruled that fossils were not organic remains but "sports of nature," perhaps put in the rocks by the devil to confuse mankind. Even so careful an observer as Georgius Agricola (1494–1555), the German scholar in whose words and woodcuts the late medieval Saxon mines and miners are still preserved for us, described only the leaves, wood, bones, and fish skeletons embedded in rocks as former organic remains. To him the fossil shells were "solidified accumulations from water" (whatever that may mean).

The restraints of tradition and authority were not thrown off until the geological pioneers of the seventeenth and eighteenth centuries repeatedly collected and compared the shells found in cemented rocks with those in unconsolidated sands along the seashore. They noticed that a few of the shells found as fossils in firm sandstone are identical with those strewn along a modern beach, but that most differ from shells of living animals. Then, between 1790 and 1815 early geologists made maps showing the distribution of strata of sandstone, limestone, and other rocks. Their mapping demonstrated that layers of soft sand may grade laterally into firm sandstone.

Today, with modern tools such as the petrographic microscope, it is easy to trace the stages whereby loose sand like that on a beach has been transformed to **sandstone**, a firm rock made of *cemented sand grains*

(Fig. 3–1). It is seen in the microscope that the individual grains of a fossiliferous sandstone (Fig. 3–1,C) are of the same shapes and are composed of essentially the same minerals as the sand grains of a modern beach (Fig. 3–1,A). Fossil shells in the sandstone, though they differ from shells of living animals, show microscopic structures so similar as to force the conclusion that they are remains of formerly living things—indeed, traces of amino acids (substances formed only by living organisms) have been found in many fossil shells now known to be several hundred million years old (See Chapter 7). The loose beach sand and the firm sandstone differ only in *cementation:* the voids or pores between the grains of the fossiliferous sandstone have been almost completely filled with calcite and other minerals. By the filling of these voids, unconsolidated sand has been made into firm sandstone (Fig. 3–1,B and C).

The sandstone just described is representative of the great group called sedimentary rocks: rocks formed at the surface of the earth, either (1) by accumulation and later cementation of fragments of rocks, minerals, and organisms, or (2) as precipitates and

FIGURE 3–1

Stages in the cementation of sand, as seen under the microscope. A: *loose sand from an Oregon beach;* B: *partly cemented sandstone from near a Brazilian coral reef:* and C: *completely cemented sandstone from Ohio.*

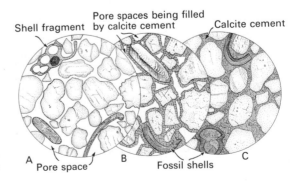

Pore spaces being filled
Shell fragment by calcite cement   Calcite cement

A Pore space   B   Fossil shells   C

organic growths from sea water and other solutions. As we shall see, there are many varieties of sedimentary rocks besides sandstone, but there are also many rocks whose characteristics are inconsistent with a sedimentary origin.

Characteristic features of sedimentary rocks

SORTING. We have mentioned only sediments transported and deposited by water. Glaciers and wind also move rock and mineral particles that may accumulate and be cemented into rock. Each of these agents of deposition leaves a characteristic stamp upon the sediments it forms.

Wind winnows the dust cleanly from sand, but does not have power enough to move coarse boulders. Hence, grains of windblown sand in a group of shifting dunes are all about the same size. Such sediment is *well sorted,* which means that it shows little variation in grain size. Water currents also remove mud and fine sand from coarser material.

In general, deposits formed by wave action are better sorted than river deposits, but not as well sorted as windblown sands. In contrast, glaciers dump *unsorted* coarse boulders, sand, and fine mud together in heterogeneous heaps.

ROUNDING. The rushing water of a swiftly flowing stream tumbles loose fragments of rock over and over, grinding them against one another and against the stream bed. This slowly wears off their sharp corners and rounds them into smooth-surfaced pebbles. Accumulations of pebbles slowly migrate downstream in bars that can be seen on the bed of any swiftly-flowing river. Sand grains also lose their corners by scraping against other particles as they bounce along in wind or water. Field observations of the rounding of particles rolled along in natural streams for measured distances agree well with ex-

perimental results from tumbling of materials in spinning barrels in proving that the degree of rounding of pebbles and sand grains depends on their original shape, on their resistance to abrasion, on the medium in which they are transported, and on the distance they have been rolled. Hence rounding can give some indication of the kind of agent that long ago shaped the particles of a sedimentary rock.

STRATIFICATION. Most sedimentary rocks show distinct layers, or **strata.** This layering, called **stratification or bedding,** generally results from variations in the supply of sedimentary detritus during deposition, or from changes in the velocity of the currents that are laying down the material.

Visits to a beach before, during, and after a storm reveal changes in the coarseness of the beach material that reflect differences in the power of the currents and waves during periods of calm and storm. A pit dug by a child in the sand nearly always shows distinct layers of varying coarseness. The strong waves and currents of a great storm may completely remove a previously deposited layer of sand and mud on the sea floor and sweep a sheet of coarse gravel over it, as has been proved by samples dredged from the same spot before and after storms. In the southwest Pacific the accumulation of shells and coral in an offshore reef is sometimes interrupted by a fall of ash and pumice from a nearby volcano, or by mud swept far out to sea during unusually heavy floods in the rivers of the nearby land. By such interruptions during deposition, distinct sedimentary strata are formed; and because such changes vary in intensity and frequency, some strata are thin and others many feet thick.

The stratification of a sedimentary rock gives important clues to the conditions of deposition. Mud that slowly accumulates on the bottom of a large lake is generally bedded into parallel, paper-thin strata. This leads

FIGURE 3–2
Stream ripples on the flat, sandy channel of the San Juan River near Mexican Hat, Utah. (Photo by A. C. Waters.)

us to suspect that many "paper shales" such as the one shown in Figure 13–34 have been laid down under similar environmental conditions. Artificial cuts through sand dunes reveal that the stratification of windblown sand is quite complex and not at all like that of a lake sediment. It runs in long sweeping curves that roughly parallel the surface of the dune. The upper strata commonly lie across the cut-off edges of older sets of curving beds that formed when the wind was blowing in a different direction, or when the surface of the dune had a different shape. These older sets may, in turn, lie across the edges of still older sets of strata. Exactly the same complex intersecting patterns of <u>cross-bedding</u> are found in many well-consolidated sandstones (Fig. 15–25).

Interpretations

Many buildings in Glasgow, Scotland, are built of blocks of just such cross-bedded sandstone quarried from the nearby rocky hills. The cross-bedding is one of the many pieces of evidence that Scotland once had a desert climate. Not only does some of the sandstone show dune cross-bedding, but individual sand grains in it are well rounded and evenly

and cleanly sorted as is typical of windblown sand. Equally significant, many grains are "frosted" like the sandblasted grains in modern desert dunes. Here and there in the sandstone are scattered pebbles like those shown in Figure 15–10 and 15–11 whose surfaces have been sandblasted by the impact of wind-driven grains.

Some quarries that yield wind-laid strata show other layers of a different sandstone containing tongues and streaks of rounded gravel like those left by the flash floods that follow infrequent desert rains. In places the lifting of a huge slab of sandstone by the quarry machinery reveals a beautifully rippled surface on the rock below. These **ripples** are complete in every detail, and identical to ripples visible today on the sandy floors of desert streams in southeastern Utah (Fig. 3–2). Moreover, many sandstone strata show cross-bedding which differs from that in windblown dunes, but is identical to that of sandbars along watercourses in the Mohave Desert.

The few shales interbedded with these sandstones contribute further evidence. They show typical shrinkage cracks like the mudcracks that form when shallow muddy pools dry up periodically beneath the desert sun.

(Fig. 3–3). In much older Scottish sandstones are the records of a second desert, including fossil skeletons of ancient fish (Fig. 3–4) that lived in the shallow pools along desert streams.

Thus the rocks of the Glasgow area record

FIGURE 3–3
Mud cracks due to drying of fine-grained alluvium deposited by a stream. Note that greater contraction of clay in the topmost layer than of the slightly coarser silty material beneath has caused curling up of the chips. (Photo by W. H. Bradley, U.S. Geological Survey.)

FIGURE 3–4
Fossils from the Old Red Sandstone, Scotland, collected by Hugh Miller.

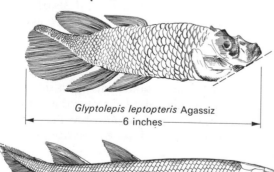

Glyptolepis leptopteris Agassiz
6 inches

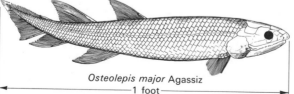

Osteolepis major Agassiz
1 foot

their story. The evidence is circumstantial; it rests upon the close comparison of all the features of the Glasgow rocks with the sands and muds in modern deserts. Taken together, however, the many different bits of evidence point unequivocally to the conclusion that long ago this area had a climate like that of the Mohave Desert and central Australia today.

How different, though, is the record of these Glasgow rocks from that revealed by certain **limestones** from the Alberta plains. These rocks consist mostly of cemented marine shells and intertwining growths of coral. In every detail of composition and structure (except that most organisms are of species and genera different from their modern analogues) these rocks closely resemble the great reefs of white corraline rock, many miles long, off the shores of northern Australia and Indonesia today. In the present-day reefs, shells of clams, oysters, and many other marine organisms are accumulating along with the limy deposits made by the coral animals themselves. Even the shells of living creatures in these reefs are being stuck together by lime-depositing algae, and open spaces between them filled by limy mud from microscopic shells. This quickly hardens into solid rock that affords a foothold on which new shells and coral can grow. The close similarity of the limestone in Alberta to these modern reefs shows that this land was not always a cold semiarid steppe far from the ocean, but once lay beneath the waters of a warm clear sea. "The present is the key to the past."

Laws of sedimentary sequence

Observations of strata now accumulating make possible the following generalizations, which though rather obvious, are nevertheless useful in interpreting ancient sedimentary rocks. The first is the **Law of Original Horizontality:** *Water-laid sediments are deposited in strata that are not far from hori-*

zontal, and parallel or nearly parallel to the surface on which they are accumulating. This law was first clearly stated in 1669 by the same Nicolaus Steno whose measurements of quartz crystals led to important discoveries in mineralogy. It applies to all sediments deposited in water except certain small-scale accumulations, such as sandbars, in which, as in dunes of windblown sand, some strata may be laid down at a marked angle to the other strata within the same deposit. This is cross-bedding, already discussed.

Steno also first stated the **Law of Superposition:** *In any pile of sedimentary strata that has not been disturbed by folding or overturning since accumulation, the youngest stratum is at the top and the oldest at the base.* In other words, the order of deposition is from the bottom upward.

Many applications of these generalizations appear in subsequent chapters. That they are not insignificant truisms may be realized from the fact that in most mountain ranges the strata of sedimentary rocks are no longer horizontal, but are steeply tilted, folded, and even overturned. Because we recognize that these deformed rocks were once sheets of sand, shells, and gravel deposited in nearly horizontal layers and then cemented together, their present contorted structures show that great forces have bent and broken the once-horizontal sheets of rock into fantastically complex patterns.

Classification of sedimentary rocks

Sedimentary rocks are named and classified mainly on the basis of their **texture** (size and shape of the constituent particles) and **composition** (kinds of materials that compose the particles and cements). We have already found that cemented sand is called sandstone; similarly, rocks composed of cemented gravels are called **conglomerate,** and very fine-grained rocks composed mainly of compacted mud and silt are called **mudstone, siltstone,** or, if they part easily along smooth planes parallel or nearly so to their bedding, **shale.** Mudstones, siltstones, and shales are collectively called **pelites,** from *pelos,* the Greek word for clay. All these belong to a class of sedimentary rocks called **clastic,** from the Greek word for "broken" (see Appendix III), because they are composed mainly of broken and worn fragments of pre-existing minerals, rock particles, or shells that were carried to the site of deposition by moving agencies such as streams, wind, waves, or glaciers, and there cemented.

The most important aspects of *clastic texture* are grain size and grain shape. The fragments may be large or small, rounded or angular. Although all kinds of mineral and rock fragments may appear, the coarser clastics such as conglomerate and sandstone generally contain much quartz because this hard and chemically resistant mineral does not rot even after long exposure to air and water, and it also resists the grinding process of transportation better than other common minerals. The cements that bind clastic rocks together are mostly calcite, clay, quartz, and limonite, but many other minerals may also cement the sedimentary grains.

Other broad subdivisions of the sedimentary rocks include the **sedimentary materials formed by organisms,** and the **sediments deposited as chemical precipitates** from sea water or other solutions on the earth's surface. Rocks of both groups generally show *crystalline texture*—the grains are interlocked by mutual interpenetration of crystals during growth and there is little or no cement. *Organic textures and structures,* from which the fossils that form the rock can be identified, are prominent in most rocks of organic origin. In reef deposits the structure and shape of each shell or other bit of organic debris is generally well preserved. Most coal also shows organic textures; well-preserved cell structures and other plant characteristics visible under a microscope prove that it is made from accumulated plant remains. Both organic and chemical sediments accumulate in place, without notable mechanical transport, and so their grains generally do not show the rounding and other effects of mechanical wear that characterize clastic sediments, although some shells and other fragments of organic origin may be broken and worn by waves and currents. Most organic and chemical sedimentary rocks also contain at least some admixture of foreign clastic fragments washed in or blown in from elsewhere.

Most rock-building organisms have shells composed of calcium carbonate ($CaCO_3$), but some organisms, especially diatoms, radiolaria, and some sponges (Appendix V) have shells or skeletal parts composed of silica. Bones, and the shells of a few marine molluscs, are largely calcium phosphate.

Chemical sedimentary rocks consist of intergrown crystals; most have precipitated from sea water, saline lakes and ponds, or hot springs. Some limestones, in contrast to the organically accumulated reefs or to clastic limestones made of worn fragments of shells and older carbonate rocks, are chemical sediments. They show features indicating accumulation by direct precipitation of calcium carbonate from solution instead of by organic processes. Rare, but perhaps more typical chemical sediments are the **evaporites** such as the salt deposits (chiefly halite) on the Bonneville Salt Flats west of Salt Lake City, Utah. These crystallized during the slow evaporation of a large lake of which the present Great Salt Lake is a final remnant. Many thick evaporites have crystallized from masses of sea water cut off from the open sea by a reef or other obstruction. They generally contain large amounts of gypsum and anhydrite in addition to halite. In chemical sediments the minerals precipitated from solution are generally tightly intergrown, giving the rock its characteristic crystalline texture.

Common varieties of sedimentary rocks

Hundreds of different kinds of sedimentary rocks have been described and named, but most are comparatively rare. For an elementary knowledge of geology, learning to recognize the common ones listed in Table III–1 of Appendix III will suffice. This appendix contains fairly full descriptions of each of the major rock varieties. The student should turn to the appendix at this point and read the descriptions of *sandstone, shale,* and *limestone*—three rocks that have been given more than passing mention in the preceding pages. Each description should be studied with a specimen of the rock at hand, so that its properties may be noted and compared with those listed in the description. In making such a comparison, do not expect specimen and description to correspond exactly, for rocks vary widely and grade into one another. Nearly all sedimentary rocks are really mixtures—organic, chemical, and clastic debris are present in varying proportions in practically all of them. Hence our classifications can do little more than call attention to the dominant constituent, and process of formation. Indeed the aim of rock study is not merely to fit rock specimens into the pigeonholes of a man-made classification. Far more important than man's classification is nature's record, shown in the compositional, textural, and other variations that give clues to the *origin of the rock* and to its *subsequent history.*

IGNEOUS ROCKS

In January 1938, a white-hot stream of molten lava issued from a fissure near the base of Nyamlagira volcano, in Africa, and flowed quietly downslope onto a forested plain. For two years and four months the lava continued to pour out, until molten rock had devastated an area of over twenty-five square miles. Finally the flow ceased and the lava congealed into the black slaggy rock we call basalt. Similar lava flows have been observed in Hawaii, Samoa, Iceland, and many other parts of the world.

On November 15, 1963, the fog-bound southern coast of Iceland was heavily shrouded with clouds of volcanic pumice as a new volcano was born 32 kilometers off-shore. By the spring of 1965 the new island, Surtsey, was 170 meters high and covered an area of 2.3 square kilometers. A smaller com-panion, or satellite volcano, Surtling, half a kilometer to the east, was 25 meters high in July of 1965.

Some volcanoes, instead of emitting streams of fluid lava, break forth in spectacu-lar explosive eruptions, blasting vast quan-tities of volcanic ash (fine bits of volcanic glass and pumice) and large fragments of broken rock high into the air. Pumice and hot ash that exploded from Vesuvius in 79 A.D. overwhelmed the ancient cities of Herculaneum and Pompeii. Recent excava-tions in the slightly consolidated ash reveal the buildings, household objects, and even the remains of some of the people and ani-mals that lived in these flourishing Roman cities. A similar explosive eruption from Mont Pelée in the West Indies destroyed the town of Saint Pierre in 1903 with the loss of more than 28,000 lives. Many spectacular eruptions from volcanoes in Japan, Indone-sia, the Andean ranges, Alaska, Mexico, and many other places have been witnessed dur-ing the last 100 years.

That rocks were made by volcanic action was well known to early civilizations because of the many active volcanoes in the Mediter-ranean countries, but the ancients did not recognize that volcanic rocks are also com-mon in regions far removed from active vol-canoes. It is one thing to watch liquid lava emerge from a fissure, flow down a slope, and congeal into a mass of basalt, and quite another to recognize a basalt flow that was extruded millions of years ago. This is espe-cially true if, after eruption, the flow has

been eroded into isolated remnants, or partly buried under younger sedimentary rocks. Volcanic and sedimentary rocks are com-monly interlayered. Basalt flows in Samoa have been seen to enter the sea and spread over reefs in which coral limestone was form-ing; today corals and shells are growing on the upper surface of the congealed lava. The great flow at the base of Nyamlagira covers older volcanic material, but earlier flows in the same region spread over a plain under-lain by lake and river deposits, and were in turn partly buried beneath later sediments. Dust from later eruptions of Vesuvius, and sand washed by rains from higher slopes, has accumulated on the surface of the ash blanket that destroyed Pompeii and Hercu-laneum. Scarcely any thick pile of sedimen-tary rocks is completely free from volcanic interlayers.

It is not surprising, therefore, that flows of lava and beds of volcanic ash interstrati-fied with sedimentary rocks were regarded by the early geologists as sediments hardened in some unknown way. Even today the un-initiated often make the same mistake. In-deed, fifty years of controversy took place before the volcanic origin of basalt was proved by careful field work.

The controversy over the origin of basalt

The interpretation of scientific as well as other phenomena is often biased by such human factors as the philosophy and back-ground of the worker. The history of geol-ogy, like that of other sciences, is replete with unsuccessful attempts to fit observed phenomena into some preconceived notion, or into results from inappropriate laboratory experiments. A classical example of the con-flict between theoretical and field interpre-tations was the controversy over the origin of basalt, which raged from about 1775 until 1822.

Some of the hills of Saxony near the fa-mous mining academy of Freiberg are composed chiefly of sedimentary rocks, but interstratified with them are a few layers of black rock long ago named basalt. The basalt resists erosion better than the associated sedimentary rocks, and stands out in picturesque colonnaded cliffs high on many of the hills.

In 1775, the Stolpen, one of these hills, was visited by Abraham Gottlob Werner, professor of mining and mineralogy at Freiberg, a scientist who was destined to wield great influence on the early development of geology ("geognosy," as he called it). From observations on this and later visits, Werner wrote, in 1787, that the hill showed ". . . not a trace of volcanic action, nor the smallest proof of volcanic origin. . . . After further more-matured research and consideration, I hold that no basalt is volcanic but that all these rocks . . . are of aqueous origin."

Convinced that basalts and most other rocks were precipitated from the ocean, Werner proceeded to divide the rocks of the earth into a series of "Universal Formations." These, he taught, could be definitely recognized in all parts of the world, each formation having the same character and occurring in the same order no matter in what country it might be found. Thus he attempted to apply to the whole earth the same kind of precision and system that he used in organizing and classifying the minerals in the laboratory collections at Freiberg.*

Werner's personal charm attracted able students, and he fired them with great zeal. They were convinced that the "Universal System" of the great teacher would explain the geologic history of every country. But other workers were reaching different conclusions. Even before Werner first visited

* Because of the errors he promulgated about the structure of the earth's crust and the origin of basalt, the remarkably effective work that Werner did in mineralogy is often neglected or forgotten. The science of mineralogy in his day was a chaos of jumbled terminology and haphazard descriptions; he reduced some of this to order, and provided the original impetus that has led Germany to excel in this branch of geology.

Stolpen, Nicholas Desmarest, a French government official who was able to study geology only in his spare time, had investigated in careful detail some basalt flows in the Auvergne region of central France. The Auvergne has had no eruptions within historic times but it contains well-preserved craters, lava flows, and other volcanic features. How different was the approach of this clear-eyed observer from that of the systematist Werner.

In his first journey into the Auvergne in 1763, Desmarest found a cliff of basalt. Searching at its base, he noticed that the soil beneath the basalt had apparently been scorched and hardened. He also noticed that the basalt grades upward into masses of **scoria,** a coarsely frothy basaltic rock filled with small, spherical holes. Scoria is common along the base, and much more abundant just beneath the top, of basalt flows. It has been observed to form in moving lava as expanding bubbles of steam rise toward the top of the flow and are trapped by congealing of the sticky lava around them. When he visited the Auvergne, Desmarest had never seen lava flowing from an active volcano, but by careful observation and by reasoning he established two criteria now universally used in the recognition of ancient basalt flows—the baking of the ground beneath, and the presence of scoria formed by the congealing of bubble-filled lava. Desmarest, however, did not consider that even these observations were proof of volcanic origin. He continued his studies and eventually prepared a map of the entire flow. He traced the flow to its source in a round, steep-sided hill which, despite modification by erosion, retains the characteristic form of a volcanic cone.

Still not satisfied, Desmarest enlarged his map to show all the different rocks of the Auvergne. By carefully following and plotting the boundaries between the lava and other rocks, he proved that the volcanic history was long and complicated. Some eruptions had been followed by quiet periods during which streams cut valleys through the flows and washed away much of the ash from the cones. Some of these valleys were later inundated and obliterated by new lava flows. Eventually Desmarest recognized three main cycles in the volcanic history. His map, one of the first geologic maps ever made, is a monument to thoroughness and ability to interpret field relations.

Ironically, although most of Desmarest's maps were published before Werner formulated his "Universal System," they remained almost unnoticed for many years. While Werner's teachings and ideas were sweeping over Europe, Desmarest took no part in the controversy. When asked his opinion on the origin of basalt, he would reply: "Go to the Auvergne and see." Eventually, two of Werner's own students, D'Aubuisson and von Buch, eager to establish the "Universal System" of their teacher in other countries, did visit the Auvergne. How great was their disillusionment as they followed, step by step, the evidence and lines of reasoning that Desmarest had so carefully recorded! They saw the scorched and indurated ground over which the lava had flowed. They saw the scoriaceous tops and bottoms of the flows where bubbles of steam had been trapped in the lava. All these features are also present at Stolpen, but Werner and his students had missed the critical details in the field.

The straightforward reports of D'Aubuisson and von Buch did much to overthrow the theory that basalt was a precipitate from a "Universal Ocean," although some disciples of the great teacher, content to work in the laboratory instead of examining rocks in the field, continued to promulgate the Wernerian doctrines. Darwin, late in life, recorded how the stubborn adherence of one of his teachers, Professor Jameson of Edinburgh, to Wernerian ideas about basalt were so contrary to common sense that as a young man he was driven away from the study of geology. Nevertheless, the failure of Werner's speculations to withstand the rigorous test

of careful field observations had shown many geologists that the ultimate worth of geologic theories can be proved only in the field.

The controversy stimulated great interest. Many ancient volcanoes were investigated, particularly in the British Isles, an area uniquely rich in varied and spectacular volcanic features despite the fact that no British volcano has been active in historic time.

Plutonic rocks

The basalts just described obviously differ from sedimentary rocks. They are called **igneous rocks** (from *ignis,* the Latin word for fire), and form by the congealing of magma—the name for melted rock deep within the earth. If magma is erupted as lava, or exploded to the surface as ash, it forms **volcanic igneous rocks, but if it crystallizes deep beneath the ground, it forms plutonic igneous rocks.**

As volcanic rocks became better understood, British geologists began to study the conduits through which magma had reached the surface. In the Midland Valley of Scotland and in the Hebrides, just as in northwestern New Mexico and central Oregon, erosion has swept away most of the lava flows and bitten deeply into the foundation beneath. A few flows, however, grade downward into pipe-like masses (**volcanic plugs**) or filled fissures (**dikes**) that cut through the basement on which the lava rests.

A few plugs and dikes can be traced downward on canyon walls into larger and more complex igneous bodies. Masses of plutonic rock formed beneath the surface are called **intrusive bodies.** Although a few such bodies can be traced directly into lava flows, many may never have had an outlet to the earth's surface. That these masses were also formed by crystallization from magma is proved by several lines of evidence: they commonly show borders of rock finer-grained than the bulk of the intrusive; tongues and stringers from the intrusive mass penetrate cracks in the adjacent rocks in the manner of a liquid, and the bordering rocks are commonly altered both in texture and in their minerals —some are even completely recrystallized.

Nearly all rocks crystallized from magma underground have much coarser mineral grains than lava flows, and in most the crystals are large enough to be readily recognized with the naked eye. The roof rock of an intrusive body acts as a blanket that permits only slow escape of heat from magma emplaced below it. Laboratory investigations prove that heat is transmitted by solid rock much more slowly than it is carried off by rising air (convection currents) above a molten lava flow. The slower the cooling, the more time available for the crystallizing silicates to grow into large crystals.

Gas bubbles, so conspicuous in scoria, are microscopic in most plutonic rocks because the load of the roof rocks tends to hold the gases in solution in the magma. Large bubbles form only when the pressure is reduced, as when the magma ascends from great depth to the surface.

The different forms assumed by intrusive bodies are systematically described in Chapter 18, but one, called a **sill,** is worthy of special comment here. Most intrusive bodies cut across the bedding of the enclosing sedimentary rocks and are called **discordant,** but a sill is a rock mass congealed from magma forced **concordantly** between sedimentary strata. The magma spreads between the

FIGURE 3–5
Sills are concordant, dikes are discordant tabular intrusions.

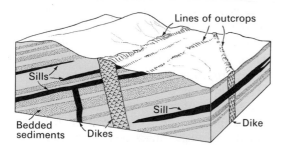

strata like the grease squirted between metal surfaces by a grease gun (Figs. 3–5, 3–6). A sill might thus be low in a sedimentary sequence and yet be much younger than strata hundreds of feet above it. Here, then is a possible source of error in applying our generalization about the Law of Superposition, for how can we tell an intrusive sill from a lava flow that had been buried under a later accumulation of sedimentary rocks?

Contacts of rock masses

The key to this question, as to many others in geology, lies in interpretation of the boundary surfaces between rock bodies. A mass of a single kind of rock, whether sandstone, basalt, or any other, does not extend indefinitely; somewhere it must abut against another. These common boundary surfaces of adjacent rock masses are called their **contacts.** There are two general kinds: **sharp,** with a definite surface of junction; and **gradational** (especially common in sedimentary rocks) in which there is no sharp boundary but an intermediate zone generally from an inch to several feet thick through which one rock mass grades into the other.

In interpreting the relative age of two rock masses in contact, the following generalizations are useful. They apply not only to sequences of igneous rocks, but to all kinds of rock bodies.

Of two rock masses in contact, that which contains fragments or inclusions of the other is the younger. Thus, a sill ought to enclose near its upper surface some fragments torn from the overlying stratum during forcible intrusion (Fig. 3–7). On the other hand, loose fragments from the surface of a buried lava flow are likely to be included in an immediately overlying sedimentary stratum because such pieces of lava and scoria would be picked up and mixed with the overlying detritus by the moving agent that deposited the sediment (Fig. 3–7).

If a rock sends tongues and branches into

FIGURE 3–6   *Sill, left and below, and cross-cutting dolerite mass (sloping from lower right to upper left) in the Beacon Sandstone, South Victoria Land, Antarctica. (Photo by Warren Hamilton, U.S. Geological Survey.)*

another, it is younger than the rock it penetrates. The sedimentary strata above most sills, or indeed older rocks in contact with any igneous intrusion, commonly contain tongues or dikes formed when the magma forced its way into fissures or other openings in the older rock and solidified there.

Although this rule applies mostly to igneous rocks, some sediments may also, in places, penetrate adjacent rocks. Thus, cracks and openings in the upper part of a lava flow may be filled with debris from the immediately overlying sediment that filtered down into the cracks during deposition (Fig. 3–9, Bottom).

The generalization must be used with care, however, when applied to sedimentary rocks. Rarely examples may be seen in which an underlying and hence *older* bed of poorly cemented sand has sent **sandstone dikes** up-

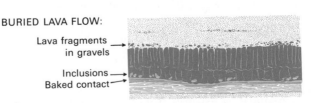

FIGURE 3–7
Criteria for distinguishing between a sill and a buried lava flow.

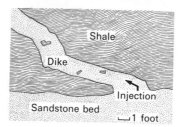

FIGURE 3–8
Dolerite dike cutting sedimentary rocks on Ala-millo Creek, near Socorro, New Mexico. (Photo by N. H. Darton, U.S. Geological Survey.)

FIGURE 3–9
Sandstone dikes. Top: *near Stanford University, California.* Bottom: *in Modelo Formation, Santa Monica Mountains, California.*

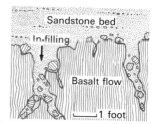

ward into younger but more consolidated overlying shale (Fig. 3–9, Top). This seems an exception to the rule stated above, though of course the actual rise of the sand into dikes did occur *after* the formation of the overlying shale and hence *the dikes* are *younger* than the rocks they cut. What apparently happened was that the underlying water-logged sand was forced upward like a viscous liquid into cracks opened in overlying rock.

If an igneous rock bakes or alters another rock with which it is in contact, it is younger than the rock it bakes. So stated, this is a truism, but recognition of baked contacts is not always easy. Some rock masses are impregnated and discolored by mineral matter deposited along their contacts by percolating waters. Careful observations or even microscopic study may be needed to distinguish such spurious features from baked contacts.

The effects of alteration by a hot magma are generally more conspicuous alongside intrusive rocks than beneath lava flows. Desmarest recognized baked rock beneath the Auvergne lavas, but this is not always possible. The interior of a lava flow remains molten after a thick rind has congealed. Many flows have been seen to creep forward beneath this rind, breaking it up into blocks and rolling it under the advancing front. Such blocks are too cool to bake the material beneath. Intrusive masses cool more slowly and invariably alter their walls, at least to some degree.

Classification of igneous rocks

With the petrographic microscope, we can learn much about the minerals in a rock, including their kinds, shapes, sizes, patterns of arrangement, order of crystallization, and the alterations brought about in them either by hot gases from the magma or by outside agencies such as air and atmospheric moisture. Great variation in so many different features yields infinite possibilities for classification, and literally hundreds of kinds of igneous rocks have been discriminated and given separate names. Nevertheless, the great bulk (approximately 95 percent) of the igneous rocks can be lumped into about 15 major groups (see the Appendix, Table III–2). This simplified list suffices for our purpose: we shall not need names for the numerous varieties within each group, or for the rare groups not included. Such a simplified classification can be based on minerals and textures visible to the eye, dispensing with the microscope. The field classification in Table III–2 is widely used when laboratory equipment is not immediately available.

Comparison of the mineral composition with the chemical composition for thousands of samples of igneous rocks shows that the kinds and amounts of different minerals depend, in general, on the chemical composition of the original magma. Magmas rich in silica yield, on cooling, much feldspar and quartz; magmas low in silica form rocks rich in the ferromagnesian minerals such as pyroxene and olivine.

Differences in the amounts of glass and crystalline material and in the size and arrangement of the crystals determine the texture of an igneous rock. Texture is important in classification (see Appendix III). The size of the mineral grains depends chiefly on the rate of cooling, although the chemical composition of the magma plays a part. It has been inferred from field observations, and confirmed by laboratory experiment, that a high content of water and other volatile substances in the magma promotes the growth of large crystals. In large intrusive masses the minerals are large enough to be readily identified with the eye, or hand lens. In a lava flow, however, rapid cooling

generally prevents the growth of large crystals after extrusion, although a few large ones may already have formed underground. Such mixtures of large crystals enclosed in a groundmass of much smaller ones form the porphyritic texture common in many lava flows, and more fully described in Appendix III. Lava erupted to the surface chills quickly to mixtures of microscopic mineral grains and glass. If cooling is extremely rapid, the magma may congeal into a glass containing hardly any crystals.

THE ENIGMATIC ROCK CALLED GRANITE

As geologists learned more about the contacts of intrusive igneous rocks, a spirited discussion arose over the origin of granite, a common coarse-grained rock composed chiefly of feldspar and quartz. The origin of granite is still a lively topic, and indeed it now seems clear that granite can be formed in more than one way.

Geologic mapping has shown that granite and the similar rock granodiorite are among the earth's most abundant rocks. They form bodies hundreds of square miles in extent. At many places, granites are overlain by sedimentary rocks containing pebbles of the underlying granite (Fig. 9–22). The sediments are therefore younger than the granite, and some geologists deduced (erroneously) that granite was the earth's oldest rock—a part of its "original crust." Werner considered granite to be the first precipitate out of his "Universal Ocean;" others thought it had formed when the earth solidified from a hypothetical molten state.

But the idea that all granites are old did not remain unchallenged. James Hutton, the Edinburgh physician who proposed the Principle of Uniformitarianism, was one of the first to become dissatisfied with the prevailing Wernerian view on the origin of granite. Hutton, familiar with the conduits through which basaltic lava had been erupted near Edinburgh, noticed that the rock of these conduits resembled granite in crystallinity, but differed in color and mineral composition. He became convinced that the ruling view of granite origin by precipitation from a primitive ocean could not be correct, and suggested that it may have crystallized from deeply buried masses of molten rock. But how could he test this hypothesis? If granite welled up in a molten or even a semiliquid state, surely it would have penetrated cracks in any rock alongside. Hutton decided to search for such "veins" (dikes in our terminology) in the Grampians, a chain of granite mountains southwest of Aberdeen, along whose lower slopes the granite must come in contact with prevailing dark schists in the deep precipitous glen of the River Tilt. Here, in the space of a mile, Hutton soon found five large dikes of pink granite that broke upward across the somber schists.

Elsewhere in Britain Hutton found place after place where granite had broken across older rock, distorting and pushing the walls aside, and forcing its way into every fissure and cranny. Abundant fragments of the adjacent rock, pried off by the intruding granite magma, are strewn through the granite along many contacts. Only in the scale of the injection features—measurable in thousands of feet rather than in feet or inches—were the contacts notably different from those of small intrusive masses. Moreover, in places the invaded rocks along granite contacts are so thoroughly recrystallized that their origin as sedimentary or volcanic rocks is difficult to establish (Fig. 3–10). Such changes in wall rocks immediately alongside granite contacts proves that the wall rocks had once been at high temperatures.

Thus many granites were shown to be igneous rocks, congealed at considerable depth. Diked contacts and flow structures also indicate that some masses are not single intrusions but have been formed by successive invasions separated by intervals of inaction.

This recalls the Auvergne, where Desmarest demonstrated three distinct periods of lava effusion separated by long interludes of quiet. Apparently large igneous bodies, whether at the surface or far beneath it, are emplaced slowly and somewhat intermittently.

If we left the subject of the origin of granite here, however, we should be greatly oversimplifying a complex problem. Not all granite contacts are either clearly erosional or clearly intrusive. Many are gradational, the granite fading gradually into rocks that are altered and recrystallized but that nevertheless show clear relics of undoubted sedimentary or volcanic structure. Moreover, some rocks, definitely granite in composition and texture, contain within themselves certain faint, nebulous patterns that resemble stratification, outlines of pebbles, or other sedimentary structures. Still other granites contain frail layers of recrystallized limestone and sandstone only a foot or two thick, which project from the wall rock for tens or even hundreds of feet into the granite body. It is inconceivable that magma could break up and engulf wall rocks in the manner shown in Figure 3–10 and yet leave such frail layers unbroken. More likely, originally sedimentary rocks have been transformed to granite by slow recrystallization and replacement in the solid state. Certain beds, less susceptible to replacement than others, have been left as

FIGURE 3–10
Intrusive relations at a granite contact.

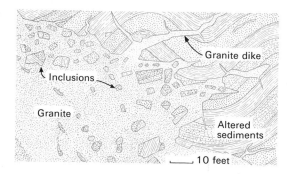

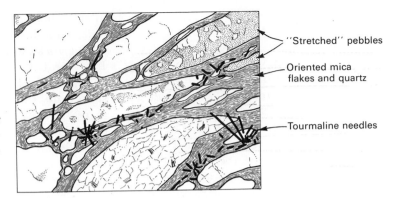

"Stretched" pebbles

Oriented mica flakes and quartz

Tourmaline needles

FIGURE 3–11
Metamorphosed conglomerate with tourmaline needles cutting the other constituents. (Enlarged about 4 times).

relics. Thus some granites appear to be products of **metamorphic** (from the Greek word for "change of form") transformations. The problem of telling a granite of metamorphic origin from one of igneous origin is decidedly difficult. We will return to this controversial subject in Chapter 18, but first let us consider other and less perplexing rocks that present unmistakable evidence of belonging to the metamorphic group.

METAMORPHIC ROCKS

The sedimentary origin of many rocks can be confidently inferred from their stratification, water-worn pebbles, and fossils. Other rocks have textures and mineral compositions that, by analogy with volcanic rocks, permit us to classify them just as confidently as igneous.

There remains a third great group, the **metamorphic rocks,** in which diagnostic features of igneous or sedimentary origin are absent or have been so obscured by the growth of new minerals that they are scarcely recognizable. For example, we find rocks showing rounded pebbles, and stratification much like that of a normal conglomerate, but in which the pebbles are stretched and flattened into spindles or pancake-like shapes and the matrix between the deformed pebbles consists not of sand and clay, but of clear

quartz interlocked with lustrous flakes of mica. Long delicate needles of tourmaline may also cut through two or more adjacent pebbles and the intervening matrix (Fig. 3–11). We infer that such a rock was once a conglomerate, but that the tourmaline and mica could not have been present when the conglomerate was deposited; they grew in the solid rock long after deposition. Evidently the original round pebbles have been squeezed and stretched, and the sand and clay that formed the matrix of the original conglomerate has recrystallized—metamorphosed—to mica and quartz. Original, but deformed, features such as the flattened pebbles must mean that the original rock did not melt in attaining its present condition. Although altered by recrystallization of some of its original minerals into new ones, the rock remained virtually solid throughout its transformation.

From such relations—and there are many rocks with relic igneous textures as well as sedimentary—we infer that the *metamorphic rocks* must have been formed by the *transformation of other rocks, while in the solid state, by heat, pressure, and chemically active fluids to which they were subjected after deep burial.* From the nature of their origin it is clear that there are innumerable gradations between metamorphic rocks and the igneous or sedimentary rocks from which they were formed.

Foliation, and the origin of slate

Most metamorphic rocks show a thin layering called **foliation,** which is due to the parallel orientation of the constituent minerals. The layers may be relatively coarse bands a millimeter (1/25 inch) or more thick, as in **gneiss** or layers thinner than a sheet of paper, as in **slate,** or of intermediate thickness, as in **schist.** Most foliated rocks split readily along these layers. The foliation appears to record slow pervasive movement within the rock mass, during which most of the original minerals were broken, streaked out, and slowly recrystallized into new minerals.

When geology first emerged as a science, coarse-grained, faintly foliated metamorphic rocks such as gneiss were often erroneously classified with the granites, whereas the fine-grained, well-foliated ones like slate were thought to be sedimentary. For example, the metamorphic foliation in slate, a rock much used for roofing, flagstones, and other building purposes, was erroneously considered to be stratification. Geologic study of European and American slate quarries disclosed, however, that many slates have *two* distinct layered structures. In some specimens one structure can be seen to cross and displace the other (Fig. 3–12). The older of these is parallel with alternations in grain size, color, and composition, and with bedding in neighboring rocks such as limestone or quartzite. It is the true sedimentary stratification. A younger structure, along which the rock splits into thin slabs, is the foliation. In many slates each foliation plane breaks and offsets the stratification surfaces by a small (usually microscopic) distance (Fig. 3–9), showing that the foliation is distinctly younger than the bedding. The foliation of some slates, however, does not appear to displace the older bedding. In most such slates foliation and bedding are nearly parallel and so displacement on foliation surfaces would be difficult to detect. Slates split easily along the surfaces of foliation, but not along the stratification as most sedimentary rocks do, unless the foliation happens to coincide with the bedding. When foliation and bedding do coincide, recognizable but distorted fossils are occasionally found on the foliation surfaces. These fossils, when compared with those of the same species from unmetamorphosed sedimentary rocks, are greatly thinned (flattened) in the direction across the foliation and are stretched out roughly parallel to the foliation (Fig. 3–13). Where the foliation cuts the stratification at a high angle, however, it is almost useless to look for fossils,

FIGURE 3–12   *Fragments of slate* (left) *showing foliation* (vertical lines)*, and relics of original bedding. The enlargement shows small offsets of the bedding along the surfaces of foliation of the cleavage.*

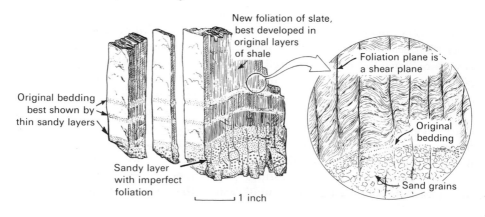

FIGURE 3–13

The fossil at the left was collected from unaltered limestone in Idaho; the deformed fossil at the right, the identical species, was found in slate in the Inyo Mountains, California.

because such rocks will not split along the stratification to disclose the fossils. Furthermore, most fossils are so broken and displaced by many microscopic slips on the foliation planes as to be unrecognizable.

Vestiges of stratification and occasional distorted fossils, show that most slates were derived from fine-grained sedimentary rocks, such as shale. This is confirmed by chemical analyses, which generally show no essential chemical differences between shales and many slates. Field and laboratory studies prove, however, that not every slate is derived from shale; some were formed from other fine-grained rocks such as volcanic tuff.

Only by the use of the petrographic microscope and of X-rays can we unravel the true nature of the foliation. Slates are exceedingly fine grained—indeed, many mineral particles in slate are ultramicroscopic. X-ray studies show, however, that slate is made up largely of tiny flakes of muscovite, the white mica. These flakes are nearly parallel. Mica has only one direction of cleavage; the cleavage of nearly all the mica flakes in slate must lie nearly parallel. This explains why slate splits so readily into thin parallel sheets. Evidently slate is merely shale or tuff that has been sheared and heated sufficiently to cause the original clay minerals composing it to recrystallize into tiny flakes of mica, all oriented nearly parallel with the foliation.

Deep-seated origin of metamorphic rocks

So far our interpretations have followed the Uniformitarian Principle rather closely. We consider slate to have been originally a sedimentary rock because of its stratification and fossils—features we can see in modern sediments. But in slate the fossils are rare and much distorted; even the stratification has become partially obliterated by growth of new minerals and by slipping on foliation planes. These changes clearly took place after the sediment was consolidated, and we have reason to conclude that they occurred deep within the earth. Furthermore, some slates may be followed through imperceptible gradations into more coarsely crystalline metamorphic rocks in which no trace of the original stratification and fossils can be recognized. The minerals of these rocks differ from those in slate, but the new minerals grew from those of the slate, gradually replacing and obliterating them just as the micas in slate replaced the clay minerals of the shale. We consequently conclude that even these coarsely crystalline rocks were derived from sediments but are yet more thoroughly metamorphosed. Moreover, the common association of metamorphic rocks with plutonic rocks that surely congealed below the surface under conditions of high temperature and pressure leads us to infer that *metamorphic rocks must have been formed deep below the surface.*

How can we interpret rocks in which recrystallization has obliterated all the original sedimentary features, leaving just a puzzling mixture of new minerals from which to reconstruct the history of past events? It is impossible to observe processes taking place at the depths where these rocks were formed, for even our deepest oil wells penetrate only about four miles—a mere pin prick in the earth's skin. Do certain subtle features of the minerals of metamorphic rocks record the changes they have gone through? And if so how can we learn to read this record?

In part we gain insight into metamorphic processes by studying transitions. We noted that slates grade into more coarsely crystalline metamorphic rocks. We find that detailed mapping of the foliation in areas of metamorphic rocks commonly reveals fantastically complex patterns of streaks and contortions indicating that the rock has flowed like putty. But how could it have flowed? The same rock is brittle and rigid under surface conditions; if put in a press it will fracture rather than flow. But, as we shall see (Chapter 13), similar highly complicated flow patterns develop in existing glaciers (Fig. 13–12). Ice, too, is brittle in our daily experience; strike a piece of it with a hammer and it shatters into hundreds of fragments. Yet crevasses in glaciers extend little more than 200 feet below the surface; at greater depths they are closed by plastic flow induced by the weight of the overlying load of ice and snow. Will microscopic comparison of the fabric of the crystals from glacier ice and of silicate minerals from metamorphic rocks reveal features in common? Does rock at great depth flow under load like a glacier, and does its foliation record such flow? Comparisons of rock and glacier ice by means of the petrographic microscope are beyond the scope of this book but they do give affirmative answers; rock flow will be further discussed in Chapters 8 and 10. Yet many questions remain unanswered. For example, at what depths, and under what actual conditions of temperature and pressure do rocks behave as puttylike masses? How can we attack such a problem?

Experimental study of metamorphic processes

One attack on these problems is to attempt to duplicate in the laboratory the conditions that might be expected at depths where metamorphism is thought to take place, and where magmas might form. Ingenious presses have been devised for squeezing minerals under confining pressures equivalent to a load of rock more than 80 kilometers (50 miles) thick. In other experiments rock material is sealed in "bombs" and subjected to high temperatures and pressures in the presence of water vapor. Under such conditions many minerals become unstable and recrystallize either by reacting with other nearby minerals, or by rearrangement of their own internal crystal structure. In such presses man has even made artificial diamonds.

From these experiments we are slowly learning about the chemical reactions that take place during metamorphism. In such studies the physical chemist and the solid-state physicist come to the aid of the geologist. Minerals, however, are highly complex chemically and so, despite epochal pioneering work in a few laboratories, knowledge of the chemistry and physics of solids, and particularly of solid silicates while they are being deformed, still lags compared with that of the chemistry of fluids. Only in the last few years has mica been successfully synthesized from clay minerals—the major reaction in the transformation of shale to slate. Much effort is now being directed toward determining the **stability ranges** of various minerals, that is, the ranges of temperature and pressure under which a given mineral will remain stable and not break down or react with adjacent minerals to form some new substance. If we knew these ranges for many minerals under varying physical conditions we might have a golden key enabling us to translate the enigmatic crystal assemblages of a metamorphic rock into a readable record of the changing physical conditions that brought about its present crystalline state.

RECRYSTALLIZATION OF THE STASSFURT SALTS. Such physical-chemical investigations must be constantly guided and tested by field work on the rocks themselves. Without "checking of the laboratory against nature," sterile leads may be followed and erroneous conclusions reached. The roles of the physical chemist and field geologist in checking one another's conclusions are well illustrated by one of the first such studies ever made— that of the origin of the salt beds at Stassfurt, Germany.

The salt deposits at Stassfurt are valuable not only for their sodium chloride, but also for salts of magnesium and potassium used in chemical industries. Since these salts are associated with sedimentary rocks, it was thought that the deposits were typical **evaporites,** that is, the residues of a former body of sea water whose connection with the open ocean was so obstructed by a reef or bar, or perhaps merely by the narrowness of a strait, that it slowly evaporated in the desert climate of Permian time, more than 200 million years ago (Chapter 7). The salt strata were intensively studied from 1900 to 1905 by the famous Dutch chemist, van't Hoff.

Van't Hoff was puzzled by one feature of the salts. Although their chemical composition is consistent with their being evaporites, their minerals are not those obtained when sea water is slowly evaporated. Patiently van't Hoff worked out in the laboratory the temperature stability ranges for many of the sodium, potassium, and magnesium chlorides and sulphates found in the deposits. He discovered that one association of minerals, a rock which the miners call *Hartsalz,* cannot be formed below 72°C (157°F) —far above the temperature of the most tropic sea. One possible explanation was that in Permian time, when the salt beds were deposited, the climate may have been much warmer than now, and perhaps the oceans of that time were near boiling. It should be emphasized that van't Hoff's work proved only that the *Hartsalz* crystallized above 72°C; the inference about Permian climates was a deduction from this fact. Geologists could not accept this deduction because fossil shells are found in sandstone and shale closely associated with the salt. It was inconceivable that these animals had lived in near-boiling seas. Clearly re-examination of the geologic and chemical evidence was needed to resolve these difficulties.

Arrhenius, a Swedish chemist, recognized that van't Hoff had shown only that the *Hartsalz* crystallized above 72°C; he had not eliminated the possibility that mineral changes might have occurred in original normal evaporites because of a rise in temperature after their burial. Further investigation of the geologic setting of the salt deposits was clearly required. It was found that after evaporation of part of the ancient sea the newly formed evaporites were warped down and covered by thousands of feet of younger sedimentary strata. Measurements in deep wells show that in the outer crust of the earth the temperature increases, on the average, about 1°C for every 100 feet of depth. Presumably such a temperature increase also prevailed in Permian and later time. Heating of the evaporites by deep burial could have caused the original salt minerals to recrystallize into *Hartsalz.* In confirmation of this, the textures of the salt rock, as seen under the petrographic microscope, reveal abundant evidence of postdepositional recrystallization. Van't Hoff's conclusion about the temperature of mineral formation was correct, but the inference that climatic temperatures had been exceptionally high was erroneous. The most interesting and significant point is that clues to all these events are clearly recorded in the composition and textures of the *Hartsalz* itself, but it took much geologic and physical-chemical detective work before they could be read correctly.

Thermal metamorphism

Salt beds are particularly susceptible to temperature changes. They recrystallize completely at temperatures so low that the silicate rocks associated with them are not metamorphosed. Thus fossil shells are still found in sandstones associated with the Stassfurt *Hartsalz.* But where a pure quartz sandstone containing marine shells has been heated to high temperatures (as at the contact with a plutonic igneous rock) no shells can be found near the contact. Sheaves of the mineral wollastonite take their place. These field relations suggest, and laboratory experiments support the idea, that wollastonite has been formed according to the following reaction:

$$SiO_2 \; + \; CaCO_3 \; \rightleftarrows \; CaSiO_3 \; + \; CO_2$$

| sand grains (quartz) | shells (calcite) | wollastonite (calcium metasilicate) | (carbon dioxide) |

Wollastonite resembles neither the quartz grains nor the shells that have combined to make it. Under laboratory conditions it requires temperatures higher than 500°C to bring about the change. The actual temperature of formation of wollastonite in the earth's crust, however, also depends on whether the carbon dioxide produced in the reaction can escape. The pressure under which the materials exist determines whether the carbon dioxide gas can escape or will be retained, and laboratory work has shown that the temperature of reaction is changed by pressure. We cannot, therefore, accept the presence of wollastonite as a safe guide to the exact temperature. Moreover, we can seldom use wollastonite as a "geologic thermometer" for still another reason. Most fossiliferous sandstones contain many other substances besides quartz—usually a little clay, some limonite or ferromagnesian minerals, and various other impurities. Some of these generally join in the reaction, which then yields not a simple mineral like wollastonite, but a more complex solid solution such as amphibole, garnet, or pyroxene.

The significance of metamorphic rocks in geologic history

Even these brief descriptions—and scores of additional examples could be given—show that many minerals are stable only within a limited range of pressure and temperature. If brought into a part of the earth's crust where the temperature is higher, or where crushing and shearing are taking place, or where hot fluids permeate them, many minerals break down and form other minerals stable in the new environment. Metamorphic rocks result from such transformations. Alteration may transform only part of the minerals of the original rock, yielding a metamorphic rock whose surviving unchanged minerals or textures still furnish clear evidence of its origin, but more commonly transformation has been complete.

From relations revealed mainly by geologic maps, but also in part from physical-chemical deductions based on the minerals we see under the petrographic microscope, we know that nearly all metamorphism takes place deep within the crust of the earth—far below the depths we can reach in mines and wells. Therefore we can make the following generalizations about regions where metamorphic rocks are widespread.

Where large areas of metamorphic rocks—particularly the foliated rocks called crystalline schists—are found at the surface, deep erosion has taken place.

This conclusion applies equally well to plutonic rocks such as granite. The geologic processes by which the rocks that formerly covered the plutonic and metamorphic rocks have been removed to expose these deep-seated rocks will be discussed in the next two chapters.

Classification of metamorphic rocks

Since any rock may be metamorphosed in one of several different ways, there are hundreds of different kinds of metamorphic rocks. For example, there are at least five different metamorphic rocks with the chemical composition of basalt—indeed, all are derived from basalt—yet each differs from the others in texture, mineral composition, and general appearance. Many minerals appear in metamorphic rocks. Therefore, metamorphism is best studied with the petrographic microscope, aided by the principles of physical chemistry and fundamentally, of course, by thorough field observations. Nevertheless, the more common groups of metamorphic rocks can be roughly distinguished by sight, as indicated in Appendix III, Table III–3.

Metamorphic rocks, like sedimentary and igneous rocks, are classified on the basis of texture and composition. The principal textures useful for determinations made without the microscope are listed and described in Appendix III.

Facts, concepts, terms

Sedimentary rocks, igneous rocks, metamorphic rocks
Uniformitarian principle
Cementation of sand; burial and preservation of fossils
Law of superposition; law of original horizontality
Texture of rocks
Volcanic and plutonic rocks
    Magma
Origin of basalt
    Importance of field studies
Origin of granite
Interpretation of contacts
    Fragments of one rock in another
    Penetration of one rock by another
    Alteration of one rock by another
Recrystallization of rocks by metamorphism
Origin of foliation
    Relation of foliation to relic sedimentary and igneous features
Stability ranges of minerals
Geologic thermometers
Checking physical-chemical deductions in the field
Crystalline schists as indicators of deep erosion

Questions

BASED IN PART ON APPENDIX III

1. The bedding in most sand dunes is curved, and some parts slope more than 15° to the horizon. How do you reconcile this with the Law of Original Horizontality?

2. According to the Uniformitarian Principle, geologists agree that large areas of South Africa and India, which now have a tropical climate, were once covered with glaciers. What kind of observations do you think have been made that lead to this conclusion?

3. The controversy over the origin of basalt in which Desmarest and Werner participated took place before the invention of the petrographic microscope. How would microscopic studies (if available) have helped in a solution?

4. If you observe two intersecting sets of structures in a rock, how will you decide which is the older?

5. The surface temperature of lavas is as high as or higher than that of most intrusive magmas. Yet evidence of metamorphism is widespread along intrusive contacts and trivial beneath lava flows. Can you suggest a reason?

6. How do you distinguish limestone from sandstone? Basalt from limestone? Phyllite from shale?

7. In examining a contact between granite and an overlying rock, what would you look for to tell whether the granite had intruded the overlying rock, or had been eroded to form it?

8. Discuss the origin and significance of porphyritic texture.

9. What holds the sand and other mineral fragments together in a sandstone? What holds the mineral grains together in a granite? What holds the fragments together in welded tuff?

Suggested readings

Geikie, Sir Archibald, *The Founders of Geology*. Baltimore: Johns Hopkins Press, 1901. [A fascinating account of the early history of geology.]

Huxley, T. H., *On a Piece of Chalk*. New York: Scribner, 1965.

Mather, K. F., and S. L. Mason, eds., *Source Book in Geology*. New York: McGraw-Hill, 1939.

Scientific American offprints

101. Philip H. Abelson, *Paleobiochemistry* (July 1956)

803. Ph. H. Kuenen, *Sand* (April 1960)

819. O. Frank Tuttle, *The Origin of Granite* (April 1955)

846. Loren C. Eiseley, *Charles Lyell* (August 1959)

chapter 4

Weathering
and Soils

WEATHERING

We paint our houses every few years because, if we neglect to do so the old paint peels off, the wood becomes etched, splintered, and ultimately rotten. We say it is "weathered" or "weather-beaten." The gravestones in an old cemetery, and even the facings of some fairly new buildings, show that originally smooth and polished stones also become discolored, pitted, and cracked where exposed to the weather.

Deep road cuts generally penetrate rock so firm at depth that blasting is required to make the cut. In most places this firm rock passes gradually upward into a zone of broken rock with softened and discolored rock particles, and finally into loose soil near the top. Many rocks that are black or steel gray in the walls of mines, wells, or deep quarries, are yellow or brown in outcrops. In some, the yellow color is a mere stain on or near cracks, but in most it is pervasive, and accompanied by drastic changes in mineral composition and in firmness. We infer that exposure to air and moisture, aided by organisms that live on or near the ground surface, has brought about the changes. We call the altered rock **weathered,** and deduce that much soil has certainly formed from the weathering and crumbling of underlying rocks.

SOIL

Soil consists, at least in part, of material weathered in place and mixed with organic matter near the surface. These two features distinguish soils from such other unconsolidated materials as gravel in a river bed, sand in a dune, or mud on a tidal flat. All these materials are easily separable into individual grains, but unless they contain some organic matter and show some evidence of rock decay in place, they are not properly called soil.

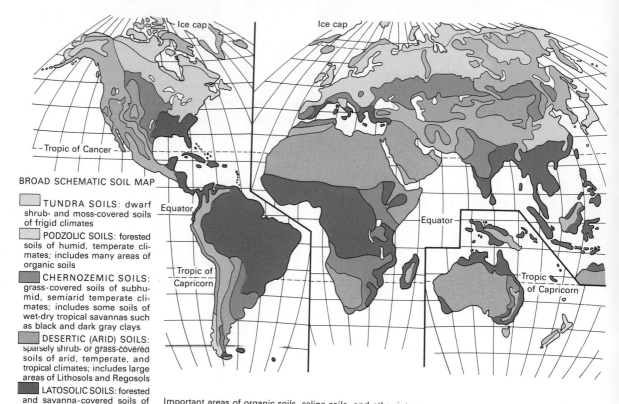

BROAD SCHEMATIC SOIL MAP

TUNDRA SOILS: dwarf shrub- and moss-covered soils of frigid climates

PODZOLIC SOILS: forested soils of humid, temperate climates; includes many areas of organic soils

CHERNOZEMIC SOILS: grass-covered soils of subhumid, semiarid temperate climates; includes some soils of wet-dry tropical savannas such as black and dark gray clays

DESERTIC (ARID) SOILS: sparsely shrub- or grass-covered soils of arid, temperate, and tropical climates; includes large areas of Lithosols and Regosols

LATOSOLIC SOILS: forested and savanna-covered soils of humid and wet-dry tropical and subtropical climates

SOILS OF MOUNTAINS: stony soils (Lithosols) with inclusions of one or more of the soils listed above, depending on climate and vegetation, which vary with elevation and latitude

Important areas of organic soils, saline soils, and other intrazonals are omitted as well as very important bodies of alluvial soils along such great rivers as the Mississippi, Amazon, Nile, Niger, Ganges, Yangtze, and Yellow.

FIGURE 4–1

Map of the world, showing six broad soil zones. In each zone a characteristic soil profile forms, though there is great variation within each. Many large areas of alluvial soils, such as the valleys of the Mississippi, Ganges, and Amazon Rivers are neglected in this summary chart. (After the Department of Agriculture Yearbook for 1957.)

Although soils vary widely from place to place they tend to be similar in areas with similar climates, despite differences in source rocks. In areas of different climate, however, soils tend to differ even if the source rocks are virtually identical (Fig. 4–1). Climate, so important in soil formation, is partly a measure of temperature, rainfall, and evaporation, and hence also controls the kinds and amounts of vegetation and of soil-inhabiting organisms such as bacteria and earthworms. All of these factors strongly influence the geological processes that change rock into soil. The differences between soils in one climatic province and those in another are great enough so that an ancient buried soil may reveal the climate under which it was formed.

ANALYSIS OF WEATHERING

Studies of soils and their transitions from their parental rocks show that weathering involves both **mechanical disintegration and chemical decomposition.** Disintegration is a mechanical breakdown; the rock loses its coherence but the composition of the materials in the rock changes little. Disintegration does not include abrasion and removal of material —these movements are part of erosion, the wearing away of the land. Decomposition or chemical weathering involves rock decay accompanied by marked changes in chemical and mineralogical composition. The complex silicate minerals that make up the bulk of most igneous and metamorphic rocks change into hydrous silicates, hydrous oxides, and carbonates; some materials are lost by solution.

Mechanical weathering

FROST ACTION. When water freezes it expands 9 percent, thereby exerting a bursting pressure on its surroundings, as every householder who has had a water pipe break during a winter freeze knows. The force of crystallization of ice is powerful, indeed; at 8° below 0°F, a not uncommon temperature, it amounts to 30,000 pounds per square inch. Freezing expands wet soils especially, because of their abundant and complex pores; thawing leaves the soil open and spongy.

Because solid rock conducts heat better than a comparable volume of fine-grained but otherwise identical material, the slow freezing of soils exerts different pressures upon materials of different grain size and tends to sort the soil components. The coarser particles are pushed toward the surface by freezing ice, the finer tend to be left behind. Both stones and fence posts are likely to move upward during deep frosts. Figure 4–2 shows the vertical sorting of rock fragments in the frost-riven surface material of a flat area near Thule, Greenland.

In high latitudes, where vegetation is shallow rooted, the upwelling of coarse fragments by this selective processes is at first guided by random differences in the size of fragments in the original soil. Gravity causes the heaved up fragments to slide away from the centers of upwelling during alternate thaw and freeze. In time the coarse fragments accumulate between the heaved up areas in sufficient volume to coalesce into a roughly polygonal network that encloses circular areas of upwelling (Figs. 4–2, 4–3). Such areas of "patterned ground" are active now only in high latitudes and rigorous climates. When similar patterns of fragment distribution are found in areas (for example, eastern

FIGURE 4–2
Vertical sorting of rock fragments due to freeze-thaw cycles. Because large fragments conduct heat more readily than equal volumes of smaller fragments with their enclosed pore space, the larger fragments are selectively displaced toward the surface by the pressure of expanding ice crystals. (Photo taken near Thule, Greenland, by Dr. Arturo Corte, National Cold Regions Laboratory, Hanover, New Hampshire.)

FIGURE 4–3
Patterned ground on a gentle slope near Thule, Greenland, formed by freeze-thaw cycles. (Photo by Dr. Arturo Corte, National Cold Regions Laboratory, Hanover, New Hampshire.)

Washington) that are today much warmer than those of "active" patterned ground, they are considered evidence of a formerly more rigorous climate (see Chapter 13).

To break rocks—not merely to sort already broken fragments—freezing water must be confined. Because water in a crack freezes from the surface downward, in the deeper crevices it may be so completely confined that a deep freeze will shatter the rock extensively. Most high mountain peaks are so mantled by frost-wedged rubble that solid, unbroken rock is difficult to find. The colder the climate, the deeper the freeze, but the many repeated alternations of freeze and thaw in cold temperate climates is much more effective in breaking rocks than the fewer, but deeper, freezes of the extreme Arctic. For example, there are five times as many freeze-thaw cycles in an average year at Montreal than in Ellesmere Land in Arctic Canada.

PLANTS AND ANIMALS AS AIDS TO WEATHERING.
Organisms help to break rock down into soil, both mechanically and chemically. Growing plant roots powerfully wedge soil and rock, as shown by the broken and heaved slabs of concrete in old tree-bordered sidewalks. Even tiny lichens and mosses pry open cracks in rock and loosen the bonds between mineral grains. Bacteria and other microscopic organisms in soil produce changes in the chemical composition of the air and water in soils, and cause complex changes in the soil minerals as well. Vegetation also affects soil processes in other ways. Roots bind the soil and slow its washing away. On rotting, roots leave tubules that allow water to penetrate and freeze.

Burrowing animals move and mix the soil effectively. Darwin estimated that English earthworms spread their casts over the ground to a depth between 0.1 and 0.2 inch (2 to 5 millimeters) per year, loosening and aerating the soil and subjecting much of it to the chemical action of the worm's digestive processes. This mixing is a major factor in producing uniform soils in humid regions. There are few earthworms in arid regions, but ants, termites, and rodents fill a similar niche.

OTHER AGENTS OF DISINTEGRATION. Wedging by ice and plant roots is most effective in disintegrating rocks, but many other processes assist: the crystallization of soluble salts washed into rock pores in deserts; the intense heat of forest fires; the shock and heat of lightning; even the impact of rocks rolling or falling from above. All these give further access to moisture and air and expose new surfaces to chemical attack.

Indeed, chemical decomposition itself may be a major cause of disintegration. Feldspars swell as they weather into clay and many other minerals decompose to substances that occupy more volume. The swelling of altering feldspar and mica crystals in time disintegrates massive granite into loose sandy loam. Alternate swelling and shrinking of the clay as it is wet by rains and dried by the sun aid in the disruption.

It was once thought that the drastic day-to-night temperature changes in deserts weaken or even break some minerals by repeated expansion and contraction. But specimens of granite have been heated and cooled in electric ovens through similar temperature ranges for many thousand cycles without appreciable disruption. Surfaces of polished granite at Assuan in Egypt, fully exposed to the tropical sun, retain their polish after 3,000 years. Without doubt the swelling of decomposing minerals—slow as is chemical decomposition in deserts—breaks down the rocks more effectively than daily temperature changes.

Chemical weathering

In discussing metamorphism, we pointed out that the quartz and fossil shells in sedimentary rocks become unstable at high temperatures and pressures—they react to form a new mineral, stable under the more intensive conditions. Conversely, most minerals of volcanic rocks, which formed under high temperatures, and of plutonic and metamorphic rocks, which formed under both high temperatures and high pressures, are unstable under the lower temperatures and pressures of the earth's surface; they slowly react with the oxygen, carbon dioxide, and moisture from the air to form new minerals, most of which are hydrous (chemically combined with water). These changes should not be thought of as taking place quickly. Most chemical reactions double in rate for each 10°C rise in temperature; we should therefore expect that rock will decompose much more rapidly in the humid tropics than in temperate and arctic zones. An arable soil may form in a few years in the wet tropics, but the same kind of rock may require centuries or even millenia to decompose into soil in temperate, arctic, or even desert regions.

Microscopic, X-ray, and chemical studies of mineral alterations show that one of the principal agents of alteration is carbon dioxide, which dissolves in water to form carbonic acid (H_2CO_3).

Falling rain dissolves carbon dioxide from the air in higher proportion—compared to oxygen and nitrogen—than its low ratio in the air. In coal-burning industrial communities the amount is considerable, as people in London may readily deduce from the marked corrosion of marble and limestone on even fairly new buildings. In the soil, however, most dissolved carbon dioxide comes from the decay of organic matter caused by soil bacteria. Plant tissues are mainly carbohydrates (compounds of carbon, hydrogen, and oxygen). In aerated soil, where oxygen is available, microorganisms feed upon the carbohydrates and form carbon dioxide by the reaction of the oxygen in the soil pores with the carbon of the plant substance. The atmosphere contains only .03 percent CO_2 but the gases filling the pores of an organic soil may contain 10 percent of CO_2, or even more. This high concentration is extremely effective in furthering the weathering process. The carbon dioxide combines with water to form ions of hydrogen and bicarbonate:

$$(1) \quad \underset{\text{water}}{H_2O} \quad + \quad \underset{\substack{\text{carbon} \\ \text{dioxide}}}{CO_2} \quad \rightleftharpoons \quad \underset{\substack{\text{hydrogen} \\ \text{ion}}}{H^+} \quad + \quad \underset{\substack{\text{bicarbo-} \\ \text{nate ion}}}{HCO_3^-}$$

In swampy areas where oxygen is deficient microscopic molds and bacteria change the leaves, fruit, and woody matter to a dark organic substance called humus. Humus is acid-forming, and the water percolating from it attacks many minerals and dissolves them.

WEATHERING OF LIMESTONE. As an example of chemical weathering, consider the action of carbon dioxide and water in soil on the chemically simple rock, limestone:

Limestone is mostly calcite, but generally contains a little clay and other impurities. Calcite dissolves very slightly in pure water, but a few calcium ions (Ca^{++}) and carbonate ions (CO_3^{--}) do enter the solution:

$$(2) \quad \underset{\text{calcite}}{CaCO_3} \quad \rightleftharpoons \quad \underset{\text{calcium ion}}{Ca^{++}} \quad + \quad \underset{\substack{\text{carbonate} \\ \text{ion}}}{CO_3^{--}}$$

But if calcite dissolves in water that already

contains some carbon dioxide, the carbonate ions formed by solution of calcite will react with the hydrogen ions formed by the reaction of Equation 1 to form more bicarbonate ions:

(3) H^+ + CO_3^{--} $\rightleftharpoons$ HCO_3^-
   hydrogen   carbonate   bicarbonate
     ion   ion   ion

Thus water that contains carbon dioxide can dissolve much more calcite than pure water. The basic reason for this is that water which has dissolved carbon dioxide contains hydrogen ions, carbonate ions, and bicarbonate ions (Equation 1), but only the carbonate ions can react with calcium ions to produce calcite. Any process that moves Equations 1 and 3 toward the right will at the same time remove carbonate ion from the right side of Equation 2, allowing this reaction to proceed toward the right so that calcite goes into solution.

In solutions, combination and dissociation of ions is constantly going on at rates governed by the temperature and by the abundance of the several ionic species present. If these rates have become so adjusted that the total amounts of the various components remain the same (although all the reactions are still going on), the system is said to have reached equilibrium. At equilibrium in the system represented by Equation 2, as much calcite is being precipitated from the solution during a given time as is being dissolved as ions entering the solution. The weight of both the calcite and of the solution remain constant, and the solution is said to be saturated with calcite. But if the ions on the right side of Equation 2 are selectively removed so that fewer are available to form the product on the left side (calcite), the reaction will so proceed as to yield more of these ions (calcite will dissolve). When limestone dissolves, the solution would soon be at equilibrium if it were unable to move. But rainwater slowly percolating through the rock carries away the ions of calcium and bicarbonate and allows new unsaturated water continuously to attack the limestone. Calcite

is dissolved, not only at the surface, but along every crack and pore through which the solutions percolate. Where the underground circulation is vigorous (Chapter 14), the limestone becomes extensively honeycombed, and large caves may be formed in the rock. The clay in the limestone does not dissolve; it remains on the surface as the calcite of the underlying rock slowly leaches away. A few inches of clay soil may thus be all that is left of many feet of dissolved limestone.

The soil that accumulates on the limestone contains practically the same minerals that were in the original rock—only their proportions have been drastically changed. Weathering merely changes the texture and mineral proportions, without producing a radically new set of minerals. The clay and other noncalcite minerals are not chemically altered. This is readily understood when we recall that the clay in the limestone was deposited under atmospheric temperatures and pressures, and that it accumulated in sea water which was constantly exchanging carbon dioxide with the atmosphere. In other words, the impurities, as well as the calcite of the limestone, at the time it was formed, were not far from being at equilibrium with the conditions at the surface of the land, and are thus chemical compounds nearly stable under these conditions.

Many other sedimentary rocks are also composed of minerals relatively stable under atmospheric conditions. Their soils contain practically the same minerals as the parent rocks, differing merely in mutual proportions. But the changes in nearly all igneous and metamorphic rocks are far more drastic; their component minerals crystallized at temperatures and pressures far different from those of the soil, and most of them are chemically unstable at the earth's surface. The weathering of granodiorite furnishes examples.

WEATHERING OF GRANODIORITE.   The individual minerals of a granodiorite weather very differently from calcite and from each other.

The component minerals differ in compressibilities and thermal expansion, with the result that the grain boundaries are differentially stressed and become sites of higher solubility and chemical reaction. The rock thus tends to disaggregate into a mass of noncoherent mineral grains.

In general, the minerals that crystallized first as the magma consolidated (Chapter 18) are less stable under soil-forming conditions than those which crystallized later, when the temperature of the cooling magma was lower. Biotite and amphibole are seen in deep road cuts in granodiorite to have been altered and stained at greater depths below the surface than potassium feldspar, indicating that they are more susceptible to weathering than feldspar. Though amphibole alters slightly more readily than biotite, it yields similar products and the alteration of both may be illustrated by that of biotite. (In the chemical reactions we list only the final products, not the complex ionic reactions by which they were largely formed).

Decomposition of *biotite:*

$$2KMg_2Fe(OH)_2AlSi_3O_{10} \; + \; \tfrac{1}{2}O_2 \; + \; 10H_2CO_3 \; + \; nH_2O \; \rightarrow$$

biotite oxygen carbonic acid water

$$2KHCO_3 \; + \; 4Mg(HCO_3)_2 \; + \; Fe_2O_3 \cdot H_2O \; + \; Al_2(OH)_2Si_4O_{10} \cdot nH_2O \; + \; 2SiO_2 \; + \; 5H_2O$$

potassium bicarbonate (soluble)   magnesium bicarbonate (soluble)   "limonite" (rust)   clay mineral   quartz or soluble silica   water

Plagioclase is the next most susceptible mineral of the granodiorite after amphibole and biotite. It alters as follows, and the higher the anorthite content of the plagioclase, the more susceptible it is to decomposition in this way.

$$CaAl_2Si_2O_8 \cdot 2NaAlSi_3O_8 \; + \; 4H_2CO_3 \; + \; 2(nH_2O) \; \rightarrow$$

anorthite   albite   carbonic acid   water

$$Ca(HCO_3)_2 \; + \; 2NaHCO_3 \; + \; 2Al_2(OH)_2Si_4O_{10} \cdot nH_2O$$

calcium bicarbonate (soluble)   sodium bicarbonate (soluble)   clay mineral

Potassium feldspar, whose glistening cleavage flakes can commonly be recognized when all the other minerals except quartz have been severely altered, weathers more slowly according to a similar scheme:

$$2KAlSi_3O_8 \; + \; H_2CO_3 \; + \; nH_2O \; \rightarrow \; K_2CO_3 \; + \; Al_2(OH)_2Si_4O_{10} \cdot nH_2O \; + \; 2SiO_2$$

potassium feldspar   carbonic acid   water   potassium carbonate (readily soluble)   clay mineral   soluble hydrated silica or finely divided quartz

Quartz in the granodiorite persists almost unchanged except for staining and some mechanical breakdown. It does indeed dissolve, but extremely slowly.

Many examples thus show that the complete weathering of granodiorite in a humid temperate climate leaves residual quartz grains enclosed in abundant newly formed aluminum-silicate clay which is stained yellow or red by hydrated ferric oxides ("limonite"). As illustrated by the equations, sodium, calcium, and much of the magnesium and potassium have been carried away as bicarbonate ions in water draining from the soil, although some magnesium and potassium ions do remain in the clay minerals, held there by feeble electrical forces. Leaching of the soluble ions proceeds much more readily in humid than in arid regions. As potassium is an important plant food, its retention is agriculturally significant. The slowness of leaching in arid soils accounts in

FIGURE 4–5   *Granite dome showing coarse exfoliation, Sierra Nevada. The sheetlike slabs of rock are tens of feet thick. (Photo by G. K. Gilbert, U.S. Geological Survey.)*

FIGURE 4–4
Exfoliation in granodiorite. Note that spherical forms have developed by rounding off the corners of angular blocks (lower part of picture) bounded by intersecting fractures, or joints. The corners are rounded because the weathering agents attacked them from two or more sides. (Photo by Eliot Blackwelder, Stanford University.)

FIGURE 4–6
Thin exfoliation slabs formed by relief of load in granite rock of the High Sierra. (Photo by N. King Huber, U.S. Geological Survey.)

part for the exceptional fertility of newly irrigated land in the arid West.

Despite the differences in their parental rocks, soils derived from both limestone and granodiorite are rich in clay. The clays of the original limestones are merely concentrated in the soil by leaching away of the calcite, but the clay in the soil on granodiorite is newly formed in place. Clay minerals are among the stablest under soil-forming conditions, both in the temperate and arctic zones.

Exfoliation

The splitting away of scale-like layers of rock from an exposed or soil-covered surface of massive rock (not a platy rock such as shale or schist) is **exfoliation.** The separated sheets or plates may be flat or curved, paper thin or many feet thick, a fraction of an inch or many hundreds of feet long. Two kinds of exfoliation may be distinguished: In massive partly weathered rocks exfoliation is shown by the scaling of decomposed material into small thin flakes (Fig. 4–4), and in fresh or only slightly decomposed plutonic rocks by the splitting into giant plates (Figs. 4–5, 4–6).

Most rocks are cut by cracks or **joints** that divide them into smooth-sided blocks whose dimensions may vary from a fraction of an inch to many feet. Dolerite, graywacke, arkose, granite, and many other medium- or coarse-grained rocks commonly show many thin concentric layers of crumbly weathered materials (Fig. 4–4) which peel away from the edges of the joint blocks like the layers of an onion. As the outermost layer weathers and expands it pulls away from the fresher rock beneath, and additional shells form successively inward. The swelling caused by the formation of hydrated clay minerals brings about much of this mechanical exfoliation. Because attack at block edges is from two sides, and at corners from three, the unweathered central kernel becomes more and more spheroidal as the deeper material swells outward on weathering.

The huge curved plates of fresh rock (Figs. 4–5, 4–6) that have split away in forming the giant domes of Yosemite in California (Fig. 4–5), Stone Mountain, Georgia (Fig. 4–7), and Sugarloaf at Rio de Janeiro, show that a different kind of exfoliation may take place without much decomposition. These domes are all in little-weathered plutonic rocks that originally consolidated beneath a cover of overlying rocks a mile or more thick. Perhaps as the weight of the thick cover lessened while it eroded away, the granite slowly swelled upward and outward, breaking into curved plates parallel to the surface.

RESIDUAL SOIL AND THE SOIL PROFILE

Some of the mechanical and chemical processes that take place in rocks during weathering have been described. Soil scientists have traced and described the various stages in the change from firm bedrock at depth to humus-rich soil at the surface. The whole series of stages visible at any one place is called the **soil profile** (Fig. 4–8). Most soil profiles are divisible into three main zones. Having already discussed the chemical weathering of the chief minerals in granodiorite, we will take for an example the soil profile of the western Sierra Nevada, whose steep canyon walls expose much hard gray granodiorite. On the gentle slopes of the forested uplands between the canyons, this granodiorite is buried beneath a soil made up of three layers. The surface layer—called the **A-horizon** —is a red-brown sandy loam (a mixture of quartz sand, silt, minute clay particles, and decomposed plant residues). In the fine-grained reddish matrix are embedded many irregular quartz grains, alike in size and shape to those in the granodiorite. At a depth of about a foot (30 cm), the clay content increases. This tough sandy clay is the subsoil or **B-horizon.** Apparently some of the clay formed by decomposition of plagioclase near the surface has been washed downward from the A-horizon, and fills pore spaces in the B-horizon. Two to four feet (60 to 120 cm) below the surface, the B-horizon becomes paler and sandier. The sand grains include not only quartz but abundant feldspar, some partly changed to clay but still readily recognized by dulled cleavage faces and some, a little deeper, by flashing cleavages nearly as bright as those of the fresh orthoclase and plagioclase. Here also are many micaceous flakes—not jet black like the biotite of the granodiorite, but iron-leached, pearly yellow scales, sometimes mistaken for gold. Rusting of its iron has changed the color of biotite from black to gold. Still deeper, this material grades imperceptibly into less-stained but still crumbly material in which the texture and characteristic minerals of the granodiorite are identifiable. The transitional material between the zone of high clay content (B horizon) and the bedrock below is called the **C-horizon,** or rock mantle (Fig. 4–8,

left). That the surface material developed by weathering of the underlying granodiorite is inescapable. Such a soil, still in place on its parent rock, is called *residual*.

Most soils show characteristic profiles, composed of two or more distinct soil horizons, that differ from place to place because of differing parental rocks, climates, vegetative cover, and maturity, that is, the length of time the soil-forming process has been operating on the material. The residual soil of the limestone region of Kentucky differs notably from that of the Sierra. The Kentucky climate, though also temperate, is more humid and the underlying rock is mineralogically simpler. The A-horizon consists of black humus-rich clay that passes downward into lighter-colored clay and broken and stained limestone, without a clear division between a B-horizon and a C-horizon such as is commonly found. (Fig. 4–8, right). The clays are the residues left when the calcite in the

FIGURE 4–7   *Stone Mountain, Georgia, a granite dome shaped by exfoliation. (Photo by Warren Hamilton, U.S. Geological Survey.)*

limestone was dissolved. Although the parental rock in these particular examples clearly did influence the soil profile, the end product in both cases is mostly clay. Soil scientists have found that mature soils are in general surprisingly similar in regions with similar climates, even though the soils have been derived from widely different kinds of rocks. If mature soil profiles can be recognized in ancient buried soils, they can thus give strong clues to past climates.

Soils on unconsolidated transported material

Many soils have developed, not on bedrock but on unconsolidated material deposited by streams in alluvial cones or flood plains. These materials were at least partly weathered before deposition. After deposition, such loose material allows easy access to air and water, so that renewed weathering quickly forms typical A- and B-horizons under favorable climatic conditions.

The soils of the Great Valley of California afford a typical example. Some residual soil of the Sierra, derived from granodiorite as we have described, has been washed into streams and transported to the valley where some streams have spread debris of partly weathered rock over hundreds of square miles of the valley floor. In places, such sediments, including even coarse gravel, have been left undisturbed long enough to have weathered into brown soils with a characteristic soil profile. The brown silty A-horizon, two or three feet (60 to 90 centimeters) thick contains scattered quartz pebbles. Faintly outlined spherical masses of clay containing clumps of closely spaced angular quartz grains are clearly the remnants of thoroughly decayed pebbles of granodiorite. The compact B-horizon, one or two feet thick, has been formed in part by minute clay grains washed down from the A-horizon. Such compact clayey B-horizons, especially when cemented by iron oxide, calcium carbonate,

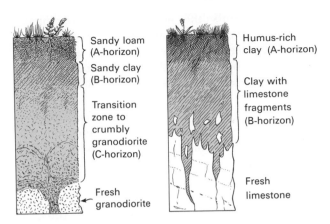

FIGURE 4–8

Soil profiles on Sierra Nevada granodiorite (left) , *and Kentucky limestone* (right) .

and other bonding materials—as they commonly are in the Great Valley and elsewhere —are called *hardpan*. This vague term refers to any tough, clay-rich deposit, not merely to B-horizons developed on transported material. The C-horizon consists of the relatively little-altered gravel or other parental transported material below the B-horizon.

Another soil formed on transported material may be wholly different. One in eastern Massachusetts, for example, derived from rock flour (very finely ground fresh rock) , boulders, and clay transported by glaciers, which formerly covered Massachusetts (Chapter 13) , has no B-horizon and the A-horizon consists of only three or four inches (7 to 10 centimeters) of dark humus-rich material overlying unweathered rock flour and rock fragments. This soil is obviously much younger than that of the Great Valley of California; the Massachusetts soil has been forming only since the glaciers of the Ice Age melted away about twelve thousand years ago (Chapter 13) , whereas the California gravels were deposited far beyond the reach of the glaciers, and the soil on these gravels has been forming for a much longer time. In short, soils differ not only because of climate, parental material, and the plant and animal life that has inhabited the soil, but also because of *maturity,* the length of time that the soil has been forming.

EFFECT OF TOPOGRAPHY. Because slope influences rate of runoff and thus both the penetration of water into the ground and its washing away of surficial grains, soils are generally thinner on slopes than they are on hilltops. In a study of soils in Manitoba, the A-horizon was more than twice as thick on flat areas as on slopes of 10°.

Colors of soils

Soils, by their colors, give clues to the climatic conditions under which they were formed. Most are colored either by iron-containing minerals, which give red, brown or yellow hues, or by organic matter, which gives black or gray. The weathering (climatic) conditions that prevail in a soil determine which colors will dominate.

Iron forms two kinds of ions, both with positive charges: ferrous, with two, and ferric, with three. A ferric ion can be formed from a ferrous ion by the loss of one electron. Because this loss is easier in the presence of free oxygen and results in a compound with relatively more oxygen, it is called **oxidation.** Thus, FeO is a ferrous compound, and Fe_2O_3 a ferric. When hydrous ferric oxide (limonite) is formed by chemical decomposition of a ferrous silicate such as biotite, the reaction is brought about by the addition of oxygen from the air. The finely divided limonite stains the soil yellow. If the soil is dried out repeatedly, as in a climate with a warm dry season, some of the limonite may lose its water and change to red hematite; the soil then becomes red. At intermediate stages or with admixed manganese oxides the soil is brown.

Iron is reduced to the ferrous state as readily as it is oxidized. A pale-greenish, dark-gray, or black soil generally indicates that the iron has been reduced by reactions with plant residues or by sulfur bacteria. Ordinarily this occurs where the soil pores are filled with water, thus excluding the air that would otherwise oxidize both iron and organic matter. Thus a black soil may indicate swampy conditions at the place of its formation; the iron has been reduced and mostly combined with sulfur to form black hydrous iron sulfide, and the soil is also rich in humus. Although soils rich in organic matter are generally dark, many well-drained forest soils of the temperate zone contain so much humic acid formed from decomposing leaves that nearly all the iron is dissolved and washed out of the A-horizon, which thus becomes very light gray.

CLIMATIC FACTORS IN WEATHERING

In moist temperate climates, as we have seen, both limestone and granodiorite yield clay-rich soils on weathering. In humid climates, either temperate or tropical, weathering takes place much more rapidly on rocks rich in ferromagnesian minerals and carbonates than it does on rocks rich in quartz, because most iron-, magnesium-, and calcium-bearing minerals are easily susceptible to chemical decomposition whereas quartz is resistant. Thus, basalt and limestone weather rapidly, granodiorite more slowly, and quartzite is almost immune.

In the driest deserts, such as those of southwest Africa, the chief weathering process appears to be disintegration caused by slight chemical weathering. Because the soils of such areas contain little organic matter and few bacteria, their moisture holds less dissolved carbon dioxide than that of humid soils. Obvious chemical changes are therefore minor, but the surface layer does disintegrate to yield a coarse, only partly weathered soil.

Generally the A-horizon has been slightly leached of carbonates and iron, and thus is slightly paler than the B-horizon, which has a little more clay.

Chemical weathering of a kind that yields soils rich in calcium carbonate and high-silica clay minerals, operates in semiarid regions such as the western interior of the United States. Here crusts, veinlets, and irregular nodules of calcite precipitate in the pores of the B-horizon, and may cement it into a nodular calcareous rock called **caliche**. The calcium carbonate accumulates because, during most of the year, the soil water evaporates within small connected capillary pores, releasing its dissolved carbonates. In a humid region the carbonate-rich water is continuously leached away into the permanent streams.

Where, in arid regions, the soil water rises almost to the surface, as along the shores of saline lakes and swamps, or where irrigation has been heavy and subsoil drainage poor, salts even more soluble than calcium carbonate accumulate on and near the surface as well. These make the so-called "alkali-soils," many of which are encrusted with sodium carbonate and sodium sulfate, poisonous to most plant life. Such soils are useless for agriculture unless they can be drained and the soluble salts washed out of the surface layers.

In arctic regions and in alpine heights elsewhere, disintegration by frost action is the dominant variety of weathering. In subarctic Finland, Siberia, and Canada, however, very siliceous clay soils are formed by chemical weathering. Where the tundra supports fairly abundant vegetation, the acid formed from decomposing plant material at low temperatures leaches most of the calcium, iron, and magnesium from the soil.

Differences in weathering due to differing climates are dramatically illustrated by the contrast between the pock-marked valleys formed by the leaching away of limestone in humid regions like the Shenandoah Valley of Virginia, and the bold ridges of comparable kinds of limestone that rise high above the desert in arid Arizona. Only quartzite forms similar resistant ridges in the humid Appalachians.

Laterite

The soils of the rain forests of the Congo and Amazon Basins have not been adequately studied, but they appear similar to the aluminum-silicate clay soils of moist temperate regions. Most of the wide belts of grass- and tree-covered savanna that lie adjacent to the rain forests, however, are underlain by tough to thoroughly indurated yellow and red-brown soils called **laterites** (from *later,* the Latin word for brick). The characteristic dark-brown upper layers of laterites dry to a brick-like consistency and are sometimes used for building materials. Parts of India, Nigeria, Brazil, the Caribbean region, and many other tropical areas have typical lateritic soils.

Because laterites differ so markedly from soils of temperate climates, and also illustrate one of the ways a chemical element may be concentrated into a valuable ore, we will discuss them in some detail.

Laterites vary widely in composition, but most contain aluminum hydroxides and iron hydroxides and oxides, mixed with a little residual quartz. A rare variety called **bauxite** is almost pure hydrous aluminum oxide, $Al_2O_3 \cdot nH_2O$, and hence valuable as an ore of aluminum. Another, diagrammatically illustrated in Figure 4–9, is derived from serpentine, a rock that contains almost no aluminum, but considerable magnesium and iron. In this laterite hydrous iron oxides are concentrated enough to make an ore of iron.

In most laterites, practically all the silicon of the original silicates has been dissolved away by rain water, along with the easily soluble sodium and potassium, and the acid-soluble calcium and magnesium. The leach-

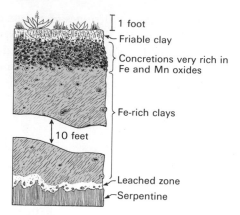

1 foot
Friable clay
Concretions very rich in Fe and Mn oxides
Fe-rich clays
10 feet
Leached zone
Serpentine

FIGURE 4–9
Profile of Cuban laterite. The concentration of iron in these soils is so great that they are mined as iron ore. (Data from H. H. Bennett and R. V. Allison, 1928.)

ing out of all these elements at the same time is hard to understand. Silica is only slightly soluble; it dissolves more rapidly in water containing many more OH⁻ (hydroxyl) ions than hydrogen ions—an alkaline solution. Calcium and magnesium, on the other hand, are not very soluble in alkaline solutions, but dissolve readily in solutions that contain more hydrogen than hydroxyl ions—acid solutions. Yet great quantities of all three have clearly been leached from the soils.

Most laterite regions have marked wet and dry seasons, the so-called "Monsoon climate." It has been suggested that during the warm dry seasons organic acids are so completely oxidized to carbon dioxide, which escapes into the atmosphere as a gas, that the dry soil contains no acid-producing materials, but retains a little material that would dissolve to give an alkaline solution. Hence, at the onset of the first rains, silica is carried off in the temporarily alkaline soil solution before the growth and decay of new vegetation again restores the supply of carbonic acid.

Some of the complex aluminum and iron hydroxides in laterite do not form directly, but first precipitate as other minerals that

are easily soluble when first formed but soon stabilize and become highly insoluble before the onset of the next wet season.

Residual laterite soils are characterized by a pale *zone of leaching* just above the parent rock, and a dark-brown *concretionary zone* at or near the surface (Fig. 4–9). Each zone is usually a few feet or a few tens of feet thick, but in places it may thicken to hundreds of feet. The concretionary zone is a concrete-like mass, composed chiefly of either dark-brown "limonite" or of many limonite nodules (concretions), of pea or marble size, cemented into a solid mass. The uppermost part of some lateritic soils retains enough unaltered quartz to make it crumbly or even sandy.

Leaching is so complete in many laterites that some elements essential to plant life are entirely removed and others, such as phosphorus and iron, are precipitated as iron phosphates or other compounds so insoluble as to be practically unavailable. Even though the lateritic soil of the Hawaiian Islands contains abundant iron, it is necessary to fertilize the pineapple plants grown there with soluble salts of both iron and phosphorus.

What happens to the silica leached out during lateritization? No definite answer can yet be given because the subtropical distribution of even so abundant a substance as silica has been little studied. Extensive siliceous crusts have been reported from Angola, just south of the Congo Basin, and from other parts of tropical and subtropical Africa, but laterite is not definitely known near them. Possibly nodules of chert (a silica-rich rock) and silica concretions form beneath the lateritic soils. From comparisons of the silica content of rocks and the silica content of the streams that drain them, it appears that silica is more rapidly dissolved in the tropical climates than in temperate. For example, the silica content of the rivers in tropical British Guiana is about twice the world average for rivers draining the same kind of rocks.

FIGURE 4–10   *Glacial polish on igneous rock, Adirondacks, New York, unscarred by 10,000 years of weathering. (Photo by V. C. Kelley, University of New Mexico.)*

RATES OF WEATHERING

The rate of weathering varies greatly with different rocks and different climates. Surfaces of igneous rocks polished by glaciers 10,000 years or more ago still glisten (Fig. 4–10) in the temperate climates of Massachusetts and New York; even the finely ground rock flour left by the same glaciers contains little or no decomposed material. On the other hand, glacial deposits in Iowa of about the same age have fairly well-developed profiles.

Chemical weathering almost surely proceeds most rapidly in moist tropical climates, but after it has gone far enough to form a deep blanket of decomposed material, the product reaches virtual equilibrium with its environment. Thus the arched roofs of Angkor in Cambodia, built of laterite, stand nearly intact after seven centuries of neglect. Though the jungle crowds close and plants spring from every cranny, the delicately sculptured walls are only slightly weathered; the laterite, already nearly in equilibrium under the prevailing climate, is slow to change further. By contrast, a fairly well-defined soil profile has developed on burial mounds left by the Huns in the Volga Valley eight centuries ago. But we should expect the stream sediments of the Volga to weather much more rapidly, even in a cool climate, than the Cambodian laterite, itself a product of weathering.

Many other data are conflicting. The slight weathering of the glacial debris of New York and New England took place in a climate not unlike that of western Europe. But in Normandy, soil with an A-horizon 9 cm thick and a B-horizon 31 cm thick has formed on a refuse pile of oyster shells at a castle known to have been abandoned in 1066. The weathering in Normandy has been many times as great in 900 years as in ten times that span in New England.

In Northumberland, England, measurements on ancient structures suggest that limestone solution has proceeded at the rate of about an inch in 300 years. But this rate is considerably higher than would be inferred from the height of pedestals in the same area supporting glacial boulders. These suggest a rate of solution less than half as rapid.

The A-horizon developed on ash from the

1883 eruption of Krakatau in Indonesia was 60 years later as much as 5 percent poorer in silica and 2 percent richer in alumina than the C-horizon. These differences suggest extremely rapid decomposition of the glassy pumice—the source rock; a crystalline rock in the same setting would undoubtedly weather much more slowly.

In Wisconsin, biotite scattered through a sand culture has been converted to a hydrous clay mineral (vermiculite) simply by growing four successive crops of wheat. Farther south, the soils developed within 50 years on abandoned plowlands in eastern North Carolina, have new A- and B-horizons with a combined thickness of 5 inches (12 centimeters).

Old gravestones also yield interesting data. In Edinburgh, within less than eighty years, the inscription on marble in memory of Joseph Black, the discoverer of carbon dioxide, was rendered illegible, chiefly by the action of the gas he discovered. Solution along grain boundaries gave access to water, which, on freezing, disrupted the rock, roughening the surface. On the average, about a third of an inch of rock has been dissolved from faced limestone in Edinburgh in a century. In small Scottish towns with less coal smoke, limestone dissolves more slowly. Slate, less susceptible to acid solutions, has been barely roughened in the same time.

Weathering is slowest in a hot dry climate. Inscriptions carved between 3 B.C. and 79 A.D. above the doors of sepulchers in the crumbly sandstone cliffs of northwest Arabia can still be read. Forty centuries ago, not far from the site of the Assuan Dam in Upper Egypt, a block (cut as an obelisk) from Syene red granite was smoothed and dated by an in-

FIGURE 4-11
Cleopatra's Needle, in Egypt (left) *and in Central Park, New York City* (right). (*Photos by courtesy of the Metropolitan Museum of Art, New York.*)

scription. Its surface, though exposed to the direct sun, is still firm and polished. At various dates between 2850 and 313 B.C., colossal statues in rock from this quarry were set up at Luxor and elsewhere in the somewhat moister climate of Middle and Lower Egypt, and blocks of the same rock were used to face pyramids near Cairo. Structures cut from Assuan granite throughout Egypt were studied in 1916 by D. C. Barton, an American geologist. He estimated the average rate of exfoliation in the slightly moister Lower Egypt was about one or two millimeters per thousand years.

Two obelisks of Syene granite, each bearing many deep-cut hieroglyphics, and each now called "Cleopatra's Needle," stood for about 3500 years in Egypt with only slight weathering. One, removed to London, has weathered appreciably but not disastrously. The other, brought to New York about 1880 and set up in Central Park, where it is exposed to frost, frequent wetting, and air rich in carbon dioxide, disintegrated so extensively that by 1950 (despite the application of shellac-like preservatives in the 1920's and 1930's) part of the pictured story was completely erased (Fig. 4–11). Frost wedging alone had produced more weathering in seventy New York winters than all processes of weathering in fifty times seventy years in Egypt.

SUMMARY

Soil profiles develop through the rotting of rock. The minerals that form the crust of the earth are not immune to the attack of oxygen, moisture, and carbon dioxide from the atmosphere, nor to the disruptive forces of frost and other agents of disintegration. Hence most of the earth's surface is mantled by a variable thickness of decayed and broken rock.

Variations in soil profiles arise chiefly from differences in climate and in the original parental rocks, though there are many other modifying influences. Thus three great soil groups are the products of three differing climates:

a. Soils of humid temperate regions, in which calcium, magnesium, and sodium are leached, aluminum and iron are washed downward into the subsoil, and silicon is concentrated at the surface.

b. Soils of the savanna tropics, in which iron and aluminum are concentrated as insoluble oxides and hydroxides, and from which silicon and other elements are selectively removed.

c. Soils of arid and semiarid regions, in which the soluble salts are redistributed by water but mostly remain within the soil system. This produces caliche, alkali, hardpan, and other subsurface accumulations of calcium, sodium, and even of soluble potassium compounds.

Source rock, whether bedrock or transported, governs the kind of material composing a soil while the soil profile is immature. Given a long time, however, the soil shows less and less resemblance to the parental material. Indeed, differences among truly mature soils due to differing source rocks are trivial compared with differences due to climatic factors. Thus soils derived from such different rocks as slate, granite, and basalt may ultimately become almost identical, provided they are exposed under identical climatic conditions.

Soil development is also influenced by such factors as topographic position (which influences drainage, vegetation, humus accumulation, soil bacteria, and doubtless other factors), the geologic environment (whether the soil is being slowly or rapidly eroded or buried, etc.), and time. Thus the rate of soil formation varies under different circumstances from several inches per century to less than an inch in 10,000 years. The fact that it normally takes thousands of years for a soil to adjust to a change of climate allows us to use soil as a clue to the climate prevailing while it was being formed. Such studies indicate that the prehistoric climates of many areas differ greatly from those they now have.

At present the range in surface temperature on the earth is at least 45°C, with very marked latitudinal differences that are in large part reflected in differences in rates of weathering from place to place. Studies of the geologic past suggest strongly that the earth has normally been without ice caps comparable to those of the present, though at other times still greater ice accumulations have been present. In general, though, the range in temperature must have been far narrower than at present, with correspondingly more-uniform rates of weathering and soil formation the world over than now prevail.

Facts, concepts, terms

Weathering
    Residual soils
    Definition of soil
Disintegration or mechanical weathering
    Frost wedging
    Influence of plants and animals
    Decomposition
    Minor supplemental processes
Decomposition or chemical weathering
    Main factors: oxygen, water, carbon dioxide
    Soil bacteria
    Weathering of limestone
    Weathering of granodiorite
    Representative reactions during decomposition of common rock minerals
Exfoliation
    In decomposed material
    In nearly unaltered material
    Influence of joints
The soil profile
    A-, B-, and C-horizons
    Variations with climate
    Hardpan; caliche
    Soils on transported materials
Soil colors; oxidation; reduction
Soils
    Of moist temperate climates—new clay and iron oxides plus residual quartz
    Of dry climates—disintegration products, caliche, alkali accumulations
    Of savanna climates—laterites, bauxite, concretions

Questions

1. In Oregon, a laterite developed on basalt is now covered by a second basalt flow, which has a soil composed chiefly of clay minerals. Explain.

2. Western Nevada is semiarid, with dry summers; eastern Iowa is moist, with considerable summer rainfall. Assuming that the soils are derived from similar parental rocks, how should the characteristic soil profiles of the two areas differ, if at all?

3. Why does calcium carbonate accumulate in the A-horizon of some soils formed on basalt in Nevada, whereas it is practically absent from this horizon in soils developed on limestone, predominantly composed of calcium carbonate, in Kentucky?

4. Few of the soils of extreme western Texas are mature, whereas most of those of eastern Texas are mature. What hypotheses occur to you as possible explanations of this fact?

5. The Hagerstown Valley of Western Maryland is underlain by limestone; the Piedmont, to the east, by gneiss and schist. How would you expect the soils of the two areas to differ, if at all?

6. Name the chief minerals in granite, and tell what happens to each of them when granite weathers in a moist temperate climate.

7. Volcanic tuff containing abundant fragments of pumice is successfully used as a building stone in southern Arizona, but not in Alaska where similar volcanic rocks are widespread. Why?

8. In the great Chicago fire, pillars of granite in burned-out buildings were greatly spalled and cracked, but pillars cut from limestone withstood the flames with much less damage. Can you suggest why?

Suggested readings

Geikie, Archibald, *Rock Weathering as Illustrated in Edinburgh Churchyards*. Proceedings of the Royal Society of Edinburgh, v. 10, 1880, p. 518–532.

Keller, W. D., *The Principles of Chemical Weathering*. Columbia, Missouri: Lucas Brothers, 1955.

Reiche, Parry, *A Survey of Weathering Processes and Products*, Rev. Ed. Albuquerque: University of New Mexico, 1950.

United States Department of Agriculture, *Soil and Climate* (Yearbook 1957). Washington, D.C.: G. P. O. [Especially p. 17–60]

United States Department of Agriculture, *Soils and Man* (Yearbook 1938). Washington, D.C.: G. P. O.

Scientific American offprints

821. Charles E. Kellogg, *Soil* (July 1950)

870. Mary McNeil, *Lateritic Soils* (November 1964)

chapter **5**

Erosion

GRAVITY

Water in a pond and coffee in a cup both assume a level surface. If we hang a plumb bob above this surface, we find the plumb line exactly perpendicular to it. Both plumb bob and liquid have approached the center of the earth as closely as they can— the liquid by flowing to the lowest level possible and the plumb bob by hanging as close to the earth as the suspending string permits. The earth evidently exerts an attraction on each particle of the liquid and of the plumb bob. This attraction is the force of gravity. Moreover the attraction on a particular volume of material must vary with the mass of the material contained within it, for a heavy stone sinks at once to the bottom of a pond, displacing an equal volume of the less dense liquid upward. If we uncork a bottle of air beneath water, the air bubbles to the surface because the water, being denser than air— that is, containing more mass in an equal volume, is more strongly drawn to the lowest level. The air is attracted too, even though it is displaced upward by the denser water.

The law of gravitation

The attraction of the earth for a plumb bob, for water, for air, and for all other objects in the universe illustrates the universal **Law of Gravitation,** first formulated by the great English scientist Isaac Newton (1642– 1727). This generalization is usually stated: *Every particle in the universe attracts every other particle with a force directly proportional to the product of their masses, and inversely proportional to the square of the distance between them.*

The mathematical statement of the law is as follows:

$$F \propto \frac{M' \times M''}{D^2}$$

In this expression, F is the force of attraction, M' is the mass of one body (in our example, the Earth), M'', the mass of the second body, and D the distance between the bodies. The symbol ∝ means "varies as."

As a numerical example of the way in which the law operates, consider the earth's attraction for a plumb bob that weighs one kilogram (2.2 pounds). At sea level, the distance of the plumb bob from the earth's center is approximately 6400 kilometers (4000 miles). If this distance were doubled, the attractive force would be only one-fourth as great, for the denominator would be $12,800^2$ instead of 6400^2, and $12,800^2/6400^2 = 4$. In other words, if it were possible to suspend the plumb bob in space 12,800 kilometers (8000 miles) from the earth's center (that is, 6400 kilometers or 4000 miles above the earth's surface), it would weigh only ¼ kilogram. Because of this relation, instruments on artificial satellites must be so designed that the pull of gravity is not necessary for their functioning, as it is for so many laboratory instruments on earth.

Erosion

The most familiar geological process in which the work of gravity is dominant is **erosion,** the wearing away of the surface of the earth and the transportation of the detritus to lower levels, either on land or in the sea. Anything that moves can pick up and carry away loose materials. Agents as different as earthworms, auto wheels, and lightning assist in erosion, but nearly all transportation of rock waste on land is accomplished by five main agents: (1) Gravity—acting directly to cause the falling or sliding downslope of solid or semiliquid masses of mud, soil, and rock; (2) wind; (3) glaciers; (4) ocean waves and currents; (5) streams.

Energy for erosion

All erosional agents are driven by gravity. Soil, rock, water, ice, and air—all are drawn by gravitational attraction toward the center of the earth's mass, and each particle tends to fall, slide, or flow to low areas on the earth's surface. Because of gravitational attraction, loosened rocks fall, bounce, and slide down steep slopes, streams flow downhill, and glaciers shear and flow outward. Winds result from the flow of dense air masses beneath masses of lighter air. Ocean currents, too, (as distinguished from the shallow roiling of the water by wind-generated waves) are caused by the flowing of huge bodies of water to restore gravitational equilibrium between water masses of different density. Except for such trivial effects as those produced by the activity of plants and animals, the shattering of rock by lightning, and its spalling by forest fires, all erosion, in the last analysis, results from gravitational attraction.

But gravity is only the immediate driving force. Wind and water, the major erosive agents, depend upon solar radiation for their effectiveness. Radiation from the sun warms the air and ocean—more in tropical areas than in polar areas—thus changing the density of different masses of air and water. Because the gravitational attraction on dense air or water is greater than on an equal volume of air or water that is less dense, the denser masses flow beneath the lighter ones, generating the winds and water currents, which then redistribute the heat. This heat transport from tropics to polar areas exactly compensates (on the average) for the differences in heating; if it did not, the equatorial zones would become steadily hotter and the polar areas colder. Measurements show that most of the heat is redistributed by the winds, but about 10 percent is by ocean currents. More than heat is carried: dust storms could not arise from the land, nor storm waves attack the coast if there were no winds. Atmospheric circulation affects erosion: water evaporated from the oceans is carried to and precipitated upon the continents. The rugged mountains etched by glaciers and the majestic rivers in fertile valleys could not form if the wind did not transport water vapor. In a windless and waterless world the land would quickly parch to barren deserts of dust and rock. Erosion, other than that caused by the falling of rock downhill under the direct action of gravity, could not occur. The landscape of Mars, a nearly waterless and airless planet, resembles that of the Moon, whose huge uneroded craters stand stark and bare, unsoftened by the effects of erosion and deposition by running water.

RELATION OF WEATHERING TO EROSION

Although weathering involves little movement, it does include some shifting of material under gravity, even on flat ground: for example, the downward transport of fine clay particles from the A- to the B-horizons in soils and the leaching away of dissolved ions by downward percolating rain water. It is thus not possible to draw a sharp distinction between weathering and erosion.

If the soils and other weathering products were not removed they would eventually bury all rocks beneath a thick mantle of the products of their own decomposition. This does happen on flat ground in warm, humid regions, where weathered rock may extend downward for a hundred meters or more. Here weathering has outstripped erosion, but even here soluble materials are slowly dissolved away by seeping water. Moreover, even on gentle slopes the almost insoluble clays, silts, and sands are gradually pushed downslope by rain splash and rills. Contrast this with steep mountainous slopes where running water and glaciers, aided by rock slides, avalanches, and the gradual downslope creep of water-saturated detritus, are so active that wide areas are almost completely denuded of soil, and the underlying rock is continually exposed to renewed weathering. Here erosion is outstripping weathering.

Erosion thus emphasizes the **transportation** of rock waste from the site of its formation, whereas weathering emphasizes the production of rock waste and soil in situ under virtually static conditions. Yet both are really interrelated parts of a single process—**denudation,** the lowering of the surface of the land. Weathering aids and abets erosion by weakening and disintegrating the rocks, thus preparing them for removal by erosional agents; erosion in turn aids weathering by removing the cover of soil and loose debris and exposing new rock to the ravages of the weather. The transported rock waste is nearly all carried to lower sites, as close to the center of the earth as the local restraints permit, and here the material is deposited. Weathering, erosion, and deposition are parts of an endless *cycle of rock change:* weathering prepares rock for transport; erosional agents move the debris to a lower site (for example, the sea), and deposit it in strata that may then be cemented into rock. Millions of years later this rock may be raised above sea level (Chapter 8), exposed to the air and the rains, and again weathered and eroded in a new cycle. The interrelations within this cycle and among its products are schematically diagrammed in Figure 5–1. Analyses of these processes are the chief themes of Chapters 11 through 16, but we give here some examples as an introduction to other geologic processes.

PROCESSES OF EROSION ON LAND

Downslope movements

Gravity plays a dual role in erosion. We have noted its indirect effects in keeping the air and water that envelop the earth in a constant state of motion. These will be fur-

FIGURE 5–1

The cycle of rock change.

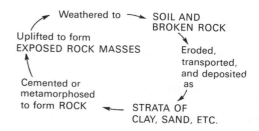

FIGURE 5–2   *Gravity movements at the head of a glacier. Sunset Amphitheater, Mount Rainier, Washington. Length of view: one mile. Note the following features: (1)
The arcuate crevasses (bergschrund) formed where the glacier pulls away from the
steep snowfield and rock at the headwall. (2) The dark streaks and fans of broken
ice and rock piled up by avalanches and rock falls tumbling from the cliffs. Much
of this cascading rock and ice has been channeled down steep ravines (avalanche
chutes) on the cliff face. (3) The precariously balanced blocks of ice at the edge
of the 200-foot-high cliff (in shadow) that caps the rock wall on the right edge
of the photo. Fans composed of broken ice and rock that have tumbled from this
ice cliff and from the rock wall below it spill down across the bergschrund. (Photo
by Miller Cowling, 116th Photo Section, Washington National Guard.)*

ther discussed in Chapters 19 and 20. Climbers threading their way along the edge of a
glacier are often forcefully reminded of the
more direct action of gravity when a boulder
loosened by frost wedging bounds down the
mountainside and crashes into a pile of similar fragments (Fig. 5–2). Larger rock falls

and avalanches have dammed rivers and buried towns (Chapter 11). Less spectacular
examples of **downslope movement** (as the
direct transportation of rock, soil, and mud
by gravity is called) are all about: banks
undercut by rivers or waves cave in; mud
and wet soil slide downslope or are trampled

FIGURE 5-3   *A "black duster" rolling into Spearman, Texas, on April 14, 1935. (Photo by F. W. Brandt, Sedimentation Laboratory, California Institute of Technology.)*

downhill by the hooves of animals; piles of loose sediment of the sea floor or at the edge of a steep delta give way and glide out in tongues beneath the water; avalanches roar down narrow chutes on mountain slopes, carrying trees, soil and boulders with them; on every sloping surface loosened detritus rolls or slips gradually downward, bit by bit, inch by inch, year after year.

If downslope movements were the only means of erosion, denudation would be restricted to relatively small areas. Gravity, acting directly, can roll or slide solid or semiliquid masses of rock and soil only to the bottom of a cliff or slope—there they must stop. But on earth other means of transportation then take over. Loose rocks crash down upon the surface of a glacier, and the glacier carries them away; banks of streams cave in during floods and the swirling waters swish the debris downstream; soil creeps slowly down a slope and the brook at its base carries it to the sea. The chief role of downslope movement is to supply a continuous incre-

ment of rock waste to the agents of long-distance transport. Operating alone, downslope movement could accomplish little, but in cooperation with stream erosion it is a major element in denudation.

Winds

Winds transport rock fragments—dust, sand, and silt—as any prairie housewife can testify. Among the best examples of its work are the great dust storms that blew out of the so-called Dust Bowl of the southwestern High Plains during the drought of the early 1930's.

When the High Plains were settled, the natural sod was plowed under and the light soils were planted to corn and wheat. Even before settlement, this area had undergone considerable wind erosion: the "sooners" who raced madly into the Cherokee Strip of what is now Oklahoma to stake out homesteads were greeted by blinding dust storms. As more and more land was put under the plow, these "black dusters" (Fig. 5–3) became larger and more frequent. In the early 1930's, a succession of dry seasons led to the tragic drought of 1933-1934. Pulverized by tillage and parched by drought, the soil had lost not only its original protective cover of grass but much of its cohesiveness. The stage was set for one of the most spectacular and destructive events of modern agriculture.

On May 12, 1934, roaring winds lifted huge clouds of dust from the fields of Kansas, Oklahoma, Texas, Colorado, and other Great Plains States and drove it swiftly eastward in a gigantic dust storm. Sweeping out of the plains as a blinding, choking mass of particles so dense as to blacken the sky and change day into darkness, the seething dust cloud rolled rapidly across the well-watered lands east of the Mississippi. Here, where little loose soil could be gleaned from the forest and grass lands, some dust settled to the ground, but the clouds were still dense enough to blot out the sun as they swirled around the skyscrapers of New York and out over the Atlantic. Twisting dirty-brown clouds of dust engulfed ships more than five hundred miles from shore.

Measurements reported by observers in points scattered widely over central and eastern North America indicate that more than 100 tons of dust per square mile fell in the areas covered by the cloud. Since the storm covered approximately two-thirds of the North American continent and much of the western Atlantic, it appears that more than 300 million tons of soil—enough to fill six million railroad cars—were removed from the Great Plains during this single storm and strewn over the lands and sea to the east. It revolutionized the economy of large parts of half a dozen States, for it put an end to wheat farming throughout whole counties, and precipitated a mass exodus of dry farmers. Measurements during a much smaller dust storm at Syracuse, Kansas, in 1954, showed that 29,000 tons of dust per hour were being transported in an air column one kilometer wide. This width of the air stream

was carrying as much dust as would fill 750 freight cars in an hour! This is equivalent to 10 trains, each a kilometer long.

Wind winnows thoroughly the material it transports. Only the finest particles swirl high in the air and travel far; most of the material moved is not this fine. Studies by soil conservationists indicate that in the Great Plains about three-quarters of the material moved by the wind does not rise as a dust cloud but is grains of silt and sand that roll or skip along the ground. Much of this coarser material drifts along the surface for only a few meters, or at most a few kilometers, and then accumulates in ditches, around clumps of vegetation, and against fences, buildings, or other obstructions. For every ton of airborne dust there are generally two or three tons of coarser (and humus-poorer) debris piled in drifts of silt and small dunes of sand near the source.

Although the great dust storms of the 1930's were intensified by changes in the soil cover brought about by man, wind erosion is constantly at work on all land surfaces, particularly in deserts. In the western Sahara, the "Harmattan," a local name for the trade winds, sweep across the desert from north to south for about six months of each year. In exceptionally stormy years they are reported to deposit as much as 30 centimeters (a foot) of silt, dust, and sand along the edge of the desert in northern Nigeria. One has only to watch this sand blowing off the surfaces of the large dunes to get a vivid picture of the effectiveness of wind as an agent of erosion. Vessels far out in the Atlantic report showers of silt when the Harmattan is at its height; such silt is conspicuous in sediments dredged from a wide area of the South Atlantic sea floor (Chapter 17).

Glaciers

Wind and water are mobile fluids that flow on application of even the slightest force. Solids, too, flow under certain conditions of pressure and temperature. Glaciers furnish excellent evidence of the flow of a solid under gravity. As a glacier slowly creeps and slides downhill impelled by its own weight, it drags with it the material beneath. Thus glaciers transport immense quantities of coarse rock waste; indeed, they are perhaps the most powerful agents of erosion per unit of area covered, but because they act upon relatively small areas they are quantitatively less effective erosional agents than downslope movements and streams.

The Nisqually Glacier (Fig. 5–4), easily reached by highway in Rainier National Park, has probably been visited by more people than any other in North America. The Nisqually is a pygmy among glaciers; less than 8 kilometers (5 miles) long and less than 300 meters (1000 feet) thick, it does not compare with the much larger Emmons and Winthrop Glaciers on the more remote, northeastern flank of Mount Rainier—not to mention the 100 kilometer (60 mile) long ice streams of Alaska or the gigantic Beardmore Glacier of Antarctica, 250 kilometers (155 miles) long and 5 to 25 kilometers (3 to 15 miles) wide.

No visitor can observe the snout of the Nisqually Glacier without being impressed by the tremendous erosive power of slow-moving ice masses. At the glacier front little ice is visible beneath the blocks of rock riding on the moving ice mass or being pushed forward before it. Many blocks are huge fragments of a distinctive porphyritic andesite torn from ledges far up the valley and carried down by the glacier. As the ice melts, the rock debris accumulates in huge hummocks in front of the glacier. Smaller piles

FIGURE 5–4   *Nisqually Glacier, Rainier National Park. The lobe in the central part of the picture is so heavily covered with rock debris that little ice is visible. Note the large streams of meltwater cascading from the base of this lobe; also the highly crevassed surface of the lobe at the left. (Courtesy V. R. Bender, National Park Service.)*

also lie on top and alongside the ice where frost-riven boulders have rolled down from the cliffs above (Fig. 5–2). Snowslides and streams of meltwater also carry debris onto the glacier surface.

For many years before 1956 the Nisqually Glacier had been slowly shrinking; since then its front has fluctuated a few meters from year to year but remains in nearly the same place. Downstream, below the glacier snout lie irregular piles of debris left as it retreated. The rock floor bared by the melting ice has been scored and polished by blocks of rock and finer material dragged across it by the glacier.

The meltwater gushing from tunnels in the snout of the Nisqually Glacier is a dirty milky white. If we collect a glassful, allow the sediment to settle, and examine it with a magnifying glass, we see that the sediment is not clay but finely ground **rock flour,** obviously pulverized by the grinding of rocks against each other and against the bedrock as they were dragged and crushed beneath the tremendous weight of the moving glacier.

The actual quantity of material carried by glaciers has rarely been measured but the few measurements that have been made are truly amazing. For example, the Susitna River, immediately below the snout of the Susitna Glacier in Alaska is carrying 0.1 percent of rock flour and sand—more than 520 million cubic feet of rock debris per year. The glacier covers about 180 square miles; it is therefore scouring into its bed at the rate of almost 0.1 foot (3 centimeters) per year —a hundred feet per thousand years! This is many times the annual average rate at which even the most voracious stream is lowering its drainage basin. Of course, thinner glaciers, or those in areas of lower precipitation can hardly be such effective erosional agents. Measurements of silt in meltwater from the Hoffelsjokul, a glacier in Iceland, indicate that it is cutting down only a sixth as fast as the Susitna, 5 millimeters per year, but even this is very rapid erosion—16 feet per thousand years.

Sea waves and nearshore currents

At the shore the sea vigorously attacks the land. Each oncoming breaker crashes against the beach, and as the wave recedes the water surges back toward the sea. Anyone who has watched the ceaseless play of the waves along an open coast (Fig. 5–5) recognizes here a powerful agent. Even moderate waves move sand and gravel; in great storms houses, breakwaters, and seaside roads have been destroyed overnight, ships driven against rocks and broken to matchwood, and huge boulders rolled about in the surf like bowling pins.

The effects of a major storm on an exposed open coast seem almost incredible. At Wick, in northern Scotland, a great storm in 1872 tore a concrete monolith (14 meters long, 8 meters wide, 3½ meters thick, and bound by 9-centimeter iron rods to the breakwater foundation) from its place, together with a huge piece of the foundation material, and dropped it unbroken inside the harbor. The total mass removed weighed 1350 tons. The monolith was replaced by one weighing 2600 tons, but five years later this, too, was torn away by the waves. At Tillamook Rock, on the Oregon coast, waves have repeatedly ricocheted stones off a curving rock platform and broken heavy plate-glass windows in the lighthouse, 40 meters above the sea. One fragment, weighing more than 60 kilograms, crashed through a roof more than 30 meters above sea level. At Dunnet Head, in northern Scotland, lighthouse windows 100 meters above the water are occasionally broken by storm-driven stones.

The shore of the open sea is clearly a zone of vigorous erosion. Storm-driven pebbles and sand act as a gigantic horizontal saw biting ceaselessly into the land. Most sea coasts of notable relief are cliffed because this ceaseless wave-driven saw rapidly undercuts the headlands. Valuable beach property must be protected from erosion, or in some places from unwanted deposits of new sand

FIGURE 5–5 *Wave breaking on a rocky headland near Yachats, Oregon. (Photo by Oregon State Highway Commission.)*

or gravel, by breakwaters, sand by-pass pumps, and other engineering works.

Detritus torn from the shore during a storm may be carried into deep water and deposited, or nearshore currents may drift it along the coast and drop it in protected areas, forming spits and sandbars. Sites of erosion and deposition shift with different storms, depending upon wind direction, tidal height, and the velocity of the nearshore currents.

One storm may drive enough sand along a beach to completely block a river; the next, with a more direct frontal attack, may sweep the accumulation of sand far out to sea. There the sand is deposited, or perhaps is transported underwater to still greater depths by currents of turbid sediment-laden water swirling down steep submarine canyons.

Streams

Although wind, glaciers, and ocean waves perform spectacular feats of erosion, their combined effect in eroding the land masses is subordinate: the streams, and such slope processes as rill wash and downslope movements, are the great levelers. Flooding rivers offer dramatic examples of erosion, as when the Milk River of Montana undermined a railroad bridge, tumbled a great Mallet engine into the swirling flood, and rolled it half a mile downstream. But the real reason that stream erosion is quantitatively important is because rain falls on all parts of the land and carries rock waste from them. Even the driest deserts and the glacier-clad slopes of Antarctica bear imprints left by running water.

In the years since the middle 1930's, rain-wash has almost completely obliterated the eroded hollows and the drifts of silt and sand left by the dust storm of May 12, 1934. Only in the driest deserts are wind-eroded features conspicuous, and even there numerous gullied slopes, dry stream beds, and sheets of water-deposited gravel show the stamp of the rare rainstorms upon the desert landscape.

At present, glaciers are confined to high mountain ranges and to polar regions; they cover only 10 percent of the lands. Although they strongly abrade the areas they occupy, their effect in wearing away the land as a whole is insignificant compared with that of streams.

Sea waves, too, are limited in scope and effect. The attack of the sea upon the land is confined to the shoreline and to the shallowly submerged margins of the land. On exposed open coasts, waves play a dominant role, but at places where the coast is protected, the tidal range low, and storms infrequent, stream deltas may advance into the sea more rapidly than the waves can carry the streamborne detritus away.

ANALYSIS OF STREAM EROSION.   To assess the role of streams in erosion let us look more closely into the source and amount of stream runoff, and the amounts of debris carried by different streams.

"What is the source of the water in rivers?" Aristotle and other early philosophers held that rainfall was entirely inadequate to account for the vast flow of water in rivers like the Danube and Nile, and that the earth's surface was too impervious to allow rain to percolate into the soil and rocks from which it could return as springs. Up to the middle of the seventeenth century, most people thought that the amount of water rising in springs and flowing to the ocean in streams was much too great to have come entirely from rain and snow.

The modern concept of **hydrology** (the science that treats of water) began with the work of a Frenchman, Pierre Perrault (1608–1680). Perrault measured both the rainfall and the amount of water flowing in the upper Seine, during a three-year period. From maps he estimated the drainage area above the point where he measured the river flow, and calculated that the Seine carried off only one-sixth of the water that fell in this basin as rain and snow. A few years later Edmund Halley, an English astronomer, showed by experiment that the moisture evaporated from the oceans entirely suffices to supply the runoff from streams. These measurements proved the fallacy of Aristotle's assumption that streams carry more water than falls on their drainage basins. Indeed, the problem of the streams was reversed—the question was no longer, "What is the source of water?" but, "What has become of vast volumes of water, equivalent to five times the flow of the Seine, that has fallen in its drainage basin but is not being carried out by the stream?"

THE HYDROLOGIC CYCLE.   The moisture precipitated on the land as rain and snow follows divergent paths (Fig. 5–6): (a) Some promptly evaporates from the ground surface and from the vegetation on which it falls. (b) Some is absorbed by roots of growing plants and is soon transpired back into the atmosphere through the leaves, although a little is locked up in the plant tissues until the plant dies and rots. (c) Some seeps into the soil and rocks where it is temporarily stored as **ground water.** Ground water fills pores, cracks, and larger openings in the soil and rocks and thus acts as a storehouse and equalizer for stream flow. Some of this ground water returns to the surface by capillary action and evaporates, some is delivered to the roots of growing plants, and much reappears at lower elevations, gushing forth in springs or seepages especially along the banks and bottoms of streams. Finally, (d) much water from rain and snow runs off in surface rills, brooks, and rivers.

Table 5–1 **Distribution of the world's estimated supply of water**

	Volume of water in 10^3 cubic miles	Percent of total
Surface water on the continents		
Polar ice caps and glaciers	7300	2.24
Fresh water lakes	30	0.009
Saline lakes and inland seas	25	0.008
Average in stream channels	0.28	0.0001
Subsurface water on continents	2000	0.61
Total water on the lands	9360	2.87
Atmospheric water	3.1	0.001
Oceanic water	317,000	97.1
Total world supply of water	326,000	100

SOURCE: After R. L. Nace, U.S. Geological Survey, 1960.

Runoff is defined as the total discharge of water by surface streams. It includes all the precipitation that flows across the surface immediately after rains, and the increments from ground water in springs and seepages that swell the streams. It is this runoff that erodes the lands.

The part of the precipitation that returns to the air by evaporation and transpiration is called the **evapotranspiration factor.** Hydrologists generally simplify the hydrologic cycle, by assuming that evapotranspiration can be determined by subtracting runoff from precipitation. Actually addition to or subtraction from the ground-water reservoir may invalidate this assumption for a short period, though in the long run it seems roughly to balance out.

The equation

Precipitation = Runoff + Evapotranspiration

is only approximate, however, even when ground-water storage remains constant. It neglects many locally important, though generally unmeasurable factors, such as the seepage of water through the soil and rock directly into the sea. For the continents as a whole, such seepage is trivial, but in areas of rock as permeable as the lava and cinders of the Hawaiian Islands, or the cavernous dolo-

mites of Yugoslavia, it may dispose of most of the rainfall. Another minor factor is the amount of water that combines chemically when minerals are weathered. An estimate of the distribution of the earth's waters is given in Table 5–1. From this table it can be seen that nearly 80 percent of the water on and in the continents is in the form of ice. Most of the rest is underground; all of the liquid surface water amounts to less than one percent of the total.

The hydrologic cycle is depicted graphically in Figure 5–6. The sun provides the energy to operate this great system of waterworks. Solar energy warms and evaporates water from the ocean and the land and stimulates the growth of plants, which transpire water vapor into the atmosphere through their pores. Winds waft the water vapor inland and raise it high, thus cooling and condensing it into rain, hail, and snow. On falling, some of the water gathers into streams that sweep soil and rock debris into the sea.

FACTORS AFFECTING RUNOFF.   The ratio of runoff to precipitation is not everywhere the 1 to 6 that Perrault calculated for the basin of the upper Seine. Measurements made by the U.S. Geological Survey in many drainage basins of the United States reveal wide variation in the ratio of runoff to precipitation. Among the many factors that affect this ratio are the following:

Amount and duration of rainfall.—The distribution of rainfall through the year greatly influences runoff. Rain uniformly distributed in many small showers may be largely evaporated or absorbed by the ground before it reaches flowing streams, but during violent and heavy rainstorms infiltration is too slow to capture much water, and evaporation is negligible. Rapid melting of the winter snowpack is another common cause of river flooding.

If the annual rainfall is high, 200 centimeters (80 inches) or more, the ground is generally waterlogged and most rain runs off, even though it is uniformly distributed. In deserts, on the other hand, the scant rainfall is quickly absorbed by the parched soil, or evaporated, and little runs off except after violent storms.

Permeability of the ground.—Soils and rocks differ greatly in **permeability** (ability to transmit water). Most rain that falls on the porous ash of a fresh cinder cone immediately sinks in to become part of the ground water, but nearly all that falls on a similar slope of shale runs off because the pores in shale are so minute that the rock is almost impermeable, even though saturated shale can hold about as much water as ash. Tests show that a sandy loam will accept more than ten times as much water in a given time than will a soil made wholly of clay. The ability of a soil to accept rain or snowmelt depends on other physical conditions besides permeability. Waterlogged soil, even though highly permeable, can hold no more water; neither can frozen ground. A highly permeable soil, once saturated, may also allow little more to sink in because the subsoil or bedrock below is impermeable. Permeability, of the surficial

FIGURE 5–6
The hydrologic cycle.

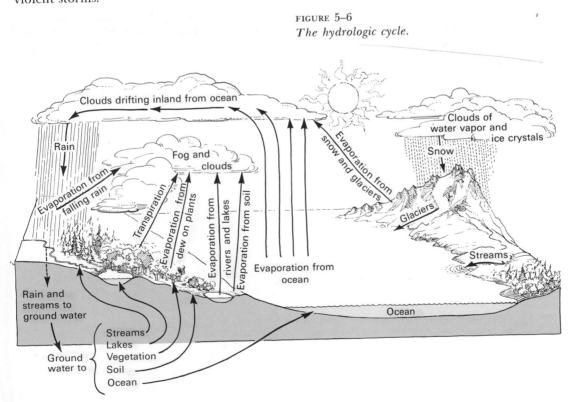

material, then, does not alone control infiltration. Hydrologists use the term "infiltration capacity" to define the maximum rate at which soil, in a given physical condition, can absorb falling rain. Tests of infiltration capacity, made by playing sprinklers on enclosed plots from which runoff is caught and measured, show, as would be expected, that the rate of absorption is high at the beginning of a rain, then quickly diminishes until a fairly constant rate, which differs with conditions of each plot, is reached.

Vegetation.—Vegetation retards the runoff. Matted sod or the mulch of decaying leaves and twigs in a forest absorb rain like a blotter. Earthworms and other burrowing animals that live in plant-rich soil aid percolation by opening tunnels to the surface. Heavy coniferous forests may hold much snow on the tree branches, increasing the evaporation losses.

Very striking increases in runoff have been observed where forests have been burned off, or the natural sod plowed under, as in the Dust Bowl. Figure 5–10 summarizes some data for areas with differing vegetative cover.

Temperature.—Temperature profoundly affects runoff. Evaporation and transpiration are much greater in warm regions than in cold; for a given rainfall, the higher the temperature, the smaller the runoff. The data for the United States have been summarized by Walter B. Langbein, an hydrologist of the U.S. Geological Survey, in Figure 5–7. The graph shows that, with an average annual precipitation of 100 cm (40 inches), more than half (54 cm or 21.5 inches) runs off where the mean annual temperature is 4°C (40°F); but only 26 cm (10.2 inches) where the mean annual temperature is 16°C (60°F), and less than 7.6 cm (3 inches) where it is 27°C (80°F).

Slope.—Slope obviously influences runoff strongly. Steep mountain slopes of barren

rock shed nearly all their rain, but on flat ground, shallow puddles hold much rain water until it evaporates or is absorbed by soil and plants.

These variables effect marked differences in runoff in different stream basins. In the western United States, for example, runoff varies tremendously with differences in rainfall, temperature, infiltration capacity, and other local conditions. The range is from less than 6 mm (0.25 inch) of runoff (about 6 percent of total rainfall) in the desert of southwestern Arizona to more than 200 cm (80 inches; about 75 percent of total rainfall) on the western slopes of the Olympic and Cascade Mountains of Washington. In the States east of the Mississippi, runoff is much less variable, rarely less than 25 cm (10 inches) or more than 75 cm (30 inches).

AMOUNT OF WATER AVAILABLE FOR EROSION. Although meteorologists estimate that the atmosphere carries enough water over the United States every year to form a layer 150 inches thick, four-fifths of this passes by; the average rainfall, determined from hundreds of rain-gaging stations is only a fifth of this: 75 cm (30 inches). The average runoff for the country as a whole is less than a third of

FIGURE 5–7

Variation of runoff with rainfall and temperature. (After W. B. Langbein, Circular 52, U.S. Geological Survey, 1949.)

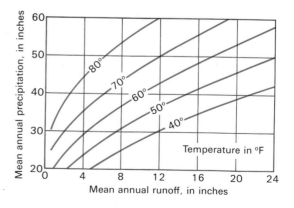

Table 5–2 **World Distribution of Runoff**

Continent (or other area)	Area, in thousands of square kilometers	Area, in thousands of square miles	Runoff, in centimeters	Runoff, in inches
Europe (including Iceland)	10,372	3734	26.0	10.3
Asia (including Japanese and Philippine Islands)	45,336	16,321	17.0	6.7
Africa (including Madagascar)	31,972	11,510	20.3	8.0
Australia (including Tasmania and New Zealand)	8541	3075	7.6	3.0
South America	19,280	6941	45.0	17.7
North America (including West Indies and Central America)	21,925	7893	29.5	12.4
Greenland and Canadian Archipelago	4164	1499	18.0	7.1
Malayan Archipelago	2811	1012	160.0	63.0
Totals	144,401	51,985		
Means			27.0	10.5

SOURCE: From Langbein, after L'vovich.

this: 22 cm (8.6 inches). The difference, 75 cm less 22 cm = 53 cm (21.4 inches), is the amount of precipitation returned to the atmosphere by evapotranspiration. The United States thus has a ratio of runoff to precipitation of about 1 to 3.5, in contrast with the ratio of 1 to 6 determined by Perrault for the basin of the upper Seine. Stream gaging shows that the rivers of the United States deliver 50,400 cubic meters (1,800,000 cubic feet) of water per second to the sea (about 1500 cubic kilometers or 330 cubic miles per year). Roughly a third of this is carried by the Mississippi.

Data for precipitation and runoff on other continents are less complete. L'vovich, a Russian hydrologist, has made estimates on a worldwide basis. His results, summarized in Table 5–2, give the world average runoff as 27 centimeters or 10.5 inches per year. Other hydrologists give somewhat lower figures, from 19 to 23 centimeters.

Despite these uncertainties, we can estimate fairly reliably the total water available for erosion: The average annual precipitation over the land areas of the earth is a little more than one meter, about 40 inches.

Thus each year approximately 160,000 cubic kilometers or 35,000 cubic miles of water falls on the land as rain and snow. The rivers return to the ocean something between 19 and 27 centimeters (7.5 and 10.5 inches) per year. As an average then, about 37,000 cubic kilometers or 8000 cubic miles of water courses off the lands into the seas each year. This is the amount available for the erosion of the land.

ENERGY AVAILABLE FROM THE RUNOFF. On the average, the surface of the land stands about 800 meters or half a mile above sea level, so that the runoff falls an average of 800 meters as it flows from source to ocean. This is only an average: runoff from a coastal plain may descend only a few meters to reach the ocean, the meltwater from the snows of Mount Everest falls more than 9 kilometers. A tremendous amount of energy is developed by the world's streams in descending to the sea: imagine all the continental runoff concentrated in one gigantic waterfall—37,000 cubic kilometers or 8000 cubic miles of water per year tumbling down a waterfall 800 meters high! Such a waterfall could continuously supply about 72 horsepower per each square kilometer, or 200 horsepower for each square mile of land, enough to keep almost 60 million bulldozers in continuous operation. All this energy is available for erosion. Although few streams work at full capacity, it is easy to see why running water is the great leveler.

Rate of denudation

Streams carry dissolved and clastic material from the lands to the sea, wearing away the mountains, hills, and plains; we are curious about the rate at which this lowering is accomplished. Clearly the rate of denudation must vary tremendously from one region to another. In humid areas a mat of vegetation protects the natural surface and holds the soil so that relatively much less is washed into the streams than in the barren arid regions. Measurements have shown brush lands more erodible than forest, virgin grass land, much less. Where slopes are steep, erosion is obviously faster than in flatlands, even in the same climatic regimen. Where the surface rocks are permeable more of the rainfall sinks into the ground, there to dissolve rock material; where they are impermeable more runs off, sweeping clastic material along. Erodibility of soils is closely related to ease of dispersion of the soil into separate particles; studies in California show that clays with much adsorbed calcium and magnesium are sticky and hence more resistant to erosion than soils depleted in these ions. Such sticky clay serves as a binder. Rocks that are well cemented or massive are obviously less readily eroded than fine-grained unconsolidated silts. These and other factors make clear that denudation of the land varies greatly from region to region. Unfortunately, we have few quantitative data.

The total load, dissolved and clastic, carried by a stream is difficult to measure, and varies widely, both among streams in different climates and between high and low-water stages in any particular stream. The load consists of three fractions: 1, that in **solution;** 2, that in **suspension;** and 3, that dragged or bouncing along the bottom, the **traction** or **bed load.** The first two are easily measured by sampling during measurement of stream discharge. But samplers that reach the very bottom of the stream obviously disturb the sediment flow and yield a distorted sample; accurate measures of bed load are few.

The dissolved load is only a small fraction of the total in the sediment-laden streams of arid regions—as small as $\frac{1}{20}$. In regions of higher rainfall it is a much larger fraction of the total, and in such humid areas of low relief as the South Atlantic and eastern Gulf of Mexico watersheds, more than half of the stream load is in solution. This is also true of the St. Lawrence because most of the clastic load of its tributaries is trapped in the Great Lakes. Estimates for the world as a whole suggest that perhaps 30 percent of stream load is carried in solution.

The proportion of the clastic load carried in suspension also differs greatly from one stream to another and from time to time in any particular stream, depending on the stage of flow. Careful estimates on the Niobrara River in Nebraska suggest that fully half the clastic detritus is carried as bed load, but study of the Mississippi indicates that only 7 to 10 percent of its load is similarly entrained. Measurements of Colorado River sediments trapped in Lake Mead suggest that its traction load is almost negligible. Most hydrologists think that on the average perhaps 10 percent of the clastic load of most streams is in the traction load, and so is not sampled when suspended loads are measured.

Not only is accurate measurement of stream load at any particular time difficult, it is even more difficult to obtain a meaningful long-term average. Load in some streams varies tremendously—often by several orders of magnitude from low-water to flood stage.

Even on an annual basis the load of the Delaware was five times as great one year as it had been the year before. Most hydrologists believe it likely that even in the rivers of relatively steady flow the exceptional "fifty-year flood" carries off as much sediment as is normally carried in an entire year. The common large floods that occur about twice in three years, however, probably transport most of the sediment. Few accurate estimates of steam flow and sediment load in the United States extend over more than a few decades; it is thus easy to see that estimates of the rate of denudation are necessarily rough, and all are perhaps somewhat below a true long-term average rate.

Each year the Mississippi pours almost 500 million tons of dissolved and clastic material into the Gulf of Mexico. Though generally thought a muddy stream, the Mississippi carries only about ½ percent by weight of rock waste. Even the Missouri, often called the "Big Muddy," rarely carries more than 2 percent. This is a high load for a big river, though it is exceeded by the Colorado, the Hoang Ho of China, and a few others. The Colorado, between 1925 and 1957, carried an annual average of more than 150,000 tons of waste past the Grand Canyon. On the other hand, the Columbia, a dashing, turbulent stream, full of rollers and gigantic eddies before it was tamed by a dozen giant dams, carried very little silt and mud above its junction with the muddy Snake. The Columbia flows on bedrock and coarse boulders, and most of its tributaries head in forested mountains; little fine debris is available to it. In contrast, the Missouri in the Great Plains crosses hundreds of miles of shale, poorly bound by scant vegetation and pulverized by cattle grazing and the plow: abundant fine-grained waste is readily at hand.

Many smaller streams in arid or semiarid regions carry enormously greater loads per unit of volume than these large rivers. During floods many desert streams may contain as much as 30 percent by weight of rock de-

bris. The San Juan, in southwestern Colorado, carried over 75 percent by weight of silt and sand during one flood; such highly loaded streams grade into mud flows. A small drainage basin in the Loess Hills area of Iowa yielded in one year more than 30,000 kilograms of sediment per square kilometer (90 tons per square mile) of drainage area. This exceptional rate was attained, however, because the hills are made of very weakly coherent silt. In semiarid western Nebraska some small streams carry each year as much as 100 kilograms of load per square kilometer of watershed, but in humid New York and Connecticut comparable streams carry less than one percent as much.

W. B. Langbein and S. A. Schumm of the U.S. Geological Survey have produced the generalized diagram of Figure 5–8 to show the variation of sediment yield in the United States with climate. This shows that sediment yield is greatest in areas of only 15 inches of rainfall, where the runoff is only half an inch! These are the conditions of central Kansas and Nebraska.

A careful study of rates of denudation in the United States has been carried out by

FIGURE 5–8

Relation of precipitation to annual sediment yield, measured in tons per square mile. (From W. B. Langbein and S. A. Schumm, 1958.)

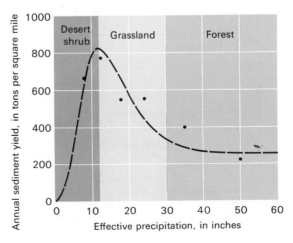

Table 5–3 **Rates of regional denudation in the United States**

Drainage system	Area, in 10³ sq mi	Runoff, in 10³ cu ft per sec	Load, in tons per sq mi per yr			Denudation in inches per 10³ yr	Years of record
			Dissolved	Solid	Total		
Colorado	246	23	65	1190	1255	6.5	32
Pacific slope in California	117	80	103	597	700	3.6	4
Western Gulf of Mexico	320	55	118	288	406	2.1	9
Mississippi	1250	620	110	268	378	2.0	12
South Atlantic & eastern Gulf	284	325	175	139	314	1.6	7
North Atlantic	148	210	163	198	361	1.9	5
Columbia	262	345	163	125	288	1.5	Less than 2
Totals	2627	1658					
Averages			121	340	461	2.4	

SOURCE: After Judson and Ritter, 1964.

NOTE: Great Basin, St. Lawrence, and Hudson Bay drainages are not considered.

Judson and Ritter. Their results are summarized in Table 5–3.

The average rate of denudation of the country as a whole, 2.4 inches per thousand years, is thus one foot in 5,000 years (one meter in 16,600 years). It is noteworthy that this figure, which is based on many more data, is nearly twice the rate estimated in 1909.

Dramatic differences occur in rates of denudation of different regions—four times as great in the arid watershed of the Colorado as in the humid Pacific northwest or the South Atlantic and Eastern Gulf States. Furthermore, the ratio of dissolved to detrital load ranges from 5 percent in the arid Southwest to more than 55 percent in the humid Northeast and Southeast, demonstrating clearly the influence of climate. Judson and Ritter have shown that there is an inverse relation in the United States between the detrital and dissolved loads of streams. The lower the runoff per unit of area of drainage basin, the higher the proportion of detrital load (see Fig. 5–9). Conversely, the higher the runoff the greater the ratio of dissolved to detrital load.

The influence of slope on rates of erosion is obvious, but there are few quantitative data. Measurements of pegs driven into weakly coherent shale in the Navajo Reservation in Arizona showed erosion on slopes of between 20 and 40 degrees at an average rate of 5.7 mm per year during a period of 14 years. On slopes of less than 10 degrees the rate was less than half as great, 2.5 mm per year, but still far higher than in more humid

FIGURE 5–9

Relations in various regions between detrital and dissolved loads. (After Sheldon Judson and D. F. Ritter, Journal of Geophysical Research, 1964.)

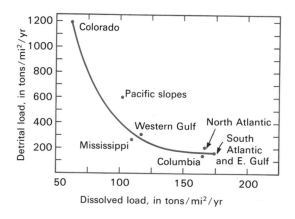

regions. Studies of root systems and tree-ring ages of the very long-lived bristlecone pines of the White Mountains, California, show that the steep slopes are being eroded at rates between 240 and 360 mm per thousand years (10 to 14 inches). Sediment caught by debris dams below the San Gabriel Mountains of southern California over a period of two or three decades show denudation ranging between 60 and 200 mm per thousand years; this measuring method, of course, neglects the solution fraction. But in the great flood of 1938 one fairly large drainage basin was lowered an average of 14 mm (more than half an inch) in only 5 days. These rates are far higher than the rate of 50 mm per thousand years of the Mississippi, and scores of times greater than the rate for the Hudson Bay lowlands.

Measurements of the detritus carried by mountain torrents of the Swiss Alps show denudation of 600 mm per thousand years —twelve times the rate of the Mississippi Basin—but the loads of the Rhine and Rhone as they leave Switzerland show that nine-tenths of this material is trapped in alluvial fans, deltas, and in bottom sediments of the Swiss lakes; it is long delayed in reaching the sea. The Kosi River, which drains the highest peaks in the world, Mounts Everest and Kanchenjunga, is lowering its basin at the rate of about 3.2 feet per 1,000 years, about twice the rate for the western Ganges or for the Durance River, which drains the French Alps. The Irrawaddy and Chindwin, which drain the eastern Himalayas, are nearly as efficient: 2.5 feet per 1000 years.

In Italy, careful estimates of transport from the various river systems over the period from 1918 to 1960 vary between 30 and 900 mm per 1000 years (one foot in 330 years and one foot in 10,000 years). From wooded areas the loss was commonly a tenth of that from the barrens; from weak sedimentary rocks the loss was generally 4 or 5 times that from crystalline rocks of comparable relief.

J. Corbel, a French hydrologist, has made estimates of erosion under various climatic and topographic conditions. See Table 5–4. His figures are of very uneven quality owing to inadequate sampling and variable estimates of bed load. Although these figures are

Table 5–4 **Estimates of the rate of erosion under various conditions of climate and relief**

Physiographic setting	*Estimated rate of erosion, in cm per 1000 years*
Lowlands—gradient = .001 or less	
Hot moist climate with dry season	3.2
Climate with cold winter	2.9
Intermediate maritime climate	2.7
Equatorial climate (dense rain forest)	2.2
Hot, dry climate (Mediterranean, New Mexico)	1.2
Mountains—gradient = 0.01 or more	
Hot moist climate (Guatemala-Mexico border)	92.
Extremely snowy climate (Southeastern Alaska)	80.
Semihumid, near-glacial climate	60.
High Mediterranean mountains	45.
Hot dry climate, (southwestern United States, Tunisia)	18.

SOURCE: After J. Corbel, 1959.

subject to considerable error (and indeed are not in very close agreement with those of Judson and Ritter, which are based on more recent data for the United States), they strongly suggest a wide range in the rate of erosion under different climatic and relief conditions—a range of more than 75 to 1. Yet even the lowest rate is noteworthy, implying, as it does, an average degradation of 12 meters per million years.

Although all these figures are uncertain and perhaps in error by many percent, they are nevertheless significant. If the present rate of erosion for the entire United States were maintained, and if there were no compensating upward movements of parts of the earth's crust, the country would be eroded to sea level in about 14 million years. This is a tremendous time span by human standards, but, as will be shown in Chapter 7, it is very short in terms of the total length of geologic time.

CHANGES IN THE RATE OF EROSION.   There are many reasons for thinking that the loads of present-day streams are higher than the average loads in the geologic past. Rivers in popu-

lous areas carry industrial and municipal wastes in addition to their normal loads. Enormous areas are roofed and under pavements that prevent rain from soaking into the ground, thereby very appreciably adding to flood heights in cities and suburbs. Vast quantities of silt and mud are annually washed into streams from cultivated fields once covered with forest or grass. That cultivation greatly increases the rate of erosion has been proved by the Soil Conservation Service of the United States Department of Agriculture, which made extensive tests of the amounts of soil and water running off plots of ground with identical areas and slope, but different vegetative covers. A few results from these tests are given in Figure 5–10.

Though the changes in rate of erosion brought about by man's activities cannot be precisely evaluated and the erosion rates during earlier times cannot be determined accurately, the present estimated rate of one millimeter in 295 years (one foot in 5000 years) for the United States is certainly greater than the average of the past. To judge from the volume of sediment on the continental mar-

FIGURE 5–10
Results of soil-erosion tests on plots of ground with different vegetative covers. (Redrawn by permission from H. H. Bennett, Soil Conservation, *McGraw-Hill, 1939.)*

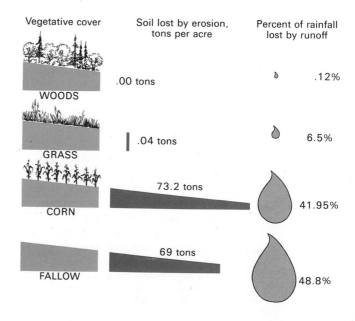

gins, however, the present rate is probably less than twice the average of prehuman times.

SOIL EROSION.   In classical Greece many cities prohibited the grazing of goats and sheep because these omniverous animals so denuded the land of vegetation that the soil washed away in a few years, leaving barren rock. Despite such regulations, in two or three thousand years, goat grazing and other damaging agricultural practices have impoverished most of the Mediterranean countries of soil. The hills of Italy and Greece today are largely barren rock; Tunisia and Tripoli were once the granaries of Rome, today they are agriculturally unimportant because of soil erosion.

In many sections of the United States, too, the productive topsoil is rapidly disappearing. From thousands of acres of once-fertile lands the A- and B-horizons of the original soil profiles have been removed, and the almost sterile C-horizons are deeply carved by steep-walled gullies. At least 300 million acres of former farmland have thus been rendered sterile. The soil conservationist has difficulty in reconciling this striking evidence of damaging erosion with a rate of denudation of only one foot in 5000 years. Most of our productive soils are at least a foot thick. How can so much damage have been done in the few decades since the sod of the frontier was plowed? Only after many studies like those diagrammed in Figure 5–10 were made on thousands of soil plots scattered all over the United States did we know: most of the soil washed from the fields is almost immediately redeposited at the foot of the slopes, in ditches, beside roads, or along the stream channels; only a small part is carried immediately to the sea. Thus, although one foot per 5000 years may be a reasonable estimate of total lowering of the continent, it does not represent the much greater local erosion and immediate redeposition of primary concern to the soil conservationist and to the farmer.

EROSION BENEATH THE SEA

The sediment eroded from the landmasses ultimately reaches the seas and there is deposited in deltas or on the floor of the shelf seas that border much of the continents, or is drifted by waves and currents into deeper waters. Deposition predominates in the seas —"the oceans are the graveyards of the lands"—but it is not the only process that modifies the sea floor. Erosion also goes on over great areas, even in the depths of the ocean. Before we can discuss this, we must describe some pertinent features of the topography of the sea floor.

The dark abyss of the sea has always been difficult to study. Until a generation ago hydrographic maps were based wholly upon scattered soundings taken from shipboard. These soundings were made by paying out a wire with a weight attached until the weight touched bottom. The ship's position was known only through astronomic observations and dead reckoning, and there was no way of telling if currents kept the wire from hanging vertically. By this tedious and inaccurate method a few of the outstanding topographic features of the sea floor were crudely outlined during the time before World War II. Since then methods of submarine sounding have been revolutionized: first with the development of sonic sounding and of position control by radio and sonic buoys, and lately by the development of the "precision profiler," an automatically recording device that emits powerful sound waves at accurately timed intervals in a narrow cone directed downward beneath the ship. The reflections of the sound waves from the narrow cone come from a much narrower area than those received from early sonic sounders, which often received interfering echoes over rough bottom topography. The new instruments receive clearly recorded definite pulses reflected from the surface of the ocean floor, and, in addition, reflections from shallow strata, some buried as much as several hundred meters within the sea-floor sediments. These advances in techniques have revolutionized our knowledge of the topography and processes beneath the sea.

Major relief features of the ocean floor

The major topographic provinces of the ocean are: the continental shelves, continental slopes, continental rises, abyssal cones, abyssal plains, ridges, and rises. Inferences about the structure and origin of these provinces are discussed more fully in Chapter 16; here we refer to some whose relations bear directly on our topic, erosion.

The **continental shelves** are the submerged edges of the continents (Fig. 16–30). Off much of the continental margins the sea floor falls off gradually at a slope that may be as little as 1:1000 but perhaps averages 3 or 4 meters per kilometer (15 or 20 feet per mile). At an average distance of about 50 kilometers (30 miles) from shore the shelf ends abruptly, and the continental slope begins. The depth of this break between shelf and slope is by no means uniform: generally it is at about 150 meters (500 feet), but in the Barents Sea and off Norway and Labrador it is as deep as 450 meters (1500 feet) and around the Antarctic continent it varies between 300 and 700 meters, averaging perhaps 450 to 500 meters. Nor is the width of the shelf uniform: off Chile and much of southwestern Alaska there is no shelf at all, whereas on the Arctic coast of Siberia the shelf is more than 1,350 kilometers (800 miles) wide. Altogether the shelves cover about 7 percent of the sea floor.

The **continental slope,** near some mountainous coasts begins at the shore line, and may drop off at slopes as steep as 1:6 and perhaps averages 1:20. Off most wide coastal plains the slope is only half as steep, but it is everywhere far steeper than the shelves. Off most shores the continental slope extends to great depths, commonly 2000 to 3000 meters, where it gives way to the **continental rise, a** considerably gentler slope with a gradient

between, say, 1:50 and 1:700. Next, at depths between 4000 and 5000 meters, are either **abyssal hills** or the extremely featureless **abyssal plains** of the ocean floor. The slopes of the abyssal plains are flatter than one meter per kilometer and may be even as low as 1:7000. An abyssal plain may cover an area of many thousands of square kilometers, and show less relief than even the flattest continental land surface of comparable size.

A most significant group of submarine features are the huge **abyssal cones** that extend offshore from the Mississippi, Congo, Ganges, Indus, and Magdalena Rivers. These cones have their apices at the river mouths and extend from shallow water across the continental slope and rise to merge at their bases with abyssal plains. They are clearly composed of sediment derived from the rivers. They are depositional rather than erosional features, but show by their form that sediment is carried to great oceanic depths by gravity.

Elsewhere most of the continental slopes are cut by a maze of **submarine canyons** of all sizes, some deeper and more precipitous than the Grand Canyon of the Colorado. Many can be traced to great depths. A few canyons begin off the mouths of large rivers such as the Hudson and Congo; others, equally impressive, begin at the shoreline, far from the mouth of any stream, and many more begin as notches in the continental shelf far from land. The origin of such canyons has been vigorously debated (the characteristics of the larger canyons and the various hypotheses as to their origin are given in Chapter 16). The fact that most steep submarine slopes are scored by countless ravines and small canyons, much like those on land except for their steeper gradients, favors the suggestion that they have been eroded by submarine currents, loaded with silt and sand, coursing down the steep continental slopes under the influence of gravity. Such currents, flowing under still water by virtue of their higher density derived from suspended sediment, are **turbidity**

currents. Observations in bathyscaphes show that sediment does indeed stream down some canyons; the question remains whether these turbidity currents are merely taking advantage of the steep slopes of the canyons, or whether the canyons owe their origin to erosion by them.

Turbidity currents

Aviators in the Arctic report that some silt-laden streams of meltwater discharged from the large Greenland icecap do not halt or spread out when they enter the sea but dive and flow on beneath the clear water of the fjords.

Soon after the building of Hoover Dam, when Lake Mead was only half-filled with relatively clear impounded water, outlet pipes more than 60 meters (200 feet) above the base of the dam discharged surges of silt-laden water from time to time. At this stage of reservoir filling the muddy Colorado River entered Lake Mead about 160 kilometers (100 miles) above the dam. Much of its sediment settled out in a delta at the head of the lake, but samples of water from the lake bottom, and data on currents from a flowmeter, revealed that muddy water was cascading over the front of the delta and flowing the full length of the reservoir on the bottom. At the dam the turbidity current still retained enough energy to boil up to the outlet pipes, 60 meters above. Similar turbidity currents have been observed in Elephant Butte Reservoir on the Rio Grande, in Lake Leman, in Switzerland, off the mouth of the Magdalena River in Colombia, and at many other places.

Turbidity currents like those in Lake Mead or the Greenland fjords can be made in the laboratory. If water made denser by dissolved colored salts, or by suspended sediment, is poured into clear water filling a tank with a sloping bottom, turbidity currents much like those in reservoirs develop (Fig. 5–11). Experiments show that such currents have enough energy to pick up loose particles from the bottom, and thus confirm the theory that currents of turbid water flowing down continental slopes with inclinations of 35 to 50 meters per kilometer (200 to 300 feet per mile) can actively erode those slopes.

THE GRAND BANKS TURBIDITY FLOW. The American oceanographers Heezen and Ewing have shown that a very large turbidity current swiftly overwhelmed 280,000 square kilometers (100,000 square miles) of the floor of the North Atlantic. New England and the Maritime Provinces of Canada were rocked by an earthquake centering at the edge of the Grand Banks off Nova Scotia on November 18, 1929. During the quake, and in the first thirteen hours following, thirteen transatlantic telegraph cables were broken: ten parted in two places and three in three places. The broken segment of each cable was more than 160 kilometers (a hundred miles) long. All the broken cables lay along the steep continental slope south of the Grand Banks, or on the gently sloping ocean floor below and south of the slope. None of the many cables that lay on the Grand Banks (a part of the continental shelf) were broken. Each break was timed precisely by the interruptions of the teletype machines and accurately located by measurements of the electrical resistance of the cables, a method long used in cable repair.

FIGURE 5–11
Turbidity current in a laboratory tank. (After photos by H. S. Bell, Sedimentation Laboratory, California Institute of Technology.)

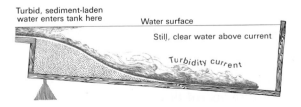

Turbid, sediment-laden water enters tank here   Water surface

Still, clear water above current

Turbidity current

FIGURE 5–12

Profile of the sea floor off the Grand Banks, showing by arrows the positions of transatlantic cables broken by the landslide and turbidity flow started by the earthquake of November 18, 1929. (Modified from B. C. Heezen and M. Ewing, 1952.)

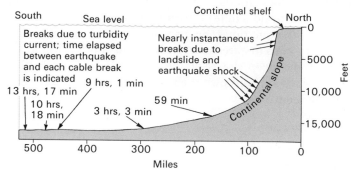

When the times and positions of the breaks were compared, an interesting correlation was found (Fig. 5–12). Eight cables high on the slope broke almost instantaneously during the earthquake. The other five broke successively in order of their positions downslope. The highest of the five parted 59 minutes after the quake, the lowest, 490 kilometers (295 miles) farther downslope, 13 hours and 17 minutes later. Heezen and Ewing concluded that the earthquake started a landslide in the weakly consolidated sediment of the continental slope. This broke the first eight cables. As the water-soaked sediment tumbled and cascaded down the steep submarine slope, the motion disrupted the weak cement binding the mineral grains together, throwing the unconsolidated material violently into suspension, to produce a rapidly flowing, heavy, turbulent liquid, which squirted forth on a wide front from the foot of the landslide. As this sediment-laden turbidity current poured down the slope, it broke each cable as it engulfed it. The velocity could be calculated from the times and the distances between cable breaks. The current was traveling about 100 kilometers (58 miles) an hour near the base of the continental slope, but had slowed to a little less than 25 kilometers (14 miles) an hour when it snapped the last cable, nearly 500 kilometers downslope. The higher speed is much greater than that of most mountain torrents and is surely great enough to erode vigorously.

Kuenen compared this turbidity flow with currents artificially produced in experimental tanks. From its calculated velocity he concluded that it must have advanced far beyond the last cable break, even on the relatively flat ocean floor, and that it may have transported fine sand more than 800 kilometers (500 miles) from the base of the landslide, and spread it over approximately 280,000 square kilometers of deep sea bottom. This far travel has been partly confirmed by the dredging of "clean sharp sand" from many points within the area.

Other evidence of submarine erosion

Since the invention of the underwater camera and oriented recording current meters we have abundant evidence of the existence of strong currents at great depths. Where the Gulf Stream sweeps across the Blake Plateau off the Florida Coast, current ripples like those in swift-flowing streams are common. Current ripples abound at many other places also: on the Scotia Ridge east of Burdwood Bank in the South Atlantic, where the cold Antarctic water pours into the South Atlantic at depths of 1,700 fathoms; in the Romanche Trench, which transects the Mid-Atlantic Ridge near the Equator; on the very bottom of the Pacific floor off Eniwetok Atoll (Fig. 5–13); and even in the bottom of the Philippine Deep. A generation ago, had features such as these been seen in consolidated marine sediments on land they would almost certainly have been interpreted as proof of shallow water; now we know that strong currents flow at depths of several kilometers below sea level.

Submarine cables, heavily armored by steel wires and thick insulation, are so abraded by sediment-laden currents where they cross the Mid-Atlantic Ridge (at depths as great as 2000 meters), that they must be replaced every twenty-five years. Clearly, such powerfully abrasive currents must wear away rocks as well. Strong currents have been measured sweeping coarse detritus down deep abyssal canyons, and the detritus they carry and deposit on great aprons at the base of the submarine slopes has been sampled in core barrels driven into the bottom.

True, strong currents probably affect relatively much less of the submarine areas than of the land. Erosion of submarine mountains undoubtedly proceeds more slowly than erosion of mountains on the land, but in both environments erosion is primarily the work of streaming sediment-laden water. The vast size of the sea and the relative inaccessibility

of its depths makes difficut the measurement of current flow and load, and leaves many fascinating questions still unanswered.

THE BASIC PRINCIPLE UNDERLYING EROSION PROCESSES

Our brief look at the processes that erode the earth's surface brings out one striking principle: Gravity is the driving force of erosion. Glaciers, downslope movements, landslides, soil creep, and fluid flow are all driven by gravity. Distant transport is nearly all accomplished by fluids—water, and to a lesser extent the wind—moving in response to gravitational forces. During their flow, fluids entrain rock waste whose added weight makes the flowing current even more powerful in seeking its lowest possible level.

Although differing in many characteristics, a dust storm in air, a turbidity current in the sea, a silt-laden river, or an ash flow of expanding pumice and gas racing down the slopes of a volcano, are all basically similar. Each is a current of fluid, with entrained rock particles, and each is out of gravitational equilibrium with the less dense fluids that surround it. This fundamental principle applies even to glaciers. Ice is a solid whose threshold strength must be exceeded before flow begins, but once plastic flow has started it responds in the same way as a viscous fluid.

The emphasis of this chapter has been upon the dominant role of gravity in *powering erosion,* but it must not be forgotten that the active agents of erosion—the rains, the snows, the winds, and the waves—could not persist without solar radiation. Solar radiation heats the water and the land surfaces, causing the density differences in atmosphere and ocean that set the wind and ocean currents in motion. Solar radiation evaporates water vapor into the air, and the winds disperse it in rain or snow over the whole earth. Gravity's role is the constant effort to restore these changes in density to a state of equilibrium.

FIGURE 5–13

Current ripples in calcareous sand on the ocean bottom at a depth of 2000 meters (6600 feet). Southwest slope of Eniwetok Atoll, Marshall Islands. (Underwater photo by C. J. Shipek, U.S. Navy Electronics Laboratory.)

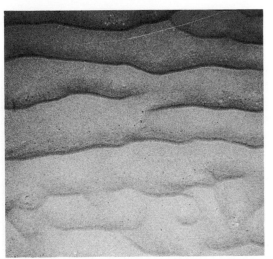

GEOLOGIC EVIDENCE OF EROSION

Nearly all of the data on which this chapter is based became known during the past hundred years, and much of it only within the past thirty or forty. Since the earliest days of the science, however, geologists have recognized the vast changes in the landscape wrought by running water. Early geologists, however, were less concerned with the analysis of the process than they were with the etched surface of the earth itself (see Fig. 5–15; also Figs. 9–6, 12–35).

Over 150 years ago John Playfair, a British mathematician and geologist, nicely summarized the evidence that streams have cut their valleys:

Every river appears to consist of a main trunk, fed from a variety of branches, each running in a valley proportioned to its size, and all of them together form a system of vallies, communical with one another, and having such a nice adjustment of their declivities, that none of them join the principal valley, either on too high or too low a level, a circumstance which would be infinitely improbable if each of these vallies were not the work of the stream that flows in it.

At first glance, the deep gash of the Grand Canyon (Fig. 5–14), or the cliffs bordering a glacier on Mount Rainier (Fig. 5–4), seem to have been produced by some great catastrophe that split the earth apart. But look more critically into the relations. Although beds of flat-lying sedimentary rock at the Grand Canyon, and of gently inclined lava flows on Mount Rainier, are cut off abruptly by the canyon walls, their continuations can be seen across the canyon in the opposite wall. Evidently the rock layers must once have been unbroken sheets, extending completely across the sites of the canyons, but parts of them have been eroded as river and glacier slowly lowered their beds into the rock.

In many mountain ranges, strata of sandstone, shale, and limestone have been tilted from their original horizontal position. The edges of the more resistant beds, etched out by erosion, project in ridges like those shown in Figures 5–14 and 5–15. Obviously the deeper and older beds in the sequence could have been exposed only by removal, through erosion, of the younger beds that once covered them. In several mountain chains great numbers of such tilted beds are exposed in belts many kilometers wide; to strip away all of the overlying beds and expose those at the surface required removal of two, ten, or even more kilometers of overlying rock. Were it not for such deep erosion, geologists would have only meager information about the internal structure of the earth's crust, and about rocks such as slate and granite that form deep within it.

The study of this phase of erosion, however, is best deferred until we have discussed geologic maps and the evidence that can be gleaned from them about the movements of the earth's crust that raise the mountains so erosion can work on them. The most striking proofs of erosion are the folded and eroded rocks themselves, but the complex relations among them can be grasped only after we have plotted them on geologic maps. Such maps are the subject of our next chapter.

FIGURE 5–14
The Grand Canyon of the Colorado River. (Photo by L. F. Noble, U.S. Geological Survey.)

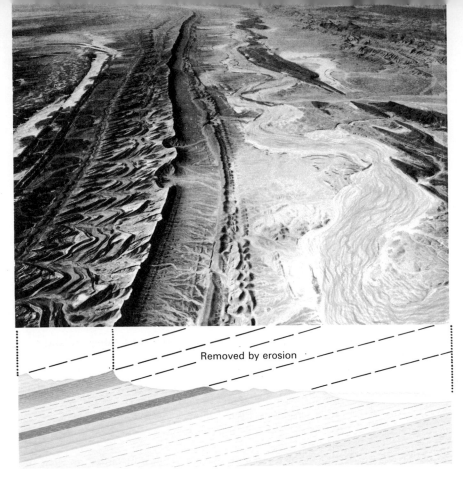

FIGURE 5-15   *Erosion of tilted sedimentary rocks. The drawing shows the rocks as they would appear if sliced vertically at the lower boundary of the photograph. The dashed lines represent only a small part of what erosion has removed. (Photo by U.S. Air Force.)*

Facts, concepts, terms

The law of gravitation
Erosion
Erosional agents
    Gravity; wind; glaciers; ocean waves and nearshore currents; streams; turbidity currents
    Energy for erosion
Relative importance of the agents of erosion
    Streams, aided by downslope movements, are the great levelers
The hydrologic cycle
    Source of the energy that powers the cycle
    Factors affecting the runoff
    Amount of runoff available for erosion
    Energy generated by the runoff
Rate of denudation
    Local, present total, and geologic rates of soil denudation

Erosion under the sea
  Submarine ravines and canyons on steep slopes
  Coarse sand plains
  Turbidity currents
  Evidence of current action at depth
Energy for erosion
  Basic principle underlying erosion processes
  Respective roles of gravity and solar radiation
Geologic evidence of erosion
  Proof that streams cut their valleys
  Revealing of metamorphic rocks and granites by erosion

Questions

1. Why can a stream move larger particles than can wind moving with the same velocity?
2. Which of the erosional agents could cut a valley on land to depths of 1000 feet or more below sea level? Why?
3. Point Barrow, Alaska, and Yuma, Arizona, have about the same rainfall (5 inches per year). Yet Yuma lies in a parched desert whereas the country around Point Barrow is largely swamp. Explain.
4. In a temperate humid climate, which will erode more rapidly: a basalt cone composed of loose cinders, or a hill of the same size composed of unconsolidated silt? Why?
5. In view of what has been said about infiltration, on what rocks would you expect the streams to be spaced closer together, assuming similar slope, vegetation, and precipitation: (*a*) basalt flows with numerous vertical cracks; (*b*) shale; (*c*) granite? Give reasons.
6. Where would you expect streams and gullies to be most closely spaced, assuming uniform granite bedrock: (*a*) steep slopes; (*b*) gentle slopes; (*c*) nearly flat terrain?
7. It has been said that "A turbidity current in the ocean is like a dust storm on the land." Analyze this statement in terms of (*a*) energy of motion, (*b*) entrainment of debris, and (*c*) the nature of the medium surrounding the moving current.
8. Rivers flow beneath air, turbidity currents beneath clear water. Assuming that turbidity currents acually do cut submarine canyons, do the above relationships help to explain why the gradient of submarine canyons is, on the average, about four times as steep as that of comparably deep canyons on land? Explain.

Suggested readings

Bennett, H. H., *Soil Conservation*. New York: McGraw-Hill, 1939.

Brown, C. B., *Sediment Transportation,* in H. Rouse, ed., *Engineering Hydraulics*. New York: John Wiley and Sons, 1950.

United States Department of Agriculture, *Soils and Man* (Yearbook, 1938). Washington, D.C.: G.P.O.

United States Department of Agriculture, *Water* (Yearbook, 1955). Washington, D.C.: G.P.O.

Scientific American offprints

803. Ph. H. Kuenen, *Sand* (April 1960)

807. Bruce C. Heezen, *The Origin of Submarine Canyons* (August 1956)

809. William O. Field, *Glaciers* (September 1955)

817. W. D. Ellison, *Erosion by Raindrop* (November 1948)

845. Willard Bascom, *Beaches* (August 1960)

chapter

Geologic Maps

No traveler can miss the contrast between a lava flow of black basalt and the prevailing light-gray granodiorite of the Sierra Nevada, or, on the opposite side of the earth, between a similar basalt flow and the gleaming white coral rock of Samoa. To record the outlines of such a flow on a topographic map we carefully plot a line showing the contact between the flow and the rocks adjoining it. This **contact line** shows the position of the boundaries of the flow not only with reference to other rock masses, but also in proper relation to valleys and hills, as shown by the contour lines on the map, and to other mapped features such as streams and roads. The result is a **geologic map.** Even so simple a map as one showing only basalt and granodiorite may be economically useful. If basalt is needed to surface a Sierran road, our map shows where it can be quarried, and, from the contours, we can estimate the thickness of the flow and thus calculate the available tonnage of useful rock. From geologic maps plotted on a topographic base map we can read information about the size and shape of rock bodies hundreds or even thousands of feet below the surface.

A geologic map is a valuable economic tool, useful in locating supplies of oil, water, coal, iron ore, and other substances buried beneath a cover of soil and rocks. Though such valuable prizes are completely hidden beneath the surface, a geologic map often reveals where tunneling or drilling will be successful. The accuracy of such predictions has been proved again and again by discoveries of valuable ores, coal, and petroleum. Geologic maps are indeed the indispensable foundation of all geology—basic to our understanding of all subsurface processes, of deciphering the stages in the development of a mountain range, the sequence of evolution of fossil organisms, the changes in local climates, and all the other vicissitudes that have marked the long and eventful history of the earth itself.

DIFFICULTIES OF
GEOLOGIC MAPPING

The distribution and relationships of rock bodies are not ordinarily so obvious as they are on the barren peaks of the Sierra Nevada or along the shores of Samoa. Indeed, in a fertile agricultural area such as Illinois or the Ukraine, it is hard to perceive any systematic arrangement of strata. Here unweathered rock is nearly everywhere masked by soil or stream silt, and can be seen only in bluffs along streams, in deep ravines, or in man-made excavations such as roadcuts and quarries. Geologic mapping in such regions is not easy; it may require digging pits and trenches at critical spots, or drilling holes and examining fragments of the rocks penetrated by the drill. Nevertheless, the principles of geologic mapping were developed in western Europe, where few rocks are well exposed.

EARLY GEOLOGIC MAPS

Among the earliest geologic maps to show the relations of strata over a considerable area are two of the Paris region in France, published jointly by the French naturalists Georges Cuvier and Alexandre Brongniart in 1810 and 1822. At about the same time (1815) William Smith, an English surveyor, published a geologic map of England that marked a great forward step in the development of geology.

Long before Cuvier and Brongniart, French scientists knew that the rocks near Paris are gently tilted layers of limestone, clay, gypsum, and sandstone. These could be seen in many natural and artificial exposures, notably in the pits dug for plastic clay by the makers of pottery and porcelain. As early as 1782, Lavoisier took time from his epochal chemical researches to show that quarry after quarry near Paris exposed the same sequence of strata, a sequence, from the base upward, of chalk, clay, sandstone, limestone, gypsum, impure limestone, and sand, with a siliceous limestone at the top. But Cuvier and Brongniart went much further. They demonstrated that characteristic fossils are present in some strata; that certain beds change in color and composition as they are followed across the countryside; and that distinct sequences of strata can be grouped into units now called formations, whose thickness and other physical characteristics are distinctive enough to allow them to be mapped continuously for long distances.

Succession of the rocks near Paris

East of Paris low ridges and narrow lowlands curve in a broad arc, partly encircling the city. Each ridge slopes gently toward Paris and steeply in the other direction (Fig. 6-1). Just beyond the outermost row of curving hills is a lowland largely covered with soil. Within this lowland scattered rock **outcrops** (natural exposures) and man-made excavations all expose chalk, a variety of limestone.

The belt of lowland underlain by chalk almost completely encircles Paris. Along the outside rim of the belt—farther from Paris—the chalk is gray, with many thin layers of pale green sandstone; on the side nearer Paris it is white and porous, and some layers are crowded with potato-shaped, lumpy nodules of black flint. Between the flinty layers, beds of massive chalk, 5 or 6 meters (15 to 20 feet) thick, contain no flint. The layering in both gray and white chalk slopes gently downward toward Paris; from this Cuvier and Brongniart concluded that the white chalk must rest upon the gray. Therefore, a well dug in the white chalk at the inner edge of the belt would penetrate the gray chalk at depth. Thus they were able to separate the chalk into two distinct formations: the Lower Chalk, chiefly gray chalk and greensand (a sandstone rich in a green iron-bearing min-

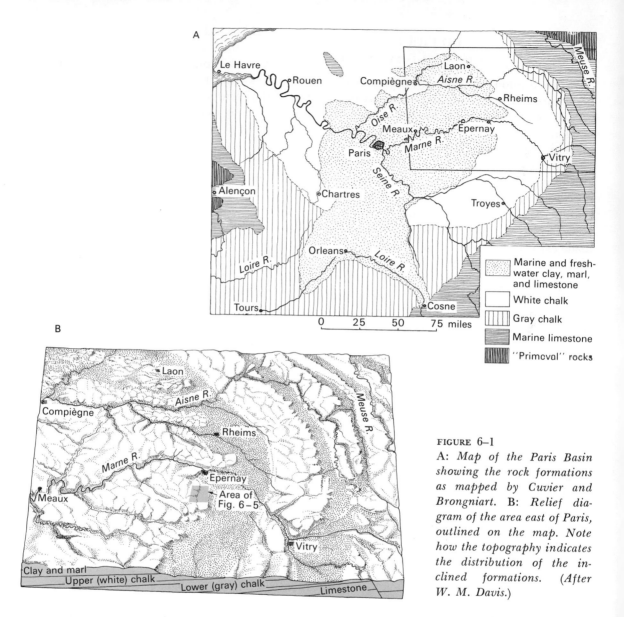

FIGURE 6–1
A: *Map of the Paris Basin showing the rock formations as mapped by Cuvier and Brongniart.* B: *Relief diagram of the area east of Paris, outlined on the map. Note how the topography indicates the distribution of the inclined formations. (After W. M. Davis.)*

eral, glauconite); and the Upper Chalk, a massive white chalk containing layers of flint nodules. It is the Upper Chalk that forms the "White Cliffs of Dover" in England.

Cuvier and Brongniart found more than fifty varieties of fossil shells and other animal remains in the Upper Chalk; these resemble, but are not identical with, shells of animals now living in the sea.

The steep outer slopes of the hills that border the Paris side of the chalk lowland expose plastic clay in the little ravines where the thin soil has been washed away by the rains. This clay rests upon the chalk. Ravines higher up the slope show weakly consolidated sandstone resting on the clay; still higher are exposures of limestone and marl (clayey limestone). All these beds show distinct stratification surfaces that slope gently toward Paris.

The clay that overlies the chalk yielded no fossils. Cuvier and Brongniart concluded that although both chalk and clay had been deposited in water, they were formed in different environments—the chalk in the sea, the clay in fresh water. Marine animals flourished while the chalk accumulated, but they could not live in the fresh water from which the clay settled. In some places, fragments of chalk were found in the lowermost bed of clay where it overlies the chalk. Cuvier and Brongniart concluded that the chalk must have been coherent when the clay began to accumulate, and hence that considerable time had elapsed between deposition of the chalk and the younger clay.

Eventually Cuvier and Brongniart systematically worked out the succession of the formations all the way to Paris. They consist of several beds of limestone, sand, clay, and gypsum. Some contain marine shells; others, the bones of land mammals and birds, skeletons of freshwater fish, and impressions of plant leaves. Each formation shows characteristic physical features and most also contain distinctive fossils.

The larger features of the succession remain the same throughout the Paris Basin, but not every bed nor even every group of the beds making up a formation could be traced all the way round the basin. Some beds had been partly eroded away before the later beds were deposited; others had been deposited as discontinuous lenses in small basins, or built up by water currents, just as spits and sandbars are now being built.

Identifying formations by fossils

The great variety of rocks made Cuvier and Brongniart's mapping task difficult; for example, the distinction of one limestone from another, among so many, could not always be made with assurance on the basis of color, details of bedding, thickness, or other physical characteristics, with the methods that they used. Cuvier and Brongniart were not entirely successful in their pioneer studies until they examined in detail the assemblages of fossils from the different strata. This work revealed that:

Each group of closely related strata contains its own characteristic assemblage of fossils.

This generalization has proved fundamental in correlating isolated outcrops of strata, even across seas and oceans. It has been checked again and again by the Law of Superposition. For example, almost exactly the same succession of fossils occurs in the same order in the sequences of strata of England, France, and North Africa. Yet it was many more years before the reason for this relationship among the fossils was grasped.

William Smith's geologic map of England

The first geologic map of England, published in 1815 by William Smith, furthered the use of fossils in geologic mapping. His map made a notable advance over those of Cuvier and Brongniart. Smith, a surveyor, took great pains to fix the contacts of his formations accurately on the map with reference to streams, roads, and other features. Starting with the exposure of a contact on a canal or river bank, he would follow its approximate position across a soil-covered hill, using as guides small rock fragments in the soil or at the mouths of rabbit holes, until he could again determine the contact precisely, perhaps on a steep bank beside the next stream.

Smith worked as a surveyor on many canals throughout England. On the Somersetshire Coal Canal, for example, he superintended the excavation for more than six years, observing details of the strata in many miles of cut. In all his work and travels he kept a record of the succession and kinds of rocks. Finally, after twenty-four years of observation, he published his colored geologic map of England, one of the great classics of geology.

This map had a profound influence. A written record of Smith's twenty-four years of labor would have been too bulky for easy reference and too detailed to remember. But the summary provided by the map could be quickly grasped and the implications deduced. It demonstrated that many problems of engineering and scientific importance could be solved by careful mapping of the rocks. For years Smith had successfully predicted the kind and thickness of rock masses that would be met in a particular excavation or tunnel. From study of his map men began to think of many other economic applications of geology.

Smith's greatest contribution, however, lay in determining and showing on his map the **stratigraphy,** the order of succession of the different sedimentary formations, for an entire country, thus proving the continuity of individual formations despite minor lateral variations, over considerable areas (though not with the rigid simplicity that Werner had assumed). Smith proved conclusively that if a given bed or stratum occurs above another in one locality, it never occurs below it anywhere else unless a structural disturbance has displaced or overturned the rocks. This is, of course, simply one aspect of the Law of Superposition. Eventually, the subdivisions that he and other pioneers established were extended and refined into the Standard Geologic Column with which we now compare sedimentary formations from all over the world. (See Table 7–1).

This brief account of early geologic maps hints of the methods and principles used in geologic mapping. We now summarize some of these principles, consider their validity, and show how they are applied.

FOUR FUNDAMENTAL POSTULATES OF GEOLOGIC MAPPING

Four fundamental postulates underlie the making of a geologic map. Two of these, the Law of Superposition and the Law of Original Horizontality, have already been discussed (Chapter 3). The third, the **Law of Original Continuity,** is merely a commonsense deduction from these two, and, like them, was first stated by Steno: *A water-laid stratum, at the time it is formed, must continue laterally in all directions until it thins out as a result of nondeposition, or until it abuts against the edge of the original basin of deposition.* An important corollary of this law, not fully appreciated by Steno in 1660, was well known to the geologists of France and England at the beginning of the nineteenth century. It may be stated: *A stratum that ends abruptly, at some point other than against the edge of the basin in which it was deposited must have had its original continuation removed by erosion* (see Figs. 5–14, 5–15), *or else displaced by a fracture in the earth's crust* (See Fig. 9–17).

These four principles— (1) *superposition* (the higher bed is the younger), (2) *original horizontality* (stratification planes are formed roughly parallel to the earth's surface), (3) *original continuity,* and (4) *truncation by erosion or dislocation*—are the basis for many of our interpretations of the relations of strata. They are not absolute rules that can be perfunctorily applied. For instance, some beds once horizontal have been highly tilted and even overturned by movements of the earth's crust (Chapters 8 and 9), so that a stratum formerly beneath another may now lie upside down upon it. Other strata, as at the front of a delta, may have been deposited on appreciable slopes; landslides may end abruptly instead of thinning out to a narrow wedge. Such exceptions, though, are not common and can generally be easily recognized by the geologist.

Although these basic principles are commonplace, a geologist still meets problems in applying them. What, for example, does he select to map in a sequence of strata containing hundreds of beds only a centimeter to a meter thick, many of which closely resemble one another? He cannot map each separate stratum, but how is he to group them?

FORMATIONS

The basic unit of the geologic map is the **formation.** There are two criteria for deciding what constitutes a formation; first, its contacts (i.e., the top and bottom of a sedimentary formation) must be recognizable and capable of being traced in the field, and, second, the formation must be large enough to be shown on the map.

Cuvier and Brongniart noticed faint stratification surfaces within the Lower Chalk. The chalk above and below such surfaces, however, was so nearly identical in appearance and fossil content that each bed of chalk was not regarded by the two geologists as either significant or capable of being successfully traced in the field or shown individually on their map. The contact between the Upper Chalk and the overlying Plastic Clay, on the other hand, was mapped as a formation boundary because of the marked contrast in the rocks. A still more cogent reason for selecting this contact to map was the evidence that it represented a considerable span of geologic time—time enough for the underlying chalk to have become firmly coherent, so that it could be incorporated as pebbles and fragments in the lowermost bed of clay.

The beds above the Plastic Clay posed a more difficult problem of mapping. Here are many kinds of rock in thin layers—limestone, shale, sandstone, gypsum, and clay. At some outcrops, an individual bed—perhaps a layer of clay only a half-meter thick—could be seen to thin out and disappear within a few dozen meters: or the overlying sandstone, perhaps 5 meters thick, could be seen to thicken when followed across country in successive outcrops, and then to thin again and perhaps end. Only on a map of a very large scale could each layer be shown, and it would take a prodigious amount of time to trace the contacts. Such a series of thin, variable beds, often including very diverse kinds of rock, were grouped together by Cuvier and Brongniart as a single formation. Although individual beds within such variable formations may be discontinuous, and also may be indistinguishable from similar beds higher or lower in the same formation or in adjacent ones, the entire group of beds constitutes a unit recognizably different from formations above and below it.

The scale of the map, the abundance and quality of exposures, the character of the beds, the intended use of the map, and, not least, the discrimination of the geologist, determine the selection of map units (formations). Any differences are adequate to justify classing a particular bed, or any closely related group of beds as a formation, provided the differences allow the unit to be recognized in scattered outcrops, and provided its top and bottom can be traced in the field.

In the United States, a geologic formation is nearly always named from a geographic locality near which it was first identified, followed by the name of the dominant kind of rock composing it, or, if its components are variable, by the word "formation." Examples: Austin Chalk, Yakima Basalt, Chattanooga Shale, Denver Formation. In Europe, the practice is less formal; many formations are named from some characteristic fossil (Lingula Flags, a thin-bedded sandstone containing abundant fossils of the brachiopod genus *Lingula*), from some economic characteristic (Millstone Grit), or even from a folk name (Norwich Crag).

Mapping of poorly exposed formations

On the barren walls of the Grand Canyon (Fig. 5–14), details of the strata are visible for scores of miles, and contacts between the several formations can be readily traced. In most areas, however, soil covers the surface, and natural outcrops, roadcuts, and quarries are scarce. On William Smith's geologic map of England, the contacts between different rock formations are shown for distances that represent hundreds of miles. Yet, in tracing an individual contact for a hundred miles,

Smith probably found, on the average, less than fifty exposures where the actual contact could be seen on a clean rock face. How, then, can his map record the real distribution of the rocks? Can it represent anything but a guess? The eyes of a geologist are no more capable of seeing the bedrock through a cover of soil and turf than those of any other observer. How can the geologist make inferences about the position of the strata underground that will withstand objective tests, such as those provided when wells are drilled or mine shafts dug?

The succession must be pieced together from scattered outcrops. Although, in an area of several square miles a geologist may find only one or two outcrops in which he sees the actual contact between two formations, he will doubtless find a hundred or more outcrops composed entirely of rock belonging to one formation or the other. Even with no clean outcrops at all, some valuable information can be gleaned. Loose fragments of rock in the soil creep slowly downslope; their bedrock source is surely above the place where they are found, for they cannot creep uphill. These fragments, called "float," thus aid greatly in fixing the position of the *upper* contact of a rock mass. Each outcrop and even each fragment of float gives an indication of the approximate position of the contact, and from many of them it is possible to "bracket" the contact closely. The problem is like that of drawing a contour line to conform to elevations determined at a hundred or more control points (Appendix I). To use scattered rock outcrops and pieces of float in this way, however, is difficult: it requires that the separate formations be accurately identified in the fragments and outcrops, and correctly correlated from one outcrop to another. How is it done?

Correlation of strata

Modern geologists use essentially the same methods of correlation as Cuvier, Smith, and the other pioneers. In a ravine on a grassy hillside we may see a bed of clay with well-marked horizontal stratification; we assume that it continues horizontally into the hill at the same elevation, for how else can its horizontal stratification be extended? If we go a hundred meters along the same level without seeing an outcrop, and then find a clay bed at the same elevation in another ravine, we suspect that it may be the same bed. If both are gray, and we have also noted several pieces of gray clay float between the outcrops, the probability is heightened. If both show lines of concretions (nodular lumps) along the stratification planes, and if the size and spacing of the concretions is about the same, we can be more confident of our correlation. If both rest on red limestone, are overlain by fine-grained brown standstone, and contain the same kinds of fossils, our confidence is greatly strengthened. We are now justified in considering that the bed is truly continuous beneath the soil between the exposures. If we go on a little farther and find a deep ravine that exposes not merely a few meters of strata but several hundred, and if in this section there is only one clay bed resembling those we saw in the two small outcrops, we have still further assurance that our correlation has been correct. We can now map the clay, for the contacts of the clay bed with beds above and below, being horizontal, will parallel the contours. We have, furthermore, gained information about the red limestone below and the brown sandstone above the clay bed, because in this larger outcrop a much greater thickness of rock is exposed. For example, we discover that the brown sandstone is 60 meters thick and is overlain by a bed of distinctive black limestone crowded with fossils.

If, now, we go to a still more distant outcrop and find there a clay bed a little thinner than that in the last outcrop, one that rests on pink limy sandstone instead of on red limestone and is overlain by a pebbly green sandstone instead of the fine-grained brown sandstone, we might question a correlation with our original bed, though we certainly would not regard correlation as impossible or even unlikely. To check, we might go to lower elevations and study the limy sandstone in various outcrops. If we found it gradually changing to sandy red limestone and then to pure red limestone in the direction from which we came, but to pink sandstone in the other direction, our correlation would be strengthened. It would be further confirmed if we walked up the hill and found that the pebbly green sandstone above the clay was overlain by a black limestone full of fossils identical to those in the limestone that rests on the brown sandstone in the large exposure. Nearly all strata are found to change in physical characters if traced far laterally—the change from red limestone to pink sandstone merely records changes in the supply of sand at different localities during deposition.

Our example illustrates the use of three most important factors in the correlation of rock formations. These are:

1. *Lithology.*—The more nearly alike are the kinds of rock in scattered exposures—in such features as grain-size, composition, color, bedding, and any other recognizable physical characteristics—the more likely their correlation; but most strata can be expected to change gradually if traced long distances.

2. *Sequence.*—Similar sequences of strata emphatically suggest correlation, and the more numerous the parallel items in sequence the better the correlation.

3. *Fossil content.*—William Smith found that, "Each stratum contained fossils peculiar to itself, and might, in cases otherwise doubtful, be recognized and discriminated from others like it by examination of them." Cuvier and Brongniart reached the same conclusion. Thus fossil assemblages are excellent keys to correlation. Although Smith only used fossils as if they were particularly distinctive pebbles, we shall learn in the next chapter that their irreversible changes in kind with time make them a much more significant guide to correlation than pebbles or other inorganic physical features.

A fourth method of correlation is obviously the best of all: *tracing a continuously exposed contact from one area to another.* But only where rocks are not covered with soil and vegetation can this be done for any considerable distance, and, of course, this method cannot be applied across a sea, or beneath a cover of younger rock. The determination of similarities in physical characters of rocks, sequence of strata, and fossil content—all of which call for the exercise of judgment—are everywhere required in geologic mapping because of the generally sporadic exposures of rocks.

Thus, sound geologic mapping can never be reduced to a mechanical routine; there is invariably an element of judgment regardless of the apparent simplicity of the rocks. Some correlations are certain, others are reasonably sure, and about others there may be doubt. Two geologists may disagree about the doubtful ones, just as two equally qualified physicians may differ in the diagnosis of identical but ambiguous pathologic symptoms. But nearly all such differences in interpretation concern minor features in a stratigraphic succession. Most thick groups of beds show enough peculiarities to lead two careful observers to identical conclusions.

GEOLOGIC SECTIONS

Geologic sections are used with geologic maps in nearly all economic applications of geology. A **geologic section,** also called a **structure section,** shows how the rocks would appear on the side of a trench cut vertically into the land surface. The edge of a slice of layer cake discloses both the layers and the filling between; a geologic section is a similar illustration of rocks in depth. As an example, let us make a geologic section of the horizontal clay bed shown in Figure 6–2, plotting our data from the geologic map, which shows the relation of the clay bed to overlying and underlying beds in a deep branching ravine. In Figure 6–2, the completed section is shown below the geologic map; the figure also shows the construction lines used in drawing the section.

This geologic section portrays the strata as they would appear on the wall of a deep trench dug along the line from A to B on the geologic map. The section was drawn by making use of the contour lines on the map and relating the outcrops to them. To simplify our task, we made the horizontal scale of the section the same as that of the map. Then lines were dropped perpendicularly from A and B to the place below the map where the section was to be drawn. A vertical scale showing the range in elevation from 1120 to 1260 feet above sea level was laid off on the line dropped from B. Horizontal lines were then drawn across the section through these points; each line represents the elevation of the corresponding contour line on the map. From each point where the line AB intersects a contour, a perpendicular line was dropped to the horizontal line corresponding to that contour on the section; the ends of the perpendicular lines provided a guide for sketching the **surface profile,** the

irregular line connecting A′ and B′ in the section. Perpendiculars were now dropped to this profile from each intersection of the map line AB with the top and bottom (contact lines) of the clay stratum. There are five such intersections—three with the top of the clay stratum, two with the base. Lines drawn through the points on the surface profile that represent, respectively, the top and bottom of the stratum (in this example, the beds are horizontal) complete the cross section, and show the relations of the clay bed to the underlying limestone and overlying sandstone.

Geologic sections have many practical uses. If the clay shown is suitable for brickmaking, we can determine from the section how much worthless soil and rock must be removed at any point along the section line to uncover the clay. If a subway tunnel is to be driven, we can foresee difficulties that may arise during excavation, such as problems of roof support and water disposal. Mines, tunnels, and wells all test the validity of our geologic maps and sections, and of the assumptions underlying their construction.

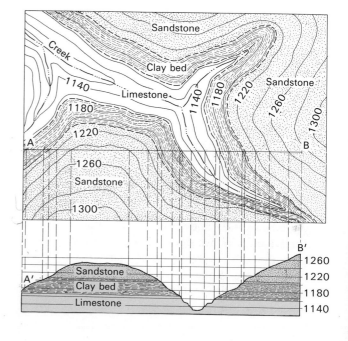

FIGURE 6–2

Construction of a geologic section from a geologic map.

ROCK STRUCTURE AND GEOLOGIC MAPPING

In most places, strata are no longer horizontal, as they were when deposited; they have been disturbed by warping and folding of the earth's crust (Chapter 8). The beds of the Paris Basin, we recall, are tilted gently toward Paris. In mapping tilted beds and plotting them on sections, the same principles apply as with horizontal beds. Outcrops of a tilted bed must appear at many elevations when traced across hilly topography. How are the amount and direction of tilt determined?

Dip and strike

The slope of a tilted plane is fixed if we know the **direction** (which may be measured with a compass) and the **angle of inclination** (which may be measured with a clinometer —see Fig. 6–4) of the steepest line that can be drawn on its surface. This is most simply illustrated by the slope of a roof—the direction in which a drop of water runs down that slope is the **direction of dip** of the roof surface. The acute angle between the track of the water and a level surface, measured on a vertical plane through the track, is the **angle of dip** of the roof. But in natural exposures of rocks it may not be possible to determine these directions so easily. We usually do it indirectly by determining the **direction of strike,** which is the direction of a horizontal line drawn on the surface of stratification. Such a horizontal line is, of course, at right angles to the direction of dip. To revert to our roof example, it is obvious that the ridge pole is a horizontal line and that it lies in the plane of the roof. The *compass direction* of the ridge pole is thus the direction of strike for the roof. Moreover, the compass direction of the ridge pole is at right angles to the compass direction of the dip of the roof.

In a geologic example, we may visualize the relations shown in Figure 6–3. Note the tilted stratum that intersects the surface of a lake: the trend of the water line where it wets this stratum—that is, the bearing, or compass direction of the line of intersection of the lake surface (a horizontal plane) with the stratification (a tilted plane)—forms a definite line of reference; this is the **strike** of the stratum. We can see that the bed will project into the hill along the strike, and we realize that it will continue in this direction unless it becomes bent, or is cut off, either by erosion or in some other way.

Strike is measured in the field with a *Geologist's compass* equipped with a *level-bubble* so that it can be held horizontally, and with a *clinometer* for determining dip (Fig. 6–4). With the level-bubble centered, the compass is sighted along the bedding plane and the compass bearing is read. The line in the bedding plane thus determined is a **strike line.** Thus a bed that intersects a lake surface along a line running exactly northwest-southeast has a strike of N45°W (north 45° west), which is, of course, the same as S45°E, or southeast-northwest. A bed on which a horizontal line trends 10° east of south has a strike of N10°W or S10°E. As we noted in the example of the roof, the angle of **dip** (it is usually referred to simply as "the dip") of a bed is the maximum acute angle between a horizontal surface and the stratification plane. In our example of the lake and the inclined stratum, the dip is the angle between the surface of the lake and the line on the submerged continuation of

FIGURE 6–3

The strike and dip of an inclined bed exposed along a lake shore.

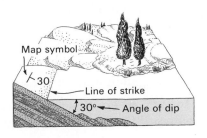

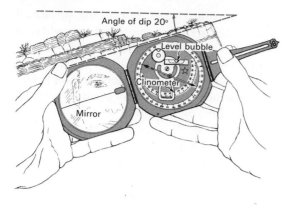

FIGURE 6–4

Determining dip with the Brunton geological compass. The clinometer is rotated by a lever on the back of the compass until the bubble is centered while the ruling edge is held parallel to the dip of the stratum; the dip is then read directly on the inner half circle.

the tilted bed that lies at right angles to the strike (Fig. 6–3). Such a line is the steepest that can be drawn on the bedding surface. Dip angles are measured with the clinometer, which is a pointer with a level-bubble attached to its top. This pointer is attached to the inside of the compass, and its lower end swings freely against a scale (protractor) graduated in degrees (Fig. 6–4). With the compass held in position and the bubble in the clinometer leveled as illustrated in Figure 6–4, the angle of dip is read directly from the graduated scale. The *direction of dip* must not be confused with the *angle of dip*. The direction of dip is the compass direction toward which the tilted bed slopes into the earth; in our example, it is the compass direction (not the inclination) taken by the water that runs down the surface of the roof. The direction of dip is always at right angles to the direction of strike.

In recording strike and dip on a map, a symbol consisting of two lines is used. The symbol $\underset{60}{N45E}$ indicates that the stratum has a strike of north 45° east and a dip of 60° to the southeast. On most maps, the letters and figures indicating the strike are omitted; thus $\underset{55}{\diagdown}$ indicates a bed striking north 45° west and dipping 55° to the northeast. The "N45W" is omitted because the top of a map is always north unless specifically marked otherwise; the direction of strike is thus shown by the trend of the strike line, which is always accurately plotted with respect to the north line on the map. Similarly the direction of dip is given by the trend of the dip line. The angle of dip in degrees cannot be similarly represented graphically on a map; it must always be given in numbers.

Topography, inclined beds, and geologic mapping

A dipping bed, in contrast to a horizontal bed, will project along a contour only when the trend of the hillside exactly parallels the strike. If the strike does not parallel the contour, the trace of the bed along the hillside will rise or fall away from the first outcrop, depending on the direction in which the bed is followed. This fact is the basis for determining the strike and dip of most beds with low dips, for it is difficult to read a measurement of less than 1° by a clinometer, but it may be relatively easy to locate two points on the surface of a bed that each have exactly the same elevation, although they may be a thousand feet apart on opposite sides of a stream valley. The compass bearing of a straight line between the two points is, of course, the strike of the bed. This relation is also the basic clue to reading the succession of beds and their direction of dip from a geologic map.

In the Paris Basin, most streams drain to the Seine. East of Paris (Fig. 6–1) they flow westward, cutting across the arcuate ridges at nearly right angles. Using the relation between the dip of a bed and its trace over a hilly terrain, we find that any particular identifiable bed, when traced westward along a valley wall, gradually decreases in elevation until it reaches a stream bed. On crossing the stream the trace of the stratum rises, but it also reverses direction and trends eastward up the opposite wall of the valley. In other words, the outcrop pattern is a V with the point of the V directed downdip (Fig. 6–5).

In Figure 6–1 the fact that the Upper Chalk crops out farther west on the banks of the Marne and Aisne rivers than it does on the intervening ridge tops shows that its contact with the overlying Plastic Clay dips west. By using such facts, the east-west section forming the lower edge of Figure 6–1, B was drawn. Each formation shown on this section is projected to much greater depths within the earth than we can actually observe in the field. We are justified in this projection to depth by the basic principles of original continuity, which holds for tilted as well as for horizontal beds. In projecting a tilted bed to a geologic section account must be taken of its dip.

Relation of topography to structure

As shown in Figures 5–15 and 6–1, a relationship is generally apparent between the landscape of a country and the structure of the underlying bedrock. Weathering and erosion etch the surface into relief, forming lowlands on the less-resistant beds and leaving the more-resistant ones standing as hills. This differential erosion produces a landscape that reflects differences in position and structure of the underlying rocks. The curving ridges around Paris (Figs. 6–1 and 6–5) mark outcrops of resistant strata such as sandstones, but porous chalk and other easily eroded rocks are found only in the lowlands. The curving pattern of both hills and lowlands, as well as the strike and dip of the rocks, shows that the formations have been warped into the shallow saucerlike form, which geologists call the Paris Basin. Indeed, the whole succession of strata resembles a pile of saucers of diminishing size, with Paris near the center of the smallest and uppermost saucer.

The interrelation between topography and structure in the Paris Basin is by no means perfect—it is much closer where soil is thin or absent (Fig. 9–6) as in deserts. In most areas, nevertheless, the topography reflects trends in the underlying rocks. Sandstone is generally more resistant to erosion than shale, and in a dipping sequence where the two are interstratified (Fig. 5–15) it forms ridges. It is also more permeable to rain, so that where it rests on shale there is likely to be a line of springs along its base which feed a strip of flourishing plants. Thus the minor features, both topographic and vegetational, nearly always give clues to the kinds and trends of the underlying bedrocks. If firm conglomerate crops out on top of a long ridge at one point, it is likely to continue the entire length of the ridge. This is easily checked by examining other outcrops along

FIGURE 6–5
Relief diagram and geologic map of the small area south of Epernay (Fig. 6–1, B). Note the strong V in each contact where it crosses a stream valley. The strike of the beds can be determined by joining points, like A and B, where a contact intersects a contour line. (Why?)

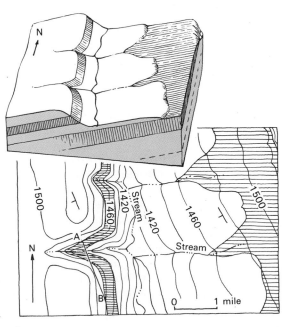

the crest. A road may expose chalk in a low-land. Perhaps a well has been dug in the same lowland a thousand feet away. Does it show chalk on its walls? By piecing together such information, the geologist can generally establish the stratigraphic succession, dis-cover the variations in thickness of beds, and ultimately plot their positions on a map and structure section.

Even in a country with thick soil, it is still possible to apply the principles of geologic mapping and correlation by using data gained from excavations and well borings, or by geophysical methods (Chapter 19).

LIMITATIONS OF SCALE

Geologic maps, like all other maps, demand rigorous selection of data; they emphasize some features at the expense of others. The smaller the scale of the map, the fewer the details that can be shown. In Figure 6–5,

which shows only a few square miles of the Paris Basin near Epernay, details of thin lay-ers above the chalk are shown that could not possibly be indicated on a map with the scale of Figure 6–1. The geologist must select his geologic units to fit the map scale. The larger the scale and the better the exposures, the greater the number of formations that can be shown within a given area, although the number per square inch of map is likely to remain about the same (compare Figs. 6–1 and 6–5).

Preparation of the geologic map, however, is generally only the first step in a geologic study. The map is a shorthand representa-tion of the geologic history recorded in the rocks—their mutual relations and structures, and the episodes these features record—but to determine the ages and environments of deposition of the various strata requires fur-ther work, and particularly a careful study of the fossils in the rocks. Fossils are one sub-ject of our next chapter.

Facts, concepts, terms

Uses of geologic maps
  To simplify and enable us to visualize complex relations among rocks
  To find valuable minerals hidden beneath soil or rock
  To clarify the geologic history of an area
Fundamental postulates in geologic mapping
  Law of superposition (chapter 3)
  Law of original horizontality (chapter 3)
  Law of original continuity
  Truncation by erosion or dislocation
Grouping of strata into formations
Correlation of outcrops
  Lithology
  Sequence
  Fossil content
  Tracing of beds
Structural attitude of rock strata
  Dip and strike
  Relation of horizontal contacts to contours
  Relation of dipping contacts to contours

V-ing of contacts in crossing stream valleys
Construction of geologic sections
Topographic expression as an aid in mapping
In desert regions
In areas partially masked by soil

Questions

1. What differences in landscape would you expect if the rocks of the Paris Basin had been warped into a dome instead of a saucer-shaped basin?
2. Express a general rule relating contours and outcrop patterns of horizontal beds.
3. If you traced a thick lava flow for a mile and could not find its continuation, what possible explanations of its termination could you suggest.
4. How would a dike of basalt that dips vertically and strikes north appear on a map? What difference, if any, would the map pattern of such a dike show as it crosses a sandstone ridge and a valley in shale both of which trend due east?
5. If you follow the contact between a shale bed and a sandstone bed across level country for several miles and it leads you in an oval path back to the starting point, what inferences can you make about the dips in the area?
6. Some of the buttes of the New Mexico desert are capped by horizontal basalt flows; others are volcanic plugs. How would you expect the map patterns of these igneous rocks to differ? (Assume there are two or more deep gullies on the sides of each butte.)
7. Draw a hypothetical geologic map showing a series of tilted beds that have been invaded by a sill and that also contain a buried lava flow. Indicate on the map a locality where you would expect to find fragments of the lava flow as inclusions in a sedimentary bed.
8. When a geologic contact V's downstream the direction of dip is always down-stream also, but if the stream is a rushing mountain torrent a contact which dips *downstream* may actually V *upstream*. Show how this might happen, and frame a general law expressing the relation between the angle of dip of the contact and the gradient (slope) of the stream bed.

Suggested readings

Adams, F. D., *The Birth and Development of the Geological Sciences*. Baltimore: Williams and Wilkins, 1938. [Especially Chapters 7 and 8.]

Harrison, J. M., *Nature and significance of geological maps*, p. 225–232 in C. C. Albritton, ed., *The Fabric of Geology*. San Francisco: Freeman, Cooper, & Company, 1963.

Mather, K. F., and S. L. Mason, *Source Book in Geology*. New York: McGraw-Hill, 1939. [Especially p. 181–191, 194–204.]

chapter 7

Fossils, Strata, and Time

No other discovery has influenced geology as profoundly as the one that fossils can be used to determine sequences in a series of strata, and to correlate widely separated outcrops, even those separated by an ocean. That fossil shells found embedded in rocks far inland are the remains of marine animals was known for centuries, but until the early years of the nineteenth century no one understood their value in chronology. At first even Cuvier, Brongniart, and Smith used fossils to identify beds in different outcrops only as unusual chert nodules or pebbles might be used, but significant new concepts developed as the work continued. Cuvier was one of the first to explore systematically the biologic relations among fossils, and the succession of fossil organisms in the history of the earth. His studies of the fossil animals and plants of the Paris Basin earned for him the title of "Father of Paleontology." **Paleontology** (derived from the Greek words for "ancient" and "existing things") is the scientific study of ancient life (Appendix V). Some of Cuvier's conclusions about fossil relationships have proved incorrect, but others, more firmly based on field evidence, are basic to modern stratigraphy.

CORRELATION AND FAUNAL SUCCESSION

The great advance made by Cuvier and Brongniart was to recognize that the differences between the fossils of the many strata in the Paris Basin are systematic. When they arranged the fossils from the various strata in the same sequence as that of the strata themselves, they noticed that each fossil assemblage differs from all the others, and that fossil shells from the lower (older) beds differ more from those of animals now living than do those from higher (younger) beds. This they found broadly true of all fossils—clams, sea snails, fish skeletons, and all others. Thus fossils are useful in correlation not only as characterizing particular strata, but more significantly because they record the successive changes in life forms through geologic time.

That older fossils differ more from living creatures than do younger ones implies two things: (1) old forms of life have died out, and (2) they have been succeeded in time and place by newly developed forms. Neither concept was generally accepted before Cuvier. In fact, the great Swedish naturalist Linnaeus, who founded the systematic classification of animals that is basic to the one zoologists use today, had declared only a generation earlier that "the existing species of animals are now as they were created in the beginning."

Cuvier's discoveries disproved Linnaeus' conclusion and raised a new question: How did new species arise? Cuvier's answer—by a succession of new creations, each following a universal catastrophe—was incorrect, as we shall see, but his discovery of extinction of old species and the rise of new ones was a portentous step in the history of science, for it was basic to the great advances in both biology and geology represented by Darwin's demonstration of evolution, and to the development of a biologic basis for geologic chronology.

Geologic chronology

Naturalists working in many lands found a wealth of additional fossil species, as well as many specimens of those already described by Cuvier from the Paris Basin. And, learning from Cuvier to seek for faunal changes, they confirmed his discovery of a progressive change in the fossils with time—in general, the more ancient the fossil, the more it differs from a living form.

As discussed more fully in Appendix V, biologists and paleontologists group individual organisms (or their fossil remains) into species. Species considered closely related are grouped into genera (singular, genus), genera into families, and so on to higher and higher categories. The studies by Cuvier,

Brongniart, Smith, and their early successors showed that many species, genera, and higher categories of fossils are limited to narrow stratigraphic intervals within the areas where they mapped. Some of the stratigraphically limited species, and more of the similarly limited genera and even larger groups are widespread geographically and imply the fundamental **Law of Faunal Assemblages** upon which geologic correlations of strata, both locally and over wide areas, are based: *Like assemblages of fossil organisms indicate like geologic ages for the rocks that contain them.*

Once Cuvier and Smith had demonstrated the systematic changes in fossil assemblages with time for their areas, other students quickly spread the work over much of the earth. Parallel successions of fossils were described from many lands. Such successions, partly overlapping in time and thus confirming their sequence, are the basis for the standard geologic column.

THE STANDARD GEOLOGIC COLUMN

Simple early column

As early as the middle of the eighteenth century, Italian and German geologists had classed their local rocks into three groups: Primary (rocks like granite and gneiss, with neither bedding nor fossils), Secondary (cemented sedimentary rocks, generally exposed in the mountains), and Tertiary (weakly consolidated sedimentary rocks of the lowlands, which rested upon the Secondary rocks). Though fossils from both the Secondary and Tertiary rocks were known, distinctions among them from bed to bed were not used in this early classification.

Standard column

The present **standard geologic column** is made up of sequences of European formations because it was pieced together in the nineteenth century by expanding the stratigraphic sequences worked out by Smith, Cuvier, and Brongniart to include strata exposed in other parts of Europe. The fossil assemblages from the standard geologic column form the worldwide standard of comparison. Correlations that may extend across a continent, or even to another continent, are based on biologic comparisons of assemblages of fossil plants and animals. Some correlations are handicapped by the restriction of certain fossils to specific environments of deposition so that they are found only in one kind of rock or in one part of the world. On the other hand, many fossil species, especially those of marine habitat, were both abundant and cosmopolitan in distribution. Correlation is greatly facilitated by the huge number of former living things; thousands upon thousands of fossil species are preserved in the rocks.

The major subdivisions of the geologic column are called **rock systems.** Most of the systems are represented, at least in part, in the area mapped by Smith and his early followers. Smith grouped his oldest strata as the Old Red Sandstone. These rocks contain few fossils, as they show evidence of having accumulated in a widespread desert, but to the south in Devonshire they interfinger with fossiliferous marine beds. The Old Red Sandstone is therefore one of the formations now included in the Devonian System (named from Devonshire). Resting on the Old Red Sandstone is a group of strata called by Smith the Mountain Limestone, which is in turn overlain by a succession of sandstone, shale, iron ore, and coal which Smith called the Coal Measures. These rocks and the underlying Mountain Limestone are now grouped together as the Carboniferous System, so named because coal is abundant in the rocks. Above the Coal Measures, Smith called one group of beds the Magnesian Limestone, followed in turn by the New Red Sandstone. These formations contain few fossils and are largely landlaid. The Magnesian Limestone is now considered part of the

Permian System, named from a province in Russia just west of the Ural Mountains, where marine fossiliferous rocks occupy a similar stratigraphic position. Next overlying was the New Red Sandstone. It is now included in the Triassic System, named from the three (triad) formations that overlie the Permian System in Germany.

Overlying the New Red Sandstone is a succession of richly fossiliferous beds that Smith was able to divide into many formations, partly because he cut many canals through them, disclosing finer details of their succession. Some years later, many identical fossils were found in the rocks of the Jura Mountains of Switzerland and France, whence the Jurassic System derives its name. Jurassic rocks also underlie the Lower Chalk of the Paris Basin.

Toward London, the Jurassic strata are overlain by greensand, and this in turn by the chalk. This succession is grouped as the Cretaceous System (from the Greek word for "chalk"). The fossils are identical to those in the chalk of the Paris Basin. Overlying the chalk, Smith found the London Clay, a group of beds rich in fossils like those in the beds above the chalk of the Paris Basin. These beds, both in England and France, are now considered part of the Tertiary System, a name that has survived from the early classification of the eighteenth century.

It was more than a generation after Smith before the stratigraphy of the complexly folded rocks below his Old Red Sandstone was worked out. Three new systems were eventually recognized: in descending order Silurian, Ordovician (both names of old British tribes), and Cambrian (from the Latin name for Wales).

The Cambrian strata are the oldest that contain fossils in abundance, although sedimentary rocks thousands of feet thick are found beneath them in some regions and many of these contain primitive fossils (Fig. 7–1). These fossils, however, are either sparse in or entirely devoid of characteristic fea-

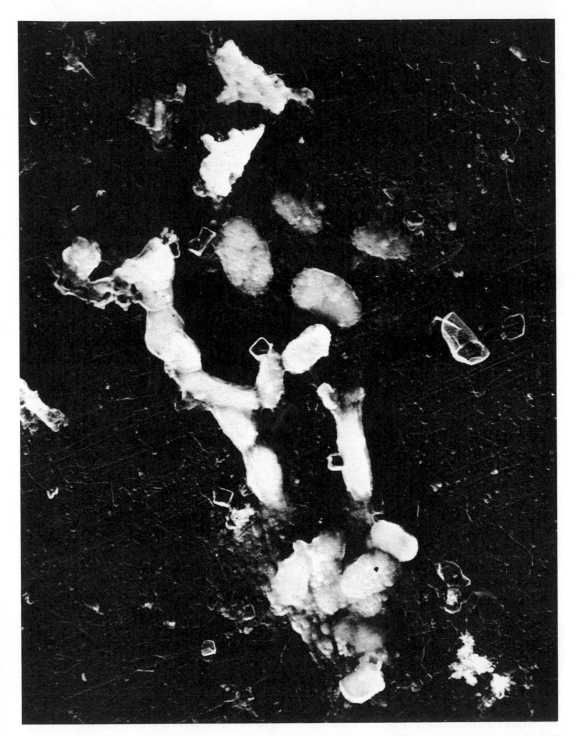

FIGURE 7–1   *Fossil bacteria from the Gunflint Formation of Ontario, north shore of Lake Superior. The Gunflint Formation has been dated as about two billion years old. (Electron photomicrograph by courtesy of Elso Barghoorn, Harvard University.)*

Table 7–1 **Geologic column and time scale**

Era	System or Period (rocks) (time)	Series or Epoch (rocks) (time)	Approximate age in millions of years (beginning of unit)
Cenozoic (*recent life*)	Quaternary (an addition to the old tripartite 18th-century classification)	Recent	.01
		Pleistocene (*most recent*)	2.0 to 3.0
	Tertiary (Third, from the 18th-century classification)	Pliocene (*very recent*)	7
		Miocene (*moderately recent*)	25
		Oligocene (*slightly recent*)	40
		Eocene (*dawn of the recent*)	60
		Paleocene (*early dawn of the recent*)	68 to 70
Mesozoic (*intermediate life*)	Cretaceous (*chalk*)		135
	Jurassic (Jura Mountains, France)		180
	Triassic (from three-fold division in Germany)		225
Paleozoic (*ancient life*)	Permian (Perm, a Russian province)		270
	Carboniferous (from abundance of coal)		
	Pennsylvanian *		325
	Mississippian *		350
	Devonian (Devonshire, England)		400
	Silurian (an ancient British tribe, the Silures)		440
	Ordovician (an ancient British tribe, Ordovices)		500
	Cambrian (Cambria, the Roman name for Wales)		550 to 600
Precambrian	Many local systems and series are recognized, but no well-established worldwide classification has yet been delineated.		3500 or more

(Handwritten annotations: "din. died out" with line to Mesozoic; "din come in" near Triassic/Permian; "Dinosaurs" beside Jurassic; "First Fish →" beside Ordovician.)

SOURCES: Approximate ages from Holmes, 1964; Evernden, Savage, Curtis, and James, 1964; and The Phanerozoic Time Scale of the Geological Society of London, 1964.

NOTES: Definitions in italics are from the Greek.

Many provincial series and epochs have been recognized in various parts of the world for Mesozoic and older strata. Most of the systems have been divided into Lower, Middle, and Upper Series, to which correspond Early, Middle, and Late Epochs, as the times during which the respective series were deposited.

* Pennsylvanian and Mississippian Systems, named for States of the U.S.A., are not generally recognized outside of North America; elsewhere the Carboniferous System is regarded as a single system.

tures useful for correlation. In this book, all the older rocks are grouped together as the Precambrian. They have great bulk and complexity and are not easily arranged according to age, although they can be mapped and classified by other features quite as well as the more fossiliferous younger strata (see Chapter 18). Dating by radioactivity, as mentioned later in this chapter, has begun to enable us to subdivide the Precambrian rocks chronologically, just as fossils have permitted us to classify the Cambrian and younger systems, but there are still many difficulties, and most results are rather tentative.

The systems of rocks in the standard geologic column are listed in Table 7–1. The ages there given (except for the Precambrian) are the current estimates of the date of beginning of the series or system referred to.

GEOLOGIC TIME SCALE

The standard geologic column is the basis for the **geologic time scale.** The same names as are applied to the systems (of strata) are also used for the respective periods (time intervals) during which the systems were deposited. Thus we use the term Carboniferous Period for the time interval during which the Carboniferous System—the Mountain Limestone and Coal Measures of Smith—were laid down. **Systems** (strata) and **periods** (time) are further divided into **series** and **epochs,** respectively. For example, we say that the time interval during which the Comanche Series of Texas was deposited is in the Early Cretaceous epoch. The fundamental elements in the classification are the strata—the systems and series—which are tangible objects; the periods and epochs are concepts derived from strata.

More subdivisions are recognized among younger than among older rocks. Just as in human history, the data are more numerous and the gaps in the record fewer the more recent the period with which we deal. The systems are grouped into larger units, formally called erathems; the corresponding time intervals are called eras: Paleozoic Era, Mesozoic Era, etc. Erathem is a rare word in geologic writing, instead the era names are used adjectively as, for example, "Paleozoic rocks."

Gaps in the standard column

Divisions of the standard column are based on abrupt changes in the fossil assemblages of the strata in Europe. The boundaries between the different systems were naturally chosen at stratigraphic levels at which fossil assemblages above and below contrast most conspicuously. These greater changes in fossils generally correspond to times of erosion or nondeposition in the European strata. The longer the episode of erosion or nondeposition the more prominent the differences between fossils of adjacent systems would generally be. As stratigraphic work was extended to other continents, however, fossil assemblages intermediate between those of adjacent European "type" systems were discovered—they had lived during the gaps in time not represented by strata in the European systems.

With more and more stratigraphic work, the gaps in the column have continued to narrow. Beds whose fossil assemblages pose "boundary problems"—that is, uncertainty about whether they are more closely related to those of the upper part of one European system or the lower part of the next higher are thus present at many places for nearly every systemic boundary. Even the gap between the Paleozoic and Mesozoic Eras, long considered an interval when none of the present continents received marine deposits, is bridged by nearly complete successions of beds in Nevada, Africa and the Himalayas. Even in Europe, where the divisions were established, further research has narrowed the gaps in the record. For example, the Paleocene was established to designate strata that could not be certainly correlated with either the typical Eocene or the typical Cretaceous. Now we find that different paleontologists refer certain strata (in Wyoming, for example) to the Cretaceous or to the Paleocene, depending on their appraisals of the relative affinities of the fossils of these beds with those in one or another European section.

The uncertainties posed by "boundary problems," however, are concerned largely with form instead of fact. Such disputed strata, it is generally agreed, must fill, at least partly, the gaps in the stratigraphic sequences from which the standard geologic column was established. Further detailed stratigraphic work is sure to fill other gaps. This is indeed a tribute to the precision of correlation by fossils, rather than a criticism of its uncertainties. It seems likely that all gaps between systems in the standard column will ultimately be bridged by sequences of fossiliferous strata at one place or another around the earth. The systemic divisions are purely arbitrary and convenient, rather than natural divisions applicable the world over. They would certainly have been placed differently if the early stratigraphic work (and hence the standard reference successions) had been in, say, western America or South Africa, instead of western Europe.

Intercontinental correlation

Thus, although the original divisions of the geologic column were based largely on the physical stratigraphic differences of the rocks, our *correlations of distant strata are necessarily based on a comparison of fossils* —not on physical stratigraphy but on biostratigraphy. An interruption in stratigraphic succession or an abrupt change in kind of rock in the type area does not help correlate beds hundreds of kilometers away. A stratigraphic break in Texas, for example, cannot logically be used as evidence that the beds above are Permian and those below Carboniferous. Such assignments of age to the Texas strata can be made only by the comparison of their fossils with those of the European type-sections of the geologic column.

Many difficult problems arise in the use of fossils in correlation. Some of these will now be discussed.

LONG-RANGING FOSSIL SPECIES.   In the century and a half since Cuvier and Brongniart began their work, studies of thousands of different species of fossils have shown that some shells, even from very ancient rocks, differ little from the shells of organisms now living. But such stable, long-enduring species of organisms are very few. Though a long-enduring species may range throughout a thick succession of strata, fossils of other species associated with it generally die out, or change from bed to bed, until finally none of the original companions of the long-enduring species accompany it. Conversely, many a species extremely abundant in lower beds becomes less so and then disappears completely in beds only a little higher, though most of its associates persist. Individual species range through quite different thicknesses of beds, which must mean that different species of organisms persist unchanged through entirely different spans of time (Fig. 7–2).

Obviously, short-ranging species are more useful in correlation than are those that persist through thick successions. But only occasionally can enough short-ranging forms, each with a slightly differing time span, be found to enable accurate correlation within a small part of an epoch. Commonly we must be content with less precise age determinations. The most suitable fossils for correlation over wide areas are obviously those species of short range but wide distribution, which were able to spread and accumulate

FIGURE 7–2

Using fossils to date beds. The long-ranging species on the left is of no value in dating the limestone beds between the horizontal lines, but the short ranges of the other species make them good time markers. The actual specimens were collected in England. (Data from S. W. Muller, Stanford University.)

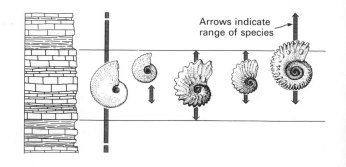

Arrows indicate range of species

in nearly all parts of the ocean. Such a species must have been abundant, otherwise its chances of preservation as fossils in widely different environments would have been remote.

SEDIMENTARY FACIES AND FACIES FOSSILS.   In correlating rock strata by comparison of fossils, we must keep in mind the limitations on the spread of organisms imposed by their natural habitats. Many different depositional environments exist: floodplains of rivers, estuaries protected from the open sea, ocean beaches, coral reefs, and hundreds more. Each environment has its characteristic group of animals and plants, living contemporaneously with the more-or-less different but equally characteristic groups of organisms in other environments. For example, we do not find antelopes thriving on a coral reef, nor living coral in a desert sand dune. Similarly, during a particular span of past geologic time, we do not expect to find the same fossils entombed in all the varied deposits formed.

By analogy with similar modern organisms, we assume that some marine fossils represent free-swimming forms that could live in almost any part of the sea. Their fragile shells, however, might be battered to pieces in the breakers and hence be preserved only rarely in deposits formed near shore. On the other hand, some fossil organisms were bottom dwellers, living only on muddy bottoms; their remains would not normally be found in limestone, or conglomerate, for they could not live in environments that permit such rocks to accumulate. Thus fossils in ancient rocks of even the same age may differ because of variations in the environments of deposition. Rocks that were formed in different sedimentary environments are said to represent different **sedimentary facies.** At any one time, either in the geologic past or now, many different sedimentary facies coexist.

Most organisms could live only in one environment; the fossils of each thus tend to occur in rocks of a particular sedimentary facies. The term **facies fossils** is generally used for groups of fossils found only in particular kinds of sediments. Thus we speak of one assemblage of fossils as the "limestone-reef facies fauna." Along the bedding the limestone may change within a few kilometers to shale containing a fossil fauna that lived on a mud bottom, a "shale facies fauna." Although the deposits were contemporaneous, the two facies faunas may have few, if any, species in common.

One relationship occasionally found between two facies fossils can give rise to errors in interpretation: in Fig. 7–3 a fossil of a long-ranging species (Fossil A) occurs *above* that of a shorter-ranging kind (Fossil B) in one region, but *below* it at another locality. At first thought, this might be considered a

FIGURE 7–3

Reversal of fossil sequence between two localities owing to differences in depositional sequence and accidents of preservation.

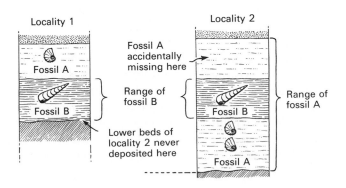

contradiction to the statement that once a fossil species dies out, it never reappears in younger strata. Such apparent reversals, however, generally result from differences in the environment of deposition of the two fossils. Likewise, a particular species may be missing from a certain bed containing a second species, though both are found below and also above that bed (Fig. 7–3). The environmental conditions (sedimentary facies) might have changed during the life-span of the first form, expelling it temporarily from the area of deposition even though its companion was able to adapt to the change. A later return to favorable conditions allowed the first species to migrate back and repopulate the area.

Despite these complexities—and there are still others—Cuvier and Brongniart's generalization has been abundantly justified: The older the rocks, the less their fossils resemble living forms. The younger the rocks, the closer the resemblance between fossils and living organisms which occupy similar depositional environments. Data from many parts of the world now make it possible to assign almost any collection of more than a few species—and even some single fossils—to a fairly restricted part of the standard geologic column.

EARLY ESTIMATES OF GEOLOGIC TIME

Cuvier's discovery of the extinction of some species of animals and the rise of new ones led him to the erroneous conclusion that there had been a series of major catastrophes in geologic history. These, he believed, destroyed all existing life. Following each, a whole new fauna was created. This doctrine, called Catastrophism, was unquestionably inspired by the Biblical story of the Deluge. Buffon, a French naturalist, had earlier estimated from some crude (and as it turns out,

wholly inapplicable) experiments that it would have taken the earth about 75,000 years to cool to its present temperature from the white heat he assumed it must once have had. Only during the last 40,000 years, he thought, would its temperature have been low enough for life to exist. Cuvier accepted Buffon's estimate and thought he could recognize four distinct faunas, so he assumed that the past 40,000 years had witnessed at least four catastrophes that had destroyed all existing creatures. Following each, a new creation repopulated the earth. The creation of Genesis was believed the most recent, having occurred about 6000 years ago—a date obtained by adding genealogical ages from Adam to Christ as given in the Old Testament.

But even as Cuvier expressed this belief, data were already at hand to disprove it: evidence showing that all coexistent species do not die out simultaneously, but that individual species change and become extinct in an overlapping sequence. One fossil species may die out, but its contemporaries continue on until they too, each in its own time, are succeeded by others. There is no basis for believing that a catastrophe destroyed all existing species, nor that new species all arose at once. Part of Cuvier's error lay in confusing facies faunas with new creations, for in the Paris Basin a continental environment commonly succeeded a marine one—but part of the confusion, no doubt, was due to the human predilection to fit ideas into those current at the time. This trait is still with us, in science as well as in other activities, and serves too often to color judgments that should be objective.

Cuvier's theory was short-lived; Hutton and Lyell urged the Uniformitarian view, and the steady accumulation of knowledge of the biologic relations among fossil forms opened a new and more consistent way of assessing evidence of the changes in fossils with time, and of the great age of the earth.

MODERN ESTIMATES OF GEOLOGIC TIME

With the framing of the geologic column came a growing appreciation of the vast duration of geologic time. Contemplation of even the time required to lay down the 500-foot thickness of chalk in the Paris Basin is disturbing to one who thinks of time only in terms of the human life span. The strata of the chalk are composed of skeletons of minute animals and plants. Similar deposits are accumulating today at rates so low as to defy precise measurement—certainly no more than a few millimeters per century and probably much less. Yet the chalk represents only part of the Cretaceous System, and the entire Cretaceous Period is a small part of total geologic time.

Not only the great thickness of sedimentary rocks impressed geologists with the immensity of geologic time, but also the vast parade of life recorded by the fossils. Thousands upon thousands of new species developed and then died out; whole fossil assemblages were gradually replaced by new ones. This can only be conceived of as involving millions of years, unless new species developed and spread far more quickly in the past than they do at present.

It would seem simple and obvious to measure the duration of geologic time by adding the greatest thicknesses of strata of each period to obtain the total thickness for all geologic time and then divide this total by the present annual rate of sedimentation to obtain the length of geologic time in years. But so many doubtful assumptions are involved in this approach that it is meaningless. What is an "average" rate of sedimentation when we know that it may take a century to lay down less than a centimeter of chalk, whereas a desert cloudburst may deposit fifteen meters of mud and gravel in an hour? Rates of sedimentation vary so greatly and so few have been measured accurately that an "average"

annual rate can only be guessed at. This method can thus give only a rough approximation of the length of geologic time; by using it the British geologist Sollas estimated (in 1899) that the time elapsed since the beginning of the Paleozoic could be between 34,000,000 and 75,000,000 years. His larger figure included a guess at the length of the lost intervals in the Standard Geologic Column: such guesses are interesting but far from reliable.

Age of the ocean

The Irish scientist Joly was more ingenious. He reasoned that the salt in the sea must have been weathered from the rocks and carried to the oceans by streams. As only a little salt is blown out by the wind or deposited by evaporation in desert lagoons or on tide flats, the oceans must be growing saltier; if we could compare their present salt content with the annual amount brought in by the rivers, we might determine the age of the sea. From the many ions contained in sea water, Joly selected sodium as the one best suited for such a measurement.

The volume of the sea has been estimated from its mean depth and area, and its composition is known from thousands of analyses (Appendix IV, Table 4). Thus, its total sodium content can be roughly computed. Similarly, we have thousands of analyses of river water, and from stream gages we know fairly well how much flows annually to the sea. From these figures, Joly computed the annual increment of sodium. Dividing the amount of sodium in the sea by the annual increment, he estimated the age of the ocean:

$$\frac{15,627 \times 10^{12} \text{ tons of } Na^+ \text{ in the oceans}}{15,727 \times 10^{4} \text{ tons of } Na^+ \text{ added annually}}$$

$$= 99,400,000 \text{ years}$$

Joly knew he was disregarding many factors. River discharge has not been constant throughout geologic time nor is all the sodium in present-day rivers directly derived from current weathering of rocks: much comes from sewage and industrial waste, some in water near the coast is windblown from the sea, and much is leached from marine sedimentary rocks that were deposited long ago in ancient seas. The present annual increment is quite certainly higher than the average for the geologic past, but how much higher we do not know.

On the other hand, great deposits of rock salt derived from evaporated sea water are among the stratified rocks. If returned to the sea, they would increase the oceanic tonnage of sodium, but how much we do not know. Furthermore, sodium ions react with clay and some are removed from sea water in muds. Finally, much sea water is trapped in the pores of marine sedimentary rocks. Thus an unknown amount of sodium has been removed from the ocean.

Clearly, Joly's 99,400,000 years is far too short a time, but we cannot make a quantitative correction; we can only conclude from this argument that the ocean has existed for considerably longer than 99 million years.

The radiometric clock of the rocks

When Becquerel discovered radioactivity (1896), he opened new vistas in every science. Among these was the discovery that it is possible to measure geologic time in years by studying the rate of decay of radioactive minerals. This method proved all previous estimates of the duration of geologic time to be far too short.

A few elements, among them uranium and thorium, disintegrate spontaneously into other, lighter elements. The intrinsically unstable atomic nuclei of such elements emit alpha particles (charged helium atoms), beta particles (electrons), and gamma rays (short x rays, not further considered here). Each nuclear emission of an alpha or a beta particle transforms the atom into one of a different element. In this way uranium 238 (U^{238}) slowly decays by way of many intermediate daughter products, all themselves radioactive, until the stable, nonradioactive isotope * of lead (Pb^{206}) is produced.

The rate of spontaneous disintegration differs greatly from one element to another. It is expressed in terms of the element's **half-life**—the time required for half of its atoms to disintegrate. The half-life of some members of the U^{238} series is only a fraction of a second; for U^{238} itself it is 4500 million years. If we start with one gram of U^{238}, in 4500 million years (hereafter abbreviated as m.y.), half a gram will be left, in another 4500 m.y. only a quarter of a gram, and so on. The rest has changed into lead, helium ions, electrons, and small amounts of intermediate elements in the decay series, which are in process of disintegrating to lead. This disintegration involves changes in the atomic nucleus and is independent of external conditions. Each radioactive element (except for a very few elements of no concern to this discussion) disintegrates at its own constant rate, without regard to temperature, pressure, or state of chemical combination.

Uranium consists of two isotopes: U^{238} (which makes up about 99.27 percent of natural uranium), with the half-life already mentioned of 4500 m.y., and U^{235} (making up about 0.73 percent), with the much shorter half-life of 713 m.y. The proportion of U^{235} was thus very much greater in the distant geologic past than it is today. U^{235} also disintegrates to yield a stable, nonradioactive isotope of lead, Pb^{207}. Thorium (Th^{232}) likewise disintegrates to yield lead with atomic weight of 208. Natural lead thus

---

* Isotopes are atoms of the same chemical element (i.e., with the same number of protons in the nucleus) which, because they have different numbers of neutrons, have differing atomic weights. Since the number of protons determines the number of electrons and hence the chemical behavior of the atoms, all isotopes of any element have virtually identical chemical properties.

consists of a mixture of the three radiogenic isotopes, Pb^{206}, Pb^{207}, and Pb^{208}, together with a fourth isotope of nonradiogenic origin, Pb^{204}.

Many minerals, most comparatively rare, contain measurable amounts of uranium, thorium, or both. By analyzing such minerals and finding the ratio of radiogenic leads to the radioactive parental isotopes (Fig. 7–4), the age of the mineral can be computed, provided that certain conditions are fulfilled. For example, it is obvious that the minerals analyzed must be absolutely fresh, for solutions circulating long after the mineral was formed might dissolve out the lead, uranium,

or thorium at different rates, thus producing great errors in the calculated age. A metamorphism after the mineral was formed would drive out lead more rapidly than uranium, thus invalidating the Pb-U ratio as a measure of age. And if the radioactive mineral happened to be deposited in close association with a lead mineral containing common, rather than radiogenic lead, it might be difficult to distinguish the two varieties of lead, especially if the common lead were much more abundant.

Nevertheless, a good many minerals have been found to meet these stringent geologic conditions and have been carefully analyzed. The analyses are difficult and, of course, require the use of complicated and delicate instruments, such as mass spectrometers. The proportions of the several isotopes of lead must be measured, as well as the total amount of lead, uranium, and thorium. Correction must be made for associated ordinary lead, whose amount can be estimated from the proportion of the nonradiogenic isotope, Pb^{204}, present. With all these meticulous measurements, it is still unfortunately true that few analyses give completely consistent results when the ratio of each daughter isotope to its parent is computed. Commonly ages computed from Pb^{208}: Th^{232} ratios differ notably from ages computed from Pb^{206}: U^{238} or Pb^{207}: U^{235} ratios. Lead behaves very differently chemically from either uranium or thorium so that even slight leaching by solutions passing through the rock is bound to produce errors in the ratio of daughter to parent element. Probably the best measure— the one likely to yield an age closest to the true date of origin, at least for the older rocks —is the ratio of Pb^{207}: Pb^{206}, for, of course, the two isotopes of lead are virtually identical chemically, and their *ratio* should be little affected by subsequent alteration, even though their *quantities* may be drastically reduced. But even allowing for rather wide differences in the ages computed from these several ratios, it is clear that many uranium

FIGURE 7–4

Graphs showing disintegration of a radioactive element, the growth of its stable daughter element, and the ratio of daughter element to parent. The small amounts of intermediate elements in the disintegration series are neglected.

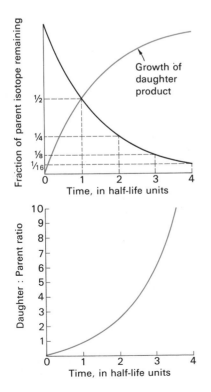

and thorium minerals are many hundreds of millions of years old.

Uranium and thorium are relatively rare elements, found in large amounts in only a few minerals. Radiometric dating began with minerals containing uranium and thorium, and suitable minerals containing these elements are still avidly sought for analysis. In 1948, however, L. T. Aldrich and A. O. Nier, physicists at the University of Minnesota, found that the very common element potassium could be used in chronology. Since then attention has focused chiefly on the far more abundant potassium-bearing minerals.

Potassium, the seventh most abundant element in the earth's crust, consists of three isotopes: K^{39}, K^{40}, and K^{41}. The first and last are stable, but K^{40} is radioactive and disintegrates in two ways. In one, an electron is ejected from the atomic nucleus, thereby converting a neutron into a proton and the original atom of potassium into one of calcium, Ca^{40}. The stable daughter, Ca^{40}, is the commonest isotope of calcium in nature, but only a small proportion of the Ca^{40} in the earth's crust is a product of potassium disintegration. Calcium minerals are so commonly associated with potassium-bearing ones that this process can only exceptionally be used in measuring mineral ages. The second scheme of decay is much more useful. In this, the decay is by capture of an extranuclear electron by the nucleus of the K^{40} atom, which thereby converts a proton into a neutron and the atom into one of argon of the same atomic weight. The half-life of the combined scheme is 1.31 billion years, with 11 percent of the K^{40} decaying to Ar^{40}.

Argon is an inert gas and enters no natural chemical compounds. From some mineral lattices it is able to diffuse readily and thus escape, but in others, notably those of biotite, muscovite, hornblende, and sanidine (the high-temperature form of potassium feldspar found in many volcanic rocks), the argon seems to be retained indefinitely, unless the mineral is reheated to high temperatures. To determine the Ar^{40}:K^{40} ratio requires painstaking and skillful analysis, but with recently improved techniques it yields consistent results, with probable errors less than 3 percent —perhaps even lower. Under favorable circumstances it is possible to date minerals as young as 50,000 years, in which radiogenic argon is sparse, indeed. It is beyond the scope of this book to detail the techniques of measuring Ar^{40}:K^{40} ratios, but the results of many careful workers on geologically dated material lie back of most of the dates given in Table 7–1.

Another pair of elements useful in radiometric dating is rubidium and strontium. One isotope of rubidium, Rb^{87}, is radioactive, and disintegrates with a half-life between 47 and 50 billion years (hence an uncertainty of about 6 percent in the deduced ages) into Sr^{87}. Common strontium consists of four isotopes, Sr^{84}, Sr^{86}, Sr^{87}, and Sr^{88}, so that it is necessary to correct for Sr^{87} that is not of radiogenic origin in the mineral analyzed. Because of the very long and somewhat uncertain half-life of Rb^{87}, and the necessity of this correction, Rb^{87}:Sr^{87} ratios are not as accurate measures of age in young rocks as in old. Although under favorable conditions this technique can be applied to rocks as young as Mesozoic, its main application is to the Paleozoic and Precambrian.

Many minerals that contain these radioactive elements crystallize from magma. Thus dikes or other intrusive bodies that cut, say, Devonian rocks, and contain radioactive elements suitable for dating, give us a minimum age for the Devonian. Pebbles recognizably from such a dated intrusive rock and found in younger strata give us, in turn, a maximum age for the beds containing them.

Many hundred analyses have been made in applying radiometry to geologic chronology, and a wealth of consistent results have been obtained. Even where the results are seemingly inconsistent, they may reveal significant events in geologic history. For example, an Ar^{40}:K^{40} date on hornblende may be, say,

750 m.y., whereas biotite from the same hand specimen gives an $Ar^{40}:K^{40}$ date of only 440 m.y. We know from many such discordant pairs, checked by analyses of the even more retentive mineral, zircon, that biotite has a crystal lattice more readily permeable to argon than that of hornblende. We may here, then, have a record of a rock formed 750 m.y. ago, and then reheated 440 m.y. ago to a temperature enabling argon to escape from the biotite but not from the hornblende. Of course, this is not the only possible interpretation of these results, and many discordant apparent ages are less readily rationalized, but it is nevertheless true that discordant results have often proved valuable and highly instructive in interpreting geologic history.

Over the last decade great advances have been made in this branch of geology. While some pessimists would disagree, it seems that the correction error involved in dating rocks that have not been reheated can be reduced to 2 percent and generally is less than 10 percent. Such accuracy is approaching that obtained by paleontologic studies of the fossiliferous rocks, and, of course, offers the only possible means of interregional correlation in the many times greater span of Precambrian time that preceded the earliest useful fossils.

Some of the most consistent measurements have been used in constructing Table 7–1. This table differs considerably in details from others compiled as recently as five years before. This is a field of most active research, and we may be perfectly confident that future work will further revise these compilations. But such changes are unlikely to be drastic. The development of geochronology is one of the great forward steps in geology. It demonstrated beyond question the tremendous sweep of geologic time: it is now certain that the geologic record encompasses at least 3500 m.y. Simple organisms such as bacteria and algae (Appendix V) have family trees nearly this old; the more complex multicelled organisms have existed at least since the beginning of Cambrian time—a span of well over half a billion years.

The oldest minerals thus far analyzed from North America (about 3500 m.y. old) came from Minnesota; comparable ages have been measured on rocks from South Africa and the Kola Peninsula in the USSR. Some meteorites have given ages as great at 4700 m.y., and many workers consider it likely that this may be the approximate age of the solar system and of the earth as a planet (Chapter 22).

RADIOCARBON, THE "SWEEP-HAND" OF THE RADIOMETRIC CLOCK. Uranium and the other radioactive elements we have discussed are naturally radioactive. Certain other elements can be made radioactive by bombardment with other particles or radiation. Among these, the most significant for geologic dating is carbon. Most carbon, such as that in coal, consists of the isotope C^{12}, with a variable small admixture of C^{13}. But carbon in the carbon dioxide of the air also contains a small amount of C^{14}. Cosmic rays from outer space bombard the nitrogen of the air to produce C^{14} by replacing one nuclear proton with a neutron. Radiocarbon, as C^{14} is called, disintegrates spontaneously, reverting to N^{14}. The half-life of radiocarbon, for some years after its discovery thought to be 5568 years, has now been determined to be somewhat longer, 5730 years; even this is a time so short that after a few tens of thousands of years very little of the original amount remains. Its use in geochronology is therefore limited to spans of up to 40,000, or at the very most, 50,000 years, rather than to the thousands of millions of years datable by the methods previously discussed. Its value within this limited span is, however, unique; such short spans cannot be measured by the methods previously described because the amounts of the respective daughter elements produced are too minute for measurement. Radiocarbon ages have proved very valuable in working out details of the history of the late Pleistocene and the Recent (Chapter 13), and have completely revolutionized archeological dating.

The theory of radiocarbon dating is as follows: the ratio of the isotopes of carbon in most living matter is virtually identical with their ratio in the carbon dioxide of the air. When an organism dies, it no longer derives radiocarbon from the air so that the ratio of radiocarbon to the stable isotopes, C^{12} and C^{13}, accompanying it in the body cells of the organism begins to decline. A comparison of the ratio of radiocarbon to the stable isotopes of carbon in a dead organism with that ratio in the atmosphere is thus a measure of the time elapsed since the organism died.

There are, however, several possible sources of error in applying this technique. Algae in a spring whose water is saturated with carbon dioxide that was partly derived by solution of the limestone (and thus from "old" carbon) have been found to deposit calcium carbonate sinter, in which the ratio of radiocarbon to stable isotopes is much lower than that of the air. Such a sinter is "born old." Conversely, porous limestone or reef corals repeatedly wet by waters whose radiocarbon content is that of the air, may exchange ions with these waters and thereby become "rejuvenated" through the replacement of part of the older carbon of the carbonate by new—and therefore more radiogenic—carbon from the air. There are still other difficulties: ages of 3000 to 5000 years determined by counting tree rings in Bristle Cone Pine (*Pinus aristata*) and Sequoia stumps are not consistent with radiocarbon ages determined on the same trees. The variations are such as to show that the ratio of C^{14} to total carbon in the air has not been constant. We know, of course, that the combustion of great quantities of fossil fuel since the beginning of the industrial revolution has added huge amounts of stable carbon to the atmosphere—as much as 3 percent of the total now present—and thus slightly reduced the ratio of C^{14} in recent years. But the variations in the Bristle Cone Pine and Sequoia carbon suggest that the concentration of C^{14} has varied by as much as 10 to 13 percent and perhaps much more in times long before the rise of industry; perhaps also before the oldest Bristle Cone Pines. The flux of cosmic rays to which the formation of radiocarbon is due varies with the intensity of the earth's magnetic field. There is incontrovertible evidence that the magnetic field has varied in both strength and polarity many times during geologic time (Chapter 19), so that variations in the rate of production of C^{14} are to be expected.

It is thus clear that radiocarbon dates cannot be considered absolute measures of age, even assuming no laboratory error. They are only approximate—"radiocarbon years" of Rubin, not astronomic years—but since the radiocarbon variations should be the same all over the earth (the time for complete mixing of the atmosphere is negligibly short), the sequence of measured ages should everywhere be parallel. And, of course, the greatest value of the age measurements is the establishment of sequence, however desirable a knowledge of the true age in astronomical years might be. Radiocarbon analyses, despite all the difficulties cited (and there are others, such as contamination by tree roots and bacteria) have yielded many consistent "age" data that have enormously expanded our knowledge of prehistory and cast new light on the events of late geologic time.

FISSION-TRACK DATING. Uranium atoms break down, not only by the radioactive decay schemes we have outlined above, but also, very much more slowly—at the rate of one atom in 69×10^{16} atoms of uranium per year—by spontaneous fission, in which an atom splits into two fragments of roughly equal atomic number. These fragments fly apart forcefully and knock many ions out of their normal positions in the crystal lattices of surrounding minerals. The lattice imperfections produced by the fission fragments are extremely small—far below the resolving power of ordinary microscopes. But the imperfections constitute weak spots and defects in crystals, making them less stable than the undamaged lattices, and therefore readily susceptible to leaching by acids, which enlarges the damaged areas and makes them visible microscopically.

Almost any rock contains a few uranium atoms as impurities, either within its minerals or on the intergrain boundaries. Thus almost any mineral, when leached in hydrofluoric acid or some other solvent of silica and silicates, reveals microscopic pits and cones that mark the paths of fission fragments.

This phenomenon has permitted development of a most ingenious method of dating rocks. A polished section of the rock is lightly etched with acid and examined under the microscope. The pits and cones of the lattice imperfections are counted in a measured area. The rock is then subjected to a measured flux of neutrons in a nuclear reactor, etched again, and the number of pits in the same area counted again. As the neutron flux is known, the increase in the number of pits in a unit area gives a measure of the number of uranium atoms present in it. Knowing this, it is easy to compute the time that was needed to form the number of imperfections first measured in the specimen.

This method is so new that it is difficult to evaluate as a practical method of geochronology, but it has yielded results consistent with those of other methods and will doubtless be thoroughly explored.

Facts, concepts, terms

Questions

1. Most of the Standard Geologic Column is based upon strata deposited in the sea. What relations between these strata and land-laid strata might be found that would permit correlations to be made between widely separated land-laid deposits?
2. Inasmuch as all paleontologists agree that new species arise suddenly by mutation, why do they reject Cuvier's Theory of Catastrophism and New Creation?
3. Why do we find that gaps in the Standard Column of western Europe are commonly bridged by transitional fossil assemblages (and accompanying rock strata) from other parts of the world?
4. In attempting to correlate two limestone sequences, one in Kansas, the other in Pennsylvania, would a comparison of the physical characters of the limestones or of their contained fossils be most useful? Why?
5. Most radioactive minerals used in age determinations are derived from intrusive igneous rocks. How can these give data about the age of adjacent sedimentary or metamorphic formations?
6. Many geologic formations contain no fossils, even though they are obviously of sedimentary origin. What relations might they show to other rocks that would permit determining their geologic age?
7. In selecting material for age determinations by the radiocarbon method, why must we be very careful to choose material that could not have been penetrated by roots, or infested by insects or bacteria, after it was deposited?
8. Why are fossil correlations over the whole earth chiefly based upon the marine organisms?

Suggested readings

Faul, Henry, *Ages of Rocks, Planets and Stars*. New York: McGraw-Hill, 1966.

Geological Society of London, *Phanerozoic Time Scale*. Supplement to v. 120, 1964, p. 13-144.

Kulp, J. L., *Geologic Time Scale*. Science, v. 133, No. 3459, 1961, p. 1105–1114.

Mather, K. F., and S. L. Mason, *Source Book in Geology*. New York: McGraw-Hill, 1939. [P. 12–13, 47–48, 174–175, 192–200.]

Simpson, G. G., *The Life of the Past*. New Haven: Yale University Press, 1953.

Scientific American offprints

102. Harrison Brown, *The Age of the Solar System* (April 1957)

811. Edward S. Deevey, Jr., *Radiocarbon Dating* (February 1952)

832. Robert Broom, *The Ape-Men* (November 1949)

837. Martin F. Glaessner, *Pre-Cambrian Animals* (March 1961)

838. Charles T. Brues, *Insects in Amber* (November 1951)

842. H. B. D. Kettlewell, *Darwin's Missing Evidence* (March 1959)

844. J. E. Weckler, *Neanderthal Man* (December 1957)

867. Norman D. Newell, *Crises in the History of Life* (February 1963)

Movements of the Earth's Crust

The many agents that erode the land were noted in Chapter 5, and the evidence for the earth's great antiquity was reviewed in Chapter 7. Clearly, if erosion were not somehow counteracted, all of the land should long since have been reduced to plains near sea level. But we have also seen that marine fossils abound in strata high in many mountains, demonstrating that beds formerly beneath the sea are now hundreds or thousands of meters above it. Marine beds as young as Pleistocene now stand in the Vale of Kashmir at altitudes of 1500 meters and are tilted at dips of 40°. Clearly this great uplift has taken place in less than 3 million years. Upward movements such as are required to explain these relations must from time to time counteract the destructive effects of erosion; otherwise great mountain chains could not still remain on our ancient planet.

Nor is the record only one of uplift. A miner deep in a Ruhr Valley coal mine, who unearths a fossilized tree stump with its roots spreading in the position of growth, can only conclude that the tree once grew on the surface of the land, even though it is now far beneath the ground and indeed even below sea level. How are these changes of level brought about? No one has ever seen a single convulsion lift or drop the land as much as a thousand meters. In this chapter we present evidence that these movements take place very slowly. Their ultimate causes are among the great puzzles of geology, but we can gain insight if we review some facts relating to them.

MEASURABLE DISPLACEMENTS OF THE EARTH'S CRUST

Displacements during earthquakes

Spectacular but relatively small earth movements have accompanied many earthquakes. In Chapter 19 we describe several earthquakes in some detail and enter into a discussion of their cause; we are here interested simply in the crustal motion associated with them.

FIGURE 8–1

Tree-denuded south-facing slopes in eastern Assam, where landslides actuated by the earthquake of August 15, 1950, devastated nearly half of an area of about 12,000 square miles. (After a photo by F. Kingdon-Ward, Geographical Journal, *September 1955.)*

FIGURE 8–2

Fault scarp (white line) 12 feet high, at the base of the Tobin Range, Nevada, formed during the 1915 earthquake. (Photo by B. M. Page, Stanford University.)

FIGURE 8–3

Cliff formed during the Mino-Owari earthquake, Japan, in 1891. The displacement, as measured on the offset road, was 20 feet vertically and 13 feet laterally. (Sketch based on photo by Koto.)

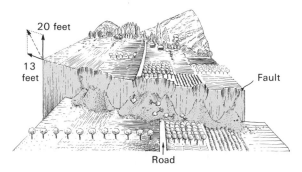

During really severe earthquakes the motion is so violent that whole mountain slopes are ravaged by landslides: in the Tibet-Assam earthquake of 1950 fully half of the mountain slopes—and nearly every one of those facing south—over an area of 12,000 square miles were completely denuded of forests by such slides (Fig. 8–1). This kind of ground motion is an aid to erosion, but other movements associated with earthquakes may oppose it.

During some earthquakes the ground has cracked open and the walls of the crack have slipped parallel to the crack. Such ruptures, along which slipping has gone on, are called **faults.** Fault displacements formed during even the most severe earthquakes rarely exceed a few meters. In some the movement is vertical, producing a small cliff (Fig. 8–2); in others, such as the destructive San Francisco earthquake of 1906, the fault walls slipped laterally, offsetting roads and fences horizontally; in many others, such as the Mino-Owara earthquake, Japan, the slipping was oblique, with both vertical and horizontal components of motion (Fig. 8–3). Table 8–1 lists some of the largest single displacements during historic earthquakes.

A few submarine earthquakes have caused

even greater fault displacement on the sea floor than the land earthquakes listed in Table 8–1. After an earthquake near Disenchantment Bay, Alaska, in 1899, the beaches stood 14.3 meters (47 feet) above the sea, and a wide expanse of sea floor became dry land. This is the greatest well-authenticated earthquake displacement known. The earthquake of 1964 that was so destructive in Anchorage, Alaska, accompanied an uplift of part of Montague Island in Prince William Sound of about 10 meters (Fig. 8–4).

Thus no single historic fault displacement accompanying an earthquake has been great enough to account for marine shells high in the mountains or for rooted stumps in mines far below sea level. Field studies show that the relatively small observed displacements are but minor steps that recur many times along the same faults. Of course, new faults of small displacement have formed during earthquakes, but most displacements have merely rebroken a pre-existing fault. The Pleasant Valley earthquake, which rocked the almost uninhabited desert of central Nevada in 1915, is a good example.

After the earthquake, the western base of the Tobin Range was marked for 28 kilometers (17 miles) by a low cliff, varying from less than 1 to as much as 5 meters (1 to 16 feet) in height along a line where only an abrupt steepening of slope had been before (Fig. 8–2). Figure 8–5 shows the break at one point along this new cliff. The 1915 fault is clearly shown by the vertical offset in the surface of the alluvium. The small patch of alluvium clinging to the upthrown Tobin Range block is nearly 4 meters (12 feet) higher than the alluvial surface of the relatively downdropped Pleasant Valley block. But the total displacement on the fault must be much more, for the dolomite of the Tobin block abuts against the alluvium of the valley block for a vertical distance much more than 4 meters. Furthermore, nearby gullies cut into the Pleasant Valley alluvium show that it rests not on dolomite like that across the fault but on lava. Immediately across the fault to the east, however, dolomite and other sedimentary rocks extend to the crest of the range, more than 600 meters (roughly 2000 feet) above the valley floor. A short distance to the north, the sedimentary rocks of the range are capped by lava like that beneath the valley alluvium. Obviously, then, the total vertical displacement along the fault has been at least 600 meters; indeed it may have been

Table 8–1 **Visible fault displacements associated with earthquakes**

Location	Maximum vertical displacement,			Maximum horizontal displacement,	
	Date	in feet	in meters	in feet	in meters
Owens Valley, California	1872	23	7	12	3.6
Sonora, Mexico	1887	20	5.1	0	0
Mino-Owari, Japan	1891	20	5.1	13	4
Assam, India	1897	35	10.7	?	?
San Francisco, California	1906	3	.9	21	6.5
Pleasant Valley, Nevada	1915	16	5.	0	0
Dixie Valley, Nevada	1964	12	3.6	12	3.6
Gobi-Altai, Mongolia	1957	30.4	9.2	28	8.5
Hebgen Lake, Montana	1959	18	5.4	small	small
Anchorage, Alaska	1964	33	10	?	?

FIGURE 8-4   *The uplifted sea floor off Montague Island, Alaska, raised during the earthquake of 1964. (Photo by George Plafker, U.S. Geological Survey.)*

enough to account for the whole difference in elevation between valley and range, locally more than 1000 meters (3300 feet).

FIGURE 8-5

Cross section showing the relation of the new 1915 scarp to the old fault surface, Tobin Range, Nevada. (After B. M. Page, Stanford University.)

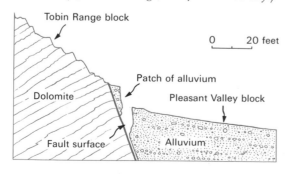

Tobin Range block

0   20 feet

Patch of alluvium

Pleasant Valley block

Dolomite

Fault surface   Alluvium

Clearly, the 1915 displacement was only the latest of many similar ones whose movements have been additive for geologically significant time.

Nearly all faults along which displacements have occurred within historic time show similar relations. Rock contacts on either side would not match if the historic displacement alone were reversed.

It should not be thought that deformation of rocks during earthquakes and faulting is confined to the immediate vicinity of the visible faults. It is, of course, more conspicuous there, but careful surveys have proved that the earth's crust is deformed in complex ways over wide areas.

An excellent example is furnished by the careful surveys of the Kanto Province, Japan, before and after the disastrous earthquake of September 1, 1923, which destroyed much of Yokohama and Tokyo, with the loss of more than 140,000 lives. Figure 8–6 shows the horizontal displacements of many reference marks; Figure 8–7, the vertical displacements. Obviously, considerable movements took place over an area of many thousands of square kilometers, with maximum horizontal shifts of more than one meter and vertical movements of as much as 2.5 meters of uplift and 1.5 meters of depression. The displacements were in many places by warp-

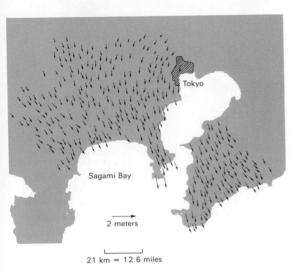

FIGURE 8–6

Horizontal movements accompanying Kanto earthquake of 1923. (After E. Inouye, Geographical Survey Institute, Japan, 1960.)

FIGURE 8–7

Vertical movements during Kanto earthquake. (After E. Inouye, Geographical Survey Institute, Japan, 1960.)

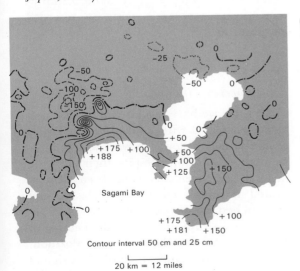

FIGURE 8–8

Displacements during Tottori earthquake of 1943. A: horizontal, B: vertical. Dotted line in (A) separates areas of dominantly eastward displacement to the north and dominantly westward displacement to the south. Irregular faults appear along this line. Vertical movements fail to show a comparable division of fields of uplift and depression. (Modified after E. Inouye, Geographical Survey Institute, Japan, 1960.)

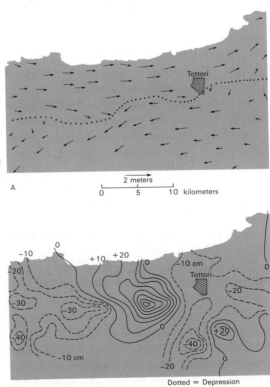

ing, as the boundaries between areas of up-lift and of depression are not marked by fault discontinuities. At first it was thought that very much greater displacements had taken place on the floor of Sagami Bay, for comparisons of soundings there showed changes deepened the harbor as much as 590 meters. Detailed study suggests, however, that most changes did not result directly from fault displacement or warping but were caused by great slides of unconsolidated muds and silts on the floor of the bay, trig-gered by the earthquake vibrations. Similar slides have been mentioned as resulting from the Grand Banks earthquake (Chapter 5), and earthquake-induced slides also deepened the harbor off Valdez, Alaska, by more than 100 meters during the Alaskan earthquake of 1964.

Displacements associated with earthquakes have many other patterns. Figure 8–8 shows the movements determined by resurveys after the Tottori earthquake, Japan, in 1943. Here almost oppositely directed horizontal move-ments took place to the north and south of an irregular easterly trending line, but the pattern of vertical displacements fails to show any corresponding division.

In earthquake-prone Japan displacements that accompany one earthquake may overlap those that accompanied another, in places reinforcing and elsewhere opposing the first movement. Accordingly, the cumulative pat-tern of many displacements has become highly complex, as seen in Figure 8–9, which summarizes the vertical displacements over a large part of Japan for a period of several decades prior to 1960.

Not all crustal movement associated with faults is accompanied by earthquakes. For example, resurveys have shown that the walls of the San Andreas fault in California, whose sudden movement in 1906 caused the San Francisco earthquake (Chapter 19), are slowly shifting past one another at a rate averaging nearly 2 inches (5 centimeters) per year in an area southeast of Hollister,

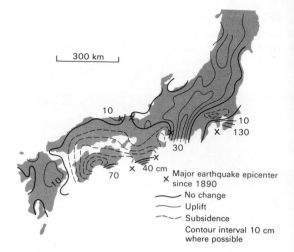

FIGURE 8–9
Vertical displacements on Kyushu and southern Honshu for several decades before 1960. (From E. Inouye, Geographical Survey Institute, Japan, 1960.)

though no earthquakes seem to be associated with the motion. A building astride the fault is being broken in two by the slow creep of the ground. The movement diminishes to-ward the south and within 300 miles is im-perceptible. Surveys show that the great Al-pine fault in the South Island of New Zealand is slipping laterally about 3.8 milli-meters per year, again with no recorded earthquakes.

Measurable slow movements not connected with faulting

Thus far we have described only displace-ments associated with faults, but the earth's crust also moves slowly in ways wholly inde-pendent of faulting. Despite their sluggish-ness, these movements have been demon-strated in many places. The classic, and perhaps best-known, example is that of an an-cient Roman ruin, the so-called "Temple of Jupiter Serapis" on the seashore at Pozzuoli, north of Naples. Only three of the original

FIGURE 8–10

Columns of the so-called "Temple of Jupiter Serapis," Pozzuoli, Italy, with high-water marks about one-third of the way up. (Photo by E. F. Davis, Los Angeles.)

columns and part of the floor of this building are still standing. About 6 meters above the floor a line circumscribes each column (Fig. 8–10); above this level the columns are smooth; below they have been bored and pitted by marine rock-boring clams, some of whose shells still remain in the holes. The history seems clear: after the building was built on dry land the ground slowly subsided until the floor was 6 meters below sea level, allowing marine clams to bore into the columns; later the land rose again; at present the columns stand in water a meter or so deep. The land has thus not quite returned to its former level of Roman times. Old

Roman wharfs nearby are submerged beneath 2 meters of water. Tide gages showed subsidence at the rates of 8 millimeters per year between 1822 and 1838 and 2 centimeters per year between 1838 and 1845; since then the subsidence seems to have slowed or stopped altogether, although the general level of the oceans has continued to rise appreciably the world over (Chapter 13). That it was the earth foundation and not merely the level of the Mediterranean that changed to bring about the submergence and the later elevation of the columns is clear from the fact that nearby sites, both north and south of Pozzuoli, have quite different histories, as recorded by old Roman docks and buildings.

Additional evidence of slow crustal movements is commonplace and virtually worldwide. Repeated surveys of high quality have shown the movements summarized in Table 8–2.

Table 8–2 **Rates of uplift and depression determined by surveys**

Locality	Rates, in millimeters per year	
	of rising	*of sinking*
Indo-Gangetic Plain, India	10.8	
Talinn, Esthonia	2.3	
Odessa, USSR		5.1
Orel, USSR	3.0	
Vilnius, USSR	3.8	
Baranovichi, USSR	5.5	
Sarni, USSR	9.5	
Krivoi Rog. USSR	10.8	
Moscow, USSR		3.7
Leningrad, USSR		3.6
Southern Denmark		.6
Northern Netherlands		.6
Southern Netherlands	.5	
Oahu, Hawaii		3.
Southern Chile		20.
Hong Kong	1.5	

NOTE: Data from repeated surveys during the last few decades.

Repeated accurate surveying in connection with large engineering projects has proved that some areas in Los Angeles are rising at a rate of 40 centimeters (16 inches) per century while others nearby are sinking at comparable rates. A large area in southeastern Alaska has been shown by tide-gage records to have risen as much as 154 centimeters (5 feet) between 1922 and 1960 (Fig. 8–11).

Even the fastest of the deformation rates mentioned seems slow by human standards, yet it is easy to see that if they continued for geologic time—say only a million years, a mere fraction of Pleistocene time—the most active uplifts in Los Angeles would attain elevations of 4000 meters (about 13,000 feet), less, of course, the height that would be lost by erosion during that time. Slow, then, as these rates of crustal movement appear to us, they are fully adequate to account for the existence of mountains on earth even after more than 3 billion years of erosion.

GEOLOGIC EVIDENCE OF DISPLACEMENTS OF THE EARTH'S CRUST

That these measured deformations do indeed persist for geologically significant times is readily demonstrable. Most of the world's coastlines yield evidence of geologically Recent (though prehistoric) crustal movement. The lobster fisherman off the Maine coast now and then finds fragments of freshwater peat, like that in the swamps on shore, fouling the wires of his traps. Almost every New England stream ends in a tidal estuary.

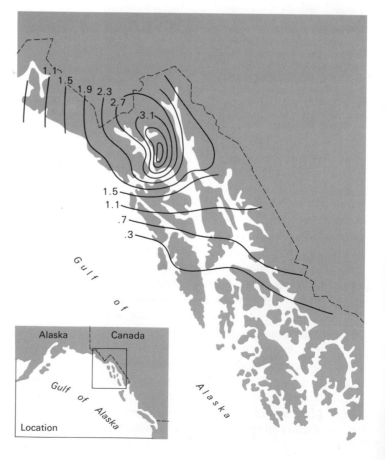

FIGURE 8–11

Map showing rate of uplift of land at various stations in southeastern Alaska between 1922 and 1960. Contour interval, 0.4 centimeter per year. (After S. D. Hicks and William Shofnos, U.S. Coast and Geodetic Survey, 1965.)

FIGURE 8–12   *Uplifted marine terraces, Palos Verdes Hills, California. (Photo by John Shelton and R. C. Frampton.)*

Dredgings from many reveal river-deposited silts with decomposed grass roots, or thinly stratified clays formed in freshwater lakes. As shown by the contained fossils, all of these must have been deposited above sea level.

Off Denmark, Japan, the Crimea, and the French Riviera, garbage heaps and campfire ashes of ancient man have been found a dozen or more meters beneath the sea. Bronze age settlements in the valley of the lower Don lie half a dozen meters below the level of the Sea of Azov. Some of these examples of apparent subsidence may be explained by the worldwide rise in sea level brought about by melting glacial ice (Chapter 13), but the facts that not all sea coasts show Recent submergence, and that those that do are not equally affected, indicate differential sinking to be real and widespread.

On a clear day, a person flying over the shallow southern part of San Francisco Bay can see former stream channels on the bay floor. These channels, though interrupted by deltas or small, wave-cut features at the shore, are clearly underwater continuations of the streams now entering the bay. They have been submerged, either by subsidence of the land or rise of the sea. At nearby Stockton, California, water wells drilled to depths of more than 300 meters below sea level penetrate buried soils, river silts containing grass roots, freshwater peat, and other land-laid deposits, throughout their entire depth.

Old roads and irrigation canals dating from the days of the Sassanian kings of Iran (third century) can be seen, from the air, to pass beneath the waters of the Shatt-el-Arab—the Tigris-Euphrates estuary—and out to depths of more than 18 meters. The downwarping in the deepest part has gone on at the rate of at least a meter per century.

High above the shores of Alaska, Newfoundland, Oregon, Italy, California, and many other lands, relics of former shorelines abound: barnacle shells still attached to rocks bored by marine clams (many shells still remain in the borings); sea cliffs, caves, and other erosional features carved from solid rock by former waves; and deposits of shell-strewn sand, drifted along former beaches by longshore currents. Conspicuous marine terraces border many sea coasts (Fig. 8–12). Although the tops of some such terraces have been buried by stream deposits washed from above, and on others former beach deposits have been removed by rainwash since their uplift, many preserve remnants of beach sand containing abundant marine fossils. Obviously these are upraised beaches of ancient seas.

Indonesia displays striking examples of geologically young changes of level, particularly in the region between Java and Borneo and in the southern Moluccas (Fig. 8–14, 8–15, 8–16). Coral reefs (Fig. 8–13) abound in these warm tropical seas. The reefs generally have nearly flat tops whose surfaces are mostly submerged but very near sea level. Reef-building corals cannot survive depths greater than 60 meters (about 200 feet) and are killed by a few hours of emergence. Limestone formed by corals, however, is by no means confined to the present depth of coral growth. High above the reach of the highest

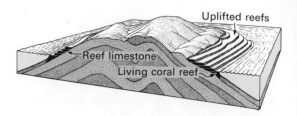

FIGURE 8–15

Uplifted coral reefs on the island of Kissa, southern Moluccas. (After P. H. Kuenen, redrawn from J. H. F. Umbgrove, The Pulse of the Earth, Martinus Nijhoff, 1947.)

FIGURE 8–16

The rivers of Borneo, Sumatra, and Java, with their submerged extensions. (Redrawn from P. H. Kuenen, Marine Geology, John Wiley and Sons, 1950.)

FIGURE 8–13

Diagrammatic sketch of a typical coral reef.

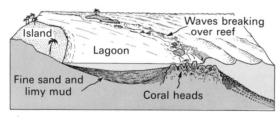

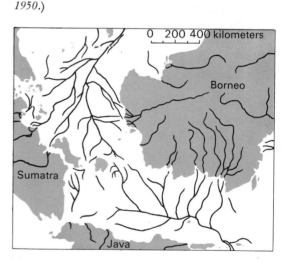

FIGURE 8–14

Height, in meters, of uplifted coral reefs and stream channels in the southern Moluccas. (Redrawn from J. H. F. Umbgrove, The Pulse of the Earth, Martinus Nijhoff, 1947.)

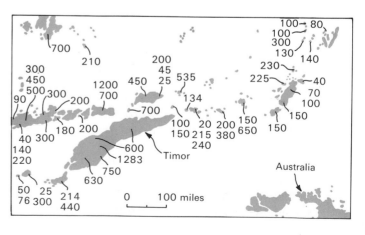

storm waves stand great terraces of white coralline limestone identical with that accumulating along the present shore. Some of these uplifted reefs are only a few meters above the sea; others surround mountaintops 1200 meters high (Figs. 8–14, 8–15).

Some uplifted reefs encircle the smaller islands like collars (Fig. 8–15). Others have been tilted; a reef a hundred meters or more above sea on one side of an island may slope down until it passes below sea level on the other side. Still other uplifted reefs have obviously been broken and displaced by faults.

Each raised reef, of course, testifies to uplift of the land relative to the sea. Equally compelling evidence shows that some former lands are now submerged, for reef corals of shallow-water habitat have been dredged in Indonesian seas from depths of many hundred meters. Most of the Sunda Shelf, between Borneo, Java, and Sumatra is less than 250 feet deep. Detailed sonic soundings have traced the courses of two large rivers across the submerged shelf (Fig. 8–16). The headwaters of these drowned rivers are the streams that still drain northern Java, southern Sumatra, and southwestern Borneo. The submerged river system accounts for the identity of the freshwater fishes and other stream dwellers of the three islands—areas now separated by a wide salt sea.

Thus Indonesia offers unmistakable evidence of both submergence and emergence in comparatively recent time. Side by side lie the submerged stream valleys of the Sunda Shelf and the uplifted, tilted, and faulted coral reefs of the southern Moluccas. Elevated reefs in Java and Sumatra point to uplift older than the drowning of the Sunda river system. Clearly, the presently active movements in this part of the earth's crust are far from simple. They involve not merely vertical uplift and subsidence, but concurrent bending and folding of the rocks. Indeed, many tilted reefs fit into a regional pattern of folds in the underlying rocks. Most of the long curving island arcs are complex upfolds or arches in the strata, separated by basins and downfolds, mostly still beneath the sea. The movements that produced these upwarps and basins still go on—warping the fringing coral reefs above the sea at one place, deeply drowning both reefs and landlaid deposits at another, and slowly building a complex system of folds in the earth's crust. Similarly warped coastal terraces are common along the coasts of California, Mexico, Japan, Italy, and many other lands.

CONTEMPORANEOUS FOLDING, EROSION, AND DEPOSITION

The crustal warping in Indonesia obviously produced widespread hills and low mountain ranges. We find, indeed, that most mountain ranges show strata, originally deposited in nearly horizontal sheets, that are now warped and folded into patterns even more complex than those of the Indonesian swells and basins. Can we find geological links between the broad warping of Indonesia and the more complex folding of the strata of the Alps and Appalachians? We can, indeed, find all stages of intermediate complexity. As an example of one such stage, consider the simple warps and folds in the lava flows that make up the eastern foothills of the Cascade Mountains in Washington and Oregon.

In central Washington and northern Oregon the walls of the canyons of the Columbia River and its tributaries reveal flow upon flow of black basalt. Most flows are between 15 and 80 meters—say, 50 to 250 feet—thick, but, unlike those seen by Werner at Stolpen, have relatively little interbedded sedimentary material. In places, however, thin sheets of river-deposited sediment do separate the flows, showing that streams advanced onto the volcanic plain after some eruptions and were later overwhelmed by new flows. Elsewhere, thin layers of ancient red or black soil are found between flows. They contain petrified (silicified) logs and tree stumps, some with roots still spreading in the soil (Fig. 8–17). Time enough had elapsed for the scoria on the lava surface to weather into soil and for a forest to grow on it before a new sheet of lava devastated the area. In certain areas, thin layers of a brilliant white rock with paper-thin stratification contrast strikingly with the basalt. The microscope shows that this white rock is almost wholly composed of the siliceous skeletons of minute one-celled plants called *diatoms* (Appendix V). Similar white diatomaceous layers are forming today in shallow ponds and lakes nearby. In a few places, river gravels, flood-plain silts, and diatomaceous deposits have buried the basalt flows under several hundred meters of sedimentary deposits.

The significant thing is that in many places the basalt flows and sedimentary rocks are no longer horizontal as they obviously once were. They rise and fall in great arches and troughs. On the flank of an arch, the scoriaceous top of a basalt flow and the diatomaceous strata above may dip at an angle of 20°; elsewhere beds of sand between flows dip at 70° to 85°. No stream tumbling down such slopes could deposit sand or gravel, nor could molten basalt maintain uniform thickness if poured out over the fold crest. Paper-thin diatomite layers would not be stable on a 20° slope in a lake. Each stratum and flow must have been virtually horizontal when deposited; the folding into the present arches and troughs developed later.

Central Washington is exceptional among mountainous areas in that the major topographic ridges coincide closely with arches, and the major valleys with troughs in the folded rocks beneath. The flanks of the arches are scored by ravines extending straight down their slopes. Flowing briskly during the rainy season, and aided by rill-wash and downslope movements, the streams have removed most of the weakly consolidated sedimentary rocks from the steep flanks of the arches, but the beveled edges of the eroded beds can still be seen on the gentle

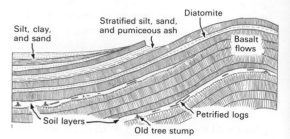

FIGURE 8–17
Cross section of lavas and interbedded sediments near Yakima, Washington. The section is a mile long, and the relief about 1000 feet.

lower slopes. Locally even the much more resistant basalt flows have been partly removed, and in places the folds have almost been erased as topographic features. Generally, however, the smooth curve of the arches, intact except for the ravines, shows that erosion has only begun to erase the uplifts. Many ravines do not have the usual concave-upward profiles of normal streams; they show humps in mid-course (see Fig. 12–26). The streams and folds have been developing at the same time, and the slow folding interfered with attainment of normal stream gradients.

How are the topographic ridges related to the adjacent troughs? The situation varies from place to place, but some partly dissected arches lie partly buried by unconsolidated stream and lake sediments that half fill the troughs. The uppermost beds of this fill are nearly horizontal, abutting against tilted basalt flows in the arches at notable angles. Younger lava flows are interbedded with the sediments in some of the troughs, but these do not extend over adjacent arches. They were erupted after the folding began and thus are confined only to the troughs (Fig. 8–18).

In a few large canyons we can see—and elsewhere we can infer from well records—that the older beds in the troughs have also been somewhat folded. Where they abut against the neighboring arch they dip with the older basalt but at a lower angle (Fig.

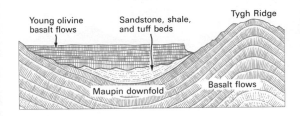

FIGURE 8–18

Cross section showing the relation of folded lava flows and sedimentary rocks to young, nearly horizontal lavas near Maupin, Oregon.

8–17, upper left). Higher beds in the troughs dip at still lower angles, and in some troughs remain nearly horizontal. These relations demonstrate that sedimentation was going on while the troughs were being downfolded. In places sediments were deposited about as fast as the troughs sank and were thus progressively warped as the fold grew.

Some of the trough-filling sediment was eroded from the adjoining growing arches, but most was brought in by rivers from the rugged Cascade Mountains to the west, as shown by the abundant pumice, andesite fragments, and quartz grains, none of which are present among the rocks of the arches.

The folds must have grown very slowly. Originally horizontal flows have been so folded that the flow on the crest of an arch may be thousands of meters higher than it is in the adjacent trough, but the folding was very slow. The first stages of folding blocked out the respective areas of erosion (arches) and sedimentation (troughs). The rising folds dammed some streams and impounded lakes in some troughs, interfering with normal stream development. In many places the growing folds interrupted sedimentation by tilting of older flows.

The folding still continues. Small streams show abnormal gradients (Fig. 12–26), and patches of unconsolidated gravel cling to tilted slopes much too steep to have originally received such deposits. Records of old surveys, although not wholly conclusive, sug-

gest that the decreased flow of water in certain irrigation canals built a generation ago may be caused by folding that is slowly changing the canal gradients.

Many examples from other mountainous regions also show that warping and folding of strata go on slowly, together with erosion and deposition. This has been clearly shown in the young (and growing) mountain ranges bordering both sides of the Pacific and in the Alpine-Himalayan belt across southern Eurasia.

FOLDS THAT HAVE CEASED TO GROW

An older mountain range (Chapter 20) such as the Appalachians shows both contrasts and similarities to the folds of Indonesia and the Cascade foothills. Figure 8–19 shows a cross section of the folded rocks of central Pennsylvania. This section depicts the structure of the rocks deep underground, as compiled from surveys of the many coal mines and from exploratory holes drilled in the search for coal. Note the independence of the surface topography from the forms of the arches and troughs in the strata; the Appalachian folds, unlike those of the Cascade foothills

FIGURE 8–19

Folds and fault in the coal fields of Pennsylvania. The solid lines represent mined coal beds; the dashed lines, their inferred continuations. The actual thickness of the coal beds ranges between 2 and 15 feet. (From N. H. Darton, U.S. Geological Survey, 1960.)

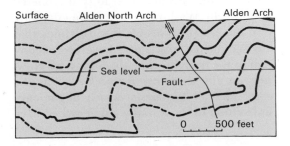

FIGURE 8–20
The relation between folds and ridges in the Appalachians near Rogersville, Virginia. (From Arthur Keith, U.S. Geological Survey, 1905.)

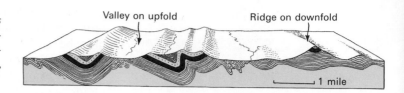

Valley on upfold   Ridge on downfold

1 mile

and Indonesia, are not growing today and have not grown in the recent past. We infer this because the arches are no longer ridges, and the troughs are not receiving sediment. Instead, throughout the folded Appalachians, the mountain summits are made of erosion-resistant rock. Some mountain summits have been left high because erosion could not yet remove erosion-resistant rock from the axes of downfolds in the strata. An adjacent upfold with more readily erodible rock now exposed in its core has been reduced to a lowland. Figure 8–20 shows typical examples. In the Appalachians, the topography is closely adjusted to the folded strata, but in a way wholly different from the adjustment in Indonesia and the Cascade foothills. Here the ridges are underlain by resistant rocks; the lowlands by less resistant. These are the common relations in mountain regions where folds have ceased to grow and erosion has had time enough to etch out the topography according to the relative resistance of the rocks. In Indonesia, the California Coast Ranges, and the Cascade foothills, the currently growing folds have developed fast enough to carry up weakly coherent strata to cap many mountain summits—erosion has not yet had time enough to strip such weakly resistant rocks away and leave the more resistant standing in relief.

Stages in the development of the folds in Pennsylvania are not so readily deciphered as those in Washington or Indonesia. Erosion has bitten so deeply into the folds that any sediments, which may have been deposited in the troughs while the folds were growing, or any shoreline features such as the coral reefs of Indonesia, which might once have clung to the initially rising arches, have

long since been removed. We can readily trace the displacements by folding and faulting of the coal beds, but we cannot tell whether they took place in a few seconds or in the course of millions of years.

Nothing, however, in the Appalachian structures differs fundamentally from its counterparts in the Cascade foothills or Indonesia. If Indonesia were deeply eroded, its topography would resemble that of the Appalachians. In the higher, more rugged Cascades to the northwest of the foothill folds, erosion has already worn down some of the basalt arches and stripped so much sediment from the intervening troughs that the best evidence of their slow growth has already disappeared. Such transitional areas show that slow movements of the crust, so readily documented in Indonesia and Japan, are fully adequate to explain the growth of the folds of Pennsylvania and the Cascade foothills. Again we see the applicability of our fundamental postulate: "The present is the key to the past." Fossil shells on mountaintops, and soils and fossil plants in deep mines are just what we should expect from our knowledge of currently active crustal deformation in many parts of the earth.

Furthermore, we see that in some places the earth's crust is broken along clearly defined faults, just as a brittle rock might be expected to break; elsewhere the strata have folded like plastic dough. In places, both kinds of deformation have gone on at the very surface of the ground. The reasons for these differing behaviors and the ultimate cause of the deformation are both obscure. The questions they raise are discussed in Chapters 9, 10, and 20. They are among the greatest problems of earth history.

Facts, concepts, terms

Crustal movement
    Fault displacements associated with earthquakes
    Fault displacements not associated with earthquakes
Warping of the crust not associated with faults
    Slow vertical movements
    Bending and folding of the crust
Warping and folding in relation to mountain structure
    Characteristics of growing folds
    Time relations between erosion and folding
    Erosional patterns on growing folds versus those on dead folds

Questions

1. You are examining a fault in the field. What evidence would you look for in the landscape to tell whether this fault is active, or long since dead?

2. Would you expect earthquakes to be more common in Indonesia or in the Central Atlantic States? Why?

3. In a certain mountain range all of the ridges and peaks are composed of erosion-resistant rocks that have been tilted, folded, and faulted. In another mountain range the rocks show about the same structure, but easily eroded rocks are locally exposed at the summits of the peaks, and many streams flow along the axes of downfolds. What can you say about the relative age of folding in the two regions? Explain.

4. As many as 13 nearly level marine terraces have been recognized at heights ranging between 100 and 1,300 feet above sea level in the Palos Verdes Hills near Los Angeles, California (Fig. 8–12). Suppose you were sent to examine this area. How could you tell whether these terraces were caused by folding and faulting of the earth's crust, or by removal of water from the ocean, perhaps to form ice sheets on the land during glacial epochs?

5. The rocks of the Swiss plain, just north of the intensely folded rocks of the Alps, show much gentler folds. The oldest rocks of the plain are marine, and about the same age as the youngest rocks of the Alps. The youngest rocks of the plain are nonmarine river gravels and sands which do not appear in the Alps. The Alps, like the Appalachians, show no direct relation between folds and topography. What suggestions occur to you to account for the differences in the two areas?

6. The dolerite sill composing the Palisades of the Hudson, across from New York City, is several hundred feet thick where exposed along the west river bank. Sandstone beds above and below the sill dip to the west. How can you account for the absence of the sill on the east side of the river?

7. Cincinnati is built on Ordovician marine rocks. Both to the east and to the west, Silurian, Devonian, and Carboniferous rocks are exposed, dipping away from Cincinnati. What is the simplest explanation for this that occurs to you?

8. Draw three geologic sketch maps to represent the evolution of one of the folds in the Cascade foothills. In the first map, show an almost uneroded arch in the basalt lavas and overlying sedimentary rocks, with a little new sediment de-

posited in the adjoining troughs. In the second, show the fold after the sedimentary rocks and some of the lava have been stripped from the crest of the arch, and the adjacent troughs are half filled with new sediment. In the third, show the area after erosion has completely erased the arch as a topographic feature.

Suggested readings

Daly, R. A., *Our Mobile Earth*. New York: C. Scribner's Sons, 1936.

Gilluly, J., *Distribution of Mountain Building in Geologic Time*. Geological Society of America Bulletin, v. 60, 1949, p. 561–590.

Hills, E. S., *Elements of Structural Geology,* 2nd Ed. New York: John Wiley and Sons, 1963.

Umbgrove, J. H. F., *The Pulse of the Earth,* 2nd ed. The Hague: M. Nijhoff, 1947.

chapter 9

Records of Earth Movements

Evidence presented in Chapters 5 and 8 indicates that the earth's crust is affected by a constant interplay between the processes of destruction (erosion) and of construction (volcanism and uplift). Most folds and other crustal structures that we see today have been much modified by erosion. In areas of intensely deformed rocks, if we are to understand the record, we must not only recognize the kinds of rocks but also their mutual relations, for in these lie clues to the changes that have taken place since the rocks were deposited as sediments or solidified from magmas.

This chapter describes the geometry of the commoner rock structures and suggests how they may be used in unraveling events of the distant past.

H. B. de Saussure (1740–1799), a Swiss geologist who was also an ardent mountain climber, did much to develop interest in **structural geology.** This branch of geology is concerned with the deformation of rock bodies, with the present geometrical relations of the rocks in terms of how they evolved, and with analysis of the forces that deformed them.

"ORIGINAL HORIZONTALITY": THE KEY TO STRUCTURE

We have seen (Chapter 3) that by the middle of the seventeenth century Nicolaus Steno had proposed the Law of Original Horizontality—that strata are generally deposited in nearly horizontal layers, parallel or nearly parallel to the surface on which they accumulated. But another century passed before geologists realized the implications of Steno's law for deciphering the complex structural relations of stratified rocks.

While climbing in the Alps, de Saussure noticed that the strata seemed to be crumpled into folds like those made when a rug is pushed together in a heap on the floor (Fig. 9–1). He did not immediately interpret these

FIGURE 9–1   *Contorted Table Mountain Sandstone (Silurian), Cape Mountains, South Africa. Such contortions are common in the Alps, also, and led to de Saussure's interest in structural geology. (Photo by Warren Hamilton, U.S. Geological Survey.)*

folds in the light of Steno's century-old law; instead, he at first assumed that the rocks had crystallized in their present contorted forms. Only when he recognized beds of water-laid conglomerate projecting vertically from the ground did he see how absurd it is to think that sheets of pebbles interlayered with sand could have been deposited in such a position. The beds must have been tilted to the vertical after they were deposited and consolidated. The stratification of a sedimentary rock gives us a plane of reference in the geologic past—at the time of its origin the stratification was nearly horizontal—if it was later tilted or folded we can therefore reconstruct the amount and direction of the tilt.

WARPS AND GENTLY TILTED STRATA

Over much of the earth the sedimentary strata still appear horizontal. If, however, we note the altitudes of several widely separated points on the upper surface of such a seemingly horizontal body, we generally find the bed not exactly horizontal. Either it had an original dip or it has been slightly warped. The gentle slopes of many such beds, however, are too irregular to be explained by original dip; these must have been tilted since deposition.

The rocks of the Mississippi Valley afford good examples. For instance, oil wells in southern Illinois penetrate the Chattanooga Shale, of Devonian age, at about 1400 meters below sea level. The shale then rises steadily eastward and finally appears at the surface about 150 meters above sea level near Louisville, Kentucky. It also rises, though less steeply, to the north, south, and west. As another example, well records and mapping reveal the bottom of the Colorado Shale, a widespread marine formation of Cretaceous age, at about 1000 meters below sea level near Williston, North Dakota; but it rises to 600 meters or more above sea level near Shelby, Montana, and to 300 meters above sea level near Sioux City, Iowa. Such differences must have been caused by movements of the earth's crust, because this uniform formation with its characteristic marine fossils could not have been deposited simultaneously both on land and in the sea.

Showing warps on maps

How can we represent broad warps on maps and sections? If the relief is high, ordinary geologic maps and sections like those of Figure 6–2, may suffice. In areas of gently dipping beds and low relief, however, few beds crop out, and hence a geologic map may be ill adapted to the needs of a mining or quarrying operation.

If we are mining a coal bed by open-pit methods (stripping away the overburden of barren rock and soil above the coal), a very slight dip may be critical to our operation. Suppose that at one place 8 meters of overburden must be stripped off to lay the coal bed bare. If the ground is flat and the coal bed dips only about 1°, a kilometer down-dip the overburden will have increased to perhaps 25 meters, a prohibitive thickness for economic operations. Up-dip, in a few hundred meters, the coal will have risen to the surface and been eroded away. If the ground is hilly, as in the Wasatch Plateau

coal field of central Utah (Fig. 9–2), or if the coal bed is irregularly warped instead of dipping uniformly, it may seem difficult to compute just what part of it can be mined economically by open pits and what part could better be mined from underground workings. To help solve such problems we construct structure contour maps of the coal bed.

Structure contour maps

A **structure contour map**, like a topographic map (see Appendix I), uses contours to represent lines of equal altitude. But whereas a topographic map depicts the surface of the ground, a structure contour map shows the surface of a single stratum as it would appear if all the rocks above were stripped away. If we removed all the overburden from a coal bed and then made a topographic map of the newly exposed surface of the coal, the result would be a structure contour map of the coal bed.

But how can we make a structure contour map without actually excavating down to the coal? Figure 9–3, a map of the area sketched in Figure 9–2, illustrates some steps that enable us to get control points for the structure contours. Figure 9–3 is a combined topographic and geologic map upon which the structure contours of the coal bed have been superposed. A heavy black line marks the outcrop of the Hiawatha coal bed. Notice that the contours of the ground surface do not parallel the outcrop of the coal—the strata have therefore been tilted since deposition. For example, there are seven places (numbered 1 to 7 on Fig. 9–3) in the ravines north of Miller Creek where the 8250-foot contour crosses the top of the coal bed. At each of these, the top of the coal is 8250 feet above sea level. Thus we have seven control points through which to draw the 8250-foot structure contour. This structure contour is a line showing where the surface of the coal bed is 8250 feet above sea level (or was,

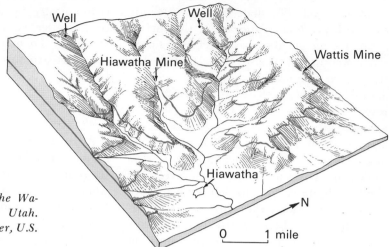

FIGURE 9–2
Relief diagram of part of the Wasatch Plateau coal field, Utah. (From a map by E. M. Spieker, U.S. Geological Survey.)

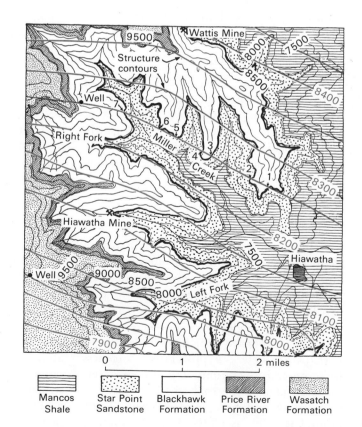

FIGURE 9–3
Topographic, geologic, and structure contour map of the area shown in Figure 9–2. (Modified from E. M. Spieker, U.S. Geological Survey.)

before erosion excavated the deep ravines and removed parts of it). On the south wall of Left Fork Canyon, the coal bed crosses the 8000-foot topographic contour at ten points; we have ten control points for the 8000-foot structure contour. Control for other structure contours is found in the same way. Borings and wells give other points. Thus, a well on the ridge north of the right fork of Miller Creek penetrates the coal at a depth of 750 feet. As the wellhead is at 9000 feet, the top of the coal must be at 8250 feet; this gives further control for the 8250-foot structure contour.

The coal is overlain by the Blackhawk Formation, whose thickness, measured in several different canyons is 750, 775, 725, 740, and 760 feet. As there is no systematic variation, we accept 750 feet as an average. Therefore, wherever a topographic contour crosses the top of the Blackhawk Formation we can assume the top of the coal is 750 feet below. A point on the 8000-foot structure contour near the west edge of the map was found as follows: a well on the 9750-foot topographic contour fails to reach the coal but does cut a thin bed of limestone at 200 feet. This limestone, we know from measurements in nearby canyons, is 550 feet above the base of the Wasatch Formation. The Price River Formation, next beneath the Wasatch, is 250 feet thick (from similar measurements). At the well site the top of the coal must therefore be 200 (depth to limestone), plus 550 (limestone to base of Wasatch), plus 250 (thickness of Price River), plus 750 (thickness of Blackhawk) or 1750 feet below the wellhead. As the wellhead is at 9750 feet, the top of the coal is at 8000. Elevations at other points are similarly found; enough to draw structural contours on the Hiawatha coal with reasonable accuracy.

Once such a structure contour map has been prepared, the amount of overburden above the coal is readily found by subtracting the elevation shown by the structure contour from that of the topographic contour directly above.

Cross sections with exaggerated vertical scale

For certain purposes, geologic cross sections are drawn with a greatly exaggerated vertical scale. Such exaggeration, of course, distorts the form of the features shown, gives a wholly erroneous impression of the dip by oversteepening it, and a false impression of the size of any structures shown. But it does permit us to plot thin formations that could not otherwise be shown, and to portray and summarize lateral changes in the sedimentary rocks. For example, Figure 9–4 shows the structure beneath the Moscow Basin. The large cross section is plotted with a vertical scale 100 times that of the horizontal. The lateral gradation of limestone to shale, and of salt to various other kinds of rock is clearly shown, although such gradations could not have been plotted on the section with a 10 to 1 exaggeration in the same figure. Had the section been drawn to true scale (vertical equal to horizontal), the entire thickness of all the beds would have fallen within a single pencil line. *It must be kept in mind, however, that when the scale is exaggerated 100 times, beds that have a true dip of not more than one degree will appear to dip 45 degrees or more in the section.*

FOLDS

The records left by intense rock deformations can be seen clearly in the great mountain chains, for example, the Alps, in which de Saussure did his pioneering work. But steep folds and large faults are not confined to mountain ranges of the present day. In some areas, repeated and long-continued periods of erosion have destroyed entire mountain ranges that must once have towered as far above their surroundings as the Alps and Sierra Nevada do today. One of the triumphs of structural geology has been the tracing of vanished mountain chains across such relatively flat areas as Finland, eastern Canada, and Brazil by the remnants of their deeply eroded structural features.

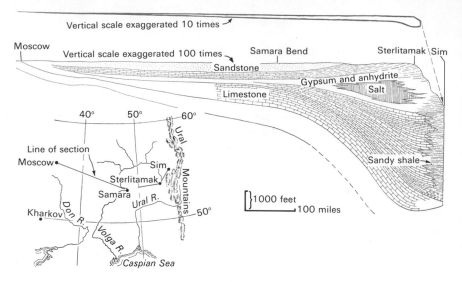

FIGURE 9–4   *Cross section of the Moscow Basin, Russia, showing long-distance facies changes in the strata. These can be plotted only because of the greatly exaggerated vertical scale. (After C. O. Dunbar, Yale University.)*

FIGURE 9–5   *Anticline in Cretaceous limestone and chert, Barranca de Tolimán, Hidalgo, Mexico. (Photo by Kenneth Segerstrom, U.S. Geological Survey.)*

FIGURE 9–6   *Air view of an eroded, plunging anticline in Iran. The plunge is away from the camera. Note the dip of the beds away from the axis of the fold. (Photo by Aerofilms, Ltd., through courtesy of John Shelton.)*

FIGURE 9–7   *Air view of an eroded, plunging syncline in northwest Africa. The plunge is to the left. Note how the ridges formed by the resistant beds indicate dips toward the trough line of the fold. (Photo by U.S. Air Force.)*

Folds are the most common structures in mountain chains. They range from microscopic crinkles through folds a mile or two across (Fig. 9–5), to great arches and troughs fifty or more miles across. Upfolds or arches in rocks are called **anticlines** (Figs. 9–6, 9–14, and 8–17); downfolds or troughs are **synclines** (Fig. 9–7). Thus on geologic maps eroded anticlines show older rocks along their central (axial) parts with younger rocks dipping away from them; synclines have younger rocks along their axes, bordered by older rocks that dip beneath them.

A **monocline** is a fold formed by the local steepening of an otherwise uniform dip (Figs. 9–8, 9–9).

The young anticlines of the Cascade foothills still form ridges, but in the Appalachian landscape all ridges are underlain by resistant rock irrespective of the position of this rock in an anticline or syncline. The terms

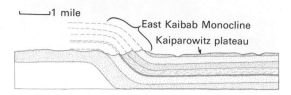

FIGURE 9–8

Cross section of the Kaibab monocline, Utah. (After H. E. Gregory and R. C. Moore, U.S. Geological Survey.)

FIGURE 9–9   *The northern plunging end of the Comb Ridge monocline, near Blanding, Utah. Note nearly horizontal attitude of rocks on the skyline to the left, the downward bend as the strata are followed to the right. Out of view in the foreground to the right the strata again are nearly horizontal. View is northward. (Photo by Tad Nichols, Tucson, Arizona.)*

anticline and syncline apply *only* to the *structure* of the *strata* and have *no reference* to *topographic form*. The original forms of most folds have been greatly obscured by erosion (Fig. 9–10). To visualize these forms, we often sketch the former extensions of the eroded beds by drawing dashed lines above the erosion surface. The monocline of Figure 9–8 has been partly restored in this way.

Another way of showing the form of eroded folds is illustrated in the lower part of Figure 9–11. The upper sketch shows part of the Jura Mountains in Switzerland. One limestone bed forms cliffs and bold ridges showing that it is somewhat more resistant to erosion than the others. The top of this limestone is shown as a heavy black line. In the lower sketch, the top of this resistant stratum is drawn as it would appear if suspended in space, entirely detached from the beds above and below, thus bringing out the form of the folds.

FIGURE 9–10
Deeply eroded limb of an anticline, Flaming Gorge, Utah. (Photo by W. H. Jackson, U.S. Geological Survey.)

Structure symbols

The best way to portray a simple fold is by structure contours (Fig. 9–12), but if we do not have enough information to draw structure contours, **structure symbols** placed on the geologic map may still bring out many details of the fold. Figure 9–13 shows some of the more common symbols used to depict structure on geologic maps.

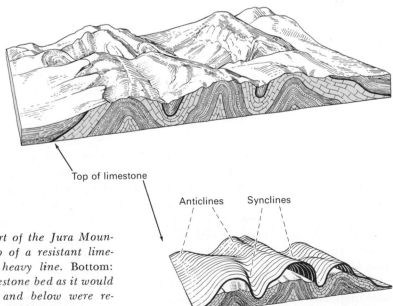

Top of limestone

Anticlines   Synclines

FIGURE 9–11
Top: *Relief diagram of part of the Jura Mountains, Switzerland. The top of a resistant limestone bed is shown by a heavy line.* Bottom: *Sketch of the top of the limestone bed as it would appear if the beds above and below were removed. (After Albert Heim, 1922.)*

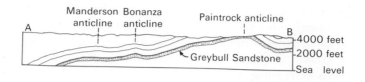

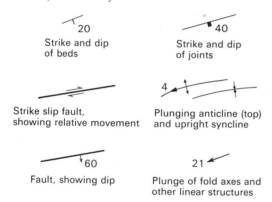

FIGURE 9–12

Structure contour map and cross section of folds in the Big Horn Basin, Wyoming. The bed contoured is at the top of the Greybull sandstone. (After D. F. Hewett and C. T. Lupton, U.S. Geological Survey.)

FIGURE 9–13

Chart of structure symbols.

20
Strike and dip
of beds

40
Strike and dip
of joints

Strike slip fault,
showing relative movement

4
Plunging anticline (top)
and upright syncline

60
Fault, showing dip

21
Plunge of fold axes and
other linear structures

The block diagram and geologic map (Fig. 9–14) of a small fold in the Jackfork Formation of Arkansas show how various structures can be shown by symbols. On the geologic map, the strike and dip of the beds are shown at several places by **strike and dip symbols** (see Chapter 6 and Fig. 9–13). While mapping, the geologist plots these symbols on his base map wherever he determines strike and

dip. The block diagram shows two layers of shale interbedded with the prevailing sandstone of the Jackfork Formation. These have been wrinkled into many small puckers that roughly parallel the major fold. The stronger and thicker sandstone has risen as a smooth arch instead of collapsing into puckers as the shale did during folding. We say that the resistant sandstone shows **competent folding,** the weak shale **incompetent folding.**

The dip of the strata in the minor puckers should not be mistaken for the general dip of the entire formation in the major fold.

The surface that divides a fold as symmetrically as possible is the **axial surface,** often loosely called the **axial plane.** The line along which the axial surface intersects a bed is the **axis** of the fold. If the axial surface stands at a high angle, as in Figure 9–14, the axis is also the line on the surface of the ground where each bed reaches its highest point as it arches over an anticline, but if the axial surface dips at a lower angle, as in Figure 9–10, the highest point for each bed —its **crest line**—may be far removed from the axis. (This distinction is not always made; many maps show the crest line as the axis, even where the axial surface has a very low dip). The crest line of an anticline is mapped as a line with diverging arrows (Fig. 9–14). The **trough line** of a syncline (the line along which each bed reaches its lowest elevation) is mapped with converging arrows.

Another feature generally mapped is the inclination of the crest line of a fold—its **plunge.** Note that the crest of the anticline shown in Figure 9–14 plunges northward into the ground at a measured inclination of 8°. The plunge is the same as the dip of a bed exactly on the fold crest or trough. It is shown by an arrowhead showing its direction, and numerals giving the amount of plunge.

Forms of folds

At one place an anticline or syncline may be either plunging or nonplunging. Clearly, though, every fold must somewhere die out, and here it must plunge. Figures 9–7 and 9–14 show why each of the strata that compose an eroded, plunging fold makes a curving or canoe-shaped pattern on the ground surface. Erosion etches the resistant beds into

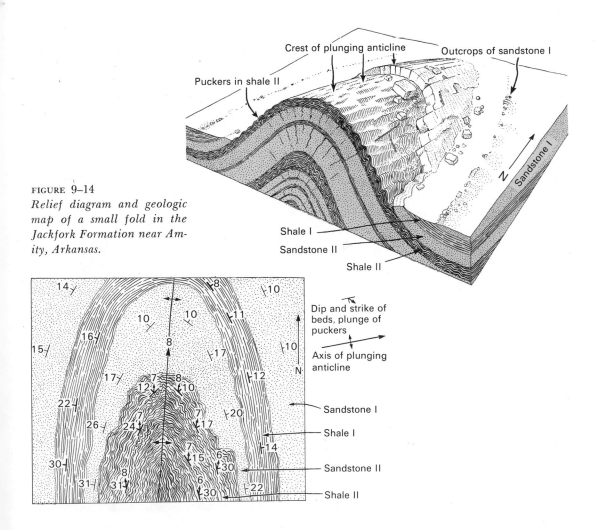

FIGURE 9–14
Relief diagram and geologic map of a small fold in the Jackfork Formation near Amity, Arkansas.

relief, and the curving ridges clearly reflect the structure. If the fold does not plunge, and if relief is low, the beds crop out as roughly parallel bands repeated on either side of the axis.

A **dome** is an anticline roughly as wide as it is long, with plunges in opposite directions from a high point. A doubly plunging syncline forms a **basin:** the Paris Basin is typical.

Many folds, such as the Paintrock anticline (Fig. 9–12) are **asymmetrical**—the strata of one **limb** of the fold dip more steeply than those of the other. Even though asymmetrical, such folds are still considered **upright,** if their limbs dip in opposite directions. In regions of intense deformation, however, many folds are **overturned**—beds on the lower limb of an overturned anticline or on the upper limb of an overturned syncline have been tilted beyond the vertical (Fig. 9–10). The strata on both limbs thus dip in the same direction, though they may differ in amount of dip. Still other folds are **recumbent** (Fig. 9–21)—in a recumbent anticline the beds on the lower limb are upside down; in a recumbent syncline the upper limb is inverted. If the beds on both limbs are nearly parallel, a fold is **isoclinal,** no matter whether upright, overturned, or recumbent. Several folds in Figure 9–21 are overturned isoclinal folds.

JOINTS AND FAULTS

Fractures in rocks are classified as joints or faults: **joints** are those fractures that have merely opened, without appreciable offset of the rock along the fracture; **faults** are those showing definite offset. This distinction is made on maps only if the displacement is large enough to be mappable; smaller offsets are generally ignored or mapped as joints. Many faults have displacements of thousands of meters.

Most outcrops show numerous joints (Figs. 4–5, 4–6, 4–7, 9–15, 9–16). Because of their profusion and irregularity, most are omitted from geologic maps. If there is some reason for showing them (for example, valuable ore veins may follow some joints), their strike and dip is commonly plotted by the symbol shown in Figure 9–13.

Joints and small faults may be formed in several ways, by erosional unloading, dessication, thermal contraction, compaction, and in other ways, but large faults traceable for many kilometers (Fig. 9–17) and whose walls are displaced hundreds or thousands of meters have certainly been formed by crustal movements.

FIGURE 9–15

Columnar jointing in basalt lava. The long, six-sided columns formed by shrinking of a thick lava flow as it cooled from the base upward. It is known from exposures nearby that the upper two-thirds of the flow has here been eroded away. Columbia River Basalt, Maury Mountains, Oregon. (Photo by A. C. Waters.)

FIGURE 9–16
Rectangular joint pattern in massive sandstone, Colorado Plateau. (Photo by V. C. Kelley, University of New Mexico.)

FIGURE 9–17
Air view of a fault near Great Bear Lake, Canada. The fault extends for 130 km (80 miles). Deformed sandstone strata to the left, granite to the right. Note the small faults and joints that cut the granite at acute angles to the fault. (Data from A. W. Jolliffe, Queens University. Photo by Royal Canadian Air Force.)

Kinds of faults

Faults are widespread, but they particularly abound in the highly deformed rocks of mountain ranges. Several kinds are distinguished by the direction of *apparent* movement along the fault fractures. A **dip-slip fault** is a fracture along which the apparent movement has been predominantly parallel to the dip (Fig. 9–18,A and D). A **strike-slip fault** is a fracture along which the apparent movement has been predominantly parallel to the strike (Fig. 9–18,F). Most faults show components of both strike and dip movement; where both are about equal the fault is called an **oblique-slip fault** (Fig. 8–3).

In nearly all dip-slip faults the fracture surface has an appreciable dip. But, direction of movement of one side of the fault with respect to the other may be either up or down the dip. Thus dip-slip faults are of two kinds. A **normal fault** is an inclined fracture along which the rocks above have apparently moved *down* with respect to those beneath (Figs. 9–18,A and D, and 9–20). A **thrust fault** is an inclined fracture along which the rocks above the fracture have apparently moved *up* with respect to those beneath (Fig. 20–2, bottom). Some geologists reserve the name thrust for faults dipping at angles less than 45°; those of steeper dip are called **reverse faults.**

M. L. Hill proposed calling strike-slip faults by the simpler name **lateral fault.** He distinguishes two kinds: if the offset continuation of the rock on which one stands while facing the fault lies *to his right* on the *other side* of the fault, it is a **right lateral fault** (Figs. 19–4, 19–5); if to the left, it is **left lateral** (Fig. 9–18,F).

Fault definitions must be precisely used or serious ambiguities will arise. Note the presence of the words "with respect to," "apparently," and "relative movement" in the above definitions. We cannot be more specific because we do not actually observe the movement itself, but only the effects of

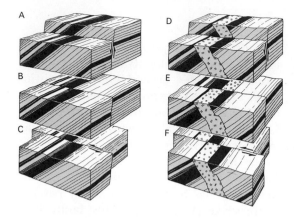

FIGURE 9–18

Diagram showing how dip-slip and strike-slip (lateral) faults can produce identical outcrop patterns after erosion (A, B, and C), and how they can be distinguished under ideal conditions (D, E, and F).

the movement. The **offset** of strata severed by a fault can be measured, but we can rarely determine the direction of movement with respect to sea level. For example, both sides of a normal fault may have moved up (but the rocks on the upper side not as far as those below) ; or both could have moved down; or the rocks above could have moved down and the rocks beneath up. The geometric relations of the rocks on either side of a fault give only the *apparent* movement *relative* to the rocks *on the other side* of the fracture. Abrupt bending of the strata as they approach the fault (called **drag**) may show the direction of relative displacement, or we may be able to tell by observing the offset of the beds across the fault plane. Both drag and offset are well shown on the normal faults illustrated in Figure 9–20.

Where the strata are uniformly tilted, it is rarely possible to tell whether dip-slip or lateral movement occurred along a particular fault. Either movement can, after erosion, produce the same pattern of apparent displacement. Consider the sketches in Figure 9–18. Block A shows tilted strata cut by a normal fault. Block B shows the same terrain

after erosion has planed off the elevated block. Note the offset of the beds at the fault surface. Block C shows similar beds displaced by a left lateral fault. B and C show identical patterns; identical offset can thus be produced by dip-slip followed by erosion or by strike-slip alone. The offset of the beds alone cannot tell us which kind of movement (or combination of both) produced it.

If, however, two rock masses with different dips intersect, and are cut by a fault, the direction and amount of relative motion is determinable. In Figure 9–18, blocks E and F clearly differ. After the normal faulting of D, erosion has caused outcrops of both dike and strata to migrate down dip, thereby producing offsets in opposite directions, as shown in block E. With purely lateral movement (block F), all offsets are in the same direction despite differences in dip of beds and dike.

Very exceptionally the attitude of drag folds permits unambiguous determination of the direction of fault movement. For example, close to the San Andreas fault in the Mecca Hills, California, the weakly consolidated mid-Pleistocene alluvium has been folded into vertically plunging isoclinal folds (Fig. 9–19). The folds die out away from the fault, so are obviously genetically related to it. Clearly, the only direction of fault movement that could drag strata into such a pattern is one of virtually horizontal (strike-slip) movement, for diagonal movement would surely produce less steep plunges.

Observations that permit unambiguous determination of the direction of fault movement are rare, but when obtainable, invaluable. In many mines (Fig. 9–20) careful matching of beds across faults, and determination of the exact amount of offset along each fault is important both in seeking displaced segments of known ore bodies and in planning the position of shafts and tunnels to extract ore whose location is already known.

FIGURE 9–19   *Weakly consolidated alluvium of mid-Pleistocene age, folded isoclinally about vertically plunging axes. The view is northwestward, parallel to the nearby San Andreas Fault, which is just out of view to the left. Mecca Hills, California. (Photo by Warren Hamilton, U.S. Geological Survey.)*

But on most faults no clues such as dike intersections with bedding, or clearly related drag folds, are observable; we cannot tell the direction of motion. The word "apparently" in our definitions calls attention to this ambiguity.

The whole classification of faults, however, is necessarily artificial; not only are there all transitions between dip-slip and strike-slip faults, but many high-angle reverse faults, when traced along strike, steepen, eventually become vertical, and farther on dip in the opposite direction, thus changing into normal faults.

A well-known example is the great Uinta fault, which extends for sixty miles along the north side of the Uinta Mountains in Utah. Everywhere the rocks on the south of the fault are thousands of feet higher than the

FIGURE 9–20

Cross section showing drag and offset on normal faults, Magdalena mining district, New Mexico. Extensive underground mine openings aided in accurate plotting of these faults. (After G. F. Loughlin and A. H. Koschmann, U.S. Geological Survey.)

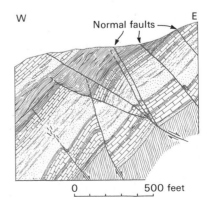

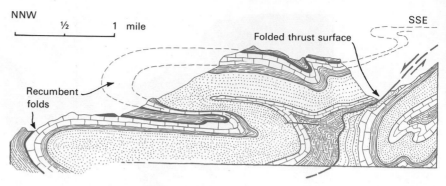

FIGURE 9–21   *Recumbent folds and a folded thrust surface, Swiss Alps. (After Albert Heim, 1922.)*

same strata on the north side. At the west end the fault dips south at a relatively low angle and is a thrust, but farther east it steepens, becomes vertical, and finally dips north, as a normal fault. Fault classification is also ambiguous if the fault surfaces have been folded and warped during or after the faulting. If we held strictly to the definitions given above, the irregular fault shown in Figure 9–21 would be classed as normal, for the rocks above it (left side of section) have apparently moved down with respect to the rocks to the right. Detailed study of a wide area beyond that of the section has shown, however, that the fault formerly dipped south at a low angle. It is really a thrust fault, warped and folded either during or after the thrusting. Such intense deformation is comparatively rare.

Exceptions abound, but most normal faults dip steeply—commonly between 65 and 90 degrees—though several with dips as low as 5 degrees have been recognized. Thrust faults similarly vary in dip; most of those with large displacements of course have low average dips, though in places they may be steep or overturned. Low-angle thrusts are conspicuous in many mountain zones. Many have demonstrable displacements of scores of kilometers and attest to great horizontal shortening of the visible part of the crust. Some lateral faults also show comparably great displacements.

Folds and faults are related and may grade one into the other. Some normal faults die out in monoclines along strike. Some thrust faults are merely broken anticlines but others show no evidence of having grown from folds.

UNCONFORMITIES

Figures 9–22 and 9–23 illustrate some common relations between rock masses. In Figure 9–22 the well-bedded sandstones that form the cliff rest on granite. The granite did not invade the sandstone, for the sandstone has not been metamorphosed by heat nor is it penetrated by granitic dikes. On the contrary, the basal layers of the sandstone contain many pebbles and grains of quartz and feldspar derived from the granite, proving that the sandstone is younger. The contact cannot be a fault, for there is no evidence of drag or offset. The pieces of granite in the lower part of the sandstone are not angular fragments sheared off by faulting but pebbles smoothly rounded by wear in turbulent water. Moreover, sandstone has filtered down into the granite along joints, indicating that it was unconsolidated sand when first brought into contact with the granite. Clearly the sandstone rests on an *ancient erosion surface carved across the granite and later buried by deposition of the sandstone*

FIGURE 9–22   *Nonconformity between granite and sandstone, El Paso County, Colorado. (Photo by N. H. Darton, U.S. Geological Survey.)*

FIGURE 9–23   *An angular unconformity, Wyoming. Tilted and eroded beds of sandstone are overlain by flat-lying clay and sandstone. (Photo by C. J. Hares, U.S. Geological Survey.)*

upon it. Such a buried erosion surface is evidence of interrupted deposition, and is called an **unconformity.** There are several kinds of unconformities; one like this in which sedimentary rocks overly plutonic rocks is called a nonconformity and is described in more detail later.

The production of an unconformity requires a reversal of the local process of erosion or sedimentation. The discontinuity

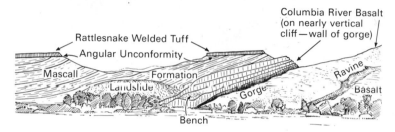

FIGURE 9–24   *Picture Gorge, Oregon. Angular unconformity between Mascall Formation (Miocene) and overlying Rattlesnake welded tuff (Pliocene). (Photo by Oregon State Highway Department.)*

between the rock masses separated by an unconformity means a lost interval in the local geologic history: the time intervening between the formation of the rocks below and those above an unconformity is not represented by rock at this locality. Elsewhere, where deposition was continuous, no discontinuity will appear at this position in the column.

In Figure 9–23, an unconformity of the kind called angular unconformity, appears as a conspicuous dark line, about a third of the way down the hill. The tilted beds of sandstone below are cut off abruptly at the unconformity. Above and roughly parallel to the unconformity, lie beds of more weakly consolidated sandstone and clay, whose basal layers contain fragments of the underlying tilted rocks. Obviously, the younger, poorly

consolidated sediments rest on an erosion surface developed across the older sediments long after they were laid down, consolidated, and tilted by movements of the earth's crust. Figure 9–24 is somewhat similar, showing the dark Columbia River Basalt (dipping left, right center of photo), which had been tilted after the Mascall Formation (smooth slope above and to the left) had been deposited, then eroded to a nearly plane surface before being covered unconformably by the Rattlesnake welded tuff, a volcanic rock topping the hill at right center. Even the Rattlesnake has been tilted slightly to the left adding to the dip of the older rocks.

These examples show that each extensive unconformity records at least three important geologic events: (1) formation of the rocks below, (2) erosion of these rocks to a surface independent of their structure, (3) burial of this surface beneath younger strata. Most unconformities also record crustal movement between (1) and (2) to give the elevation necessary for erosion, but a volcanic cone might be eroded to a flat surface, then buried by a new lava flow without any crustal movement. Unconformities buried beneath marine rocks may also record a second movement of the crust—the warping of the eroded surface below the sea—between (2) and (3), but a land area might also be buried by riverborne sediment, volcanic flows, or sand dunes without downwarping of the crust.

Landscapes preserved beneath unconformities

Locally soil and minor irregularities of a former landscape are preserved in their entirety beneath an unconformity, but generally they are eroded during burial. Erosion

FIGURE 9–25

Trees killed by burial in volcanic ash, and silicified during later alteration of the ash to clay. Later erosion has removed the ash and uncovered the unconformity at its base. Petrified Forest, Yellowstone National Park, Wyoming. (Photo by Erling Dorf, Princeton University.)

surfaces buried beneath lava flows or volcanic ash commonly preserve every detail of the former landscape, including such features as tree stumps still rooted in growth position (Figs. 9–25, 8–17). Soils and weathered bedrock also may be found beneath stream deposits but they are extremely rare where the overlying rocks are marine. Exceptionally, they may be preserved by rapid subsidence in an estuary sheltered from the strong waves of the open ocean. In Chapter 8 we mentioned the drowned stream channels at the south end of San Francisco Bay. Twenty-five miles to the west are the gravel and coarse sandy beaches of the Pacific. The same subsidence that lowered the floor of San Francisco Bay also affected the coast, but wave attack on the ocean beaches has obliterated all evidence of subaerial topography. All the soil has been removed and a wave-cut platform covered with coarse gravel and sand is developing across the bedrock.

Basal conglomerate

When a broad erosion surface of low relief is warped undersea, the rate of submersion is generally so slow that the shore advances inland only a few meters per century.

Waves are powerful agents of erosion (Chapter 5). During the slow transgression over the land, they strip away the soil and generally some of the bedrock beneath. They plane down irregularities of the erosion surface, finally producing a nearly flat rock floor strewn with storm-swept gravel and sand: finer debris is carried into deeper water. The thin layer of gravel and coarse sand directly overlying the smooth rock floor is commonly buried beneath finer sediments as the subsidence continues. It thus comes to be at the base of an overlying marine series and when lithified, forms a **basal conglomerate.** Such conglomerates, nearshore deposits of encroaching seas, are common but by no means invariable records of slow marine transgressions over land surfaces.

Kinds of unconformities

Cross sections of six simple unconformities from different areas are sketched in Figure 9–26. In A and C the beds above and below the surface of unconformity are parallel: these are **disconformities.** Many are difficult to recognize; all the strata may appear **conformable,** that is, deposited without any erosional break (Fig. 9–27). In Figure 9–26,C, however, disconformity is certain because Silurian strata are absent, as proved by fossils collected from beds immediately above and below. Perhaps this area was land during Silurian time. If it had been under the sea it would have received Silurian marine deposits, but if this did occur, the area must later have been uplifted and the Silurian eroded before the Devonian shale was deposited. Thus in either case, the disconformity records a former land surface. In A, the time break between the beds above and below the unconformity is vastly greater, embracing nearly all of geologic time since the Cambrian.

Unconformities in which the beds above the unconformity transgress the eroded edges of folded and tilted beds, as do those shown in Figure 9–23 and B and D of Figure 9–26, are **angular unconformities.**

Figure 9–22 and Figure 9–26,E and F, show another common kind of unconformity wherein bedded rocks rest on the eroded surface of plutonic or metamorphic rocks such as granite, gneiss, or gabbro. These are **nonconformities.**

Dating geologic events by unconformities

The examples sketched in Figure 9–26 also illustrate the use of unconformities in dating geologic events. For example, at Siccar Point, Scotland (B of Fig. 9–26), the Ordovician and Silurian beds were obviously folded before the unconformity was formed, as the overlying Devonian sandstone is unaffected by the folds. On the other hand, the folding in central Alabama (C of Fig. 9–26), was younger than the unconformity, for the strata and the unconformity itself have been

FIGURE 9–26   *Cross sections showing different kinds of unconformities.* A: *Baltic region, U.S.S.R.;* B: *Siccar Point, Scotland;* C: *central Alabama;* D: *Palos Verdes Hills, California;* E: *Grand Canyon, Arizona;* F: *central Washington.*

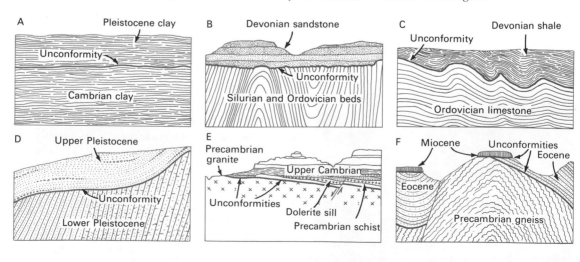

FIGURE 9–27   *Disconformity in an early Pleistocene stratigraphic section, thin-bedded sand below, silt above, near Apaxo, Tlaxcala, Mexico. (Photo by Kenneth Segerstrom, U.S. Geological Survey.)*

folded together. The folding was thus also later than the deposition of the Devonian shale. The unconformity shown in D, Figure 9–26 demonstrates that the lower Pleistocene beds were tilted during the Pleistocene, for younger Pleistocene beds lie much less disturbed upon it.

In part E of Figure 9–26, we see that the tilted rocks beneath the Upper Cambrian sedimentary rocks in the Grand Canyon were invaded by a dolerite sill and later cut by a normal fault and tilted before the invasion of the Cambrian Sea, for the unconformity at the base of the Cambrian strata truncates sill, fault, tilted beds, and even the metamorphic rocks upon which the tilted series itself rests nonconformably.

Similarly, the relations of the two different unconformities in F—one beneath the Eocene, the other beneath the Miocene lava flow—tell us that the fault offsetting these unconformities has moved at least twice, once during post-Eocene but pre-Miocene time, and again after the faulted area had been eroded to a plain and the Miocene lava spread over it.

Time significance of unconformities

Every unconformity marks a time interval unrepresented by strata in the area of the unconformity. Either no strata were deposited because the land was being eroded, or, any that were laid down were eroded away before the beds above the unconformity were deposited. In Chapter 7, we noted that the breaks in the geologic time scale built up in Europe represent times of local nondeposition: the major unconformities in the European section. Many of these times are recorded by "transitional series" elsewhere.

It is important to try to estimate the time represented by an unconformity. A common assumption is that an angular unconformity must imply a greater interval of lost geologic time than a disconformity. In some areas this is indeed true but certainly not everywhere. Contrast, for example, the unconformities shown in A and D of Figure 9–26. At several places in the Baltic region (A) Pleistocene lake clays rest directly upon marine clays that contain Cambrian fossils. The time interval represented by the disconformity includes all the Mesozoic and nearly all the Paleozoic and Cenozoic—a gap of more than 400 million years. Yet, in some places, the unconformity can hardly be recognized, so similar are the clays of both Cambrian and Pleistocene. In D, however, the marine sediments both above and below the angular unconformity are of Pleistocene age, as shown by abundant fossils. Thus the Pleistocene events in southern California included deposition of lower Pleistocene strata; folding; erosion of the newly deposited beds to a comparatively flat surface; sinking of this surface below the sea; and deposition of upper Pleistocene strata. All of these events took place in perhaps not more than a few tens of thousands of years— almost surely less than 2 million.

Unconformities, and the historical record they preserve, are often recognizable even after the rocks have been folded and meta- morphosed. On the other hand, widespread erosion has unquestionably obliterated all record of many unconformities. Those remaining are but a fraction of those that must have existed in one place or another on our restless earth.

REGIONAL GROUPINGS OF STRUCTURAL FEATURES

We have described the commoner structural features of the earth's crust. We turn now to their regional distribution and their association in time and space.

Continental plates

Broad warps, monoclines, and normal faults of small displacement are the main structural features in the relatively stable parts of the continents, the **continental plates.** The great area of low relief between the Appalachians and the Rockies, extending from the Gulf of Mexico to the Arctic, is the continental plate of North America. It is interrupted by only minor mountain masses: the Ouachita, Arbuckle, and Wichita Mountains, and the Black Hills. Another huge continental plate extends from eastern Germany to the Urals, a third extends beyond the Urals far into Outer Mongolia and Turkestan. Nearly all of Africa and most of Brazil, Uruguay, and Paraguay are continental plates as well, but in them ancient metamorphic and plutonic igneous rocks are widespread at the surface. These extensive plains or low plateaus of metamorphic and plutonic rocks, not now covered by sediments are called **shields.** The Canadian Shield, composed of highly deformed Precambrian rocks, occupies nearly all of eastern Canada and extends westward beyond Hudson Bay and into northern Minnesota and Michigan. Geologic mapping and drilling for petroleum show that the sedimentary rocks of many continental plates are generally only a few hundred, or at most a few thousand, feet thick, and that they rest nonconformably upon shields of granite and metamorphic rocks beneath.

Folded belts

Strongly folded and faulted strata form mountain belts that adjoin or in places divide the slightly deformed sedimentary rocks of most continental plates. Steep, even overturned, folds and thrust faults characterize these belts, just as broad warps characterize the continental plates. Moreover, these strongly deformed rocks occupy linear belts that contrast sharply with the broad rounded outlines of the continental plates. Bundles of closely packed parallel anticlines, synclines, and thrust faults make up most mountain chains. In many, the rocks have been squeezed and mashed into isoclinal and overturned folds and moved great distances on thrust faults.

These features contrast with the little-deformed sedimentary rocks that thinly cover the continental plates. The broad warps and monoclines of the continental plates could have been formed by differential vertical movements alone; the bundles of overturned and recumbent folds and associated thrusts of great mountain chains required great horizontal compression of the shallow crustal zones. Rocks that formerly occupied wide belts now lie crowded together in a much narrower zone.

Where deep erosion has revealed the cores of large mountain chains, the folded and faulted rocks along the edges of the mountain belt commonly grade gradually into metamorphic rocks in the more deeply eroded cores. Furthermore, many—but by no means all—ranges contain large masses of plutonic rocks that have invaded the sedimentary and metamorphic rocks deep within the range. These relations suggest that when

the outer rocks of the crust are squeezed to form a mountain belt, the rocks at depth, beneath a heavy load of overlying rock and where the temperature is higher, are slowly transformed to metamorphic varieties. Perhaps, indeed, the temperature may rise high enough in some places to melt some of the recrystallizing rock into magma. Many plutonic rocks are not however, associated with intense crustal deformation so that not all magma is associated with the processes involved in mountain making.

BROADER IMPLICATIONS

The earth pictured in this chapter is a lively one; its crust is not static and dead. Few strata remain in the horizontal position in which they were formed. Most have been warped upward and downward, many have been bent into folds, broken and displaced by faults, invaded by igneous bodies, and crushed and recrystallized into metamorphic rocks. Unconformities allow us to relate many of these events in time, and show that the complex structure of the crust did not form all in one great paroxysmal movement but sporadically and intermittently throughout geologic time.

The mountain belts are keys to earth history. How were the rocks deformed? What conditions govern metamorphism, origin of magma, and emplacement of granite masses? Structures remnant in the roots of old mountain chains after deep erosion give us glimpses into the processes that must occur deep within the crust. In trying to comprehend both the movements now going on and those of the geologic past, we shall return again and again to the earth's mountain chains. Some are young and growing, others have long since ceased to grow, but reveal, in the levels laid bare by deep erosion, early chapters of earth history that may be paralleled today beneath younger, growing ranges.

Other questions arise from the study of the structures of mountain systems. The crowding together of wide areas of rocks into intensely deformed narrow mountain belts means great horizontal transfer of mass. How is this accomplished? Does the deformation penetrate deeply into the body of the earth or did the mountain folds slide over a solid basement, like the wrinkles in a rug crumpled across a smooth floor? Can the earth's crust support a huge load of crumpled rocks crowded together in this way? What are the consequences of the great transfer of load that must occur when erosion erases a great mountain chain and spreads its detritus in an adjacent sea? In the next chapter we approach these difficult questions which lie at the heart of our understanding of earth structure.

Facts, concepts, terms

Warps
   Structure contour maps
   Exaggerated-scale cross sections
   Continental plates
Folds
   Plunging, asymmetrical, overturned, and recumbent folds
   Folded belts
   Mountain roots
Joints and faults
   Normal, thrust, and strike-slip faults
   Right lateral and left lateral faults
   Apparent versus real displacements on faults
Unconformities
   Disconformities, angular unconformities, nonconformities
   Basal conglomerate
   Dating events by unconformities
   Time involved in an unconformity

Questions

1. How do you know that the 1500-meter difference between the elevation of the base of the Colorado shale at Shelby, Montana, and its elevation at Williston, North Dakota, is the result of warping since deposition of the shale, rather than the result of uniform deposition in an ocean that was shallow near Shelby and 1500 meters or more deep near Williston?
2. We have described the method of getting control points for drawing structure contours on a deeply buried bed. Describe how it would also be possible to get control points that would enable you to project above the ground surface the former position of a bed that has been completely eroded from the top of an anticline.

3. Draw a geologic map showing two anticlines and an intervening syncline that have been eroded to an almost flat surface. All three folds plunge to the north, and all are asymmetrical. Four sedimentary formations are exposed on the map.

4. Draw a geologic map showing a syncline plunging to the south which has been cut by an east-west normal fault that dips north. Assume that erosion has reduced the area to an almost flat surface.

5. Why is it more common to find overturned folds grading into thrust faults along their strike than into normal faults?

6. In the field, what criteria would you use to tell an angular unconformity from a thrust fault?

7. In the field, what criteria would you use to distinguish between a nonconformity developed across a granite mass and an intrusive contact formed by invasion of the sediments by molten granite magma?

8. An extensive but thin basal conglomerate contains Lower Jurassic fossils in one locality but Middle Jurassic fossils when traced 230 miles to the west. How is this possible?

9. Why are broad warps that have bowed up the deeply eroded surfaces of a former mountain chain difficult to detect?

10. Draw *one* cross section showing *all* of the following features:

    a) A series of folded marine sediments that lie unconformably on granite and metamorphic rocks.

    b) A series of nearly flat lava flows that lie with angular unconformity on the folded sediments.

    c) Two thrust faults that are older than the lava flows, but younger than the sedimentary rocks.

    d) A normal fault that is younger than the lava flows.

    e) A dike that is younger than the thrust faults, but older than the normal fault.

Suggested readings

Bucher, W. H., *The Deformation of the Earth's Crust.* Princeton, N.J.: Princeton University Press, 1933.

Hutton, James, in Mather, K. F., and S. L. Mason, *Source Book in Geology.* New York: McGraw-Hill, 1939. [p. 92–100.]

Umbgrove, J. H. F., *The Pulse of the Earth,* 2nd Ed. The Hague: M. Nijhoff, 1947.

chapter

10

Geodesy, Isostasy, and Strength

We have seen in Chapters 8 and 9 that forces within the earth fold and crush rocks together and greatly change their elevations relative to sea level. In Chapter 5 we noted that rock waste is continually eroded from high elevations and transported to lower. Do still other factors influence the relief of the earth's surface, and the amount of its departure from perfect sphericity? How, indeed, do we know that the earth is roughly spherical, as all of us were taught as children?

THE EARTH'S SIZE AND SHAPE

Early measurements

The ancient Greeks noted the earth's round shadow upon the moon during eclipses, and also that the surface of the sea is curved, for only the upper part of a ship's mast is visible at a distance, and an approaching ship appears to rise gradually out of the water. The Greeks thus correctly inferred that the earth is not flat, but spherical. Today this conclusion is commonplace; the earth's curvature shows plainly in rocket photographs; airplanes circle the globe in a few days and man-made satellites in a few hours.

More than two thousand years ago, Eratosthenes, a Greek geometer and astronomer, first measured the curvature of the earth and computed its dimensions. Though measuring techniques have been greatly refined, his reasoning is still used in modern geodesy. (**Geodesy** is the science of measuring the earth, its dimensions and curvature and the distances and directions of points on its surface from each other.) Eratosthenes heard that in southern Egypt, at Syene (now Assuan), the sun shines vertically down a well only at noon on the longest day of the year. But at Alexandria, a part of every well is always in shadow. Alexandria lies 5000 stades (the ancient Greek stade equals about 185 meters or 607 feet) north of Syene. Eratosthenes measured the angle between a plumb line and the edge of the shadow cast by the noon sun in a well at Alexandria on the longest day of the year (Fig. 10–1). He then calculated the size of the earth on these premises:

a. That the sun is so far distant that its rays to Syene and Alexandria are virtually parallel.

b. That Alexandria lies due north of Syene, so that a plane through Alexandria, Syene, and the center of the earth also includes the noon sun.

c. That the plumb line points directly toward the center of the earth.

d. That the earth is a sphere.

On these assumptions, the angle between the plumb line and the shadow at Alexandria is equal to the arc of the earth's curvature between the two points (Fig. 10–1). The circumference of the earth is, therefore, given by solving the equation:

$$\text{Circumference} = \frac{360°}{\text{Angle of sun's rays to vertical at Alexandria}} \times 5000 \text{ stades.}$$

Eratosthenes' result was, in modern measure, about 45,000 kilometers or 28,000 miles. For reasons partly explained in Figure 10–1, this is about 14 percent larger than the circumference now accepted. About a century later, Poseidonius, another Greek geographer, measured another arc, but was not so favored by compensating errors. His earth was a quarter too small, and his error may have led to Columbus's mistaking America for India.

In these early crude measurements, it was assumed that the earth is a sphere. Later more accurate measurements forced several modifications of this assumption. Few better examples of scientific method, and of improvements in theory required by improved observations, can be found than are afforded by the history of investigation of the shape of the earth.

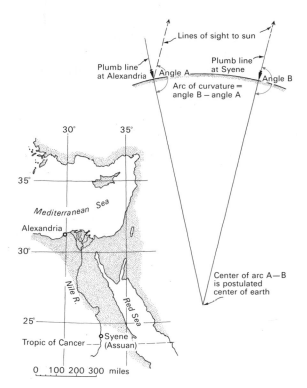

FIGURE 10–1

Eratosthenes' method for measuring the size of the earth. Note that Syene does not lie due south of Alexandria, so that the distance between Syene and Alexandria was not measured along a meridian, as he assumed. And Syene is not exactly on the Tropic of Cancer, as he thought, but a little to the north, so the arc he measured was too small. For both these reasons, his result was too large. Note that Angle A in the diagram to the right is greatly exaggerated.

Modern measurements

In the seventeenth and eighteenth centuries expanding navigation demanded more accurate charts and Eratosthenes' method came into wider use. North-south lines, "arcs of meridian," were measured in several localities: in high-latitude Finland and low-latitude France and Peru; and the angles of arc were calculated. These surveys showed that a degree of latitude is longer near the poles than near the equator. Stated another way, if we retain the assumption that the earth is a sphere, its radius as deduced from surveys near the pole is somewhat greater than that deduced from surveys near the equator. This is shown, greatly exaggerated, in Figure 10–2. The dashed circle with the center P represents the size of the earth deduced from high-latitude surveys, the dotted circle with center E, that deduced from equatorial observations. Note the discrepancy in size. If the earth were really a sphere these differing observations could not be reconciled. The simplest modification by which the differences may be satisfied is the assumption that the earth is slightly flattened at the poles, or, more specifically, that it is an *oblate ellipsoid,* the solid figure obtained by revolving an ellipse about its shorter axis. The solid line in Figure 10–2 is an ellipse with its center at C. This line reconciles both polar and equatorial observations. In the drawing the flattening is much exaggerated, for the earth departs so little from a sphere that if drawn to true scale the ellipticity would be imperceptible to the naked eye. The measurements now accepted and used internationally as the basis for official mapping are:

Equatorial radius 6,378,388 meters (3,963.5 miles)
Polar radius . . . . . 6,356,912 meters (3,950.2 miles)
Difference . . . . . .   21,476 meters   (13.3 miles)

Satellite orbits not parallel to the equator are, of course, modified by the stronger attraction of the equatorial bulge as compared with those of the lower polar regions. Computations based on the deviations of satellite orbits from those expected if the earth were a sphere give the difference between polar and equatorial radii as 21.39 kilometers instead of 21.48 kilometers, but this slightly smaller figure has not yet been incorporated into the international formula.

What does this difference of 21.4 kilometers between polar and equatorial radii

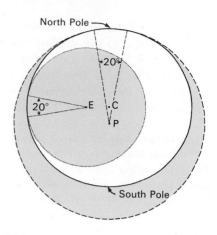

FIGURE 10–2
Diagram showing how the differing lengths of equal arcs of meridian measured in high and low latitudes suggest that the shape of the earth is ellipsoidal rather than spherical.

mean? And does the oblate spheroid that we now substitute for the sphere really fit the actual surface of the earth closely? Certainly in mountainous areas the peaks and gorges must be real departures from the ideal ellipsoid. How much do these departures amount to?

THE EARTH'S MAXIMUM RELIEF

Sea level is the conventional reference surface with which we compare heights on the earth (see Appendix I). The earth's highest peak, Mount Everest, towers 8884 meters or 29,141 feet—more than 5 miles—above sea level. The greatest oceanic depth thus far reported lies in the Nero Deep in the Mariana Trench 11,035 meters or 36,204 feet—not quite 7 miles—below sea level. Great as are these distances by human standards, they are trivial compared with the radius of the earth. If the largest ellipse that can be drawn on this page represented the earth, a normal pencil line would, on the same scale, include within its width all the earth's surface irregularities

North & South Hemispheres

ranging from Mount Everest to the Nero Deep. Actually, therefore, the irregularities of the earth's surface are hardly greater, relatively, than those of a billiard ball, though to a Tibetan, amidst the towering peaks of the Himalayas, this must seem a gross misstatement.

The extreme heights of mountain peaks and depths of ocean trenches occupy insignificantly small fractions of the areas of the continents and ocean basins, which are the major relief features of the earth. Measurements from the best available maps and charts show:

Area of the sea......	361,059,000 sq km	70.8%
Area of the land.....	148,892,000 sq km	29.2%
Total............	509,951,000 sq km	100.0%

Land and water are very unevenly distributed. The earth can be divided into two

FIGURE 10–3
The land and water hemispheres.

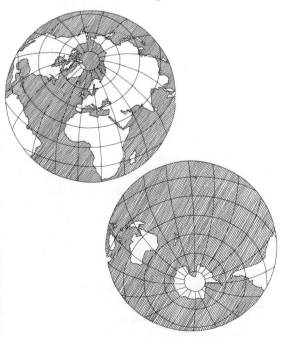

hemispheres: four-fifths of all the land lies in one and nearly nine-tenths of the other is covered with water. Figure 10–3 summarizes this distribution.

What are the differences in elevation between the continents and the ocean floors? From available maps and charts careful estimates have been made of the total areas of the earth's surface that lie between various altitude limits. Figure 10–4 summarizes these estimates and shows the two important relations already noted: (1) The high mountain peaks and the abyssal depths of the sea occupy relatively very small areas. (2) Within the extreme range—of nearly 20 kilometers —from the Nero Deep to Mount Everest, altitudes are by no means evenly distributed, by area. Two altitude ranges are especially prominent. One, the range between 4000 and 5000 meters (13,120 to 16,400 feet) below sea level, includes nearly one-fourth of the earth's surface. The other, from 200 meters below to 500 meters above sea level, includes approximately one-fifth of the earth's surface (Fig. 10–4). The under-sea part of this second range is the continental shelf. The ocean basins are overfull; the seas spread beyond their confines and inundate the continental shelves, which are really parts of the continents. At the outer edge of the continental shelf the sea floor descends rapidly in the continental slope to the ocean floors proper, which lie within the first altitude range mentioned, about 4000 to 5000 meters below sea level.

Why are there two dominant levels in the architecture of the earth? Why is the boundary between continental shelf and ocean floor so marked? Before we can even start to answer these difficult questions we need to know more about our datum of reference, sea level. Does the sea's surface everywhere correspond to the smooth surface of an oblate ellipsoid, or does it, like the surface of the land, show real departures from this form? If it does,

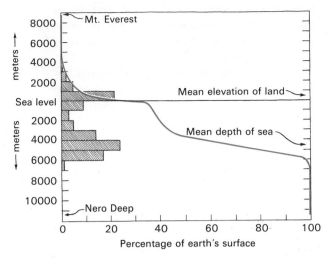

FIGURE 10–4

Graph showing percentages of the earth's surface lying between various levels above and below the sea. The bars at left represent percentages (scale below) lying between the respective levels, at intervals of 1000 meters. Note the two broad flat areas in the curve, one near sea level, the other 4,000 to 5,000 meters below sea level. (Data from Kossinna, redrawn from H. U. Sverdrup, M. W. Johnson, and R. H. Fleming, The Oceans. *Copyright 1942 by Prentice-Hall, Inc.)*

FIGURE 10–5

Two common weighing instruments. Left: *Spring scale.* Right: *Beam balance.*

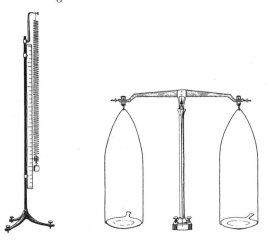

how can we account for them? Some inkling of the answers, and of the reason for the difference of 21.4 kilometers between the polar and equatorial radii as well, can be obtained from a study of gravity and of the centrifugal force of rotation upon the body of the earth.

Gravity and a level surface

In making a topographic map, or in setting the floor joists of a building, what do we mean when we speak of a level surface? The surface of a quiet pond is level, and appears to be a plane, but in fact it is curved, as we know the surface of the ocean is curved. A level surface is, therefore, not a plane but a surface so curved that it is everywhere exactly perpendicular to the direction of the local plumb line. All plumb lines converge toward the central part of the earth although, as we have seen, not toward a single point at the center. The direction of the plumb line is of course the vertical—its projection overhead defines the *zenith,* the point directly above us among the stars. When Eratosthenes set out to measure the size of the earth he determined the angle between two such vertical lines and thus calculated the earth's curvature.

Weighing a mass

Careful measurements of the exact force of gravity at various points on the earth's surface yield valuable information about the size and form of the earth. Before discussing these measurements we must first outline the ways we can weigh an object. The **weight** of any mass is the measure of the force of attraction between the earth and itself. There are two common methods of weighing—the spring scale or the beam balance (Fig. 10–5).

A spring scale measures weight by the stretching of a spring; it is calibrated by marking the stretching produced by the earth's pull on a series of standard weights. We assume that Hooke's Law holds, that the stretching of the spring is proportional to the weight, and thus can mark on our scale points for fractions and multiples of one kilogram. By international agreement, such calibrations are based on the standard kilogram mass preserved at the International Bureau of Weights and Measures at Sévres, France. At Sévres, we so calibrate our spring scale that the pointer reads exactly one kilogram when the standard kilogram mass is placed on the scale. A second weight that brings the pointer to the same mark weighs, of course, exactly one kilogram and will counterpoise the standard kilogram mass when the two are placed in opposite pans of a beam balance. But if we move our equipment from Sévres to some other point, we generally find that these relations no longer hold precisely.

EFFECT OF ALTITUDE.   If, for example, we take scale, weights, and balance to a peak in the Alps, 3 kilometers above sea level, we find that on the spring scale our kilogram weight will no longer weigh one kilogram but slightly less, although it will still exactly counterpoise the standard kilogram mass in the beam balance. All our equipment is identical with that at Sévres, but, at the alpine peak, the distance to the earth's center is roughly 6363 kilometers, whereas at Sévres, nearly at sea level, it is only 6360 kilometers. The product of the masses of the earth and our kilogram weight must be divided, at Sévres, by 6360^2 and, at the alpine peak by 6363^2 (see Chapter 5). This is a difference of nearly 0.1 percent, or one gram. Newton's law thus shows us immediately that the distance from the earth's center must be considered when we weigh on a spring scale, though not when we weigh on a beam balance.

EFFECT OF THE EARTH'S ROTATION.   Because the earth spins on its axis, all objects not at the poles tend to be thrown off, just as mud is thrown from a spinning automobile wheel, or sparks from an emery grinder. This force, the **centrifugal force of rotation,** tends everywhere except at the poles to counteract the force of gravity. It is very small—even at the

FIGURE 10–6   *Diagram showing a familiar demonstration of centrifugal force, and* (A) *how the centrifugal force due to rotation varies from equator to pole, or, stated differently,* (B) *how the linear velocity of a point on the earth's surface varies from equator to pole.*

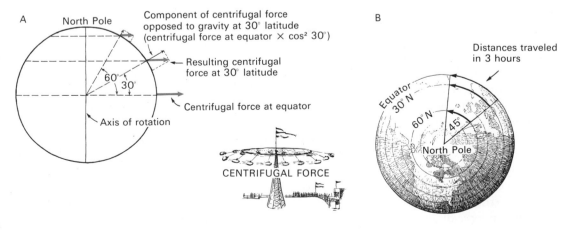

equator, where it is greatest, it amounts to only about 0.33 percent of gravity and it steadily diminishes toward the poles. Solid objects do not fly off the equator into space, but the centrifugal force does produce the equatorial bulge and the polar flattening, as Newton showed long ago (Fig. 10–6). Thus is explained the 21.4-kilometer difference between polar and equatorial radii actually found.

But this difference in distance to the earth's center also brings about a difference in measured gravity at pole and equator—as we saw in contrasting the gravity at Sévres with that at the alpine peak—in addition to that due to the centrifugal force. The sum of the two effects is approximately 0.5 percent of gravity, with the polar measurement the greater. Thus, if a polar bear weighing 1000 kilograms in his natural habitat were instantly transported to an equatorial zoo, he would there weigh only 995 kilograms.

EFFECTS OF LOCAL VARIATIONS IN ROCK DENSITY. Still another factor affects the weight of an object at different points on the earth's surface. This is the local distribution of rock masses of different density. Let us imagine that the gold buried at Fort Knox, Kentucky, as part of the United States Treasury reserve, forms a single huge block of pure metal (Fig. 10–7). A cubic meter of gold weighs 19.4 metric tons (more than 21 short tons). The inverse square relation in the Law of Gravitation tells us that an object immediately above the gold should weigh a little more than the same object would if weighed on the roof of one of the great limestone caverns nearby. Although at the same latitude and altitude, the dense gold immediately beneath the object pulls on it harder than an equivalent volume of air in an empty cavern. We know that the exposed rocks do differ considerably in density from place to place, though not, of course, to the extreme degree of our artificial example at Fort Knox. Clearly, the force of gravity must everywhere

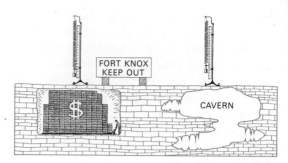

FIGURE 10–7
The effect of differences in density of nearby masses on weight.

vary with the density of the immediately underlying rocks.

This principle has had many valuable applications where the density contrasts sought were very much less than in our exaggerated example. Precise gravity measurements have been successfully used to prospect for dense ores concealed beneath soil or slide rock, and, at Carletonville, South Africa, have been used to search for dangerous caverns in the dolomite on which the town was built. During the mining on the West Rand goldfield, great quantities of water were pumped from the dolomite, dewatering hitherto unknown caverns, and thus removing some of the support of their roofs. Several consequently collapsed with great loss of property and considerable danger to life. Because of the danger, so many workers fled the town that continuation of the industry was threatened. The mining companies made many thousands of very precise gravity measurements around the town and its environs. Where gravity was notably lower than elsewhere drilling soon revealed caverns at shallow depth. The houses were removed from such areas and reestablished where the gravity measurements were higher than average. Though the collapses are still going on, they no longer seriously threaten life and property; the hazardous areas have been pinpointed by the gravity measurements.

MEASURING GRAVITY

As we have seen, the local force of gravity depends on (1) altitude, (2) latitude, and (3) variations in density of the underlying rocks. The effect of each is small and to measure the differences in the gravitational force from place to place we need a very sensitive instrument—one far more sensitive than an ordinary spring scale. The *gravity pendulum* is a relatively simple but accurate instrument that fills this need.

A free-swinging pendulum—that is, one not driven by clockwork or other external means—oscillates to and fro because of the force of gravity. If we suspend a heavy weight from a string, pull the weight aside and release it, the weight falls toward the earth, following the arc controlled by the length of the string. The force of gravity pulls it downward along its path, but the weight's **inertia** —the resistance any object offers to any change in its motion—carries it past the low point of its swing, and thus it rises against the force of gravity. It continues upward along the arc until its inertia is overcome by gravity, when it reverses and falls again toward the lowest point, repeating the swinging again and again. But each swing rises a little less because of friction with the air. Gradually the oscillations die away; finally the pendulum hangs straight down, perpendicular to a level surface. It has become a plumb bob.

The great Dutch scientist, Huygens (1629–1695) discovered the law governing the *period of oscillation*—the time for one complete to-and-fro movement—of a pendulum: *The period varies inversely with the square root of the local acceleration of gravity, and directly with the square root of the length of the pendulum.* Thus,

$$P \propto \sqrt{\frac{l}{g}}$$

(The symbol $\propto$ means "is proportional to.")

where P = period, l = length, and g = acceleration.

Newton showed that this law explains why pendulum clocks systematically gain or lose time when moved from place to place. This is why all pendulum clocks have pendulums slightly adjustable in length. A pendulum clock that keeps good time in Paris systematically loses time high in the Alps because of the lesser gravity there. This relation enables us to measure the force of gravity by using a pendulum of known length. We count the swings of the pendulum during a measured time interval and determine gravity from Huygens' Law.

Modern gravity pendulums are so constructed that they are almost frictionless. They hang on knife-edge jewel bearings, swing in chambers from which nearly all air has been evacuated, and are timed by precision chronometers accurate to $\frac{1}{10,000}$ second. Such equipment enables scientists to measure gravity to within a few parts per million. Gravity pendulums are extremely unwieldy to transport, so most gravity measurements are now made with gravimeters. These easily portable instruments compare the distortion of a quartz fiber at an observation station with that at an accurately measured pendulum station. The principle is exactly that of a spring balance, but because the distortion must be read to 1 part in 10 million, many refinements are necessary in the construction. By means of these instruments the variations in gravity over large areas are known with considerable accuracy. Such instruments have recently been developed to operate from airplanes in flight and also on surface vessels at sea where ordinary gravity pendulums cannot operate because of wave disturbances and ship motion. Before their development, the only gravity data available from the seas were obtained with the multiple pendulums developed by the Dutch geodesist, F.A. Vening-Meinesz, which had to be used in submarines, submerged beneath the zone of strong wave motion. In these instruments pendulums swing at opposed phases and by measuring their differential motions we are able to compensate for minor wave motion. Thanks to better gravimeters, we have obtained thousands of measurements of gravity from both sea and land. These measurements, as we shall see, have permitted important deductions about the relations between topography and the differences in density of the earth's crustal materials.

DEFLECTIONS OF THE PLUMB LINE

Other important relations that supplement and confirm those obtained with gravimeters, were discovered during analysis of some puzzling systematic errors in triangulation. **Triangulation** (described in Appendix I) is the method of fixing the position of a third point by sighting on it from each of two points of known position. But a point's position can also be fixed without recourse to triangulation by determining its latitude and longitude astronomically, as is done in navigation. The astronomical observations involve reading angles between the horizon and lines of sight to the stars. Such angles allow us to determine the zenith—that is, the direction of the vertical—at any point because, of course, this is everywhere at right angles to the hori-

zon, like the plumb line. If the plumb line invariably pointed directly to the earth's center, determination of position made by astronomical methods would coincide with those made by triangulation. (This statement would be strictly true only if the earth were a true sphere; as may be seen in Fig. 10–2, the slight modification required by the polar flattening is here disregarded.)

As we saw, however, other factors than latitude affect the plumb line. According to the Law of Gravitation, a plumb bob is attracted by a given mass one kilometer away with a force one hundred times that exerted by an equivalent mass ten kilometers away. We ought, then, to find the plumb line deflected sideward toward a nearby mountain. And it is.

Consider the situation in a deep Norwegian fjord. A narrow arm of the sea lies between massive cliffs 2000 meters high. A plumb line suspended near one side of the fjord will be deflected toward the nearby mountain mass. The sea surface also will be tilted slightly upward toward the mountain and downward toward the middle of the fjord. (Fig. 10–8, *Right*). Such tilts are extremely small, generally only a few seconds of arc, but they lead to appreciable errors in astronomical positioning of a point. Moreover, we now see that the concept of an oblate

FIGURE 10–8   *The relations between spheroid and geoid, tremendously exaggerated to show the qualitative effect of irregular topography.* Left: *Broad view of their relations as between continental and oceanic segments.* Right: *The hypothetical relation (greatly exaggerated) in a Norwegian fjord.*

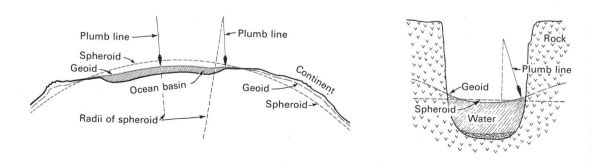

spheroidal earth, though closer to the truth than that of a spherical earth, still is not precise. In detail the true shape of sea level over the entire earth's surface is not an oblate ellipsoid. Because of local attractions, a horizontal surface of wide extent—although everywhere at right angles to the plumb line—is vastly more complicated than the surface of a simple oblate ellipsoid.

ISOSTASY

The mass of even the largest mountain, however, is very small compared with that of the whole earth. Despite its nearness, we expect the deflection of the plumb line to be small. To calculate the theoretical deflection at any one station requires considerable computation, for it is usually necessary to calculate the gravitational pull of many irregular topographic masses in different directions and at different distances from the station. When this is done for a large number of stations, however, an exceptionally interesting relation appears: *Mountain masses do not deflect the plumb line sideways as much as it would be deflected if the mountain were actually a load resting on top of an otherwise uniform crust.*

This conclusion, somewhat surprising at first glance, is also confirmed by measurements of the force of gravity with pendulum and gravimeter. If a mountain were really a load heaped on a perfectly rigid crust, the force of gravity (after being corrected for the effect of the added altitude) should be greater on top of a mountain than on an adjacent plain because of the added gravitational pull of the mass of the mountain beneath. Many investigations show, however, no close relation between topography and the force of gravity over wide areas.

These relations have led geologists and geodesists to infer that *the major irregularities of the earth's crust are not loads supported by the strength of a rigid earth crust, but are instead buoyed up by flotation upon a dense plastic interior.* The idea is that the mass of the material composing a mountain range is balanced or compensated for by a lower density of the material beneath it as compared to the material beneath an adjacent plain. The earth's interior must yield and flow laterally to equalize the loads on areas of equal size, at least approximately.

The flotation may take place in either of two ways, or by a combination of both. One is illustrated by the differing heights at which planks of the same size but of different density—say oak and pine—float in a pond. The lighter pine plank floats much higher out of the water than the heavier oak. Thus the mountains may stand higher than the continental plates because the rocks composing them are less dense; similarly the continental rocks are less dense than those underlying the oceans (Fig. 10–10). A second possibility is to assume that all rocks of mountain, plain, and ocean floor are equally dense, though less so than a deeper plastic layer that underlies them all. In this scheme the surface relief results from the thicker masses of crustal rocks standing higher than thinner masses of the same rock. The analogy is with icebergs, which float with nine-tenths of their volume submerged. A berg that projects 10 feet above the surface may extend 90 feet below it; one twice as thick will stand 20 feet above the surface (Fig. 10–11).

Such a condition of flotational equilibrium between large blocks of the earth's crust is called **isostasy** (from the Greek, "equal standing"). The theory of isostasy is one of the most helpful concepts in geology—one that we will return to again and again to explain otherwise puzzling relations. It will be well, therefore, to recount the evidence by which it was discovered—the analysis of some puzzling deflections of the plumb line detected during an early survey of the landmass of India.

The Trigonometrical Survey of India

In the middle of the nineteenth century, the Trigonometrical Survey of India was organized under Sir George Everest (for whom Mount Everest is named) to establish the control points needed for mapping that huge subcontinent. These points were established by very careful triangulation (See Appendix I). Scores of points were located and the distances between them accurately calculated. For many the latitudes and longitudes were also carefully determined by astronomical observations.

If latitude, longitude, and the angle between the line of sight to any other station and a north-south line are known at any one station in a triangulation net, it is relatively easy to calculate latitudes and longitudes of all other points. Such calculations do not, of course, depend in any way on astronomical observations except at the reference station, although they do depend fundamentally upon assumptions about the curvature of the earth's surface. If the latitude and longitude of a second station is also determined astronomically, the two independently determined fixes can be compared.

In the survey of India it soon became apparent that geographic positions determined by triangulation for some stations did not agree with those determined astronomically. Errors were sought in the triangulation, but resurveys showed the results to be consistent. Moreover, several of the apparent "errors" were far too large to be accountable to inaccuracies in this careful survey.

Two such stations, Kaliana and Kalianpur (Fig. 10–9), are among those discussed by Archdeacon Pratt, a British cleric and amateur mathematician, who, in seeking an explanation of the discrepancy, discovered the isostatic relation. Kaliana is on the Indo-Gangetic plain, close to the towering Himalayas; Kalianpur lies far to the south, near the center of the Indian peninsula. Archdeacon Pratt surmised that the plumb line at Kaliana would be deflected northward by the gravitational pull of the mountain mass so that the latitude difference between the two stations measured astronomically would be less than that calculated from the triangulation. This proved to be true. The differ-

FIGURE 10–9

The effect of the Himalaya Mountains on the computed distance between Kaliana and Kalianpur. Note the difference in the arc distance between the two cities produced by the deflection of the plumb bob, so that Angle 1 is greater than Angle 2. The angles are greatly exaggerated in the diagram.

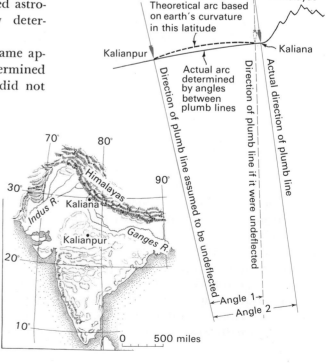

ence in latitude between the stations as determined by each method was:

Difference in latitude
  measured by triangulation . . . . 5°23′42.29″
  measured astronomically . . . . 5°23′37.06″
Discrepancy . . . .   5.23″

The discrepancy of 5.23 seconds of arc corresponds to a distance of about 500 feet—far more than could be attributed to surveying error.

Enough was known of Himalayan topography and geology for Pratt to compute the approximate mass of the mountains above sea level and their average distance from each of the stations. Assuming that the mountains rest on an otherwise uniform crust, Pratt computed what the deflection of the plumb line should have been at each station and thus the difference in astronomical latitude that should result.

The results were at first surprising: According to the calculations, the plumb line should have been deflected far more than the amount measured. The northward deflection should have been 27.853 seconds at Kaliana and 11.968 seconds at Kalianpur. The difference, 15.885 seconds, is more than three times the 5.23 seconds discrepancy actually measured, and far greater than could be explained either by errors in triangulation or in the estimate of the mass of the Himalayas.

Pratt's hypothesis of isostasy

Pratt saw that his assumptions must be wrong. A basic one was that the density of the material of the earth's crust was uniform, whether beneath the plains of India or beneath the Himalayas. If this assumption were dropped, the discrepancy could be explained by assuming that the rocks extending to a certain depth below sea level beneath the Himalayas were of lower density than those extending to the same depth beneath the plain. Thus both mountain and plain are "floating" on a deep layer of denser material,

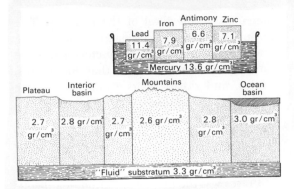

FIGURE 10–10

Pratt's theory of isostasy. The densities shown on the lower diagram were not specified by Pratt, but are based on modern estimates. (Modified from W. Bowie, Isostasy, *E. P. Dutton, 1927.)*

and the heights at which their surfaces stand are inversely related to the densities of the two "blocks." In other words, the high-standing mass of the Himalayas is "compensated" by a corresponding deficiency of mass in the rocks beneath: the rocks beneath the mountains are less dense than those beneath the plains to the same depth.

A simple illustration of Pratt's idea is shown in Figure 10–10. In the upper diagram, blocks of four different metals, each weighing exactly the same and each with the same horizontal cross section, float in a pan of mercury, a liquid of very high density (13.6 grams per cubic centimeter). The heights at which the metal blocks stand are inversely proportional to the ratios of their densities to that of mercury; each block sinks until it displaces its weight of mercury, and since their weights and cross sections are identical, all sink to the same depth. Their tops project to different heights. As an example, for ease of computation assume each block to weigh 136 grams and to have a cross section of 10 square centimeters. Each sinks until it displaces 136 grams of mercury, that is, one centimeter. Lead has a density of 11.4, antimony of 6.6. The lead column is 13.6/11.4 centimeters long and thus projects .19 centimeter above the level of the mercury. The antimony column is 13.6/6.6 centimeters long and thus projects 1.06 centimeters above the same level. Pratt assumed that mountains, plains, and ocean floors show comparable relations: the mountains stand higher above the surface of the "fluid" substratum because they are composed of (and to a considerable depth are underlain by) material less dense than that beneath the plains.

Pratt's was the first formulation of a theory of isostasy, and his scheme of "compensating" for differences in elevation by variation in density of the rocks of the crust is known as the **Pratt Hypothesis of Isostasy.** Pratt did not use the word "isostasy"; some thirty-four years later the American geologist C. E. Dutton coined this word for the condition of equilibrium Pratt had discovered.

Airy's Hypothesis of Isostasy

The same volume of the *Transactions of the Royal Society* (1855) that contains Pratt's formulation also has a brief note by G. B. Airy, the Astronomer Royal of Great Britain. Airy said that Pratt's conclusion should have been anticipated because it could be shown that no rocks are strong enough to sustain loads as great as plateaus and high mountains. The rocks beneath would crush and flow laterally until balance was restored. The only possibility, then, is to regard mountain chains as floating masses, as Pratt did. But Airy suggested a different mechanism of flotation. He saw no reason to believe that the rocks immediately beneath a mountain differ significantly in density from those beneath a plain. If the blocks are of equal density, but of unequal thickness, the difference in surface height may still be readily explained. The thick mountain block floats higher above the surface, but it also sinks deeper into the heavier "fluid" below. The height of the mountain block is compensated by a "root" of its own material that projects into the underlying denser "fluid" layer and displaces it. Airy's view is called the **Roots of**

Mountains Hypothesis of Isostasy. It accounts for the "errors" in the India Survey just as well as Pratt's, and accords much better with what we know about the composition of rocks at the surface and in deep mines and drill holes. It is much more widely accepted by geologists, but, as we shall see, Pratt's hypothesis must be called on in explaining the differences between continents and ocean basins, and in many other places. Neither mechanism operates to the exclusion of the other.

A simplified view of the Roots of Mountains hypothesis is shown in Figure 10–11. In the upper diagram, several blocks of copper, all having the same density and cross-sectional area but differing in weight because they differ in height, float in a pan of mercury. The tallest block projects highest above the surface and also sinks deepest into the mercury. The lower diagram shows how blocks of the earth's crust, all composed of identical rocks, may nevertheless float to different heights provided they differ in thickness.

The diagrams shown in Figures 10–10 and 10–11 are, of course, greatly oversimplified. Good evidence presented in later chapters shows that the earth's crust is not divided

FIGURE 10–11
Airy's theory, also called the Roots of the Mountains Theory of Isostasy. The densities shown in the lower diagram were not specified by Airy, but are based on modern estimates. (Modified in part from C. R. Longwell, Geographical Review, *1925.)*

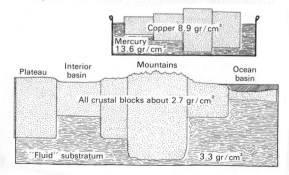

into simple blocks free to move past one another along frictionless boundaries. The substratum, also, is not a fluid, although it may respond by plastic flow to heavy loads of long duration, reacting to these large stresses virtually as a viscous fluid. We know, furthermore, that the strength of the earth's crust is very great; loads must reach a certain weight before this strength is overcome and the rock beneath yields and begins to flow.

THE GEOID AND THE SPHEROID

We have seen how modern measurements of arcs of meridian at different latitudes changed our concept of the "Figure of the Earth" from Eratosthenes' sphere to an oblate ellipsoid. But a moment's thought about the facts just discussed shows that still further refinement is necessary.

Though mountains do not deflect the plumb line as much as we might expect—a fact explained by the theory of isostasy— they nevertheless do deflect it. Even the surface of the sea, therefore, cannot be a perfect oblate ellipsoid. Near shore it is warped upward by the gravitational pull of the adjacent lands. This irregularly warped surface of the sea, which is, of course, everywhere at right angles to the plumb line, is called the **geoid** (Fig. 10–8) . The geoid may be thought of as the surface of the ocean, and in continental areas, as the surface of the water in a system of narrow sea-level canals that we imagine to be cut through the continents.

The geoid—the imaginary level surface corresponding to sea level over the whole earth—obviously does not correspond to any regular mathematical figure; unlike the ellipsoid, for example, it cannot be formed by rotating an ellipse on its axis. Analysis of satellite orbits shows them to be irregularly disturbed. The disturbances indicate the presence of upward bumps of the geoid as great as 57 meters centering near New Guinea, of 30 meters in the South Atlantic and of 35

FIGURE 10–12   *Geoid heights in meters relative to an ellipsoid with a flattening of 1/298.3. The major features include a depression in the Indian Ocean and a rise centered near Indonesia and the Philippines; there is also another rise in the South Atlantic. (After G. J. F. MacDonald,* The Use of Artificial Satellites for Geodesy, *Interscience Publishers, 1964.)*

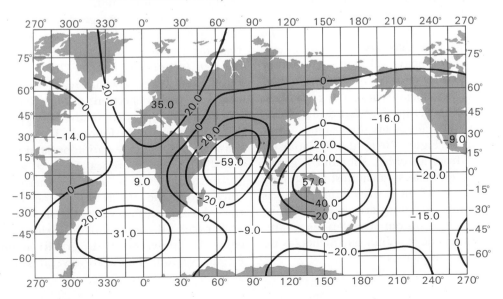

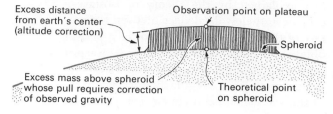

Excess distance from earth's center (altitude correction)

Observation point on plateau

Spheroid

Excess mass above spheroid whose pull requires correction of observed gravity

Theoretical point on spheroid

FIGURE 10–13

The factors involved in correcting observed gravity for comparison with the theoretical value by the Bouguer method. Height above the spheroid taken alone diminishes the observed value as compared with the theoretical, but the added attraction of the mass between spheroid and the observation point increases it. When both corrections are made, most land stations yield negative anomalies (that is, the actual value, when corrected, is less than the theoretical value), and most sea stations, positive (the actual value after correction is greater than the theoretical value.) This constitutes very strong evidence for isostasy.

meters near Scandinavia. There are comparable depressions in the geoid centering in the northern Indian Ocean and the eastern Pacific. See Figure 10–12. These and other irregular bumps and warps offer great mathematical difficulties to geodesists, who need a definite surface to which they can refer observations and thus make comparisons between different measurements and establish latitudes and longitudes of map points. To get around this difficulty, geodesists have accepted a mathematical figure called the **spheroid,** which corresponds approximately to the world-average form of the geoid. The spheroid is the ellipsoidal figure of revolution that most closely fits the geoid.

As seen in Figure 10–12 the deviation of the geoid from an oblate spheroid is generally only a few meters—an almost vanishingly small fraction of an earth radius. Slight as they are, the deviations are very significant in setting limits on our speculations regarding conditions deep within our planet, as we shall see in Chapter 19.

GRAVITY MEASUREMENTS AND ISOSTASY

At any point on the spheroid, the force of gravity has a theoretical value that depends only on the latitude of the point. Both the distance to the center of the earth and the centrifugal force of the earth's rotation are identical for all points having the same latitude. With pendulum or gravimeter we can measure the actual force of gravity, but in order to compare this with the theoretical value of gravity on the spheroid, we must take several factors into account: the altitude of the station above or below sea level and the gravitational pull of the rock between the station and sea level (if the station is above sea level) or the lack of pull of rock between station and sea level (if the station is below). For all stations we must also take account of the attraction of the nearby topography, as we saw in the Indian example. Clearly, many complex measurements and computations are needed before the measured and theoretical values of gravity can be compared in any meaningful way (Fig. 10–13).

When this is done, however, as it has been for many thousands of stations on land and sea, a most significant fact appears. The regional variations in the force of gravity prove that, on the average, *the materials of the earth beneath high land are less dense than those beneath low—if the computation is taken to sufficient depth.* This conclusion is, of course, precisely that reached by Pratt and Airy, from deflections of the plumb line —a wholly independent method of approach. The reasoning is as follows: The value of gravity measured at a station on land is compared with the theoretical value at a point vertically beneath it on the spheroid. By convention, the theoretical value is subtracted from the observed value after this has been corrected for various disturbing influences. The difference is the **gravity anomaly** for the station. There are several kinds of gravity anomalies, each computed by taking account of one or more disturbing influences. The first correction is for altitude: the measured value is increased to the computed amount it would have if the measurement could have been made on the spheroid (almost at sea level), directly beneath the station, that is, if it were closer to the earth's center. Subtracting the theoretical value from this corrected value gives the **free-air anomaly.** It is as though we assumed that the rock between station and spheroid had no mass—hence it is sometimes called the "mountains-are-empty-egg-shells" assumption. But, of course, rock is present, and its pull does add to the measured value. Hence the measured value, when corrected in this artificial way, is nearly everywhere greater than the theoretical. Free-air anomalies are thus positive for nearly all stations on land. It would be amazing if they were not.

When we further correct the measured value by subtracting the theoretical pull of the rocks between station and spheroid (having already made the free-air correction), we have a **Bouguer anomaly,** named for the French geodesist who first suggested this. Bouguer anomalies offer perhaps the strongest of all support to the theory of isostasy: they are chiefly negative on land areas and in general, the higher the station, the larger the negative anomaly (Figs. 10–14, 10–15); conversely, sea stations generally have slightly positive Bouguer anomalies. The correlation is by no means perfect, but the parallelism is unmistakable.

Neither of the two corrections we have made to the measured value of gravity in computing the Bouguer anomaly can be seriously in error. Altitude we can measure more accurately than gravity; though an average density is used rather than one specific for the region, this deviation is also small, on the average. So too, with the disturbing effects of nearby topography, except in rugged mountain areas.

But the theoretical value of gravity at the spheroid is based on the average of the whole earth. That Bouguer anomalies are generally negative in mountainous areas, and the more strongly negative the higher the mountains, indicates that the material underlying such areas is less dense, on the average, than that underlying lowlands. But this is precisely the conclusion reached by Pratt and Airy on the wholly different basis of plumb-line deflections: *the excess mass of the rocks above sea level is in general compensated for by a deficiency of mass below sea level.*

Conversely, the positive anomalies at sea

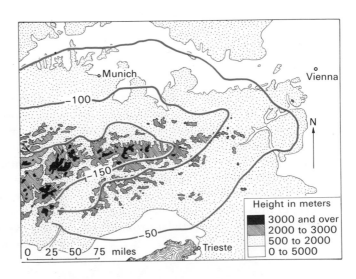

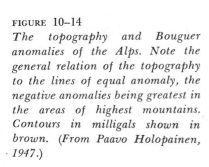

FIGURE 10–14
The topography and Bouguer anomalies of the Alps. Note the general relation of the topography to the lines of equal anomaly, the negative anomalies being greatest in the areas of highest mountains. Contours in milligals shown in brown. (From Paavo Holopainen, 1947.)

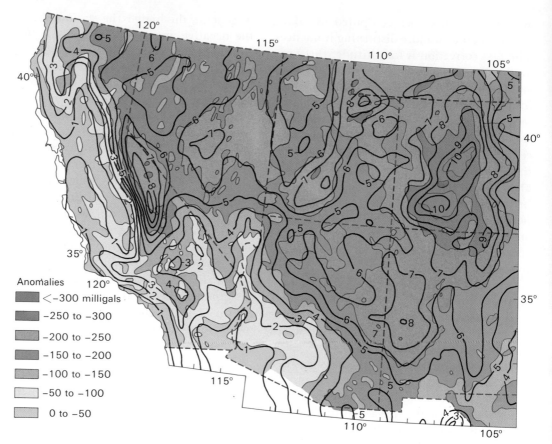

FIGURE 10–15   *Bouguer anomalies of the southwestern United States (shown by patterns), superposed on a generalized topographic map (altitudes, averaged over areas of approximately 2000 square miles, shown by contours with interval of 1000 feet). As in Figure 10–14, the anomalies tend to be greater (and more negative) the higher the topography. One milligal equals .001 gal (Named for Galileo). One gal corresponds to an acceleration of 1 cm per second per second. A milligal is thus approximately one millionth of the normal value of gravity at sea level. (Bouguer anomalies from American Geophysical Union-U.S. Geological Survey map, 1964.)*

may be explained by assuming that the oceans are underlain by denser material than the continents. We shall see in Chapters 18 and 19 many other reasons for accepting this assumption.

Both the deflections of the plumb line and the relations between measured gravity and earth relief thus indicate the same thing: the larger segments of the earth are roughly in floating equilibrium (isostatic balance) one with another. Large areas of high land stand above large areas of lowland because: (1) they are composed of less dense materials than underly the lowlands (Pratt), or (2) they are made of the same material, but it is thicker beneath the highlands (Airy), or (3) because both factors are operating together—probably the most common case for large mountain chains.

STRENGTH

The prevailing condition of isostasy suggests that the earth has a plastic interior that buoys up irregularities of the crust by flotation. What does this mean? Ordinary rocks seem rigid and do not behave at all like fluids. The great mountain ranges do not seem to be flattening out under their own weight: as far as we can see they are made of strong, rigid rocks. Furthermore, we shall see in later chapters that there is good evidence that some small areas—say a small mountain mass or a moderate-sized delta—are not in isostatic equilibrium. Some areas are definitely being held lower or higher than their equilibrium positions by the strength of the earth's crust and by forces operating on them (Chapter 20). Must we conclude from these evidences of surface strength and bodily weakness that the earth has a strong solid crust floating on a liquid interior? We shall see in later chapters cogent evidence that the subcrust is not by any means liquid—under some short-term stresses it behaves as though it were twice as strong as steel.

Perhaps we might clarify our ideas if we think of just what we mean by "strength," and especially the strength of huge masses the size of the earth. Airy gave us a significant clue when he emphasized that a solid or rigid interior could not possibly support the earth's crust no matter how strong we think the strongest rocks to be: the subcrust must behave plastically, almost as though it were a fluid. Furthermore, in areas where deep erosion has exposed metamorphic rocks the foliation and fantastically complicated fold patterns show that deeply buried rocks have flowed, bent, and recrystallized in patterns like those we can form in putty or toothpaste at the earth's surface. The folds in the basalt flows of the Columbia Plateau or in the limestone strata of the Jura Mountains described in Chapter 20 show that rocks in large masses can deform plastically, even near the earth's surface. The patterns of many metamorphic rocks are those of viscous flow.

Definition of strength

The **strength** of a body is defined as the force (load) per unit area that is required to break it, under room temperature and pressure.

Thus, we say that a cube of granite one centimeter in diameter that breaks under a weight of 2200 kilograms has a *compressive strength* of 2200 kilograms per square centimeter. A steel cable with a cross section of one square centimeter that does not break until a weight of 10,000 kilograms is suspended from its end has a *tensile strength* of 10,000 kilograms per square centimeter. For each solid substance there is a definite force per square centimeter that must be reached to cause it to rupture. This is the *rupture strength*.

Fluids, both liquids and gases, have no strength; they yield continuously under the slightest load or stress, though they vary tremendously in the speed with which they yield. At first glance, tar seems "stronger" than water—an iron bar will not sink into it so quickly. Yet the bar does gradually sink and eventually will reach the bottom; the tar is simply more viscous than water—it has no true strength to support the bar.

Most solids are not brittle; they begin to deform at lower stresses than the rupture strength and some will yield greatly before breaking. They do, however, cease to deform if the stress drops below a minimal value, the **yield stress.** But those stresses differ greatly at high temperatures and pressures from those at room conditions.

EFFECT OF TEMPERATURE. Whether a particular solid breaks or flows under a given load depends greatly on the prevailing temperature. At red heat, a bar of iron is solid, but will flow under stresses much smaller than those needed to make it bend at room temperature—a fact utilized in forging iron.

In earlier chapters we saw that many solid rocks buried deep within the earth's crust have flowed and bent in response to the heat and pressure of the earth's interior. The same rocks at the surface will not yield perceptibly without breaking. The flow and recrystallization of solids should not be confused with liquid flow; the rock does not melt, and a definite stress (equivalent to the yield strength of the material under the prevailing environment) must be applied before flowage begins. The general rule is that *all solids are weaker at high temperatures than at low.*

EFFECT OF SIZE, OR SCALE. In everyday life we seldom think of how size affects the strength of material. The earth, however, is a very large structure. How are we to think of rock strength in so huge a mass? A dramatic illustration of the effect of size has been given by M. King Hubbert in the quarry operation illustrated in Figure 10–16. Suppose we are to quarry a single block of granite the size of the State of Texas. It is roughly 1200 kilometers (720 miles) across, and we want to hoist a piece one-quarter as thick as it is broad—that is, 300 kilometers (180 miles) thick. Grant that we have a quarry crane capable of hoisting it. The rock is assumed to be flawless and to have the crushing strength of average granite, about 2500 kilograms per square centimeter. Will it be strong enough to hold together while being hoisted? Obviously we cannot test this directly, but we can investigate the properties of such a block by using a scale model.

What should be the properties of a model reduced to a size suitable for our experiment? To obtain a convenient model we could reduce the true length of 1200 kilometers to 60 centimeters (about 2 feet). Our model would then be on a scale of 1 to 2,000,000.

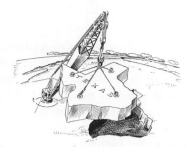

FIGURE 10–16
Quarrying the State of Texas. (After M. King Hubbert, reproduced by permission, American Association of Petroleum Geologists, Bulletin, *1945.*

On this scale, the 300-kilometer thickness would be reduced, in the model, to 15 centimeters (about 6 inches). Both original and model are at the earth's surface so the force of gravity is the same on both. Our model also can have the same density as the original, about three times that of water. What other factors must be considered?

If the model is to act like the original—that is, if it is to behave the same mechanically—clearly the strength of the model material should be reduced in the same ratio as the size. Thus, if the ratio of strength to load is to be the same in the model as in the original, we must use material whose strength is $\frac{1}{2,000,000}$ that of granite. The material in our model then must have a strength of $\frac{1}{2,000,000}$ of 2500 kilograms per square centimeter, or about 1 gram per square centimeter. It is difficult to envisage so weak a solid. A crushing strength of 1 gram per square centimeter, for a density of 3 grams per cubic centimeter, would be the pressure on the base of a column $\frac{1}{3}$ centimeter high. Any higher column would collapse of its own weight. Yet the model is about 15 centimeters (6 inches) thick and its total weight 81 kilograms (about 180 pounds). The pressure at its base would be about 45 grams per square centimeter or 45 times the crushing strength of the model materials.

Thus if we tried to lift the block in the way shown in the figure, the eyebolts would pull out; if we should support it on a pair of saw-horses, its middle would collapse; were we to place it on a horizontal table, its sides would fall off. To lift it at all would require the use of a scoop shovel. That this is not unreasonable can easily be verified by direct calculation upon the original block (the State of Texas). As Hubbert remarked: "For it, too, the pressure at its base would exceed the crushing strength of its assumed material by a factor of 45. The inescapable conclusion, therefore, is that the good State of Texas is utterly incapable of self-support!"

EFFECT OF CONFINING PRESSURE. A substance becomes stronger when it is placed under pressure from all directions simultaneously —that is, when it is under *confining pressure*. (If the pressure is equal on all sides it is *hydrostatic pressure*.)

Laboratory experiments show that the crushing strength of limestone from Solnhofen, Germany is six times as great under a confining pressure of 10,000 atmospheres (about 10,000 kilograms per square centimeter) as it is under room conditions. Under a confining pressure of one atmosphere (1 kilogram per square centimeter or 14.7 pounds per square inch), its strength is 1700 kilograms per square centimeter; under 10,000 atmospheres, 10,200 kilograms per square centimeter. Such a pressure is equal to the weight of a column of granite about 36 kilometers (22 miles) high. Presumably, then, it is also equal to the hydrostatic pressure at a depth of 36 kilometers within the earth. Despite the increased strength due to the confining pressure, Solnhofen limestone should yield by rupture or flow at greater depths.

From temperatures measured in drill holes and mines, we know that the earth is hotter inside than at the surface. Clearly, then, factors of opposite tendency affect rock strength deep within the earth: the increased hydrostatic pressure increases strength; the higher temperatures weaken it.

We thus see that confining pressure caused by weight of overlying rock is an important factor in the earth's strength. In short, there is nothing really inconsistent in the apparent incongruity of an earth whose rocks are "rigid and strong" enough to maintain large relief features on its surface, yet at the same time so "weak" that, in the long course of geologic time they react plastically to loads as large as mountain chains. Our chief difficulty is in visualizing how a substance must act in very large masses and under pressures and temperatures unfamiliar to us.

Facts, concepts, terms

The earth's gross form
Sphere? Oblate ellipsoid?
Measuring an "arc of meridian"
The geoid and the spheroid
Gravitation
Law of gravitation
Mass, weight, density
Relation of level surface to plumb line
Measurement of gravity

Questions

1. What evidence can you give that the earth is approximately an oblate ellipsoid and not shaped like a football or a doughnut?

2. What assumptions underlie Eratosthenes' measurement of the earth? Neglecting measuring errors, are there reasons for doubting the validity of these assumptions?

3. When we sight along a telescope accurately adjusted to a level position, are we sighting parallel to the (*a*) geoid, (*b*) spheroid, or (*c*) ellipsoid? Where, in general, would you expect all three of these surfaces to be most nearly parallel?

4. How would you expect the plumb line to be deflected from the line at right angles to the spheroid at Denver, just east of the Rockies? If surveys failed to show any such deflection what might you suspect as the cause?

5. Geologists commonly assume that the hydrostatic pressure at depths of a few miles is equal to the weight per unit area of the overlying rocks. How can this assumption be justified?

6. There is a very large negative anomaly at Seattle, nearly at sea level. Within less than 20 miles east or west of Seattle measurements show practically no anomaly. What suggestions can you offer to explain this fact?

7. Would the rate of swing of a gravity pendulum be faster or slower at a station on the surface than at one at the bottom of a 5000-foot mine shaft? At Seattle (see question 6) or at a station 20 miles west or east of Seattle?

8. In a certain valley in Turkestan the plumb lines are actually deflected *toward* the center of the valley rather than toward the mountains. Suggest a possible explanation of this anomalous behavior.

9. Account for the fact that rocks that are brittle and break under stresses in the laboratory have obviously been folded and have flowed under stresses within the earth.

10. Why don't the continental masses spread out over the ocean floor?

Suggested readings

Daly, R. A., *Strength and Structure of the Earth*. Englewood Cliffs, N.J.: Prentice-Hall, 1950. [Especially the Introduction and Chapter 1.]

Hubbert, M. K., *Strength of the Earth*. American Association of Petroleum Geologists Bulletin, v. 29, 1945, p. 1630–1653.

Poynting, J. H., *The Earth*. Cambridge, England: Cambridge University Press, 1913.

Scientific American, *The Planet Earth*. New York: Simon and Schuster, 1957.

Scientific American offprints

268. Marcus Reiner, *The Flow of Matter* (December 1959)

273. George Gamow, *Gravity* (March 1961)

812. Weikko A. Heiskanen, *The Earth's Gravity* (September 1955)

11

Downslope Movements of Soil and Rock

Chapter 5 outlined the role of gravity in causing erosion. Chapters 12 through 16 describe the erosive effects of such agencies as streams, glaciers, waves, wind, and ground water. Here we consider erosion by the direct action of gravity.

From the principle of the parallelogram of forces, we know that an object weighing one kilogram, resting on a 30° slope, may be thought of as having a force of .5 kilogram $(1 \times \sin 30°)$ acting to push it downhill (Fig. 11–1). Any factor that weakens the cohesion of the object with its base may allow this downslope force to overcome the friction with the base and start movement downhill. Factors that may so operate include: the expansion and contraction when water freezes and melts, the wetting of clay, the uplifting force (Archimedes Principle) of water in a saturated mass of soil and rock, the weight of a heavy snowfall, the tremors of an earthquake, or even such seemingly trivial forces as those of a high wind or the tread of a sheep.

VARIETIES OF DOWNSLOPE MOVEMENTS

Masses of rock or soil that glide or roll directly downslope under gravity range from individual grains pelted by raindrops, through small patches of water-soaked soil creeping slowly down hillsides, to great landslides crashing down a mountain.

Creep involves slow movement of broken rock and soil downslope. Weakly consolidated grass-covered material may bulge in low wavelike swells; where grass is absent, the motion may be grain by grain, usually too slowly to be readily determined, but over the years becoming significant (Fig. 17–4).

Slow slides and **debris flows** differ from creep in that the individual moving masses are bounded by distinct well-marked slip surfaces. Open, gaping cracks or rough scars

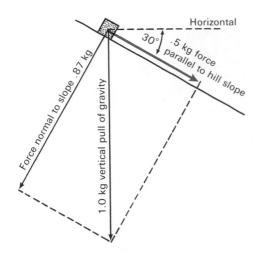

mark their sources (Fig. 11–2) . Some slides remain almost intact internally for long distances of travel, but others are jumbled and stirred together. Debris flows generally advance in tongues or broadly rounded projections. Both slides and debris flows range from a few meters to several kilometers in length.

Landslides and **rock falls** move rapidly,

FIGURE 11–1
The resolution of the force of gravity, directed vertically downward, into a force parallel and one normal to the slope on which the object rests.

FIGURE 11–2   *Slide near Orinda California. Four-lane highway and large dump trucks give the scale. (Photo by Bill Young, courtesy of the* San Francisco Chronicle.)

some in free fall. They range from small fragments rattling down fissured cliffs to huge rock falls and landslides hurtling down mountain sides—some to overwhelm whole villages or dam rivers.

RAINWASH

Rainwash on hill slopes is the first stage in the flow of surface waters that later gather into well-defined streams and rivers. We consider it here because its effects blend indistinguishably with the sliding of water-soaked soil, and with slow downslope creep of soil and rock. It is most effective on slopes of slightly permeable materials; creep predominates on slopes with more permeable soils.

Large rain drops may attain a velocity in free fall of as much as 17 miles per hour in still air; at higher speeds they break up into smaller drops, which fall slower. But in storms, downdrafts of turbulent air may increase the fall velocity to as much as 60 miles per hour, making the impact of the raindrops on unconsolidated material an effective agent in erosion. During rainstorms the hillslopes may thus be quickly covered with a thin sheet of moving water, heavily charged with mud, silt, and humus churned up by the pelting raindrops. Some of this heavily laden water soaks into the ground, but some quickly gathers into shallow rills that course downslope. Rainwash alone affects the slope angle very little; most shallow rills are filled and obliterated in a single season, but some persist as larger, steep-walled **gullies** that modify the topography much more dramatically (Fig. 11–3).

MUDFLOWS

Long-continued heavy rains may so saturate the surface material that instead of the pelting rain driving individual particles down-

FIGURE 11–3
Rill furrows in fresh volcanic ash from Paricutin Volcano, Mexico. (Photo by Konrad Krauskopf, Stanford University.)

slope, the whole of the surficial material, if it is weakly consolidated, becomes a mass of mud and moves like a lava flow. During a torrential rain that fell upon Aberfan, a small coal-mining town in Wales in 1965 a huge dump of broken rock waste from the mines became so saturated that it flowed downvalley overwhelming the village school and killing more than 100 children.

In northwestern Europe and eastern Canada, many valleys are floored with unconsolidated clays and sands deposited in lakes dammed by the Pleistocene glaciers (Chapter 13). These clay plains extend long distances inland and rise to elevations of several scores of meters. During the spring thaw these weakly consolidated sediments become saturated with water and a mass of mud as much as several square kilometers in area may suddenly break through a slightly more resistant barrier and roll rapidly downvalley as a destructive mudflow. The front of one such flow moved 10 kilometers in a single hour. A flow may pile up behind a temporary dam of logs or sandy clay until enough water collects to breach the dam. A mudflow leaves a clean-cut scar at its head, with a rough floor and steep walls a few meters high. One night in 1893 such a mudflow moved down a Norwegian valley so fast that 111 persons were caught by it and lost their lives; others escaped after being jostled about in their staunch wooden houses as the mudflow rafted them down the valley.

Arid regions show still another kind of mudflow. A thick mass of silt, sand, and coarser debris, even including boulders several meters in diameter, scoured from the walls and floor of a canyon by an exceptional rain may roll forward for miles, damming, piling up, breaking through, and gradually coming to a stop as it thickens through loss of water, or spreads out over a plain. The abrupt edge of such a flow may be a wall several meters high, with a slope of fully 45°.

FIGURE 11–4

Small lobate mudflow caused by heavy rains, Cape Fear River, North Carolina.

Small lobate mudflows are common at the base of steep slopes in unconsolidated material after heavy rains, even in humid climates (Fig. 11–4).

Some of the largest and most destructive mudflows develop in loose pyroclastic ejecta from active volcanoes (see Chapter 18).

Underwater flows

Of all downslope movements of solid or semiliquid material, the most obscure and difficult to study are those that take place on the floors of lakes or seas. The submarine gravity movement off the Grand Banks has already been described in Chapter 5. One thoroughly studied example started at the shore of the Lake of Zug, in Switzerland, and squirted out under water along the lake floor.

The source of the flow lay within the city of Zug. It extended from a lakefront retaining wall to a building-lined street about 70 meters inland (Fig. 11–5). In the two years after the retaining wall was built, water began to appear in previously dry cellars behind it, and, in the spring of 1887, the ground settled and pavements cracked slightly. The first disastrous movement abruptly dropped a small section of the retaining wall and three houses beneath lake level, causing several deaths. Half an hour later, wooden piles from the broken retaining wall suddenly rose to the lake surface a hundred meters offshore, showing that lateral movement as well as sinking had occurred. The main spurt of the flow came three hours later; streets and many houses suddenly settled beneath the lake. The average drop was about 8 meters, and some buildings moved 10 to 20 meters toward the lake.

The material that flowed out into the lake was incoherent silt and fine sand from the submerged part of a small stream delta, mobilized by its thorough saturation and the weight of the city buldings. The flow exca-

vated a trench 60 meters wide and as deep
as 6 meters that extended almost 300 meters
along the lake floor in the similar silt and
sand on the lake bottom. At the end of the
underwater trench, a new deposit of sandy

silt extended onto the lake floor as a thin
debris tongue 800 meters long, with an uneven hummocky surface (see the cross section of Fig. 11–5). The end of the tongue was
40 to 45 meters lower than the land surface

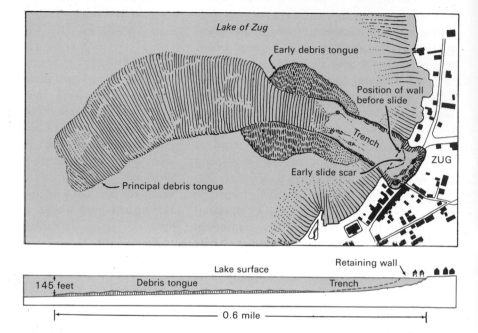

FIGURE 11–5   *Map and cross section of the underwater flow at Zug, Switzerland. (After Albrecht
Heim, 1888.)*

FIGURE 11–6   *Waterfront at Seward, Alaska before* (left) *and after* (right) *the Alaska earthquake of 1964. The small boat harbor, the railroad yards, the large docks, and
other waterfront facilities were removed by underwater landslides. Windrow-like
heaps of railroad cars and other debris were rolled ashore by the tsunami waves.
(Photos by U.S. Geological Survey.)*

at the head of the flow, so the slope was less than 3°. The deposit was more than 3 meters thick in places, and contained about 150,000 cubic meters of material. Less than half came from the land, the remainder was eroded from the lake floor by the flow. The Zug flow, like the turbidity current off the Grand Banks, was a gravity current of silt and sand, heavier than the lake water.

The Zug mudflow undoubtedly was triggered by water rising in the unconsolidated deltaic sediments behind the newly built retaining wall. But comparable flows may be engendered otherwise. For example, similar flows were set off by Alaska's Good Friday earthquake in 1964. This, one of the greatest of all recorded earthquakes, devastated a vast area of Alaska, centering at the head of Prince William Sound. Several of the many gravity movements triggered by the vibrations of this earthquake seem pertinent to our subject. The cities of Seward and Valdez are built on deltas extending into deep fjords. The footings of their docks were in fully saturated unconsolidated silts and gravels. When the earthquake struck, the still unconsolidated deltaic sediments, which had been deposited in still water, became thoroughly unstable when agitated by the earthquake's vibrations and flowed out into the fjords as great submarine slumps and mudflows. Large sections of the dockage fronts of both cities slid to great depths in their fjord-like harbors (Fig. 11–6). More than a score of people were lost in the catastrophe at Valdez; fortunately Seward did not suffer so severely.

Similar slides have been common in artificial reservoirs. As the impounded water rises it wets and buoys up the grains in weakly consolidated sediments of the reservoir walls. The result has been recurrent sliding. Such slides in Roosevelt Lake on the Columbia River above Grand Coulee Dam have caused much damage; the reservoir on the Eel River in northern California has lost much of its capacity because of them.

CREEP

Creep, the slow gliding of soil and broken rock downhill, is the most widespread downslope movement; generally it operates by slow distortion of soil, mantle rock, or weakly consolidated sediments. Observations over several years show creep to be most active during the wet seasons and shortly thereafter. Ordinarily, the movement does not extend far below the surface and no distinct slip surface develops between the creeping mass and the underlying rock. Many rock bodies whose previous shape or structure is known show distortion by creep. For example, weathered and softened boulders (Fig. 11–7), that once must have been nearly round like those in the undisturbed source material beneath) are stretched downhill into thin ribbons; thin-bedded, steeply inclined strata bend sharply downhill as they approach the surface of a steep hillside (Fig. 11–8) or even on a relatively gentle slope (Fig. 17–4). On many slopes, rock structures, trees, posts, and even buildings, all show the effects of creep (Fig. 11–9).

As would be expected, the rate of creep

FIGURE 11–7
Decayed boulders on a hillside, stretched into spindles by creep. (Photo by S. R. Capps, U.S. Geological Survey.)

varies widely with climate and slope, as well as with the material making up the slope. Measurements in the semiarid West of the United States and in Arctic Greenland, on slopes of about 25°, yielded rates of 0.2 foot per year (6 centimeters); on very steep slopes of 39° in both Sweden and Colorado the rate was 0.33 foot (10 centimeters) per year for the surficial layer. These are very high rates indeed, far higher than on the grassy slopes in England where even a 33°

FIGURE 11–8
Bending of thin vertical strata by creep on a steep hillside in Washington County, Maryland. (Photo by G. W. Stose, U.S. Geological Survey.)

FIGURE 11–9
Common effects of creep. (After C. F. S. Sharpe, Landslides and Related Phenomena, *Columbia University Press, 1938.)*

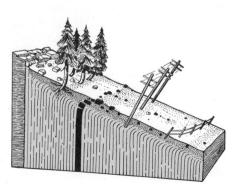

slope showed a rate of only .0006 foot (0.18 millimeter) per year and another 22° to 30° slope a rate of only 0.25 millimeter per year. But even these rates, slow as they are, are not negligible in geologic time.

The exact mechanics of creep are somewhat conjectural, but the process is generally understood. Wetting of clay-rich soil (which expands the layered structure of the clay minerals), or freezing of pore water causes soils to swell as diagrammed in Figure 11–10. A particle of soil at *a* is pushed upward at right angles to the surface by the swelling and comes to rest at *b*. When the clay dries or thaws, the soil contracts. But the particle does not return to point *a*, it tends instead to slump downslope toward point *c*. If the soil is wet enough to flow slightly under gravity, the particle will slide even farther downhill. Repeated wetting and freeze-thaw cycles move it, step by step, farther and farther downhill. Because water expands 9 percent on freezing, soil crusts may be raised several centimeters and paved roads may be bulged upward and broken into rubble by this *frost heaving* in regions with cold winters. On thawing, the shrinkage does not retrace the path of expansion; the net movement is downslope.

Other processes that cause creep include wedging by plant roots, the moving of soil by earthworms, rodents, and other burrowing animals, and the trampling of muddy

FIGURE 11–10
One mechanism of creep. The arrows show the gradual downslope movement of a particle with alternate swelling and contraction.

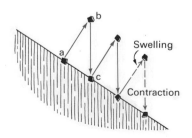

FIGURE 11-11
Paths formed by grazing animals on a steep hillside in central Oregon. After each rain hooves push the softened soil a little farther down slope. (Photo by A. C. Waters.)

soil downslope by grazing animals (Fig. 11-11). Any random movement of loose material gives gravity a chance to displace it downslope.

Creep passes imperceptibly into downslope sliding of definitely bounded masses. In the California Coast Ranges a black, sandy, clay soil develops on several kinds of sedimentary rock. On many slopes a homogeneous soil, doubtless formed by intimate stirring of A and B soil horizons farther upslope, is sharply separated by a smooth slip surface from the fresh rock beneath. The surface layer, in slow downslope transit, has scraped the underlying rock to a smooth surface. Movement in the past two or three score years is recorded by tilted fence posts and telephone poles, but the lack of scars or irregularities on the surface indicates a general movement, not concentrated into landslide tongues.

Solifluction

In arctic and subarctic regions, and above the timberline in temperate zones, slow downslope movements called **solifluction** (literally: "soil flow"), are intermediate between creep and debris flows. Frost and other weathering agents produce abundant fine rock fragments. When this debris is saturated with water, which freezes and melts, it spreads slowly down slope and along the valley floors. A. L. Washburn, an American student of the Arctic, has found that on Victoria Island, northwest of Hudson Bay, most movement takes place immediately after the spring thaw. Rows of stakes driven into the lobe shown in Figure 11-12 proved that there was a slight local tilting and forward motion during the spring and summer of 1940. The seasonal movement was only a little more than 4 centimeters, and almost all took place during the 33 days following June 14. Apparently solifluction proceeds by very slow seasonal flow of water-saturated soil, year after year.

FIGURE 11-12
Solifluction lobe on Victoria Island, Canada. The rows of stakes were used to measure rate of movement of the lobe. (Photo by A. L. Washburn, University of Washington.)

FIGURE 11–13 *Rock glacier on Cerro del Plomo, Andes of Chile. Note the smooth talus at the lower left, and at the terminus of the glacier. (Photo by Kenneth Segerstrom, U.S. Geological Survey.)*

Rock glaciers

In many alpine areas, even including Mount Ruwenzori, on the equator, many large natural amphitheaters in the high mountains are strewn with angular rock fragments, heaped in lobate ridges (Fig. 11–13). They resemble solifluction ridges, and are also like the ridges on some rock falls, later to be described. These tortuously twisted ridges of debris have been called **rock glaciers** because they resemble the debris that covers the ends of some glaciers. Rock glaciers prob- ably result from large-scale frost heaving and solifluction. The material of their sinuous ridges consists of fragments small enough to be moved readily by frost, and excavations have shown that the ridges contain consider- able ice at moderate depths. Not much is known of the mechanism of their motion, though the cores of ice they contain must play a role. The smooth talus slopes that ter- minate some of the most contorted ridges suggest that where the ice core is near enough the surface to be melted, it releases individ- ual blocks that accumulate as ridges of talus.

Gros Ventre debris flow

The Gros Ventre River is a tributary of the Snake River south of Yellowstone Park. In the spring of 1909, the Gros Ventre was dammed in midcourse by rock debris that, as early as May, 1908, had begun to flow slowly down the moderate slope (10 to 20°) of the Gros Ventre Mountains to the south of the river (Fig. 11–14). The slide was of weak shale with some thin interbeds of sandstone and limestone, all thoroughly soaked by heavy rains. Some strata probably glided along bedding, which almost parallels the slope. The sliding was imperceptible to the eye, but notably altered the landscape within a few weeks. Telephone poles tilted slowly downhill, snapping the wires. A wagon road paralleling the river soon became hopelessly twisted and broken beyond repair; eventually it was so churned up by the movement that even traces were hard to find.

Many gaping fissures opened at and near the sources on the east and south sides of the flow. Farther down, where the already churned material of an earlier flow (see Fig. 11–14) was set in renewed motion, earth domes swelled and broke open in broad cracks. The flow thickened toward the river, developed a very irregular surface, and was stirred into a gigantic jumble of clay and rock fragments.

The flow did not move as a unit, but in sections, spreading westward week by week. The debris moved faster in the wet spring months of 1909 and more slowly in the autumn. Movement continued through 1910, but almost ceased by 1911. The river was then able to trench the debris dam and partly drain the lake that had formed on the upstream side.

Many slides do not break up as completely as the Gros Ventre flow. A mass of rock may break away from a cliff and slip as a unit along a sloping water-lubricated surface for many meters, leaving only a gaping fissure at its head as evidence of movement. In weak materials, small slide blocks commonly rotate on curved slip surfaces so as to tilt each slide unit backward, as shown in Fig. 11–16.

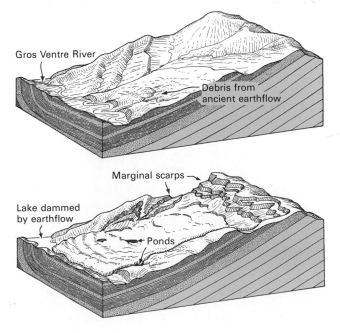

FIGURE 11–14
The south slope of the Gros Ventre River valley before (top) *and after* (bottom) *the 1909 debris flow. (After Eliot Blackwelder, Stanford University, 1912.)*

FIGURE 11–15   *Tilted blocks in the Turnagain Heights landslide, Anchorage, Alaska. (Photo by the U.S. Geological Survey.)*

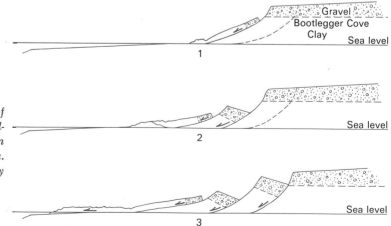

FIGURE 11–16

The pattern of movement of the Turnagain Heights landslide, as reconstructed from surveys and drilling data. (After U.S. Geological Survey Circular 491, 1964.)

TURNAGAIN HEIGHTS LANDSLIDE. This kind of movement was seen in the Alaskan earthquake of 1964. The city of Anchorage is built on glacial outwash gravels a few tens of meters thick toward the north and thinning to a very few meters toward the south. These gravels rest upon a thick, weakly consolidated flat-lying deposit of water-saturated clay, the Bootlegger Cove Clay of Tertiary age. In the southwestern part of the city, the scenic residential area of Turnagain Heights, commanding a magnificent view of Cook Inlet and the snow-capped peaks of the Alaska Peninsula beyond, was built on a bluff a few tens of meters above the sea. The darkness of Arctic evening had settled over the town just before the earthquake struck. The ground began to heave, shake, and slowly slide toward the sea. The power lines snapped and in total darkness and falling snow, scores of houses and their terrified inhabitants rode the slide down the bluff. An area of many thousand square meters, gliding on a mass of clay rendered semiliquid by the shaking, broke into crazily tilted blocks and moved on a rapidly flattening gradient toward the sea. Houses were canted at high angles and some were broken into fragments, porches drifted away from entrances, great chasms several meters deep and wide gaped open and then closed, and with water from broken mains adding to the liquification of the clay, nearly the whole of this residential area was demolished. By remarkable good fortune, casualties were few, but the property destruction was virtually complete for several hundred meters inland from the bluff (Fig. 11–15). Surveys and drilling carried on after the slide indicate that the mechanism of its motion was somewhat as diagrammed in Figure 11–16.

The hazards of the Turnagain Heights site had been specifically pointed out in a geologic report more than a decade earlier, but as commonly happens, the potential hazard, though recognized, was discounted because of the superb scenic advantages of the site. Similar ignoring of comparable hazards is widespread in many earthquake-threatened areas in California, Yugoslavia, Italy, and elsewhere.

RAPID SLIDES, FLOWS, AND FALLS

Small rapid slides

Most rapid gravity movements involve only small volumes of soil or rock, but their aggregrate effects are large. In humid temperate regions small rapid slides abound in soil or weak sedimentary rock, especially on steep slopes after unusually heavy rains. The depression or scar left at the head of a typical slip may be several meters wide. At the base of the scar the soil piles up in crumpled and disordered masses as indicated in Figure 11–2, an unusually large but typically shaped example. Such avalanching of water-soaked soil down the walls of Hawaiian canyons, was estimated by C. K. Wentworth to be lowering the general land surface at the rate of one foot in 400 years.

Talus piles

The most abundant, and in the aggregate the most voluminous, rockfalls are the countless small fragments, in the millimeter-to-meter range, that, loosened by frost, rain, or wind, drop from cliffs or steep walls, bound down the slope, and accumulate in **talus piles** (Figs. 11–17, 11–18, 11–19). A talus pile maintains a nearly uniform slope as it grows. The slope angle, commonly about 30°, though varying with the mean size and shape of the rock fragments, is called the *angle of repose* because it is the steepest slope on which the talus material will rest without rolling farther. Steep-walled valleys in arid regions are widened chiefly by the fall and continued downward rolling and sliding of large and small talus fragments.

RATE OF TALUS FORMATION. Climbers on steep slopes of closely jointed rock in lofty, snow-clad mountains know well the danger from rock fragments tumbling from cliffs above and bounding, whirring, and crashing down long talus slopes. Where frost works on well-jointed rocks (Figs. 5–2, 11–13) talus accumulates rapidly. Mere presence of talus, though, is no proof of concurrent rapid erosion of the cliffs above. In southern Arizona, great talus piles below many granite cliffs are composed of huge, thoroughly weathered blocks that could not, in their present state, have withstood the impact of fall. They must have weathered in place after the pile accumulated—a slow process in this arid land; they are one of many indications that the Arizona climate was formerly wetter and colder than today's.

Most falls are not triggered by earthquakes

Large rockfalls

Large rock slides occasionally crash down steep slopes and, deflected by flatter benches below, may even hurtle through the air in free fall. Large rapidly moving mudflows also occur, and if well lubricated they may glide swiftly over very gentle slopes. Several such rapid slides, flows, and falls have destroyed villages or portions of cities. From the many such catastrophes, we select for description some rock slides and falls in Alaska, Peru, and the Alps.

Another gravity phenomenon triggered by the great Alaskan earthquake of 1964 was the rock fall on Sherman Glacier. Sherman Glacier is in the Chugach Range, near the head of the Copper River delta, close to the site of greatest shaking during the earthquake. The

FIGURE 11–17 *Talus slopes masking most of the canyon walls of the Salmon River canyon at Riggins, Idaho. (Photo by Warren Hamilton, U.S. Geological Survey.)*

FIGURE 11–18
Sheep Rock, John Day State Park, Oregon, showing sheet talus at the upper left, trains of talus following ravines in center and right. Nearly all the talus fragments are from a basalt flow capping the peak. (Photo by Oregon State Highway Commission.)

FIGURE 11–19
Talus slope at the base of a basalt butte, Grand Coulee, Washington. (Photo by Washington Department of Conservation and Development.)

FIGURE 11–20   *Air photo of the rock fall on the Sherman Glacier, Alaska, brought about by the earthquake of 1964. Note "stream-lines" radiating from the head of the slide. (Photo by Austin Post, U.S. Geological Survey.)*

shocks loosened a mass of rock, estimated to have a volume of more than 23 million cubic meters, which crashed down one wall of the glacier and raced as far as 150 meters up the opposite wall of the valley, finally settling down to cover an area on the glacier of more than 6 square kilometers to depths averaging 1 to 3 meters but locally up to 30 meters. Much of the rock slide did not scrape off the wet snow that had lain on the glacier at the time of the fall, so it appears that the slide rode partly supported by a cushion of air compressed beneath it (Fig. 11–20). It will be interesting to learn the effects of this insulating blanket of rock on the regimen of the glacier during the next few years.

Comparable rock falls have clearly taken place many times in the earthquake-prone area of southern Alaska. At Lituya Bay, farther southeast, a minor earthquake in 1958 dislodged a mass of rock, estimated to have weighed 90 million tons, which fell into the bay from a maximum height of 3000 feet. The disturbance of the bay was equivalent to what might be caused if 2000 battleships were dropped from a height of half a mile. The gigantic wave that resulted was so powerful as to sweep the dense mature evergreen forest—containing many trees half a meter in diameter—cleanly off the promontories and islands to heights of as much as 500 meters, leaving naked rock where once a rain-forest had flourished (Fig. 11–22). Study of tree distribution and ages by Don Miller of the U.S. Geological Survey showed that similar gigantic waves had swept different parts of Lituya Bay at several times during the last few centuries. Doubtless many of these waves also resulted from rockfalls. We have already noticed that nearly every south-facing slope in the mountains near the source of the Assam-Tibetan earthquake of 1950 was laid bare by similar earthquake-triggered slides.

Perhaps one of the most destructive rockfalls of historic time took place on January 10, 1962, when, from the summit of Nevada de Huascarán in Peru, a fall of rock and ice estimated to have a total volume of 6 million cubic yards ricocheted down the mountain slope, gathering additional material as it went until it had doubled in size. It overwhelmed seven villages and killed 3500 people; the whole tragedy lasted less than 15 minutes from start to end, though the fall and land slide traveled 11 miles. It was not triggered by an earthquake; indeed most falls and slides are not.

FIGURE 11–21
Promontory in Lituya Bay, Alaska, swept free of trees to heights of more than 500 meters (1760 feet) above the sea by the gigantic wave of 1958 caused by a rock fall. (Photo by Don Miller, U.S. Geological Survey.)

ELM ROCK SLIDE AND FALL. A tremendous rockfall took place at the little Swiss village of Elm in 1881. A steep crag, 600 meters high, on a ridge, had been undercut halfway up by a quarry for slate. In the course of a year and a half, a curving fissure 10 meters deep slowly grew along the top of the ridge about 350 meters above the quarry (Fig. 11–22). This fissure was nearly perpendicular to the stratification and foliation of the rocks. In late summer, the local runoff from

FIGURE 11–22
Cross section of the rock fall and slide at Elm, Switzerland, showing the original position of the slide block. After Albert Heim, 1882.)

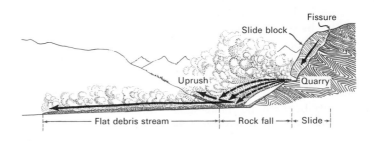

heavy rains poured into the fissure, saturating the shattered rocks. Late one September afternoon, two small earth slides started just above and on either side of the quarry. A few minutes later, the whole mass outlined by the fracture crashed down, filled the quarry, and shot forward into the narrow valley as a free-falling rock avalanche (Fig. 11–22). On striking the valley floor, it rushed obliquely up the opposite slope to a height of 100 meters, turned almost 90 degrees, and shot down the valley in a debris stream that destroyed houses and everything in its path, killing 115 people. Ten million cubic meters of rock fell an average of about 450 meters and spread as rubble over about 3 square kilometers to a depth of 10 to 20 meters. A dense cloud of dust covered the scene for several minutes.

All observers agreed that after the mass gave way and slid on the fissure to the quarry floor it shot forward into free fall. The villagers could see the hillside across the valley beneath the cascading torrent of shattered stone.

From eyewitnesses' reports, it was estimated that the debris at the front of the tongue traveled 5.5 kilometers in a little less than one minute. Calculations based on the acceleration of gravity make this appear reasonable. In free fall, the acceleration, or increase of velocity, of a falling object is 9.8 meters per second in each second. The short preliminary sliding and the free fall at Elm are calculated to have taken about 17 seconds, and the velocity of the falling rock when it hit the valley floor was about 310 kilometers per hour. Including the time it took the rock to come to a stop downvalley, the whole duration was calculated at roughly 53 seconds—in good agreement with estimates by eyewitnesses. The average velocity of the blocks that traveled farthest was calculated to have been 155 kilometers per hour. In such massive falls, the moving mass must in part be buoyed up by the air it compresses beneath it. That such compression may be very great has been shown by many snow avalanches. The tremendous air blasts partly entrapped beneath some avalanches both in Switzerland and Idaho, have been known to knock down well-built masonry structures. The uplifting effect of such an air cushion must be a factor in the distant travel of some large rockfalls.

The Elm debris was composed mostly of fragments a few centimeters in diameter, and included much intermingled soil and rock dust. Larger blocks, as wide as 6 meters, were scattered through it, especially in the central and higher parts of the debris tongue. The margins were abrupt. The top of the debris stream was hummocky and irregular, and low ridges festooned its surface. Fifty years later, almost all the devasted area had been restored to pasture and potato fields.

THE VAIONT RESERVOIR DISASTER. The worst dam disaster in history took place October 9, 1963, at the Vaiont Reservoir in the Italian Alps, when a rockfall plunged down the valley wall and, from the dam to a point 2 kilometers upstream, completely filled the reservoir to depths as great as 175 meters above the reservoir flow line (Fig. 11–23). The volume of slide material was more than 240 million cubic meters; the whole mass slid within a period of less than a minute, much of it from heights as great as 600 meters (nearly 2000 feet) above the dam. The slide created strong earth tremors recorded as far away as Stuttgart, Vienna, and Brussels. It fell so quickly as to create a tremendous updraft of compressed air before it, hurling rocks and water up the opposite canyon wall to heights of 260 meters and pushing the displaced water completely over the dam in a wall of water 100 meters high. The water front was still more than 70 meters high when it burst upon the heavily populated valley of the Piave River 1.5 kilometers below the dam (Fig. 11–23). As the water surged both up and down valley, it overwhelmed and destroyed everything over a belt more than a kilometer wide and many kilometers long, causing a

loss of nearly 3000 lives. The dam itself—
the second highest in the world, 265.5 meters
—proved to be superbly engineered and remained structurally sound even after with-
standing the combined load of slide and over-
topping water, a load many times greater
than anticipated when it was designed.

During construction of the dam, in 1960,
while the abutments were being excavated
for the dam footings it was found that the
canyon walls were under great elastic strain,
with tendencies for rock bursts. This condition was attributed by George Kiersch, an
American geologist who examined the area

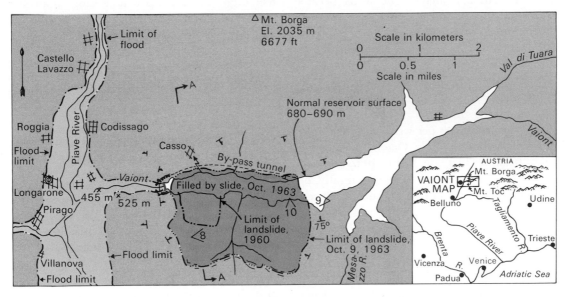

FIGURE 11–23   *Map of Vaiont Dam area and Piave River Valley in the Italian Alps, showing
area of slide and flood caused by the 1963 rock fall. (After George A. Kiersch,*
Transactions of American Society of Civil Engineers, *v. 34, 1964.)*

FIGURE 11–24   *North-south cross section of Vaiont slide and reservoir canyon, showing slide
surface and water levels in 1960 (pre-reservoir) and 1963, when the slide occurred. Location of the section is shown on Figure 11–23. (After George A.
Kiersch,* Transactions of American Society of Civil Engineers, *v. 34, 1964.)*

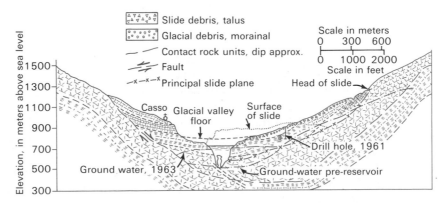

shortly after the slide, to exfoliation due to unloading of the rocks caused by rapid cutting of the deep canyon in Pleistocene and Recent time (Fig. 11–24). At the dam itself, much cement grout was used to control the tendency of the walls to spall, but, of course, this was not practical for the reservoir as a whole. When the reservoir filled to depths greater than 250 meters, the walls became water saturated and the buoyant pressure (Archimedes principle) on the much jointed rock weakened its cohesion. Slow sliding began almost immediately after the reservoir was filled in 1960, and a set of surveying stations was established to measure the rate of movement. At times the rate was as much as 25 to 30 centimeters per week, at other times much less, but in early October the movement began to increase, first to 10 to 20 centimeters per day, then 20 to 40 and finally, on the day of the rock fall, to as much as 80 centimeters per day. An attempt was made to lower the water level in the reservoir but the creep was so rapid that the reservoir capacity was diminishing faster than the spillways could discharge the water and the level continued to rise. Finally, at 10:41 P.M. came the catastrophic slide.

Although the catastrophe was triggered by man's interference with the natural regime of the Vaiont River, the condition of high elastic stress revealed during the abutment excavations undoubtedly prevailed throughout the reservoir area and in the normal course of further stream erosion and creep from the valley walls the slide would have taken place eventually in any case.

OTHER SLIDES.   Vaiont was not the largest historic rock fall, by any means. Early in 1911 an enormous mass—estimated at 6 billion metric tons—of broken rock plunged down the Pamir Mountains of Central Asia to form a giant dam about 800 meters high and with a volume of some 2½ billion cubic meters. It blocked the Murgab River, and the water accumulated behind the dam to form Lake Sarezkoye, now 75 kilometers long and 500 meters deep. The lake never overtopped the slide but continues to discharge by seepage through it, making a new source for the Murgab 150 meters lower than the lake level.

Similarly, the great Indus River has several times been dammed for months by rock falls in its canyon through the Himalayas. One slide, in December 1840, formed a dam 1000 feet high, backing up a lake more than 40 miles long. When the river overtopped the dam, rapid downcutting released a great flood, which overwhelmed with great loss of life a Sikh army encampment thoughtlessly placed on the river floodplain near Attock.

PREHISTORIC SLIDES AND DEBRIS FLOWS

Thousands of ancient slides have been recognized in all parts of the world. One is just over the hill from Elm; it is the enormous Flims landslide, at least 11,000 million cubic meters—a thousand times as big as that at Elm and twice the volume of the Pamir landslide. This mass probably first moved as a unit, but gradually broke up, especially in the farthest traveled parts. Long ago, probably in late Pleistocene time, it slid down the plane of an old fault and blocked the valley of the upper Rhine, forming a lake. When the Rhine overtopped the landslide dam it cut a gorge 600 meters deep and 15 kilometers long. All these events left traces still clearly visible; the hummocky slide surface, somewhat modified by erosion; the well-marked margins of the landslide dam; and the abrupt changes in the Rhine valley—broad and open both above and below a steep-walled gorge through the slide. One thing remains uncertain: did the slide move rapidly or slowly? A hint is perhaps furnished by the hummocky surface, much like that of the slow Gros Ventre debris flow.

A more complex lobate mass of debris extends northward from the San Bernardino Mountains into the southern Mojave Desert in southern California (Fig. 11–25). The

FIGURE 11–25   *Dissected breccia lobe on the Mohave Desert. Note how the breccia laps up against the range of hills on the left. The lobe is 2.5 miles aross at its near end. (Photo by R. C. Frampton, Claremont, Calif.)*

landslide mass lies in front of the outcrop of two thrust faults. On the lower, granite overrides Late Tertiary sediments; on the upper, crystalline limestone overrides the granite. The landslide rests on Tertiary sediments; it may have slid in Pleistocene time. A most puzzling feature is a broad lobe of poorly cemented breccia that extends 7 or 8 kilometers out over the flat desert floor, and is made up almost exclusively of small-limestone blocks. The breccia is somewhat eroded—one stream has cut entirely through it—but its abrupt margins are still between 8 and 30 meters high. This appears to be the debris from a giant rock fall, perhaps a hundred times as large as that at Elm. Several features suggest this: first, the predominance of limestone unmixed with other rocks; second, the breccia is piled against low hills far out on the desert, with a slight deflection like that at Elm; and, finally, at the edge, erosion has exposed an underlying breccia of sheared and crushed Tertiary strata. This material was probably plowed up as the lobe of limestone debris poured over a low ridge in the weak Tertiary rocks beneath. A similar but less sharply defined segregation by rock types was present in the Elm debris. The corrugations of the breccia surface, unlike the lobate ones at Elm, are almost straight. They nearly parallel the trend of the partly overridden low bedrock hill shown at the left in Figure 11–25, and may record these barriers. The differences between this and the Elm deposit, however, raise some doubt as to the origin of the limestone breccia.

Slides or flows preserved in sedimentary rocks

The form and textures of certain breccias, or brecciated strata, now parts of Paleozoic, Mesozoic, and Tertiary formations, suggest that they are ancient slides or debris flows. Most convincing are distortions in thin-bedded marine sediments and lenses of heterogeneous debris that lie in troughs resembling that developed in 1887 on the floor of the Lake of Zug. Such features have been recognized in strata from many parts of the world (Figs. 17–11, 17–12, 17–34).

SIGNIFICANCE OF DOWNSLOPE MOVEMENTS

Grand Canyon example

The Grand Canyon of the Colorado River (Fig. 5–14) not only gives evidence of extensive erosion, but makes possible at least a rough estimate of the parts played by different erosional processes in forming it. Figure 11–26 is a structure section across the Grand Canyon and its tributary, Phantom Creek, approximately from south (left) to north (right). The section shows the wide upper canyon cut in nearly horizontal strata, and the Granite Gorge cut into the gneiss that nonconformably underlies the sedimentary rocks. The canyon of Phantom Creek is eroded entirely in the overlying strata. The total depth of the canyon is about 1½ kilometers and the width from rim to rim about 12½ kilometers. The inner Granite Gorge is about 400 meters deep at the line of section. The profiles of the side slopes of the Granite Gorge are relatively straight; those of the upper canyon and of Phantom Creek are in steps, with the more consolidated strata forming cliffs above more gentle slopes cut on the less-resistant strata. Phantom Creek furnishes an especially favorable example for analysis of the relative roles of stream transport and downslope movements. The stream follows a normal fault of about 45 meters vertical displacement. It was apparently fixed in position by the ready erosion of the shattered rock along the fault zone. The dashed vertical lines on the right in Figure 11–26 indicate a trench as wide as the creek bed and represent the downcutting ascribed to the stream. But if the stream directly eroded only this narrow vertical slot, what processes account for the much wider valley? Judging the past

in terms of the present, these other processes include rainwash coursing down the canyon walls in minor rills and deep gullies, and many kinds of downslope movements, among which the fall and continual streamward movement of talus fragments is particularly important.

The Grand Canyon itself has been cut by the Colorado River and widened by rainwash and downslope movements in the same manner. Since the course of the Colorado was not determined by a fault, however, the river may have wandered somewhat to reach its present position as indicated by the curved dashed lines in Figure 11–26, instead of following a straight path like that of Phantom Creek. Similar relations seem probable for streams and stream systems in other regions. We conclude that in a rock-walled canyon whose floor is little or no wider than its stream, a volume equal to depth of canyon multiplied by stream width is a measure of the rock cut by stream erosion (in any particular cross section), whereas the remainder of the valley cross section is an indication of the proportion of material dumped into the stream by rainwash, tributary streams and gullies, and by many kinds of downslope movements.

Downslope movements of rock and soil are, of course, not limited to the matched sides of valleys. They are equally effective in reducing the steepness of single slopes or cliffs, as along shores. Gravity movements

FIGURE 11–26
Section across Grand Canyon, Arizona. The vertically trending dashed lines above Granite Gorge and Phantom Creek indicate the narrow trenches that would have been made by stream-cutting alone. (Bright Angel Quadrangle, U.S. Geological Survey Topographic Atlas.)

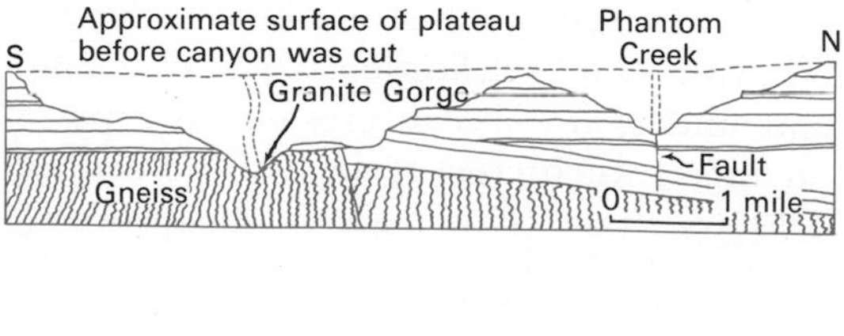

extend to the very summits of ridges, reducing their height. Rocky summits are lowered by the fall of fragments loosened by weathering or frost action (Fig. 5–2). This has reduced the summit ridge between Phantom Creek and the Grand Canyon well below the level of the plateaus to north and south. Rounded hills with soil-covered divides, on the other hand, are lowered chiefly by creep and rainwash of material softened by weathering.

EFFECT OF PLANT COVER

Downslope movement of material varies with the plant cover, which, in turn, depends primarily upon climate.

Even in humid regions, plant cover varies widely, being thin on cold moors and thick in the tropics with year-round rainfall. Where trees, shrubs, and grass abound, topographic forms are generally smoothly rounded, and creep is the principal downslope movement. Minor differences in rock resistance on a single slope are commonly masked by the almost continuous cover of soil and vegetation, but major differences are made apparent by differences in the steepness of the slopes and in the general pattern of ridges and valleys.

In arid regions, trees and shrubs are few and grass may be absent. Little soil masks the resistant rocks; they stand out in knobs, ridges, and cliffs. Poorly consolidated rocks are reduced rapidly by downslope movements and rainwash, and their outcrops are obscured by talus accumulations derived from the resistant rocks (Figs. 11–17, 11–18, 11–19). The etching out of the less resistant rocks, as shown in Figures 9–6, 9–7, and 8–20 is called **differential erosion.** In an arid region differential erosion brings out even slight differences in rock resistance, as shown in Figure 5–15. Hence, the underlying rock structure stands out much more clearly in the landscapes of arid than in those of humid regions.

CONCLUSIONS

Considered in terms of the areas affected, downslope movements and rainwash are the most important of all processes of erosion. For every square meter that is directly subject to erosion by a permanent flowing stream there are hundreds of square meters over which soil is slowly creeping—flowing a centimeter or two downhill after frost heaving or clay hydration, being pushed downslope by burrowing rodents or by the feet of grazing animals, and gliding and falling in debris flows, slides, and talus.

The critical factor for most gravity movements is the presence of enough water to lubricate slide surfaces or to produce a semiliquid flow mass. Many rocks that are relatively strong when dry become weak and plastic when wet. Where great volumes of rock are so weakened, gliding on a gigantic scale may occur.

Downslope movement is very important and widespread, but it rarely goes on alone. Streams cut valleys, downslope movements widen them, and the streams carry away the debris. Glaciers gouge valleys deeper, and gravity movements load the glacier margins with rock fragments that the ice transports away. Waves driving on shore undermine cliffs, whose upper portions then fall into the sea, to be broken up and carried away by wave-generated currents. In brief, the role of gravity movements is to provide a continuous supply of material to the agents of long-distance transportation.

Downslope movements can operate beneath the sea as well as on land. Though the buoyant effect of the water lessens the effective pull of gravity on material immersed in it, the soaking of the material is complete. As a result, even though submarine weathering is thought to be slight, downslope movements should be common there. We have cited several such movements witnessed by man; their existence in the geologic past is proved by disturbed beds and brecciated areas in marine sedimentary rocks. Downslope movements on land bring debris to the streams, and the streams in turn push the shorelines seaward in their deltas. Downslope movements in the oceans tend to reduce submarine heights to the level of the ocean floor. Thus downslope movements contribute to the formation of both of the two dominant levels of the earth—one near sea level, the other the floor of the ocean (see Fig. 10–4).

ENGINEERING APPLICATIONS

Gravity movements of soil and rock affect man-made structures, such as roads, dams, and houses. In the United States alone, clearing highways of the debris that slides or rolls from the slopes above, and the repair of sections of roadbed that have settled and slumped downslope, costs millions of dollars annually. Many newly built railroads and highways have had to be rerouted within a few years in order to bypass slide areas, or cliffs that shed many talus fragments.

These expensive repairs and reconstruction can often be reduced by careful geologic inspection along the right-of-way. Areas of active sliding are readily recognized: the hillslope is generally hummocky, with undrained depressions; the rock may show slip surfaces roughly parallel to the hillside; landslide scars and curving debris ridges are other telltale features; fences, trees, and telephone poles are tilted downhill, and tree trunks bend uniformly as they enter the ground.

A highway or railroad cut obviously increases danger of sliding because the excavation removes support from the slope above. Many an ancient landslide or debris flow, virtually stationary for tens or even thousands of years, has been reactivated by removal of debris from its toe during the construction of a roadbed. Slides of weakly consolidated volcanic ash, activated by the excavation of the Gaillard Cut in the Panama Canal have been moving for fifty years, on extremely low gradients because the clayey rocks are thoroughly saturated by the heavy rainfall.

Although highways and railroads can generally be relocated to detour dangerous slides, some structures endangered by gravity movements cannot be moved. Geologists and engineers must then take steps to stop, or at least to slow down and minimize, the sliding. An oil field near Ventura, California, affords an example. Oil wells drilled through a slide were slowly bent out of line as it moved. Some well casings were completely sheared off at the basal slip surface of the slide. Movement was most rapid in winter while the ground was saturated by seasonal rains. Unless the slide could be controlled, this valuable oil field would have been lost. The problem was solved by paving the entire hillside with asphalt and boring galleries along the base of the slide to drain off any seepage from the rains that was not caught by the paving. By thus preventing access of water, which transformed the clays into a lubricant, the slide was stopped.

During the building of the huge Grand Coulee Dam on the Columbia River, construction was threatened when a tremendous mass of water-soaked silt began to creep into the excavation for the north abutment of the dam. To stop this threatened slide, engineers hit on the ingenious idea of penetrating the silt with numerous pipes in which a refrigerant was circulated. The refrigerant froze the pore water of the silt, thus cementing its particles and increasing its strength. This effectively stopped the movement, and the area was kept refrigerated until the concrete for the dam was poured, and the excavation thus filled and stabilized.

Similar problems have to be met when heavy structures such as large bridges and dams must be built on weak clay or on creeping ground. Many soils behave plastically when loaded, and will flow radially outward from beneath the load. One pier of the San Francisco Bay Bridge was purposely made extra large at its base so that the weight of the heavy structure could be distributed over a wide area of the clay on which the pier was set. Many laboratory tests have been devised to determine the load that various kinds of sand, clay, and other loose foundation materials will bear. These tests are the basis of a relatively new branch of engineering science called **soil mechanics.** It includes the study of such field conditions as the attitude of stratification or other slip surfaces, amount of contained water, slope, and other factors, as well as of the properties of the materials as shown by laboratory tests. With such knowledge, it is often possible to forestall or control gravity movements, even in places where weak materials are covered by massive structures.

Facts, concepts, terms

Gravity movement of rock
Creep; slides; debris flows; rock falls; talus
Rainwash
Causes and effects of creep
Solifluction; rock glaciers
Slow debris flows
Rapid slides and rockfalls
Underwater flows
Recognition of ancient slides and rock falls
    On land
    In the sea
Relative roles of downslope movements and stream erosion
Engineering applications

Questions

1. What is the lowest level to which downslope movement on land can deliver material? Downslope movements in the sea?
2. On steep mountain slopes that receive a heavy snowfall, even trees that are rooted in rock crevices have trunks that are bent downhill as they emerge from the ground, then straighten to a vertical position a few feet above the surface. Why?
3. In warm humid regions, compact clay-rich soils are more subject to creep than sandy or gravelly open soil, but the latter move readily in arctic regions. Why?
4. Describe the structures you might find in a marine sedimentary rock that would indicate that the area had been the site of an ancient underwater flow.
5. A symmetrical, almost perfectly round soil-covered hill is underlain by vertical weak shales containing two thin beds of resistant sandstone. One sandstone is red, and it exactly bisects the center of the hill. The other sandstone is white, and it extends through the hill about halfway down from its summit. Draw a map or sketch showing the two sandstone beds and indicate on the sketch the areas of the hill over which you would expect to find (*a*) numerous loose fragments of red sandstone, (*b*) numerous loose fragments of white sandstone.
6. Building sites on a hill with a fine view are restricted to two locations: Both are underlain by weak shale, but at one site the stratification dips steeply into the

hill, at the other it dips roughly parallel to the hill slope. Which site would you choose, and why?

7. Basalt cliffs on the Columbia Plateau have large piles of coarse talus at their base. On the Colorado Plateau, where climatic conditions are similar, equally large cliffs of crumbly sandstone have little or no talus. Can you suggest an explanation?

Suggested readings

Eckel, E. B., ed., *Landslides in Engineering Practice* (Highway Research Board, Special Report 29). Washington, D.C.: National Research Council, 1958. [Of special interest because of applications to highway and construction problems, but also contains an excellent chapter by D. J. Varnes, *Landslide Types and Processes.*]

Heim, Albert, *Bergsturz and Menschenleben* (Beiblatt zur Vierteljahresschrift der Naturforschenden Gesellschaft in Zürich, No. 20). 1932. [Data concerning Swiss and other landslides, rock falls, and debris flows, including Elm and Flims.]

Howe, Ernest. *Landslides in the San Juan Mountains, Colorado, Including a Consideration of Their Causes and Their Classification* (U.S. Geological Survey, Professional Paper 67, 65 p.). Washington, D.C.: G.P.O., 1909. [Many photographic illustrations.]

Kiersch, George A., *Vaiont Reservoir Disaster*. Civil Engineering, March, 1964.

Sharpe, C. F. S., *Landslides and Related Phenomena*. New York: Columbia University Press, 1938.

U.S. Geological Survey, *Alaska's Good Friday Earthquake* (Circular 491). 1964.

chapter # 12

Stream Erosion and Deposition

The importance of rivers to navigation, flood control, irrigation, water supply, erosion, and sedimentation and their widely varying behavior have led to intensive studies by engineers, hydrologists, and geologists. Though many questions remain, we here try to apply some of these studies to an understanding of the work of streams and their effects on the landscape about us.

Flowing streams are powered by gravity. As we saw in Chapter 11, for any object resting on a slope a component of its weight acts parallel to the slope (Fig. 11–1). The surface of a flowing stream slopes downstream. The downstream component of gravity is proportional to the sine of the slope angle shown in Figure 11–1. Most streams flow on such low angles that the tangent of the slope angle —the vertical fall divided by the horizontal distance of flow—is virtually the same as the sine of the angle, and, because it is easier to measure accurately, the tangent of the slope angle, called "s," is used in all hydraulic engineering.

If a stream slopes only 12 meters per kilometer—a steep but not unusual gradient— particles of water gliding down this slope would accelerate at a rate of almost 12 centimeters per second if movement were not restrained in some way. In an hour (3600 seconds), such unrestrained flow would attain a velocity of 430 meters (1400 feet) per second, or more than 1500 kilometers (900 miles) per hour!

No natural stream even remotely approaches such a velocity. Most flow at a meter or a very few meters per second—generally less than 8 kilometers per hour. The greatest velocity ever measured for a large river in the United States—about 25 kilometers (15 miles) per hour—was in the Potomac River during the flood of March, 1936. The greatest ever recorded in any flood is 33 kilometers (about 20 miles) per hour in the Lyn River, England, in August 1952. Clearly the flow is restrained. The only restraining agent we can imagine, aside from the trivial resistance of the air, is the friction of particles of water against one another, against the stream bed and banks, and against particles of sediment suspended in the water. Before considering frictional losses more closely, we turn to some other aspects of stream flow.

FLOW IN NATURAL STREAMS

If streams of dye are injected into most natural streams they do not advance downstream in parallel lines as they do in water flowing very slowly through a glass tube (Fig. 12–1, *top*); instead, they swirl about and are rapidly mixed by the flow. This mixing indicates that flow is **turbulent** (Fig. 12–1, *bottom*) rather than **laminar,** as in the glass tube. Viscous fluids, such as honey or molten lava, may flow at low velocities in laminar flow; winds, ocean currents, and natural streams are nearly always turbulent.

Experiments have shown that the laminar or turbulent nature of fluid flow in open channels may be evaluated in terms of Reynolds' number:

$$R = \frac{\text{velocity} \times \text{depth} \times \text{density}}{\text{viscosity}}$$

The numerical value of R obviously depends on what units are used in measuring velocity, depth, and viscosity; whatever the units, though, at lower values flow is laminar, at higher values, turbulent.[*] Thus any increase in velocity, depth, or density of a fluid (increasing the numerator in Reynolds number) favors turbulent flow; any increase in viscosity (increasing the denominator) favors laminar. In laminar flow one layer of water slides past another—the frictional loss is proportional to the difference in velocity of the fluid layers involved. For a fluid in

[*] If metric units—centimeter, gram, and second— are used, the critical value of Reynolds number separating laminar from turbulent flow lies in the range of 500 to 3000.

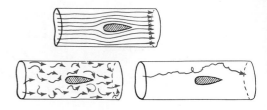

FIGURE 12–1
Top: *laminar flow,* Bottom: *turbulent flow.*

FIGURE 12–2
Distribution of velocity and turbulence in a symmetrical channel. (After John Leighly, 1934.)

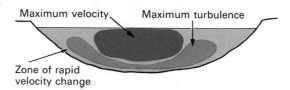

laminar motion as a whole, the frictional drag is proportional to the mean velocity. In turbulent flow, on the other hand, mixing takes place by eddies and swirls; experiments have shown the frictional drag to be proportional to the *square of the velocity.* This is the situation in virtually all natural streams, and explains why even streams in flood seldom attain velocities of more than 10 kilometers per hour. Although the velocity may approach zero and flow be laminar in a thin film immediately adjacent to the channel boundaries, both velocity and turbulence increase abruptly away from the boundaries. Farther from the banks the velocity changes are less rapid (Fig. 12–2). In broad, straight channels the velocity may be nearly constant across most of the central part of the stream with the thread of maximum velocity usually (see Fig. 12–6) near the middle and above the deepest part of the channel. But in crooked or meandering channels, as we shall see later, the fastest flow is not in the center, but is shifted far toward the outside of each bend—an important factor in undermining

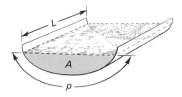

FIGURE 12–3
Cross section of flow in a stream channel.

FIGURE 12–4
Three channel cross sections of equal area. Section A contains this area within the smallest possible wetted perimeter and therefore opposes the least frictional surface to the running water. (After W. W. Rubey, 1952.)

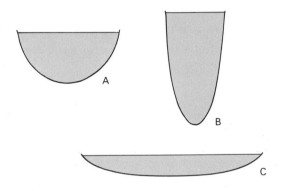

the bank on that side. Figure 12–2 shows the regions of most prominent turbulence in relation to the average velocity distribution.

If velocity is to remain uniform along a stream segment, frictional effects—the heat generated by turbulence and friction against bed, banks, and suspended particles—must precisely balance the downstream component of gravity. That the friction in flowing water does develop heat is shown by the fact that a meltwater stream on a glacier, even at freezing temperature, is able to melt its channel down into the ice.

The down-valley force exerted by a stream is the product of the *weight of the water* times the slope, *s*, the weight being given by multiplying the area of the stream channel, *A*, by the length, *L*, and the *unit weight of the water*, W. See Figure 12–3. The frictional

drag is obtained by multiplying *drag per unit area*, *T*, by the *surface area of the wetted channel*. This area is the product of the *wetted perimeter*, *p*, and the *length*, *L*. In an equation, then:

(1) $WALs = TpL$

or

(2) $T = \dfrac{WAs}{p}$

Since A/p (the area of cross section divided by the wetted perimeter) is the average depth, *d*, this may be written: $T = Wds$; that is, the drag is proportional to the product of slope and depth.

As the flow is turbulent, the drag—the shear stress along the channel boundary—is proportional to the square of the velocity. Natural streams obviously differ greatly in average velocity and in any one the velocity may fluctuate greatly from season to season, or, indeed from hour to hour. These variations result from changes in many factors but chiefly from those in (1) **gradient** (the slope, *s*) (2) channel **shape**, A/p, (3) **discharge** (which influences both the **area**, *A*, and the **wetted perimeter**, *p*) and (4) the **roughness**, *r*, of the channel. Increases in either volume or slope obviously should increase the velocity; the first reduces the ratio of frictional drag to water volume and the second increases the downstream component of gravity. Clearly, also, increase in either wetted perimeter or roughness implies an increase in friction and thus tends to diminish the velocity. Hydraulic engineers have found by experiment that:

(3) $V^2 \propto \dfrac{As}{rp} = \dfrac{ds}{r}$

Velocity also varies with cross-sectional shape of the channel. Figure 12–4 shows three channels with cross sections equal in area but of different shapes. The channel of semicircular cross section offers the least resistance to flow because it has the smallest wetted perimeter. Because channel B opposes more friction than A and because steep walls are less stable than more gently sloping ones, the stream tends to erode its walls to form a more "efficient" channel. Channels such as B can only form where the walls are coherent. Channel C has a much longer wetted perimeter than A but is nevertheless the much commoner shape of rivers flowing in weakly coherent materials. The relative instability of steep walls near the angle of repose causes widening and deviation from the ideal shape A.

Mountain torrents flowing at several meters per second over resistant rock tend to form channels similar to A. As tributaries enter and flow increases downstream, the channel enlarges, generally increasing more in width than in depth, chiefly because the lower valley banks are generally alluvial and more easily eroded than those upstream. Cross section A is favored by engineers attempting to construct stable irrigation canals in erodible material.

Roughness caused by channel irregularities and by the sediment in the channel greatly affects both velocity and channel shape. The effect on velocity is well shown by Figure 12–5. Pole Creek, near Pinedale, Wyoming, flows in a channel whose bed material averages 1.28 centimeters in diameter. The slope is .003. The Hoback River, near Bondurant, Wyoming, with the same depth and a considerably steeper slope of .0051 does not flow proportionately faster because the bed material averages ten times as large: 12.8 centimeters. The ratio of the square roots of their velocities is 1 to 1.13 (Equation 3); the ratio of their slopes is 1 to 1.7. Many measurements show that the mean velocity is at a depth .6 of the distance from surface to bed and the average of the velocities at .2 and .8 of the depth is close to the mean.

Not all streams, however, show their greatest velocity at the surface. Figure 12–6 shows three cross sections along a straight stretch of

Baldwin Creek, Wyoming. As can be seen from the current-meter readings, the maximum velocity in two of the sections is well below the surface, as is common in small rivers and at river curves.

The discharge, Q, is the quantity of water passing a given point during a unit of time. Clearly, the discharge of a stream is a function of gradient, velocity, and size of channel. Discharge is equal to the area of cross section times mean velocity of flow:

(4) $Q = AV_m$

But since the area of the stream cross section is equal to the surface width times the mean depth, D_m, we can also write

(5) $Q = AV_m = WD_mV_m$

As we have seen, the mean velocity is also

FIGURE 12–5

Current-meter measurements of velocity in rivers, plotted as a function of depth; the two rivers are chosen because their depths are identical but they differ in slope and in the mean size of their bed materials, Pole Creek measurements are on the left, Hoback River, on the right. (After Luna B. Leopold, M. Gordon Wolman, and John P. Miller, Fluvial Processes in Geomorphology, *W. H. Freeman and Company, San Francisco. Copyright 1964.)*

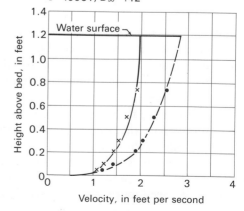

× Pole Creek near Pinedale, Wyo.,
   $S = .003, D_{50} = .042'$
• Hoback River near Bondurant, Wyo.,
   $S = .0051, D_{50} = .42'$

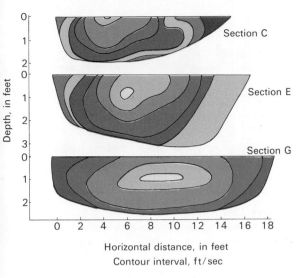

FIGURE 12–6

Velocity distribution in the channel of Baldwin Creek, near Lander, Wyoming, at three sections along a straight reach a few hundred feet long. Flow is near bankful. (After Luna B. Leopold, M. Gordon Wolman, and John P. Miller, Fluvial Processes in Geomorphology, *W. H. Freeman and Company, San Francisco, Copyright 1964.)*

influenced by the roughness of the channel and by the amount and grain size of the rock debris that the stream carries. Many of these variables are closely interrelated: for example, an increase in slope at one point along a stream increases its velocity and erosive power, and thereby changes the size and shape of the cross section. Downstream from the point of erosion, sediment may be deposited, thus decreasing the depth. In general, where a stream is eroding its bottom it is lowering its slope; where depositing, it is generally steepening it, but there are local exceptions to these broad generalizations.

Some factors fluctuate greatly even within a few days—notably discharge. Floods rage after heavy seasonal rainfall, rapid snowmelt, or even after brief cloudbursts; during drought a river may dwindle to a chain of stagnant pools. These changes in discharge are accompanied by corresponding adjust-ments in velocity and in the size and amount of sediment load carried.

Clearly the interrelations between gradient, velocity, channel irregularities, shape, and sediment load are extremely complex. Study of them is greatly aided, however, by a wealth of engineering measurements made during the past fifty years. Intelligent handling of flood control, river-bank erosion, sewage disposal, bridge and dam stability, seasonal fluctuations in hydroelectric power, and a host of other problems demand detailed records of stream flow. Hence measurement of streams, rainfall, and the ratio of precipitation to runoff within drainage basins, are now routine. Voluminous files of such data for the rivers of the United States have been published by the Water Resources Division of the United States Geological Survey.

STREAM LOADS

A stream carries material in three ways: as **suspended load**—sediment supported by the turbulent water, **bed load**—sediment largely supported by other sedimentary material and only in part by the fluid, and **dissolved load** —ions that are really a part of the fluid and move with it.

The suspended load

The suspended load of a stream consists of two classes of material. One, called the *wash load* consists of clay particles so fine—even colloidal (10^{-5} centimeters in diameter or less) in size—as to remain in suspension almost indefinitely, though, of course, they would eventually settle out from perfectly stagnant water. Even sluggish streams carry such material with virtually the same average velocity as the stream itself. Only in local backwaters is such material deposited; it is almost lacking in the sediments along channel bottoms. The amount depends, not on stream characteristics, but on external conditions, such as rain intensity, grain size of soil, grass cover, and other independent factors. Probably no stream is ever loaded to capacity with wash material.

Turbulence accounts for a stream's ability to sweep up and carry away fine silt and clay particles suspended within it. Because the tangled skein of turbulent currents actually keeps small sedimentary particles buoyed up in the stream, this part of a stream's load is supported by the fluid itself. It is the *upward* currents of turbulence that allow the particles to be picked up and transported. Once a grain has been lifted by an upsweeping eddy, it is kept from sinking only by other upward moving currents. True, downward currents are necessarily even more common than upward, but both are so distributed at random that an individual particle may be suspended for a long time before it settles to the bottom or is carried there by a downward swirl. Other grains are simultaneously set in motion by upward currents. Importantly, during the time a grain is picked up, jostled around, and redeposited, it moves downstream. An underwater observer moving with the current would see the grains rise, gyrate, bob, and fall, although an observer on the bank would see only an apparently homogeneous mixture of water and sediment, steadily moving downstream though interrupted by swirls and eddies. Sampling of suspended loads of many streams, one of which is summarized in Figure 12–7, shows that only unusually swift rivers are turbulent enough to lift particles larger than medium-sized sand from their beds.

The bed load

Some material too coarse to be lifted is pushed or rolled along the bottom by the swirling currents, thus becoming part of the bed load. The bed load is supported chiefly by the other grains on the channel floor and

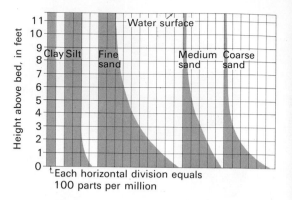

FIGURE 12–7
Graph showing variations in sediment content with depth, Missouri River near Kansas City, Missouri, January 3, 1930. Note the nearly homogeneous distribution of the particles of clay and silt throughout the stream and the concentration of coarser grains near the bed. (After L. G. Straub, in Hydrology, *courtesy of Dover Publications.)*

only partly by the fluid. As natural stream flow is turbulent, except in a narrow film along its bed and banks the frictional drag varies as the square of the water velocity. In turbulent flow a momentary swirl may speed one strand of current at several times the mean velocity; the drag of such a strand is many times that of the average current. Accordingly, except during great floods, when stream velocities are high throughout, the bed load particles move downstream, with many stops and starts, much more slowly than particles of the suspended load.

Observations through windows in the walls of experimental flumes reveal that most bed-load grains roll, some slide, and others bounce or momentarily vault into suspension. As the velocity of a stream flowing on a bed of sand is gradually increased, the motion of particles on the bed progresses from (1) short leaps of a few individual sand grains through (2) spasmodic movement and deposition of groups of grains, to (3) smooth, general transport of many grains. At still higher velocities, large numbers of grains spring into temporary suspension, hopping forward in such dense clouds that the bed load blends indistinguishably with the suspended load. This gradation of bed load into suspended load is indicated graphically for the Missouri River in Figure 12–7. In general the larger the stream the smaller is the ratio of bed load to suspended load, though there are exceptions: some streams with large bed loads of sand have the same discharge as smaller muddy channels with little bed load.

The dissolved load

Streams also carry material in solution. Transport of dissolved material does not depend on the nature of stream flow, for the dissolved material is actually part of the liquid. The dissolved load comes chiefly from inflowing ground water that has percolated slowly through the weathered mantle of soil and rock. Probably little is dissolved from channel walls except by streams flowing on limestone.

Chemical analyses show that few rivers carry more than a thousand parts per million (0.1 percent) of dissolved materials. A general average for many American rivers is about 200 parts per million. Yet these amounts are far from negligible. As an example, streams on the northeast flank of the lofty Wind River Range in Wyoming drain a terrain of granitic and sedimentary rocks; those on the southwest flank are wholly in granitic bedrock. Although the runoff per square kilometer on the southwest flank is $1\frac{1}{2}$ times that on the northeast, the northeastern drainage carries nearly 16 metric tons per square kilometer of drainage area per year, or 63 parts per million of dissolved material, while the southwestern drainage carries only about 18 parts per million or 8.5 metric tons per square kilometer, little more than half as much. The northeastern flank is

being degraded by solution alone at the rate of one meter in about 140,000 years, the southwestern at one meter in about 275,000 years. (These figures have been corrected to take account of the fact that precipitation in this region contains about 6 parts per million of dissolved matter.) Clearly, degradation of the land by solution is by no means negligible, even in mountainous terrain. In areas of lower relief and slower runoff, such as the South Atlantic and Eastern Gulf States, solution is now lowering the surface at the rate of 57 metric tons per square kilometer per year, about one meter in 25,000 years. Here the dissolved load is considerably greater than the solid load of the streams.

Competence to erode and capacity to transport load

As we have seen, the largest particles moved by a stream are in the bed load. The force exerted by a stream on the particles on its bed acts in three ways: (1) as the impact of a water mass against the exposed face of a particle, (2) as the frictional drag of the current across its surface, and (3) as the fluid pressure is greater at the bottom of the grain than on its top (because pressure varies inversely with the fluid velocity), there is a tendency for the grain to be ejected from the bottom into the stream. For a grain to move, the sum of these forces must exceed the grain's inertia, measured by its weight.

→ Hydraulic lift

(1) The impact of the mass of water that strikes a grain is proportional to the exposed cross section of the grain and to the square of the velocity of the water. Doubling the velocity thus involves four times as great a force, tripling the velocity increases the force nine-fold, and so on. Theoretically, then, according to the impact mechanism, the diameter of the largest grain that the current can move varies as the square of the velocity. Since the volume and weight of a spherical

grain vary as the cube of the diameter, the weight of the largest movable grain varies as the sixth power of the velocity. This theoretical relation—the so-called "Sixth Power Law"—was suggested before 1830. It is unfortunately of little practical value in estimating stream competence, however, for most grains on the bottom are partly shielded by their neighbors so that by no means all the momentum of the current is effective. Nor is it possible to measure stream velocity at the very bottom of a channel.

(2) The second mechanism operating is frictional drag of the column of water over a particle. This water column presses down with a weight proportional to its depth, and the downstream component of this weight, determined by the slope, tends to drag the particle along. The frictional drag increases with the exposed area of the particle so that the size of the largest particle a stream can move is proportionate to the product of depth times slope (Equation 3). As with the impact mechanism, few grains are fully exposed to this drag.

(3) The third operative mechanism, sometimes called *hydraulic lift,* is illustrated in Figure 12–8. Because the pressure in a moving fluid at any particular level is inversely proportional to the velocity—a fact that is exploited in aspirating pumps and in water injectors for steam engines—there is a large pressure difference across a thin layer of water at the stream bottom. The pressure in the stagnant water at the very bottom of a particle lying in this layer is greater than that at the top of the particle, thus tending to eject the particle into the stream. Once the particle has been lifted into the current, where velocities are more nearly uniform, the lift diminishes, and it may settle again to the bottom. This mechanism favors the selection of certain sized grains for transport, for the thickness of the boundary layer of highest velocity-contrast obviously affects the size of grains that can be moved.

All these mechanisms operate together to determine the maximum size of particles that a stream can transport. As the velocity increases, the impact, frictional drag, and hydraulic lift all increase—so, too, the maximum size of the particles that can be moved. The bed load depends on the velocity of the water within a very few grain diameters of the bottom. This is always less than the mean velocity, and in big rivers very much less. The proportion of stream load carried as bed load is therefore generally much greater in small than in large streams.

The maximum size of particle that a stream can carry is called its **competence.** The competence of many natural streams in flood is enormous: many have moved boulders more than 3 meters in diameter. When the St. Francis dam in southern California broke in 1928, the released mass of water tumbled blocks of concrete weighing as much as 10,000 tons apiece (20 × 18 × 10 meters) for a kilometer downstream. A flood in the Wasatch Mountains in August, 1923, carried a boulder 14 feet long, weighing between 80 and 90 tons, for more than a mile. During the Lyn River flood of 1952 in England boulders weighing 15 tons were moved several miles.

It is notable that in well-sorted material,

FIGURE 12–8
Hydraulic lift caused by the steep velocity gradient near the stream bed. (After W. W. Rubey, 1938.)

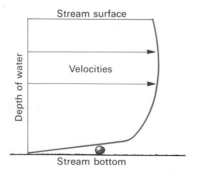

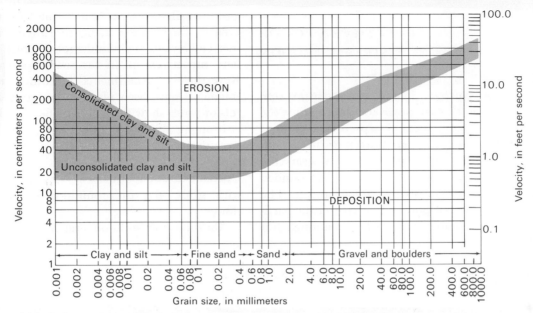

FIGURE 12–9   *Curve showing slowest velocity of flow at which sedimentary particles (quartz in sand sizes, other materials in coarser and finer sizes) begin to erode. The width of the brown band indicates approximate variations, depending on stream depth and cohesiveness of material. Note that fine sand (0.06 to 0.5 mm in diameter) erodes most readily, both finer and coarser materials require greater velocities. These curves are based upon experiments with carefully sized materials, not upon mixtures of a wide size range. (After A. Sundborg, Geografiska Annaler, Vol. 38, 1956.)*

particles of fine sand, from about 0.06 to 0.5 millimeters in diameter are those most easily moved. See Figure 12–9. The same velocity, or even one slightly greater, is required to move smaller grains, perhaps because they do not project above the film of laminar flow lining the channel. It is particularly significant that a still higher velocity is needed to erode fine silt- or clay-size particles if these are closely packed or slightly consolidated.

The graph of Figure 12–9 shows the behavior of well-sorted material. Poorly sorted material behaves about like a mixture of well-sorted material, one-third of which is coarser, and two-thirds finer than the average grain size of the poorly sorted material. Striking and puzzling is the fact that in poorly sorted sediments, grains of sizes between 1 and 6 millimeters in diameter—and especially between 2 and 4 millimeters (coarse sand and fine gravel)—are very much less abundant than grains either coarser or finer. Apparently, grains of this size range are selectively washed out of coarser materials and selectively kept in motion when associated finer particles settle out. This is an empirical fact, well-supported by much sampling in many streams, yet no really adequate explanation for it has yet been advanced.

Stream competence should not be confused with **capacity**—the total load a stream can carry. Capacity depends not only on velocity (which alone governs competence), but also on the total volume—the discharge of the stream.

MECHANICS OF
STREAM EROSION

Abrasion of bed and banks

The particles moved by a stream constantly jostle each other and dash against the channel boundaries. Sharp corners of joint blocks and cobbles are broken or rubbed off. Travel of a few hundred meters wears the coarser fragments into the subrounded shapes characteristic of stream gravel. The longer the transport and the coarser the particles the more perfect the rounding, but grains of silt or fine sand are rounded little, even by long transport, because their small inertia prevents their undergoing many violent impacts except in the swiftest streams. Nevertheless, experiments in which rock fragments have been placed in rotating barrels of water show that part of the rounding is brought about by solution of projecting irregularities, for rounding proceeds more rapidly if the water is continually replaced. Unchanged water quickly became saturated with silica, and the rounding was much slower.

Abrasion and solution are, however, not

FIGURE 12–10   *Potholes in the bed of Susquehanna River, Conewago Falls, exposed during the drought of 1947. (Photo by* Lancaster Intelligence Journal; *courtesy of H. H. Beck, Franklin and Marshall College.)*

the only causes of the downstream diminishing grain size of stream sediment. Stream flow fluctuates widely from day to day and from season to season. The load is not carried continually but pebbles and boulders may move only a few feet or a few miles during a single flood and then remain for months or years before moving again.

During these long stationary periods the sediment is exposed to weathering like any other surficial material, and weathering processes act on it to reduce grain size just as they do on bedrock. It is thus apparent that the downstream reduction of grain size of stream load is due to several cooperating processes.

Particles rolled or bounced along the bed of a stream actively abrade the bedrock. Below Great Falls, Maryland, where the Potomac River rages in flood through a narrow gorge, 40-centimeter boulders have been lifted as high as 20 meters above the channel bottom. The impact of such missiles shatters both bed and banks. In this and less rampant streams, swirling currents armed with coarse sand and small pebbles strongly abrade both the moving rock fragments themselves and the exposed bedrock. Even fine sand is an effective abrasive in swift currents. Eddies in flooded streams round the projecting rocks, tear angular blocks from the channel walls, and drill cylindrical pits (potholes) in solid rock by whirling stones round and round in holes in the stream bed (Fig. 12–10).

Water near a stream bottom is more heavily charged with sediment than that above, and since gravity always operates vertically, the abrasion of the bottom tends to be greater than that of the channel walls.

The extreme turbulence along steep cascades and at waterfalls gives the water tremendous erosive power. The swirling currents may pluck and carry away large joint-bounded blocks of bedrock from the brink of the waterfall. Water falling freely is accelerated by gravity about 980 centimeters per second during each second of fall. At Niagara Falls the water and entrained rock debris

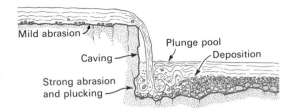

FIGURE 12–11
Erosion in the plunge pool of a waterfall.

strikes the base of the 50-meter-high fall at about 80 kilometers per hour and scours deep **plunge pools** that undermine the rock beneath the lip of the fall, making it susceptible to caving (Fig. 12–11). Thus undercutting at the plunge pool and caving of the walls above contribute greatly to the erosion of some stream valleys. Below Niagara Falls, for instance, the 7-mile gorge between Queenston and the Falls was cut principally by headward migration of the waterfall, not by slow downward erosion along the entire channel, though, of course, all the material was carried off by the turbulent stream.

Importance of flood erosion

The dependence of erosion upon discharge and velocity is most impressive during floods. The flood discharge of most rivers is many times that at low water; of the Mississippi, 30 times, of the Vistula, 120 times. The Ohio River, notorious for its destructive floods, has a ratio of annual maximum to minimum flow of 313 to 1. As the discharge increases so does the velocity. The Columbia River, 280 kilometers above its mouth, had a measured mean velocity of 57 centimeters (1.9 feet) per second and was discharging 2200 cubic meters (78,000 cubic feet) of water per second on March 12, 1945. Following the snowmelt in early May, the flood discharge was about 13 times as great (29,000 cubic meters or 1,018,000 cubic feet per second), and the mean velocity had risen to 330 centimeters (11 feet) per second, nearly six times the low-water velocity, greatly increasing the competence of the stream. The added discharge and velocity also greatly increased the stream's capacity.

During such floods streams transport huge loads and rapidly abrade the bedrock; slackening water leaves the coarser debris stranded on the stream bed. Changes in the channel of the San Juan River at Bluff, Utah, during a flood in 1951 were carefully measured by the United States Geological Survey (Fig. 12–12). On September 9, the river was discharging only 18 cubic meters (635 cubic feet) per second, and was flowing over deposits of sand, silt, and gravel that nearly filled the deep bedrock channel (Fig. 12–12, A). By mid-September, the discharge had increased to 190 cubic meters per second; with the increased velocity parts of the coarse fill in the stream channel were set in motion. At the peak discharge of 1700 cubic meters (59,600 cubic feet) per second on October 14, the channel was swept completely free of sand and gravel (Fig. 12–12,B), and the material in transit actively abraded the

bedrock floor. As the flood receded and the velocity slackened, the stream could no longer move some of the coarser material brought from upstream, and the bedrock was again mantled by a new gravel deposit. By the next low-water period the channel had virtually the same cross section it had on September 9—but a huge quantity of gravel, sand, and mud had been moved downstream, much of it so coarse that the river is utterly incompetent to move it during low water.

Such fluctuations in channel depth with river stage are sometimes astonishing. During the excavation of the foundations for Hoover Dam, the workmen found a railroad tie buried beneath 60 feet of coarse gravel. The 60 feet of scour and fill is impressive, yet a flood in Kanab Canyon, Utah, in 1883, cut a channel 50 feet deep and 260 feet wide in less than 8 hours.

Bed form

Changes in discharge of streams flowing on beds of sand bring about systematic changes in the shape of the stream bed. Few stream beds are really smooth, but if they are at low stream velocities they soon become rippled as the velocity rises enough to set many particles in motion. Ripples in sand are usually less than about 30 centimeters (one foot) long from crest to crest and 0.5 to 6 centimeters high. Their amplitude is independent of both stream depth and sand size. Though the water in the stream shadow of the ripples is more sluggish than that flowing over the ripple crest, the difference in velocity is not enough to influence the water surface, which may remain smooth or be wavy in a pattern independent of the ripples. The individual sand grains climb in linear trains up the gentle upstream faces of the ripples and roll down the steep downstream faces, so that the ripples slowly migrate downstream (Fig. 12–13).

If the stream speeds up, the sand forms larger sand waves, called dunes. A *dune re-*

FIGURE 12–12

Changes in the channel of the San Juan River, near Bluff, Utah, during the flood of October, 1941. Three stages are shown (A) on September 9 before the flood, when the river was discharging only 635 cubic feet per second, and was flowing over a shallow channel floored with silt, sand, and gravel, (B) at the height of the flood on October 14, when the discharge was 59,600 cubic feet per second and the river had removed all loose debris from its channel, and (C) during an early stage in the recession of the flood on October 26. (After L. Leopold and T. Maddox.)

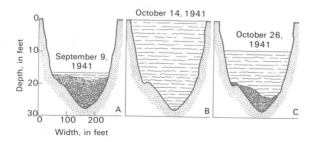

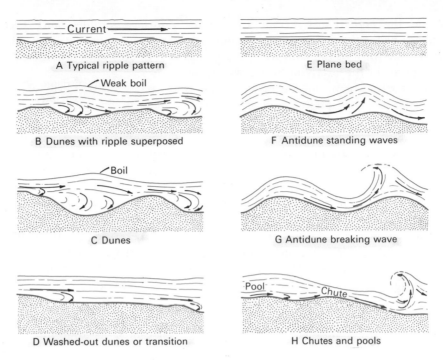

FIGURE 12–13   *Idealized diagram of the forms of bed roughness in an alluvial channel. (After Fig. 3 of R. B. Simons, E. V. Richardson, and Carl Norden, p. 3 in Special Pub. 12 of the Society of Economic Paleontologists and Mineralogists, 1965.)*

gime may form in streams carrying either coarse or fine sand. The coarser the material, the shorter the dune and the steeper its slopes. Dune forms resemble those of ripples but are much larger, ranging from perhaps 60 centimeters (2 feet) to many hundred meters in length and from 6 centimeters to many meters in height. In the lower range of the dune-forming velocities, they may carry ripples on their backs, but the ripples disappear at higher velocities. In large streams, channel dunes may reach great size; in the Mississippi near Memphis, heights of 34 feet have been measured, and in the Amazon, dunes more than twice this height have been sounded.

Dunes disturb stream flow much more than ripples; the threads of fast-moving water do not follow the form of the dune but shoot over its crest, leaving a vertical eddy in its lee. At the bottom of these vortices upstream currents may run at half to two-thirds the speed of the stream as a whole, and may form ripples whose slip-faces face upstream between the dunes. The flow is swiftest over the dune crests and slowest over the troughs, so that the water surface bulges into boils over the troughs. Streams in the dune regime carry relatively much more suspended sediment than do those with rippled beds.

Hydraulic engineers consider ripple and dune bottoms as typical of streams in what they call the *lower flow regime*. With increasing velocity, a *transitional regime* follows in which the dunes are washed out so that a smooth stream bed evolves. Although much sediment is entrained—often as much as 2000 to 6000 parts per million—most of it remains near the stream bottom. The stream surface is smooth.

With somewhat higher velocity the stream

enters the *higher flow regime*. In this the smooth bed is transformed into **antidunes** in which the form of the sand wave travels upstream as do the overlying water waves, because the downstream side of the dune is eroded while the upstream side is added to, though of course the particles of sediment move downstream at higher velocities than before. The height and length of the waves and of the antidunes beneath them depend, of course, on the size of the stream and the character of the bed load available. In some flume tests the sand waves range from 0.03 to 0.5 foot in height and the water waves above them are about twice as high, but in the Rio Grande waves 2 to 3 feet high and 10 to 20 feet from crest to crest have been measured.

At still higher velocities the antidunes break up, all available bed material is thrown violently into suspension, and sediment concentrations reach as much as 3000 to 40,000 parts per million, even where little fine material is available. When fine material is also available, concentrations as high as 600,000 parts per million—60 percent solids!—have been measured.

The highest velocities of the higher flow regime (short of that in waterfalls) produce a stream bed characterized by chutes and pools. This consists, in experimental flumes, of a reach 10 to 30 feet long where flow speeds up, followed by a jump in the surface at the downstream end, and a tranquil but still-accelerating reach of about the same length. Both chutes and pools migrate slowly upstream, over a bottom in violent disturbance. Such flow is rare in natural streams except in rockwalled channels, perhaps because the stream power, turbulence, and sediment supply needed for this are so great that a natural stream in this regime attacks its banks, widening the channel, and thus slowing the velocity and reducing the flow to a lower regime such as builds antidunes or smooth bed.

All these types of flow are shown, with surface profiles and bed roughness diagrammed, in Figure 12–13.

In Reynolds' number,

$$R = \frac{\text{velocity} \times \text{depth} \times \text{density}}{\text{viscosity}}$$

the viscosity of the fluid appears in the denominator. Thus any decrease in viscosity will give a larger value of Reynolds' number, a measure of the tendency toward turbulence. A very interesting study of the flow of the Rio Grande below Las Cruces, New Mexico, found that in winter, when the water temperature was about 40°F the river bottom was virtually flat, but in summer, the same discharge of water at 70°F produced a dune-covered bottom. At both times the grain size of the sediments was the same. The lower viscosity of the warmer water allowed the stream to speed up into a higher flow regime. The Loup River in Nebraska reacts in the same way. The temperature of the Mississippi at St. Louis ranges from a winter low of 33° to a summer high of 87°, at which the viscosity of the water is less than half its winter value. The stream regimes must surely change notably with so great a range of viscosity but no systematic observations have yet been recorded.

Ultimate source of a stream's load

Particles abraded from the bedrock add to a stream's load, but, as indicated in Chapters 5 and 11, most of the load is not derived from abrasion of the bedrock of the stream channel, but from rainwash and downslope movements over the entire drainage basin. In the great process of erosion, downslope movements supply the freight and the ephemeral rills and gullies formed during heavy rains are the loading depots. Permanent stream channels occupy far less than one percent of the land surface, but solution, downslope movements, and rillwash operate over all the rest. Both the stream's load and its water are almost wholly supplied from the interfluve areas upstream. The size, climate, and geologic nature of the drainage basin control the discharge, and also the size, amount, and mineral composition of the particles transported. The river is adjusted to these general conditions but modifies the channel shape and gradient in accordance with fluctuating conditions of discharge. It does this by downcutting where its velocity is high and its load small, or by depositing sediment and building up its bed where its velocity drops and it becomes unable to carry the detritus. If load and discharge are relatively constant, the river may in time achieve a balanced condition in which it is just able to transport the sediment and water along the slope within its channel.

THE LONG PROFILE AND THE CONCEPT OF GRADE

Much of a stream's behavior is only revealed by studying its entire length—particularly its changes in gradient, stream pattern, discharge, and load—from the headwaters to the mouth. Let us follow the full length of the Arkansas River.

The **long profile** (also called longitudinal profile) of a stream is a graphic outline of the stream's gradient over long segments of its course. It is made by plotting the elevations of points on the water surface against distances along it and connecting them with a line (Fig. 12–14). The vertical scale on such a plot must be greatly exaggerated, if we are to read it, for the length of almost every stream is many hundred times as great as its vertical fall.

Shape of the long profile

The long profile of the Arkansas River is representative of many streams, although each one differs in profile from every other, not only because of differences in discharge, load, and the other factors mentioned, but also because of more subtle differences related to the bedrock structure and geologic history of the area traversed. The Arkansas River rises in the southern Rocky Mountains and flows across the Great Plains, joining the Mississippi about 440 miles (730 kilometers) from the Gulf of Mexico. Above Canon City, Colorado, the gradient is steep and irregular; the river plunges swiftly through deep mountain canyons, including the awe-inspiring chasm of the Royal Gorge cut deeply into the resistant granites and gneisses of the Front Range. By contrast, the gradient of the lower 300 kilometers of the river is very low and regular, nowhere greater than 18 centimeters per kilometer (.00018): here the river winds in serpentine bends (like those shown in Fig. 12–22) on a gently sloping plain of sand and silt—material almost exactly like the load now being carried by the stream.

FIGURE 12–14

Long profile of the Arkansas River, from Tennessee Pass, Colorado, to the Mississippi River. Note the great vertical exaggeration, almost 5000 to 1. (Modified from Henry Gannett, U.S. Geological Survey.)

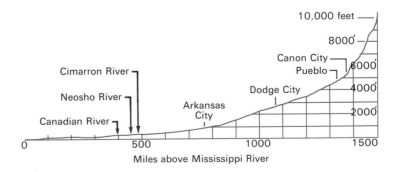

Between these extremes the gradient of the middle course of the river varies regularly and gradually, so that the entire profile approximates a smooth concave-upward curve that steepens notably near the river's head. The entire profile roughly resembles a segment of a hyperbola, but in detail it is far from a simple mathematical curve.

The concept of an ideal graded profile in relation to stream gradient

Most large streams show concave-upward profiles resembling that of the Arkansas, although details vary widely. What does this similarity mean? Is the concave-upward form an equilibrium curve toward which the stream tends constantly to adjust its gradient? We have seen that an underloaded stream may sweep loose debris from its channel and cut down into its bed, thereby flattening its gradient and decreasing its velocity. Alternatively, however, it may flatten its gradient and accommodate its underloading by becoming more sinuous without downcutting. Similarly an overloaded stream may build up its bed by depositing part of its load, thereby steepening its gradient, or it may accomplish the same steepening by straightening and shortening its course without deposition. By these processes a stream adjusts its gradient to conform to its average discharge and the average amount and size of sediment supplied from upstream. Eventually it may make such adjustments through most of its length.

Thus we come to the concept that ideally the **graded profile,** which the stream is constantly approaching by these adjustments, is a gradient of dynamic equilibrium—one nicely adjusted to the particular discharge and load inherent in each stream's particular drainage system. Though the actual profile has many irregularities and local changes in slope, it seems clear that the stream itself creates its concave-upward profile by cutting or filling, straightening or lengthening its course until it approaches a gradient of dynamic equilibrium, changing, it is true, with every fluctuation in discharge or load, but approximating to a steady shape.

But such a concept is too simple; adjustments other than in gradient are necessary before a stream is truly graded. Before considering these complexities however, let us look into the factors that tend toward flattening the long profile downstream so that it superficially resembles a hyperbolic form. Among them are: (1) limitations in downcutting imposed by base level, (2) the increase in discharge downstream, and (3) the downstream changes in grain size and load.

BASE LEVEL.   No stream can deepen its channel more than a few meters below the level of the ocean—even the Amazon is less than 100 meters deep at its mouth. This limiting depth, below which a stream cannot erode is called **base level.** Base level accounts for the generally low gradients of stream profiles near the ocean, for the streams are nearing the level below which they cannot lower their beds; they can deposit sediment to steepen the gradient, but cannot cut deeper to lower it.

Although the ocean is the ultimate base level for stream erosion, a lake or a particularly resistant mass of rock through which a stream can cut only with extreme slowness (for example, the gneiss at the Royal Gorge on the Arkansas) may form a *temporary base level.* Such levels are temporary because in the long course of geologic time even the largest lakes are ultimately drained by downcutting of their outlets or are filled with sediment. Moreover, even the most resistant rock ledge will eventually be sawed through (as the gneiss at the Royal Gorge is being sawed) by the abrading bed load of a swiftly flowing stream. But until such obstructions are removed from the stream's course, they cause the profile to flatten upstream.

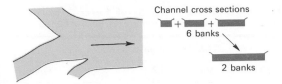

FIGURE 12–15

Decrease in channel friction area due to confluence of tributaries.

INCREASE IN DISCHARGE DOWNSTREAM.   If the Arkansas' profile is indeed a graded profile of equilibrium, how can it be that the river is at the same time in balance on a slope of .00018, less than 18 centimeters per kilometer, near its mouth, and on the much steeper slope of more than .001 (one meter per kilometer) between Pueblo and Dodge City (Fig. 12–14). Also, why are the gradients of different segments transitional so that the headward steepening is along a fairly smooth curve?

A partial answer to these questions is that the profile does not represent a stream of constant size throughout. The Arkansas, like

most rivers, grows downstream by the confluence of tributaries and the seepage of underground waters. The ratio of friction surface to channel cross section diminishes as a stream grows. For example, if the channels in Figure 12–15 were all one foot deep with nearly vertical banks, their union would remove four feet of cross-sectional friction surface—in the diagram, a 30 percent reduction. The energy previously dissipated in friction against these banks is available below junction to speed up the water, eroding the channel and lowering the gradient.

CHANGE IN GRAIN SIZE AND AMOUNT OF LOAD DOWNSTREAM.   Confluence of two streams affects the amount and kind of load as well as the discharge. If a tributary is considerably steeper and so more competent than the trunk stream, its junction necessarily affects the trunk stream's gradient. The huge load of sand dumped into the Missouri River by the Platte causes a hump in the Missouri's profile. The Colorado River of Arizona offers an extreme example in that its steep tribu-

FIGURE 12–16   *Rapids over a debris dam at the junction of Tapeats Creek (lower left) with the Colorado River, Arizona. (Photo by B. M. Freeman, U.S. Geological Survey.)*

Table 12–1 **Percentages of different grain size fractions of lower Mississippi River sediments, 100 to 1000 miles (160 to 1660 kilometers) below Cairo**

Grain size	Miles below Cairo					
	100	*300*	*500*	*700*	*900*	*1000*
Gravel	29	8	14	5	trace	none
Coarse sand	30	22	9	8	1	none
Medium sand	32	50	46	44	26	9
Fine sand	8	19	28	41	70	69
Silt	trace	trace	2	1	2	10
Clay	trace	trace	1	trace	1	10

SOURCE: After Charles M. Nevin; from data of the U.S. Waterways Experiment Station, Vicksburg, Mississippi.

tary canyons, though dry through most of the year, dump huge fans of coarse debris into the main river when in flood. Many great boulders swept down these tributary chutes during floods are too heavy to be moved by the Colorado despite its roaring torrent. Such boulders and coarse gravel accumulate at the mouths of the tributaries to form **debris dams** (Fig. 12–16). Since these boulders can be transported only after they have been slowly reduced in size by abrasion, debris dams cause very persistent convexities on the main river's profile.

Though the debris dams of the Colorado strikingly show the effect of grain size on a river profile, they are abnormal. More characteristic, though more subtle changes are found in the meandering lower courses of most large rivers. A careful study of the bed material of the Mississippi River shows a marked decrease in particle size downstream. The grain sizes of 600 samples collected between Cairo, Illinois, and the Gulf of Mexico are indicated in Table 12–1.

The average composition of delta sediments, 70 percent silt and clay, also confirms this general change. On the Rhine, between Basel and Bingen, a marked decrease in pebble size downstream closely correlates with a flattening of the river profile, although the river's discharge increases only slightly in this stretch. Thus attrition of the

bed load by friction so that the grain size decreases downstream lessens the roughness of the channel and is one of the factors that allow most streams to flow on an ever-decreasing grade. Indeed, paradoxically, the velocity of many large graded rivers increases near their mouths even though the gradients lessen. Increased discharge and depth, diminishing grain size of load, and lessened friction against smooth banks that contain proportionately more sticky clay than easily entrained silt and sand, outweigh the effect of the lessened gradient.

The concept of grade in relation to cross section and channel pattern

We have seen that a stream adjusts its gradient in conformity with variations in discharge and load. Nevertheless, because the transporting power of a stream cannot be measured by its slope alone, the graded condition of a stream cannot be rigorously defined solely by its gradient. The profile depends both on the shape of the stream cross section and on the channel pattern. In approaching dynamic equilibrium a river adjusts both gradient and cross section. Its channel must be adjusted both to discharge and to the size and kind of load carried. Furthermore, a stream also adjusts its channel pattern, flowing in serpentine bends or

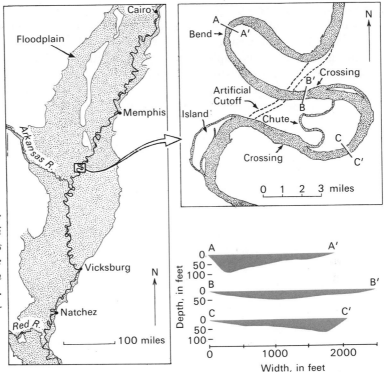

FIGURE 12–17

Left: *The meandering course of the Lower Mississippi River.* Right: *Map and cross section of three bends. The artificial cutoffs were dug in 1941 and 1942. (After H. N. Fisk, Mississippi River Commission, 1947.)*

straight chutes depending on local conditions of discharge, gradient, load, and the kind of material that forms its beds and banks.

All such adjustments must obviously be transitory. Erosion does not stop with attainment of quasi equilibrium. The river still transports material to the sea, constantly lowering land upstream, thus imposing changes in sediment load and discharge that are inevitably reflected in changes of gradient and other parameters.

PATTERNS OF RIVER CHANNELS. As already noted, the lower Arkansas winds in serpentine bends, called **meanders.** Far from following the shortest route to the sea, its intricate path is several times as long as a straight course would be. Between Pueblo and Dodge City, however, (before irrigation controlled its regimen) the river was **braided,** that is, it was subdivided into a plexus of interconnected small channels between many low

islands made up of sand and gravel bars that the stream had deposited in its bed. Elsewhere the channel is relatively straight, though only for short stretches and under most unusual conditions is any river completely without bends and kinks. The Mississippi River, from Cairo, Illinois, to the mouth of the Red River, has a typical meandering course (Fig. 12–17); the lower Amazon braids intricately between low alluvial islands. But meanders are also common in small creeks, as are braids in sediment-loaded rills that form after every rainstorm.

ORIGIN OF MEANDERS. Why does a stream meander instead of flowing directly down valley to the sea? Some streams follow meandering courses carved in bedrock (Fig. 12–18), but this is uncommon; most meandering streams flow on floodplains. The meanders of the streams now flowing in bedrock canyons probably formed on floodplains, and have been incised as the stream deepened its channel because of a lowered base level. Our real problem is to account for the meanders on floodplains.

Some local causes of stream curves are obvious: deflections caused by fallen trees, by large boulders and landslides, by tributaries whose detritus is too coarse to be moved by the main stream. But most meanders are much more regular than one would expect if all the curves were due to such accidents. A general cause must be operating.

Observation shows that meandering streams have relatively light bed loads. Their banks have a high proportion of sticky clay and are much steeper than those of braided streams. We have noted that there are two ways an underloaded stream may adjust its gradient: it may either cut into its bed or lengthen its course by becoming more sinuous; either process lowers its slope. Some meandering streams are so near base level that they cannot cut deeper; the only mechanism available for lowering gradient is to become more sinuous. Other meandering

FIGURE 12–18   *Entrenched meanders of the San Juan River, Utah. (Photo by Tad Nichols, Tucson, Arizona.)*

streams are not near base level; perhaps their meandering is due to the difficulty (Fig. 12–9) of entraining fine sediments in absence of a considerable bed load.

A stream in random turbulence must attack now one bank, now the other, thereby forming a sinuous channel. As the water rounds a bend, its inertia carries it toward the concave bank, just as a passenger is swayed to the side when a speeding automobile rounds a curve. The faster current enables the stream to undermine the concave bank; on the inside the velocity simultaneously decreases and sediment is deposited there.

The inertia of the stream brings about an almost-or-quite-imperceptible tilting-up of the water surface toward the outer bank, thereby increasing the slope of the stream surface there. This tilting tends to make the water run toward the opposite bank as it proceeds downstream; thus a curve of comparable sinuosity and opposite curvature tends to form next downstream. The tilting of the water surface at curves and the reversal of tilt in the intermediate reaches produces an almost uniform water slope along the middle of the stream course, which means that the stream is expending its energy almost uniformly through its course (Fig. 12–19). Leopold and Langbein of the U.S. Geological Survey have shown that most meandering streams change direction at an almost uniform rate.

Soundings show that the shape of the Mississippi's channel changes greatly from bend

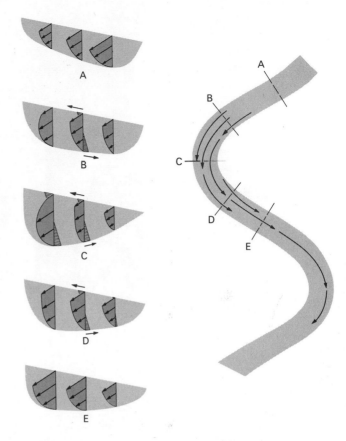

FIGURE 12–19
Idealized flow pattern of a typical meander. Left: *The velocity vectors downstream for five cross sections of the curve (arrows on brown background); lateral components of velocity indicated by the triangular brown areas.* Right: *Streamlines at the surface of the meander. (After Luna B. Leopold and W. B. Langbein, "River Meanders." Copyright © June 1966 by Scientific American, Inc. All rights reserved.)*

FIGURE 12–20
Localization of erosion and deposition of marked sands in an experimental sinuous stream. (After J. F. Friedkin, U.S. Waterways Experiment Station, 1945.)

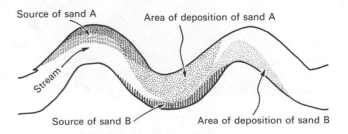

Source of sand A   Area of deposition of sand A

Stream

Source of sand B   Area of deposition of sand B

FIGURE 12–21   *Caving bank of Belle Fourche River at a meander near Shoma, South Dakota.
(Photo by N. H. Darton, U.S. Geological Survey.)*

to bend, and is deepest near the outer bank of each bend (Figs. 12–19, 12–20) . The inner bank slopes gently or is even convex, and commonly consists of shifting sandbars to which the stream is adding. This is true of all meanders (see frontispiece) . In the short straight stretches between bends, the river shallows notably and the channel is nearly symmetrical. These shallows between bends, the **crossings,** troubled the old-time river pilots. Some are less than 3 meters deep at low water, less than a fifth the depth at the bends.

During a flood, when velocity and turbulence are greatest, the channel deepens and the outer banks cave in rapidly (Fig. 12–21) . Most fine-grained material caved from the banks is carried off in suspension, but the coarser material moves more slowly as part of the bed load. Experiments (Fig. 12–20) show that almost all the coarse debris cut from a bend is deposited on the next crossing or on the inside slope of the next bend (Figs. 12–17, 12–22, and end papers) .

Erosion of the outer banks and deposition on the inner cause the meanders to shift

FIGURE 12–22
Migration of meanders of the Arkansas River in eastern Colorado between 1936 and 1957, from aerial photographs. At the left (upstream) end of the figure, the channel was fixed by concrete bridge abutments; elsewhere it was not artificially restrained.

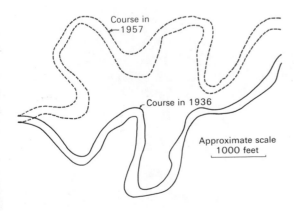

Course in 1957

Course in 1936

Approximate scale
1000 feet

position and ultimately to migrate widely over the valley floor (Fig. 12–22) . In time the stream reworks the deposits of older meander channels and forms new deposits that in turn are cut away as the channel continues to migrate. Thus a meandering river moves its coarser sediments only slowly to the sea. The residual deposits on the concave sides of the curves make up in the aggregate the river's **floodplain.** A study of the Klarälven River, in southern Sweden, showed that in a century and a half the meandering of a 100-kilometer length of the stream had destroyed about 13,000 square meters of arable land yearly and rebuilt almost an equal area of floodplain at elevations about 4 meters lower. Thus about 50,000 metric tons of sediment yearly was eroded by this stretch of river.

Even meandering streams incised deeply into bedrock, so that they cannot sweep freely over a floodplain, nevertheless attack the concave parts of their banks and thereby undercut them. The remarkable natural bridges of southeastern Utah (Fig. 12–23) were formed in this way.

Studies of natural rivers contributed to our knowledge of flow in meandering channels, but many variables are so intricately interrelated that their effects are difficult to evaluate. Accordingly hydrologists are turning more and more to stream models for help in solving both theoretical and practical problems of stream flow. Simple wooden flumes used in early experiments have been superseded by carefully constructed scale models that not only closely reproduce channel and valley shapes, but also have devices to control and measure nearly all the variables of flow.

The Mississippi River Commission used large scale models in studies of stream flow at the United States Waterways Experiment Station at Vicksburg (Fig. 12–24) . In one experiment a straight channel was carefully molded in a uniform light-weight artificial material scaled to simulate Mississippi sand and silt. Then water, with the artificial sediment added, was allowed to run in the channel for a few days. The stream promptly developed a sinuous course but no complete meanders. The artificial material simulated loose sand and silt, and was not rich in clay like that in most meandering streams.

During the experiments, discharge, slope, load, and erodibility of material were individually varied to evaluate the effect of each on the pattern of the artificial river. Increas-

ing discharge widened the curves systematically, verifying the general rule that big rivers have big bends, little rivers little ones, but the sinuosity only approached a meandering pattern during declining stages of flow, after a larger discharge had flowed more directly downslope. (Fig. 12–24, right).

The valley gradient directly affected the width of the belt of curves, also; the steeper the gradient, the larger the bends. Where

FIGURE 12–23   *Double Arch natural bridges, Arches National Monument, Utah. (Photo by Tad Nichols, Tucson, Arizona.)*

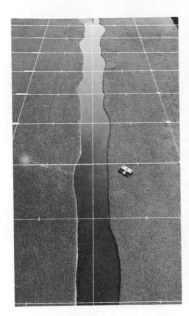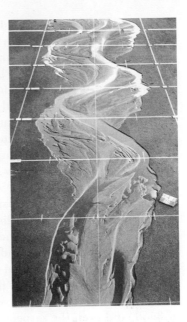

FIGURE 12–24   *A straight channel* (left) *molded in hadite, an artificial material scaled in density to simulate Mississippi River silt and sand, developed a sinuous course* (middle *and* right) *after a few days of stream flow.* (*U.S. Army Photographs.*)

the curves are tight—their radii small relative to the channel width—the resistance to flow may be twice that due to friction with the channel. When a stream was not given a load at the head of the model channel, it became sinuous only after acquiring a load from its banks.

Most meandering streams have much deeper channels relative to their width than braided streams; their flood plain sediments are more cohesive, their bed loads smaller and composed of finer materials on both bed and banks. Streams flowing over glaciers can attack their walls by melting as well as by abrasion; they commonly show meandering patterns also. Much remains to be learned about the factors governing meandering in streams.

Even straight streams flowing on bedrock show features hydrologically allied to meanders. Pools and riffles along a straight stream succeed each other in a definite periodic way, just as they do in a meandering stream (where the riffles are at the crossings between bends). Moreover, the **thalweg**—the line following the deepest part of a natural river channel—nearly everywhere wanders from side to side of even a straight channel, coming close to one bank only to cross over to the other as in meander bends. Indeed this seems to be the pattern shown in Figure 12–24. Perhaps both meanders and wandering thalwegs exemplify a wave phenomenon brought about by random fluctuations in turbulent flow.

ORIGIN OF BRAIDED CHANNEL PATTERNS.   In braided streams the channel constantly subdivides around low alluvial islands that grew from bars in the stream bed. The bars develop by accumulation of material too coarse for the stream to move except during a flood. This coarser material traps additional debris, and by its roughness diminishes the stream's velocity, causing still more deposition. The bar grows both in height and length until eventually it becomes an island, perhaps temporarily anchored by vegetation.

Braided channels characterize heavily loaded streams with easily erodible banks, such as those carrying active glacial outwash, but they are not confined to these. Indeed one of the finest examples, prior to stream control by dams, was the Platte River in Nebraska, far from any modern glacial influence. This formerly braided stream is now modifying itself to a single channel of greater sinuosity. Braids seem to form wherever the bed load is relatively large and much of it is too coarse for the stream to handle except during floods, in other words, wherever there is both a wide range in grain size of the load and a wide fluctuation in discharge. Thus the smaller particles are winnowed out even more effectively than in meandering streams. Yet it seems that the braided course of the lower Amazon can hardly be thus explained for its bed load can hardly be very large, even in flood, and even the suspended load is not great. Clearly other factors are also involved.

Summary: channel pattern, gradient, and channel shape in relation to the concept of grade

We have seen that changes in discharge, amount and character of sediment load, velocity, gradient, width and depth of channel, roughness of channel surface, and channel pattern are all closely interrelated. Change in any one affects the others, and a rough balance must exist between all of them in the graded stream. Two streams of equal discharge but different gradients may both be graded—the difference compensated for by such factors as load or channel roughness. Channel patterns—meandering, straight, and braided—are merely other ways by which a stream adjusts gradient and cross section to discharge and load imposed from upstream. By meandering, a river lengthens its course and decreases its gradient; by braiding, a stream can move the smaller grains and leave the larger ones stranded as mid-channel bars. Other changes in gradient and cross section, treated earlier in this chapter, have been nicely summarized by an American geologist, W. W. Rubey:

Cutting on the bottom increases the load of downstream parts of the stream and so eventually lowers the slope and decreases the velocity. Cutting at the sides widens the cross section, thereby decreasing the relative depth, and so reduces the efficiency of the stream. In either case, the load increases and the capacity decreases until an approximate balance is struck between the two. Conversely, an excessive load causes deposition on the bottom or at the margins of a stream or at both places. Deposition on the bottom, being greater upstream than down, tends to steepen the slope and thus to increase the velocity. Deposition at the side of the channel . . . narrows the cross section, thereby increasing the relative depth, and so increases the efficiency of the stream. . . . It is true that [the] factors [leading to the stream's adjustment] may vary seasonally or even daily and, therefore, the stream may never actually attain complete adjustment. Nevertheless, with changing conditions, the stream is constantly cutting or filling and modifying its slope, velocity, and cross section so as eventually to accomplish the imposed work with the least expenditure of energy. The recurrent floods of each season carve out or build up a channel that the stream is unable to destroy at lower stages . . . In short, the stream constantly approaches, even though it rarely attains and even then is unable to maintain, a condition of equilibrium in which the capacity for . . . cutting and filling are exactly equal. This equilibrium, which the stream constantly approaches, is one in which the imposed load is transported without either net gain or loss. . . . If discharge, load, grain size, and sorting are considered the controlling factors, then velocity, slope, and the depth of the channel are dependent variables that are affected not only by the independent variables but also by one another.

Departures from the ideal graded profile

The smoothly concave curve of the ideal profile is closely approached but probably never attained by natural streams. Even in the lower Mississippi, probably as well graded a stream as could be found, the profile shows many slight but abrupt changes of slope (Fig. 12–25). This is normal; as we have seen, inflow of most tributaries demands

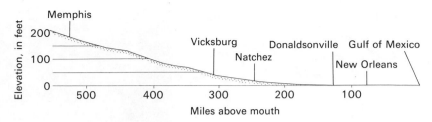

FIGURE 12–25
Long profile of the lower Mississippi River at low water. (After H. N. Fisk, Mississippi River Commission, 1947.)

changes in gradient. Such changes are not inconsistent with the concept of grade, for dynamic equilibrium may still be closely approached in each segment of the stream's course. The result, however, is a profile neither ideally smooth nor ideally concave.

A principal value of the concept of the ideal graded profile is that great departures from it point up modifications of stream regimen. Lava flows, landslides, or drifting sand dunes may encroach on and displace a stream channel, thus upsetting its graded condition and making its profile strongly irregular. Glaciation in the recent geologic past has greatly modified the slopes of nearly all major streams of the northern United States (Chapter 13). Earth movements are also disturbing factors. Some anticlines in the south central part of the State of Washington (Chapter 8) have been folded rapidly and recently enough to destroy any former adjustment of the streams flowing down their flanks. The profiles in Figure 12–26 illustrate the local broad convexity (instead of concavity) of stream gradients on some of these folds. Similarly, stream beds displaced during the 1915 Pleasant Valley earthquake (Chapter 8), all show rapids or waterfalls, some of which have retreated far upstream of the 1915 fault scarp (Fig. 12–37).

Resistant rocks cause changes in slope even in long-established streams. Because the concave profile forms slowly on resistant rocks, many structural or climatic "accidents" may intervene before the graded profile can be attained. That most large streams flow on grades that approximate the ideal profile and join at the same elevation is the most persuasive evidence of the power of stream erosion.

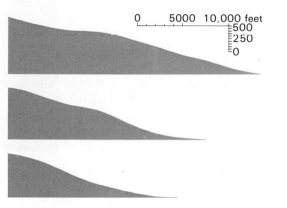

FIGURE 12–26
Profiles of streams flowing down flanks of anticlinal ridges in southern Washington. (From maps of the U.S. Geological Survey.)

STREAM DEPOSITS

Floodplains

Large trunk rivers commonly meander, or much more rarely braid, within broad, smooth valleys sloping so gently seaward as to appear flat. The flat surface of such a valley is called a floodplain, for at flood stage —usually once or twice a year—the river overflows its channel and floods at least part of the valley floor. Some floodplains are little wider than the channel of the stream—the meanders impinge against bedrock at almost every bend. Most, however, are far wider, and their streams meander everywhere through unconsolidated alluvium.

Low indistinct ridges, called **natural levees,** border most river channels on floodplains. They are highest next to the stream bank, and slope away from it. When a stream in flood overflows, the velocity and turbulence decrease as it overtops its channel;

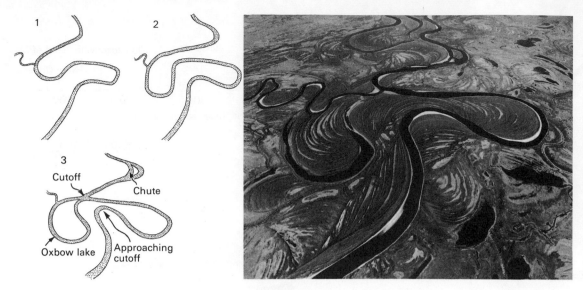

FIGURE 12-27   Top: *A river meandering on a broad floodplain. Note the lowridged deposits on the insides of bends and the abandoned meander channels, including oxbow lakes.* Bottom: *Possible stages in the evolution of the meander cutoff that has recently taken place in the center of the view. (Photo by U.S. Air Force.)*

some of the suspended load quickly settles. Most of the coarsest part drops where the flood first overtops the banks, thus building up the low natural levees. Finer sediment is carried farther and deposited on lower ground. Since natural levees interfere with tributary drainage, the floodplain behind them is generally partly covered with shallow lakes and swamps.

The silty deposits that build natural levees are individually thin, and seldom accumulate in great thickness, even over long periods of time. The Nile floods that have renewed the soils of lower Egypt for millenia are perhaps the best known example of overbank deposition, but although some Egyptian structures have been buried by 10 meters of silt—as much as 2½ meters since the Arab conquest in 1300 A.D.—this amounts to only about 30 centimeters per century; in much of the Nile Valley the accumulation is only about a third of this. The muddy Hoang Ho of China when in flood is 40 percent silt and 60 percent water; it is building up its floodplain three times as fast, at about 90 centimeters per century.

Migration of meanders constantly changes the sites of deposition for new floods. Most of the floodplain is channel deposits dropped on the inside bends of a meandering river, or bars and islands built by a braided stream. The ratio of channel deposits to overbank deposits varies, of course, for different streams, but is large for those reliably measured.

The fact that most streams reach the bank-full stage nearly two out of three years is good evidence that overbank deposits form but a small part of the total floodplain volume. Much the greater volume must be made up of sediment dropped on the inside of meander bends as they migrate laterally; if the overbank sediments were very great in proportion, the bank-full stage would become increasingly rare as time went on, except where a river is greatly aggrading. Most floodplains show crescentic lakes, and other relics of abandoned meanders, not masked and healed by later overbank deposits. In the photograph in Figure 12–27 the low stripelike ridges almost paralleling the inside of the bends are sand bars left behind as the bends migrated. The **oxbow lakes** (Fig. 12–27) are abandoned river bends left wherever a stream crosses the neck between bends and thus shortens its course. Such **cutoffs** may form when a meander is slowed in its downstream migration, allowing the next bend upstream to overtake it and sever the narrowing neck between the two. The drawing in Figure 12–27 illustrates a hypothetical sequence that might have produced the river pattern shown in the photograph. Another kind of cutoff—a **chute**—forms when a river in flood simply overtops its banks, flows directly across a bend, and persists in this shortcut. The new chute is more efficient than the old channel, because it is shorter, its gradient steeper, and the velocity correspondingly higher. Velocity and turbulence in the abandoned bend drop so low that sand deposited at both ends soon dams it off to form an oxbow lake.

THE FORMATION OF FLOODPLAINS. A few floodplains have apparently formed by lateral planation of the bedrock by shifting meanders during long stream erosion, but wells show that most broad floodplains top thick stream deposits instead of a thin alluvial veneer resting on bedrock. Meandering or braided channels atop these deeply alluviated valleys carry more than three-fourths of all the runoff of the United States.

The Mississippi River Commission used several hundred drill holes and water wells in studying the deposits underlying the lower Mississippi floodplain. They found stream deposits ranging from 30 to over 125 meters (100 to more than 400 feet) thick. Near Natchez, this debris is about 80 meters (260 feet) thick, with its base 65 meters (215 feet) below sea level. Drill holes through the floodplain show that the buried surface—the valley of a prehistoric Mississippi—was not a smooth plain but a shallow, steep-sided valley with many tributaries. The Santa Ana River in southern California also has buried its former channel beneath stream deposits more than 40 meters (140 feet) thick at the river mouth. Most other large rivers show similar filled channels near the sea. As will be seen in Chapter 13, many of these thick fills result from the rise of sea level that followed the glacial epoch, which ended a few thousand years ago.

Deltas

On entering quiet water such as a lake or sea, a stream drops part, at least, of its load because of lessened velocity, though, if it is heavily silt-laden, it may sink beneath the surface and proceed along the bottom as a turbidity current, spreading part of its sediment widely over the basin floor. In northern Sweden measurements showed that a density difference as little as .0003 between river and lake water is enough to permit a density current to form. Along an exposed coast, however, a greater contrast seems to be needed.

Where the Nile emerges from its valley near Cairo, it splits into distributary channels, which further subdivide and enter the Mediterranean on a front more than 200 kilometers long. The roughly triangular shape of the Nile's depositional plain prompted Herodotus to call it a **delta,** from the Greek letter Δ.

Deltas may be triangular, generally with a convex sea margin, or irregular, with lobe-like extensions like the "bird-foot" delta of the Mississippi (Fig. 12–28). The bird-foot distributaries are flanked by low natural levees and the whole delta surface is gradually sinking because of crustal warping and compaction of the underlying delta clays. The shapes and sizes of deltas are affected by the strength of the local waves and tides. The Mississippi and Colorado empty into relatively tideless gulfs and have prominent del-

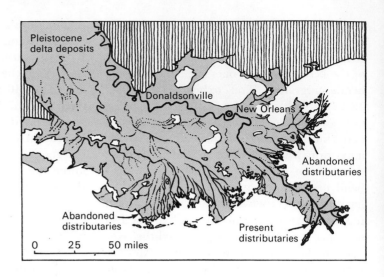

FIGURE 12–28

The delta (brown) of the Mississippi River. Note the old meander courses, the numerous lakes, the positions of the abandoned distributaries, and the bird-foot pattern of the present distributaries. (After H. N. Fisk, Mississippi River Commission.)

tas. The muddy Tiber carries 4 million cubic meters of sand and mud a year and its delta is extending seaward at the rate of 9 meters a year. The Po, also advancing into the nearly tideless Mediterranean, has left the Roman naval base at Ravenna 10 kilometers from the sea. But the Columbia and Congo have no deltas at all. The Columbia's load is scattered by ocean waves and currents for hundreds of miles along the sea coast; most of the Congo's load settles out in a stillwater called Stanley Pool, a few miles upstream. The little remaining flows down a long deep submarine canyon into the depths of the Atlantic. The heavily laden Niger, 1400 kilometers to the north, supplies a huge and growing delta.

Where sand-laden streams flow into a deep, still body of water, they deposit the layers of deltaic sediment in a characteristically discordant arrangement (Fig. 12–29). The stream deposits on the top of the delta—the **topset beds**—are thin overbank sediments of the distributaries. Thicker **foreset** beds accumulate on the front slope of the delta over which both low-water and flood debris is dumped. The finest sediments remain in suspension for a long time and come to rest beyond the frontal slope where they spread over the lake or sea bottom as **bottomset beds** in front of the advancing foreset layers.

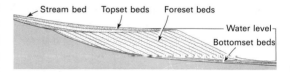

FIGURE 12–29

Diagrammatic section of a simple delta.

Most large deltas, built in storm-swept or tidally disturbed seas, are much more complex than this. The Mississippi delta, for example, shows little discordance between topset, foreset, and bottomset beds except beneath rapidly advancing lobes. Large compound deltas formed by many streams filling a structural basin are discussed in Chapter 17.

Alluvial fans

In arid and semiarid regions—less commonly elsewhere—a stream emerging from a steep, narrow valley onto a more gently sloping lowland builds an **alluvial cone** of intermediate slope whose apex lies in the valley at the side of the lowland. After debouching from the canyon the flow is no longer confined; both depth and gradient may diminish abruptly, and the stream drop its load. In dry regions much water is

FIGURE 12–30

Small alluvial fans formed when leaks in a high-level canal caused rapid gullying, near Leadville, Colorado. (Photo by M. R. Campbell, U.S. Geological Survey.)

promptly lost by infiltration in the loose sediments of the cone, hastening deposition.

The slopes of alluvial fans differ with the size of the stream and the grain size of its load. Small streams moving coarse particles may build fans sloping as much as 15° (as in Figs. 12–30, 12–38). The slopes of many larger fans (Fig. 15–5) decrease from between 3 and 5° at their apices to less than 1° near their bases. A decrease in the average grain size of the fan deposits goes hand-in-hand with such a decrease in slope. Unlike deltas, fans have no long foreset beds, though as they build out, shorter and more steeply inclined beds come to overlie the more gently sloping distal beds. Bedding is generally indistinct and highly irregular in such accumulations.

SCULPTURE OF THE LAND

Land forms are products of the interplay of constructional and degradational processes. Earth movements and volcanism uplift parts of the crust or extrude volcanics upon them; erosion constantly works to level them to the sea. Most hillslopes owe their shapes to downslope movements and the incision of the land by streams.

Drainage density (D) is the ratio of the total length $(L,$ in miles) to the area $(A,$ in square miles) of the drainage basin: $D =$ $L/A.$ Obviously the average distance between stream channels is the reciprocal, $A/L,$ of the drainage density, and the average horizontal distance from divide to stream channel is $1/2D.$ The angle of a hillslope, $a,$ is thus a function of D and of relief (H) in miles:

$$\tan a = \frac{H}{\dfrac{1}{2D}}.$$

Therefore, the greater the drainage density in an area of uniform relief, the shorter and steeper is the average slope; the greater the relief in an area of constant drainage density, the longer and steeper is the average slope.

The form of hillslopes varies greatly from region to region, depending on differences in rocks, soils, vegetation, climate, and the stage of development of the drainage, but within a region of similar rocks, structure, and climate a characteristic hillslope angle tends to develop. The Soil Conservation Service of U.S. Department of Agriculture has made extensive studies of the influence of different vegetation covers on soil erodibility. They found that for a given soil both volume of runoff and erosion of soil increase with increasing slope up to angles of about 12°, but that the longer the slope the less soil removed per unit of length. Some of the sediment on long slopes is deposited farther down the slope, leading to a reduction of slope. Deposition goes on because the longer the downslope distance the better the opportunity for the runoff to infiltrate the soil. On relatively impermeable soils, of course, this effect is small and such slopes tend to remain constant; the slope wears back at a constant angle. This is well illustrated in the badlands area of Nebraska where studies by S. A. Schumm, of the U.S. Geological Survey, have shown that slopes cut on siltstone retreat with a constant angle under attack of rainwash, whereas slopes cut on shale gradually flatten because of downhill creep. For parallel retreat to continue, it is, of course, necessary that the sediment be continually removed from the foot of the slope.

FIGURE 12–31   *Book Cliffs, northeast of Grand Junction, Colorado, showing contrasting slopes carved in shale and sandstone strata. (Photo by G. B. Richardson, U.S. Geological Survey.)*

FIGURE 12–32   *Monument Valley, Utah. Mesas and pillars of sandstone rising above shale slopes. Two structural terraces are visible in the distance. (Photo by Tad Nichols, Tucson, Arizona.)*

It is clear that hillslopes vary greatly in steepness depending on the cohesion of the rocks. In Figures 12–31 and 12–32 the coherent sandstones form nearly vertical slopes, the less coherent interbedded shales much gentler ones, embayed by gullies. The contrasts are more striking in arid or semiarid climates than in more humid areas, where they are blurred by soil creep.

An eroding stream not only deepens its valley, its headwater tributaries lengthen by **headward erosion** until halted by competing streams, similarly extending headward from the opposite side of the divide. If one of the competing drainages has a lower base level, or if it is eroding less-resistant rock, it is able to extend headward at the expense of the less-effective stream. If the process continues, one stream may capture the drainage of another, an act of **stream piracy** (Fig. 12–33). A stream whose upper course has been cap-

tured is, of course, less competent than it was prior to the capture. It may be so incapable of keeping its valley clear of alluvial fans from the sides that lakes are formed along it. Because it is generally true in mountainous areas that the drainage on one side of the divide has the advantage over that on the other, it is very common to find lakes in segments of beheaded valleys at or near divides.

Stream patterns are generally markedly affected by the rock structure. Where the underlying rock offers uniform resistance, tributaries subdivide headward like the limbs of a tree, producing a **dendritic** pattern (Fig. 12–34, *left*). Headward extension of streams, however, closely follows differences in the erodibility of rocks. If the rocks are of unequal resistance, the tributaries lengthen and cut down most rapidly in the less resistant, wearing-out valleys or lowlands, and leave ridges or uplands of resistant rocks between

FIGURE 12–33   *Unaweep Canyon, on the Uncompahgre Plateau, Colorado, the former course of the Gunnison-Uncompahgre River, which was beheaded by the capture of its upper course by the headward growth of a tributary of the Colorado River. This tributary was working in the outcrop belt of the readily erodible Mancos Shale (Cretaceous) whereas the Gunnison-Uncompahgre was held up by resistant granite. (Photo by C. B. Hunt, U.S. Geological Survey.)*

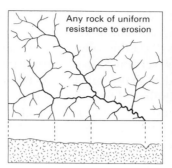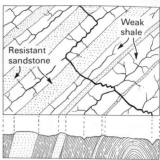

FIGURE 12–34
Structural control of stream patterns. Left: *Dendritic pattern.* Right: *Trellis pattern.*

(Fig. 5–15) . In steeply dipping parallel beds, this development of drainage along the more readily eroded rocks produces a rectangular or **trellis** pattern (Figs. 12–34, *right,* 8–20) . Other examples of **structural control** of drainage are the concentric patterns on eroded domes and basins (Figs. 9–6, 9–7) and the strikingly linear stream courses along some faults (Fig. 9–17) . Though a stream system constantly changes because of earth movements and its own activity, in the stretches where it is downcutting it continually accentuates the differences in rock resistance.

In temperate regions where soil creep is active, structural control of land forms is much more subtle than in the desert examples shown in Figures 12–31, 12–32, 5–15, and 9–7. In the area of Figure 12–35, for example, the major ridges are underlain by resistant rocks, the larger valleys by less resistant. The systematic asymmetry of the hills suggests a dip to the left, but the drainage pattern gives only slight clues to this. Even on the ground in such an area, it is sometimes difficult to tell which resistant rock supports a particular ridge because downslope creep of grass and soil masks the rock contacts and rounds the hills.

Structural terraces and plains

Etching out of the less resistant rocks by rainwash, creep, and stream erosion produces striking effects, even in areas of flat-lying rocks. In horizontal strata, streams tend to be uniformly spaced. They cut through the less resistant beds readily but may be arrested by a resistant stratum that makes a widespread temporary base level. Above this bed, headward erosion may extend the drainage over a wide area, stripping off the weak strata to form a **structural plain** upon the resistant stratum below (Figs. 12–36, 12–32) . In an arid or semiarid climate, the eroded edge of a resistant layer that is being undercut by the retreat of a less-resistant bed below it may rise in a steep embayed slope or cliff. Small detached segments, **mesas** and **buttes,** are commonly left to attest the former extension of the resistant layer above the entire plain. A stream valley in such an area displays the eroded edge of each resistant bed as a cliff whose top forms a step, or **structural terrace,** along the valley wall. Such terraces are common in and near the Grand Canyon of the Colorado (Fig. 5–14) .

Stream terraces

Not all terraces are structural. Many are made up entirely of stream deposits; others are cut in bedrock, but have veneers or residual patches of river gravel on their flat surfaces. These terraces are obviously remnants of older floodplains now incised by the streams that made them. A stream may entrench its floodplain for any of several reasons: uplift by earth movements, lowering of sea level, climatic change affecting the stream regimen, or any event that increases the stream's ability to cut down.

FIGURE 12–35   *Structural control of land forms, subdued by soil creep on weakly consolidated Tertiary rocks, San Jose Hills, Los Angeles County, California. (Photo by Robert C. Frampton, Claremont, California.)*

FIGURE 12–36   *A broad structural plain along the Colorado River, Arizona, formed where weak shale overlies a more resistant rock. The shale is in turn overlain by more resistant massive sandstone, remnants of which form cliffed buttes in the center of the view. (Photo by John S. Shelton and Robert C. Frampton, Claremont, California.)*

The 12-foot offset along the front of the Tobin Range (Fig. 8–2) formed during the Pleasant Valley earthquake of 1915 produced waterfalls on streams crossing it. Headward erosion at this step was rapid: by 1930 one waterfall had retreated far upstream and become a rapid, leaving the old floodplain as a pair of matched terraces bordering the newly entrenched channel (Fig. 12–37). Because the stream is now sidecutting at its newly graded level 12 feet below the old floodplain, the terraces are slowly cut away, though probably some parts protected by ridge spurs of resistant rock will long remain.

Other terraces caused by faulting lie on the west side of the Panamint Mountains, Cali-

FIGURE 12–37
Newly entrenched channel formed after relative uplift of the Tobin Mountain block, Nevada, at the time of the earthquake of 1915. The former valley floor now forms paired terraces. (Photo by Ben M. Page, Stanford University.)

fornia (Fig. 12–38). After faults formed a series of small cliffs across the huge alluvial fans bordering the range, streams cut deep trenches in the uplifted parts of the fans and dumped steep new fans on the older ones below the scarps.

Careful mapping of terraces along the Mississippi suggests more complex earth movements. Several terraces extend from Cairo, Illinois, to Natchez, Mississippi, approximately parallel to the present river profile and from about twenty to a few hundred feet above it. South of the Mississippi-Louisiana line the terraces converge and lie on Pleistocene alluvium instead of on older rock. Near Baton Rouge they disappear beneath the present floodplain. This pattern of warped terraces is striking evidence of slow earth movements; the delta has subsided while the area upstream has progressively risen.

Many stream terraces are not formed by earth movements, but by a climatic change, a diminution in total load, or some other factor that increases a stream's transporting power.

EXTENSIVE EROSION SURFACES OF LOW RELIEF

Under ideal conditions of crustal stability, a stream might cut a wide floodplain across even resistant bedrocks and mask them with a relatively thin film of alluvium. Theoretically such a floodplain might coalesce with neighboring ones to produce an extensive erosion surface of low relief. Because a long time is needed to cut such erosional floodplains, however, some geologic change is likely to occur before one can become very extensive. Simple, laterally eroded floodplains are rare; most present-day plains are constructional surfaces. Most existing streams have been affected by crustal movements, sea-level changes, and climatic changes; the history of their valleys is far more complex than one of simple lateral planation.

Most widespread erosion surfaces of low relief apparently result from downcutting by large rivers, small rills, and rainwash, aided by downslope movements, all operating over great lengths of time and constantly being interrupted by crustal movements and climatic changes. Such an undulating surface of low relief is the "Harrisburg surface" in the central and southern Appalachian Mountains (Fig. 12–39). This smooth-to-hilly surface is really a complex of coalescent erosion surfaces. At the base of the mountains, as near Harrisburg, Pennsylvania—whence its name, it is many miles wide. The Susquehanna and other rivers have cut gorges 60 to 100 meters deep into the surface, and many lesser streams have partly dissected it. Deep residual soils mask most of its surface, which transects flat and tilted beds almost indifferently, though low hills are underlain by the more resistant rocks. In parts of the Appalachians dominated by ridges of sandstone, the Harrisburg surface, if recognized at all, forms only valley terraces (Fig. 12–40). The terraces are between 60 to 100 meters above the streams in their lower courses, but slope less steeply than the present streams, so that they converge upstream with the present stream levels. Most river valleys in the southern Appalachians have terraces approximately correlative with the Harrisburg surface, though it is significant that the surface may lie at very different elevations in the valleys on either side of a pass.

FIGURE 12–38   *Faulted and entrenched fans at the mouth of Tuber Canyon, Panamint Range, California. Note the new fans growing on the downdropped block, and their relation to the newly entrenched channels on the upthrown block. (Photo by John S. Shelton, Claremont, California.)*

FIGURE 12–39

The erosion surface at Harrisburg, Pennsylvania (foreground and middle distance). The level summits of the distant ridges are remnants of an older, more thoroughly dissected erosion surface called the Schooley surface. (Photo by G. H. Ashley, Pennsylvania State Geological Survey.)

FIGURE 12–40

Relief diagram showing distribution of the Harrisburg surface in a strip across southern Pennsylvania, just south of Harrisburg. The underlying structure is much generalized. (After maps and folios of the U.S. Geological Survey.)

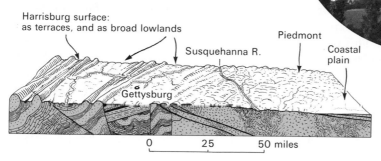

Harrisburg surface: as terraces, and as broad lowlands — Susquehanna R. — Piedmont — Coastal plain — Gettysburg — 0 25 50 miles

Peneplains

Remnants of extensive erosion surfaces, commonly called **peneplains** (from Latin, *paene,* meaning "almost") occur widely over the earth. Some, as in the central United States, from Missouri and Kansas south, lie near but above the graded streams that flow through them. Others, as we shall see in Chapter 19, have been uplifted and deeply eroded, leaving only scattered remnants as nearly flat mountain summits of accordant elevations. How are such extensive surfaces of low relief formed? Study of the better preserved ones indicates that many result from erosion by many streams flowing very near base level and constantly aided by rillwash and downslope movements. Others apparently result from subequal rates of degradation by roughly equally spaced streams acting on similar bedrocks so that the stream divides

are lowered at roughly equal rates over considerable areas.

Evidence for such an origin lies in the facts: (1) that the surfaces truncate all but the most resistant rocks, in all attitudes, (2) residual stream channels and alluvium are common upon them, and (3) superposed marine deposits are absent. They are, as a whole, not truly featureless plains formed by lateral migrations of meandering streams, though, of course parts, of them may be. Peneplains result from long-continued erosion of a large land area by downslope movements, solution, rillwash, and many streams operating over vast periods of time, despite minor warping and climatic changes. Because of such complexity, peneplains are not flat, but undulating, their low ridges and rounded crests the last remnants of former much higher drainage divides underlain by the more resistant rocks.

Though it has been suggested that peneplains are the end product of erosion, careful study of the earth's landscapes shows that all such surfaces are, like the Harrisburg surface, variously uplifted, warped, dissected, or otherwise imperfect. It is unlikely that all areas on them reached their present erosional form at the same time, and most parts of them are being actively eroded today by rainwash, creep, solution, and the work of the streams that drain them. Nevertheless, such widespread erosion surfaces of low relief do imply that the land did stand near base level for long periods of time. Like stream terraces, they help to interpret the nature and amount of crustal deformation in the relatively recent geologic past.

Reference to the rates of erosion cited in Chapter 5 shows however, that peneplains must be geologically ephemeral features, which can hardly be expected to remain recognizable after uplift followed by rejuvenated erosion for more than a very few million years. The Ozark Plateau, in southern Missouri and northern Arkansas, for example, is now being lowered at the average rate of 66 feet per million years by solution alone. A peneplain formed in the Oligocene, for example, 30 million years ago, would have been lowered roughly 30 times 60 feet—say, 1500 to 2000 feet. The more soluble rocks would lose more than this thickness. Furthermore, there would have been much additional clastic sediment removed. The relatively flat surface of the Ozark Plateau seems more likely to be the product of roughly equidistantly spaced drainage channels attacking the flat-lying rocks between interstream divides at roughly equal rates of downcutting than to be the remnant of a peneplain cut near base level many millions of years ago.

We conclude our discussion of peneplains and other widespread surfaces of erosion by some queries based on Figure 10–4, which summarizes the total areas of the earth that lie between various altitude limits, and emphasizes two especially prominent altitude ranges.

What are the reasons for these two dominant altitude ranges in the architecture of the earth? Does the upper range, embracing areas between 200 meters below sea level and 500 meters above, represent the continual tendency of streams to erode the landmasses to sea level, and to pile the detritus derived from them upon the continental shelves? What isostatic effects may be expected from the continual unloading of the landmasses by erosion and the concurrent loading of the continental shelves by deposition? Why is the boundary between continental shelf and ocean floor so abrupt? Is this due to a fundamental difference in density between continental and oceanic blocks? These questions are not easily answered, although some progress is being made. We will return to them in Chapter 17 after we have discussed other processes of erosion and deposition.

Facts, concepts, terms

Laminar and turbulent flow
Factors that determine stream velocity
Distribution of velocity and turbulence in a stream's cross section
How streams acquire and carry their load
    Wash load; suspended load; bed load; dissolved load
    Abrasion of channel bottom and banks
Competence and capacity of streams
    Bed form and flow regime

Source of stream load
Long profiles of streams
Concept of the graded river
    Adjustment of gradient
    Adjustment of channel shape
    Adjustment of stream pattern
Base levels; ultimate and temporary
Channel patterns: meandering and braided
Meanders, cutoffs, oxbow lakes
Natural levees; channel deposits; river bars
Scale models of streams
Stream deposits
    Floodplain deposits, deltas, alluvial fans
Sculpture of the land by streams
    Dendritic and trellis stream patterns; headward erosion
    Stream terraces
    Floodplains
    Peneplains

Questions

1. Would you expect the dissolved load per cubic meter of water to be higher in the Columbia (high rainfall) or in the Colorado River (low rainfall)? Why?
2. At most stream junctions the surface of the tributary and of the main channel are identical in elevation at the point where they join. Why?
3. Engineers have made many artificial cutoffs (Fig. 12–17) in the lower Mississippi and other meandering rivers. Considering the nature of meandering streams, can you suggest reasons for these projects?
4. List several criteria for distinguishing between floodplain, delta, and alluvial-fan deposits in ancient sedimentary rocks.
5. Suggest how a change in climate might produce stream terraces in areas with which you are familiar.
6. The St. Lawrence, one of the great rivers of the continent, has no delta, even though it runs into a landlocked estuary. Can you suggest why?
7. The longitudinal profile of most large rivers resembles the land portion of the graph in Figure 10–4. Can you offer any explanation of this?
8. At what point of an alluvial fan is the sediment coarsest? Why?
9. The Yazoo River, on a common floodplain with the Mississippi, parallels that stream for scores of kilometers before joining it. Why doesn't it join sooner?
10. Assuming flat-lying strata, would you expect stream spacing to be closer on a thick sandstone bed or on a thick shale formation? Why?

Suggested readings

Fisk, H. N. *Fine-Grained Alluvial Deposits and Their Effects on Mississippi River Activity*. Vicksburg, Mississippi: Waterways Experiment Station, 1947.

Gilbert, G. K. *Geology of the Henry Mountains* (U.S. Geographical and Geological Survey of the Rocky Mountains Region, 1877). [P. 99–150, *Land Sculpture*—a classic paper, outlining the principles of stream erosion and applying them to the origin of the land forms of central Utah. Its publication marks a milestone in the study of physiography.]

Leopold, L. B., M. C. Wolman, and J. P. Miller, *Fluvial Processes in Geomorphology*. San Francisco: W. H. Freeman and Company, 1964.

Rubey, W. W., *Geology and Mineral Resources of the Hardin and Brussels Quadrangles, Illinois* (U.S. Geological Survey, Professional Paper 218). Washington, D.C.: G. P. O., 1952. [P. 101–137, *Physiography*. P. 129–136 gives a clear concise account of the adjustments a stream makes in adjusting its grade.]

Sundborg, Äke, *The River Klarälven, a study of Fluvial Processes,"* Geografiska Annaler, v. 38, 1956, p. 127–316. [A good description of the hydraulics of river channels and their relation to the morphology of a particular river.]

Scientific American offprints

826. Raymond E. Janssen, *The History of a River* (June 1952)

836. Gerard H. Matthes, *Paradoxes of the Mississippi* (April 1951)

869. Luna B. Leopold and W. B. Langbein, *River Meanders* (June 1966)

13

Glaciers and Glaciation

Glaciers are slow-moving, thick masses of ice. **Snowfields** are thinner, almost motionless masses of permanent snow (Figs. 13–2, 13–7).

During the last century most glaciers have been shrinking; the snowfall, on the average, has not balanced melting. Exceptions occur: two glaciers flow from the same ice field in New Zealand, one is advancing, the other retreating. The Taku glacier, in southeastern Alaska, advanced 5 kilometers in the last fifty years; ten others nearby rapidly receded. The Bruggen glacier in Patagonia advanced fully 7 kilometers between 1830 and 1962. Nevertheless, most, by far, of the glaciers of both hemispheres have retreated markedly. For example, the Guyot glacier of southern Alaska retreated 23 miles between 1900 and 1961.

Tide records from all oceans prove that sea level is rising. A concurrence of oceanic rise of about 10 centimeters in the last century with simultaneous glacial retreat emphasizes that snowfields and glaciers act as savings banks in the water economy of the earth. Each year some water evaporated from the seas and lands falls as snow, and on the high mountains and in polar regions some is stored in snowfields (Fig. 13–2). Careful estimates by R. L. Nace of the U.S. Geological Survey indicate that 2.24 percent of the water of the earth—but 77 percent of all water not in the oceans—is presently in glaciers and snowfields.

THE SNOWLINE

The lower limit of permanent snow is called the **snowline.** The altitude of the snowline varies from place to place, depending on latitude, snowfall, temperature, wind direction (which controls drifting of the snow), and topography (which controls both snowsliding and shading from the sun).

Mean annual temperature decreases at higher altitudes and latitudes; precipitation is also affected by latitude, being less in the

Horse Latitudes than at either the equator or higher latitudes. Accordingly, the snow-line, which is at 14,000 feet on Mount Kenya and 15,000 feet on Mount Kilimanjaro in equatorial Africa, is at 20,000 feet in Tibet in the rain shadow of the Himalayas, and at more than 21,000 feet in the Andes of arid northern Chile (see Fig. 13–41). On the dry eastern slope of the St. Elias Mountains on the Alaska-Yukon border, the snowline is at 8000 to 9000 feet; on the wet western slope it is 5000 feet lower. It is lower in well-watered Norway than in the far colder, but dry, Taimyr peninsula of Siberia. Permanent snowfields and glaciers are lacking in most of Siberia, Northern Alaska, and Canada. The mean annual temperature is low enough to preserve masses of ice, but the snowfall is too scanty to supply them. In these areas moisture in the pores of soil and rock remains frozen throughout the year in a great sheet of permanently frozen ground, or **permafrost.** In many places it is hundreds of feet thick, and in parts of Siberia as thick as 2000 feet. One-fourth of all the land surface of the earth overlies permafrost.

SNOWFIELDS

Permanent snowfields cover all but the steepest and windiest slopes above the snowline (Figs. 13–2, 5–2). Excavations in snowfields where downslope movement is slight, reveal the annual additions of snow as a kind of stratification brought out by slight textural variations. The beautiful geometric patterns of new-fallen snowflakes (Fig. 13–3) do not persist at depth. Instead the snowfield consists largely of small granules of ice, about the size of birdshot. This material, called **firn,** grows by compaction of the feathery snowflakes and by thawing and refreezing of their edges.

This melting and freezing is not wholly due to variations in air temperatures above the snow. Water expands 9 percent on freezing, hence pressure lowers the melting point. This is why a snowball sticks together when squeezed and released. Snow and firn absorb rain or summer meltwater like a sponge. All precipitation contains a minute admixture of salt derived from sea spray. As the melting point of a salt solution is lower than that of

FIGURE 13–1 *Ten year running means of spring temperature (March–May, inclusive) from 1700–1950 in northern England (black line) and Holland (brown line); below, the behavior of Iceland glaciers: A = advance, R = retreat. (After Gordon Manley,* Journal of Glaciology, *1950, by permission of the Glaciological Society.)*

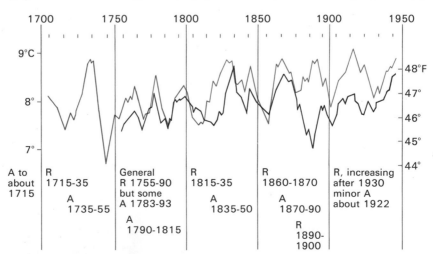

FIGURE 13–2   *Snowfields above the head of a valley glacier in Alaska. Clearest relations are at right foreground and left background: much of the flat in mid-distance is a snowfield, but it merges into moving ice—becoming a glacier below the crevasses that mark the head of a steep slope.*

pure water, an intergranular film of salt solution (the more concentrated and smaller in amount, the colder the ice) is excluded on freezing. This film of mildly salty water makes up about 3 percent of the mass of an Alpine glacier, sampled at a depth of 500 meters, and is present in small amounts in the deeper parts of snowfields and glaciers. Even at temperatures slightly below the normal freezing point, 0° Centigrade or 32° Fahrenheit, snowflakes at depth in a snowfield are under enough load to melt slightly at their points of contact, refreezing in the

intergrain spaces. Thus most mountain glaciers, even as far north as central Greenland and Spitzbergen, are always (except near the

FIGURE 13–3
Forms of fresh snowflakes. (After A. E. H. Tutton, 1927.)

surface where the effect of winter cold may prevail) at a temperature very near the pressure-melting point appropriate to the depth of ice. These are **temperate glaciers.** The grains press together, the film of salt water gradually sinks through the mass and the ice granules grow and coalesce. In stagnant icefields, single crystals of ice 24 centimeters across have been excavated from depth. The walls of a glacial crevasse commonly show all stages in the transformation: snowflake to firn to solid ice with depth. We can trace all steps in the metamorphism of snow, a sediment, into ice, a metamorphic rock.

GLACIER MOTION

Ice appears rigid and brittle; a piece shatters like glass under a blow. Under short-term load it appears very strong, but if it were, even the highest mountains above snowline would eventually be buried in accumulated snow, firn, and ice. But under long-term load, ice is a weak rock; when only a few meters of ice have formed beneath firn and snow it begins to flow downhill. Laboratory experiments show that pure ice at the freezing point begins to flow under shear stress of about one kilogram per square centimeter, but many scientists hold that under natural conditions of sustained load it may flow at stresses less than a tenth as great. The rate of flow increases under higher stress at a rate proportional to the cube or fourth power of the stress. Glaciers are perfect examples of the influence of size and time on strength (Chapter 10).

Load adequate for notable creep is reached at a depth of about 20 meters in temperate glaciers. In **polar glaciers** where temperatures are far below the pressure melting point, ice is stronger and crevasses as deep as 60 or 70 meters are found in stagnant ice. Crevasses of greater depths are only kept open by continual movement.

Glacier motion is imperceptible to the eye but is readily demonstrated by surveying transverse rows of stakes driven into the glacier. The velocity is greatest over the thickest part of the glacier—generally near the middle, where frictional resistance is least (Fig. 13–4). The speed varies seasonally, in winter the higher part of the glacier is more heavily loaded with snow and hence moves faster, in summer the more rapid melting at the end of the glacier lowers the resistance and the lower part speeds up. The speed may suddenly increase throughout the whole glacier in a **surge.** Surges are explained by melting at the base because of frictional heat when the velocity exceeds some critical value. Speeds as great as 113 meters per day were measured on the Kutiah glacier in the western Karakorum in 1953; during a three-month period it advanced fully 10 kilometers. Speeds of 50 meters per day have been measured on a few Alaskan and Greenland glaciers, but such velocities are exceptional (Fig. 13–8). The Beardmore glacier of eastern Antarctica, one of the longest in the world, moves about .8 meter per day. Figure 13–4 shows a common pattern of movement in the Alps. In the Gorner glacier, on the north flank of Monte Rosa, the mean annual speed is .5 meter per day. Some Alaskan coastal glaciers are so nearly stagnant that their debris-covered margins are overgrown with forests. These are virtually at sea level

FIGURE 13–4

Records of flow and frontal shrinkage of the Rhone glacier, Switzerland. (After Albrecht Heim.)

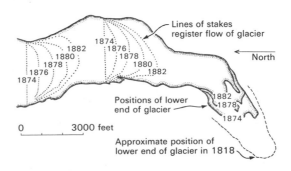

and their gradients are almost negligible (Fig. 13–11).

The mechanism of flow is complex. Microscopic studies show that some ice crystals bend, others glide along sheets of atoms composing the crystals, still others granulate and shear, and, of course, they melt and refreeze. Thus, though the mass as a whole flows, some crystals break, as in many other examples of flowage during metamorphism. The ice crystals, even at the front of a moving glacier, rarely exceed 2 or 3 centimeters in diameter, though in stagnant ice they are many times larger. As in other foliated metamorphic rocks, many crystals are strung out in parallel planes, suggesting that they recrystallized during movement.

Ice at the glacial snout * or in deep crevasses generally shows layering that superficially resembles the true stratification found in snowfields. The layers roughly parallel

* Glacial terminology is somewhat confusing to the layman. The *head*, for example, is the upper end— the highest part; the *snout* or *ice front* is the down-glacier end—the lowest part. The rock channel in which the glacier flows form the glacier *walls* and *floor*.

the floor and curve upward along the glacial walls. Measurements show that adjacent layers move at slightly differing speeds; close to the wall each successive layer inward flows slightly faster than its neighbor. The layers, therefore, are not really bedding, but foliation surfaces caused by friction against the floor and walls of the glacier. In tunnels cut into several moving glaciers, measurements have shown that the shearing is by no means uniformly distributed. Much of the movement, ranging from as little as 12 percent in a thick temperate glacier to as much as 90 percent in a thin polar one, is concentrated into a narrow zone just above the glacier bed, in which a thin layer of water is present. For example, the bottom 2 meters of a vertically drilled bore hole in the Blue glacier of the Olympic Mountains of Washington was bent through an angle of 55° in a single year.

In the Grindelwald glacier, Switzerland, a crevasse gave access to the floor of the glacier at a point where the ice was about 50 meters thick. Here an upward projection of bedrock obstructed the glacier flow. A shear zone separated brittle ice above, moving at 36.8 centimeters per day, from a mass below, about 30

FIGURE 13–5

Concentrated zone of shearing over a roche moutonnée at base of Grindelwald glacier, Switzerland. (After Hans Carol, Journal of Glaciology, *1941, by permission of the Glaciological Society.)*

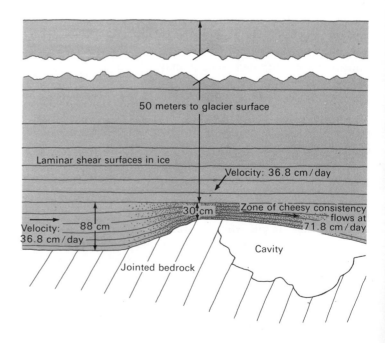

FIGURE 13–6   *Overfolded silt band at front of Taylor glacier, South Victoria Land, Antarctica, showing how ice, overriding the basal slip surface has dragged the silt band into a flat fold. (Photo by Warren Hamilton, U.S. Geological Survey.)*

centimeters thick, which had the consistency of cheese. In this cheesy layer the velocity was 71.8 centimeters per day, nearly twice the speed above, The whole basal meter of ice up-glacier from the obstruction was squeezed into the thin cheesy layer. As the cheesy ice passed over the obstruction's crest it immediately became brittle like that above the shear zone, and was stiff enough to bridge

a cavity several meters wide in the lee of the obstruction (Fig. 13–5). Had the ice been much thicker such an open cavity could not have been maintained.

The shear banding of glaciers is commonly emphasized by streaks of dust and other rock debris dragged into the glacial mass (Fig. 13–6). The foliation—very like that of many gneisses and schists—proves that the ice is

FIGURE 13–7

Portage glacier, Alaska, showing concave profile above and convex profile below firn line, which is just below steep glacial slope in mid-distance. (Photo by U.S. Air Force.)

no longer brittle, but reacts to differences in pressure by flowage and recrystallization.

The upper parts of most glaciers are covered with snow, even through the summer. Farther down, snow accumulates in winter, but is melted or evaporated by the end of the summer, exposing the underlying firn. Still farther down-glacier the firn ends: evaporation and melting have exposed the underlying ice. This lower limit of firn in summer is the **firn line.** Above it is the zone of net accumulation, below it the zone of net loss.

Above the firn line the transverse profile of a valley glacier is always concave, sloping toward the glacier's axis. Below the firn line the transverse profile becomes convex (Fig. 13–7). Above the firn line a particle of ice tends to move down, into the body of the glacier, as it becomes buried by increasing thicknesses of snow, firn, and ice; below the firn line it tends to move toward the surface as the overlying ice melts. The shear zones within the glacier are curved the same way:

downward at decreasing slopes above the firn line and upward with steepening slopes below it. The maximum velocity of a valley glacier is generally reached near firn line.

KINDS OF GLACIERS

The topography over which a glacier flows largely controls its form. **Valley glaciers** (Fig. 13–8) are ice streams flowing down steep-walled mountain valleys. Fed by large snowfields above, such glaciers may extend far below the snowline. All glaciers end where the ice front melts as fast as it is replenished by flowage.

Glaciers occupy lofty mountain valleys the world over—even in the tropics, as in the Carstenz Range in New Guinea, Ruwenzori in Uganda, and Cotopoxi in the Ecuadorean Andes. The valley glaciers of the United States, except those of Mount Rainier (where the astounding total of more than 80 feet of snow has been measured in a single year) are short ice streams only a few hundred feet thick. Many are hardly distinguishable from snowfields; indeed there are all gradations between. The Rocky Mountains, Cascade Range, and high Sierra hold hundreds of small irregular ice masses, called **cliff glaciers** or **hanging glaciers,** in well-shaded clefts opening out over steep cliffs (Figs. 13–9, 13–10).

In contrast to these puny streams, many valley glaciers in the Himalayas and Alaska are as long as 70 miles and over 3000 feet thick, with many tributaries merging into an integrated system (Fig. 13–8) draining hundreds of square miles. At the foot of the St. Elias Mountains in Alaska several of these valley glaciers emerge, spread over the plain, and join to form Malaspina glacier (Fig. 13–11), a lobate ice mass covering 800 square miles—a **piedmont glacier.** Behind the stagnant frontal area, the ice emerging from the valley glaciers above is forced into horizontal fold patterns of fantastic scale and complexity (Fig. 13–12).

FIGURE 13–8 *Steele glacier, Yukon Territory, Canada. A surging glacier. (Photo by Austin Post, U.S. Geological Survey.)*

FIGURE 13–9 *Small cliff glaciers, Sierra Nevada, California. Note how the rock in the foreground has been shattered by frost action. (Photo by François Matthes, U.S. Geological Survey.)*

FIGURE 13–10   *Hanging glacier on the north side of Mount Athabaska, Jasper National Park, Alberta. (Photo by Warren Hamilton, U.S. Geological Survey.)*

FIGURE 13–11   *Map of the Malaspina glacier, Alaska. The arrows indicate the flow of the valley glaciers that feed the Malaspina. (After R. S. Tarr and Laurence Martin, 1914.)*

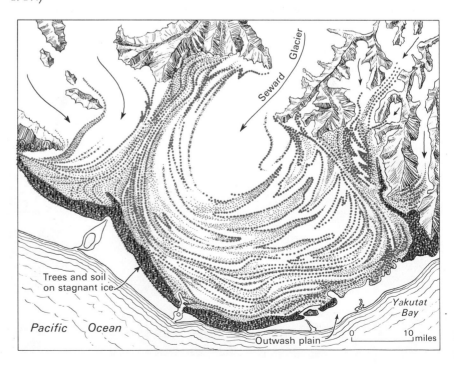

FIGURE 13–12   *Folds in the Malaspina glacier, Alaska. Seward glacier in right rear. The scale of folding is in miles, in places as much as 10 miles. (Photo by Austin Post, U.S. Geological Survey.)*

FIGURE 13–13

Top: *Ice in the Bay of Whales, Antarctica. The Bay of Whales is a reentrant in the Ross Shelf Ice, protected in part by islands. The bay ice, 30 to 50 feet thick, is folded by the pressure of the advance of the much thicker shelf ice around the protecting islands. The individual folds are several tens of feet high. Similar folds nearby are caused by the drag of the shelf ice over its morainal deposits. (Air photo by T. C. Poulter.)*
Bottom: *Sections through the Ross Shelf Ice and Bay of Whales. The thickness of the ice has been determined by seismic methods, described in Chapter 19. (After T. C. Poulter, Stanford Research Institute.)*

The great Ice Barrier of the Ross Sea in eastern Antarctica is also formed partly by coalescence of valley glaciers at the mountain front, but here most of the ice is floating, rather than lying on a coastal plain (Fig. 13–13).

Small masses of radially spreading ice are found on Iceland, Spitzbergen, parts of Scandinavia, and the islands north of Canada (Fig. 13–14). These are **ice caps.**

The largest of all glaciers are huge ice

FIGURE 13–14

Ice caps of Iceland and Spitzbergen. (After Stieler's Atlas.)

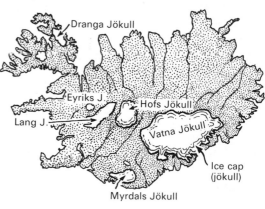

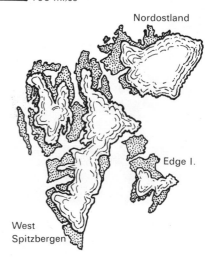

sheets, called **continental glaciers,** now found only in high latitudes, though they were formerly much more widespread. All of interior Greenland—over 630,000 square miles—is ice covered, leaving only a coastal fringe of land. The Greenland glacier spreads in all directions from two high swells in the interior. Parts of the coast are bordered by lofty mountains through whose valleys the glacier spills, and flows in tongues to the sea. Geophysical soundings (See Chapter 19) show that much of the inland ice is several thousand feet thick, indeed, the ice-blanketed rock surface of central Greenland is below sea level.

Antarctica supports a much larger continental glacier that covers about 13,000,000 square kilometers—an area larger than the United States and Mexico. Over much of this area the ice is 2 to 2.5 kilometers thick; its total volume has been estimated at 24 million cubic kilometers (more than 5 million cubic miles), enough to cover the United States to a depth of nearly 9000 feet. At the pole the ice surface is nearly 3 kilometers above the sea, but bedrock is close to sea level. The glacier overrides the coast in places and projects into the shelf ice formed by the freezing of the sea. In places the ice escapes between mountains in huge valley glaciers. The famous Beardmore glacier, ascended by several of the early explorers in their quest for the South Pole, is one of these. The Beardmore glacier, 300 miles long and 12 miles wide, flows from the interior plateau at more than 10,000 feet altitude far out into the shelf ice of the Ross Sea.

GLACIER LOADS

Frost weathering and avalanching

Glaciers acquire rock debris in several ways. Valley glaciers generally cover only small parts of the mountains from which they flow. Gentle slopes hold extensive snowfields, but steep slopes are swept bare by wind and avalanche, exposing great expanses of crags, peaks, and cliffs above the glaciers (Figs. 13–8, 13–10). Frost action strongly shatters these bare rocks (Fig. 13–9). During the day, meltwater from snowbanks seeps into the crevices; that same night it may freeze. Small grains, loose chips, and even great blocks of rock thus freed tumble down the slopes and accumulate in talus piles along the edge of the glacier. Landslides and rockfalls from cliffs undermined by the glacier crash down upon it. Much debris tumbles down with avalanches (snowslides). The power of these slides may be truly stupendous. Wet snow has been found to slide on slopes as low as 15°, and snow fences at Fionnay, Switzerland, designed to withstand pressures of 4 tons per square foot, were swept away by a slide on a slope only slightly steeper. A large avalanche thus can sweep a huge load of loosened blocks onto a glacier. Additional debris washes down in freshets from melting snow and summer rains (see Fig. 5–2).

In this way the glacier, especially along its edges, becomes charged with rock material, which forms conspicuous dark streaks along it. These stripes of dirty ice and loose rock are **lateral moraines.** If two valley glaciers join, the inner lateral moraines unite to form a **medial moraine** marking their union below the junction. If tributaries are many, several medial moraines may streak the surface of the trunk glacier (Figs. 13–8, 13–12, 13–15). The moraines are not merely surface features; they extend into the body of the glacier. Glaciers also drag shattered rock debris across their floors; much is loose rock scooped up as the glacier scrapes its floor; some is plucked bodily from the bed by pressure of the moving ice, some is rasped off by boulders frozen into the ice and dragged along with it. Rock fragments from the surface also become embedded deep in the ice; they tumble into crevasses opened during glacial motion or are brought down by avalanches and gradually sink to the bottom because of their high density.

FIGURE 13–15   *Valley Glacier in Alaska Coast Range, near Skagway, Alaska. Note medial moraines, springing from spurs between branches of the glacier. (Air photo by Tad Nichols, Tucson, Arizona.)*

FIGURE 13–16
Progressive stages of erosion at the head of a valley glacier (left), *with a detail of the bergschrund* (right). (*In part after W. V. Lewis,* Journal of Glaciology, *1938.*)

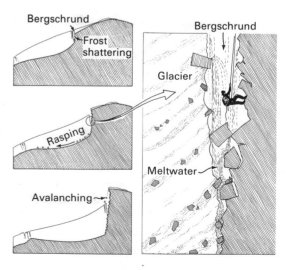

Meltwater shattering

At the head of most valley glaciers is a deep arcuate crevasse, or a series of closely spaced crevasses, called the **bergschrund** (Figs. 5–2, 13–16). Such crevasses open because the downstream flow of ice low in the glacier breaks the brittle ice above away from its rock wall. The bergschrund yawns open in summer but is generally filled or bridged with snow in winter.

Adventurous observers have descended into bergschrunds on ropes and found that the lower parts have a rocky wall on the upstream side and an ice wall on the other. The rock wall is cracked and riven with joints, some gaping, as the blocks they bound are pulled loose. Many blocks are broken free but are still nearly in place; others lean out against the ice in precarious imbalance; still others, entirely separated from their parent ledges, are embedded in the ice (Fig. 13–16). During the summer day, meltwater pours over the bergschrund cliff, filling the joints; the almost nightly frost loosens new blocks to tumble into the chasm. Gradually the cliff at the headwall is thus eaten back and the glacier grows headward.

Crevasses deeper than about 20 or 30 meters are normally closed by the plastic flow of the ice. Nevertheless, the fissures at the bergschrund must extend far deeper and remain open because the ice continues to move downvalley. On hot summer days of warm winds and rains, huge quantities of meltwater cascade into the bergschrund, yet never fill it; the meltwater must open its own channels to the bottom of the glacier, where, of course, the melting point is slightly lower than at the surface. The meltwater carries heat downward, keeping the tubes open. Meltwater deep within the glacier, however, is protected from daily temperature changes so that shattering by frost must be much less at depth than nearer the surface.

Cirques

The moving glacier carries off the shattered rock of the bergschrund and continually exposes new surfaces to attack. Where valley glaciers have melted completely away, exposing their headwalls, the glaciated valley generally ends in a semicircle of steep cliffs that bound a rock basin holding a pond or lake. Such cliffed valley heads are called **cirques.** (Figs. 13–9, 13–30). The cliffs at the cirque head are shattered through their full height and generally meet the grooved and polished valley floor at a high angle. The jagged and shattered cliffs, products of the frost erosion and plucking in the bergschrunds, contrast strikingly with the smoothed valley floor, the product of rasping by the glacial debris.

The glacial rasp

At the head of a valley glacier, the thick accumulation of snow and ice, heavily charged with rock debris, moves outward along curved shear surfaces as in many landslides (Figs. 11–15, 11–16). As this heavy rock-charged ice slides over the bedrock it abrades the bed like a gigantic rasp (Figs. 13–17, 13–18, 13–19, 13–40), gouging into and scraping off irregularities, and polishing and grooving the rock beneath. In places, the glacier breaks off semiovoid wedges of rock—**chatter marks**—resembling the tracks of a horse going down-glacier (Fig. 13–19). The polishing and planing off of irregularities continues all the way down-glacier, but because cutting tools are especially concentrated near the head, this is the favored place for rapid deepening of the floor.

FIGURE 13–17
Rock surface showing glacial grooving, polishing, and, at the left, plucking, near Mount Baker, Washington. The ice flowed diagonally from the upper left to the lower right. (Photo by H. A. Coombs, University of Washington.)

FIGURE 13–18
Glacially polished columnar basalt, Devil's Post-pile, California. (Photo by Tad Nichols, Tucson, Arizona.)

FIGURE 13–19
Lunate chatter marks on the back of a roche moutonée, near the lower end of Florence Canyon, Sierra Nevada, California. (Photo by François Matthes, U.S. Geological Survey.)

Debris in continental glaciers

A continental glacier covers so much of the ground that frost shattering and avalanche accumulation take place only around islands of rock that rise above the ice sheet. Also, meltwater can deliver proportionately much less debris than is present in a valley glacier. Yet the ice at the margins of the Greenland glacier is as heavily charged with debris as any valley glacier. How was it entrained? One source of debris is the soil and loose rock that was present before the glacier became established. Where continental glaciers have melted away, the rock floor lain bare is nearly everywhere free of soil and such unconsolidated materials as stream gravels and flood-plain deposits, except where the glacier has packed this material into depressions that it overrode. The moving ice drags off most loose material bodily. Therefore preglacial soil should long ago have been carried into the sea, for the Greenland ice has surely existed for a very long time. The present load of the Greenland ice must be derived by presently acting processes—by plucking and rasping of the floor and by the action of subglacial meltwater streams—but the problem is still poorly understood by glaciologists.

Erosion by continental glaciers

Rock floors exposed by the melting of continental glaciers are scratched and deeply grooved (Fig. 13–40); clearly the glacier has gouged and abraded its bed. Continental glaciers are thicker and heavier than most valley glaciers—even though not as abundantly charged with rock debris, they are very effective rasps. The preglacial valleys of New York's Finger Lakes region were deeply hollowed out and widened by continental glaciers.

How quickly a glacier cuts down its bed depends on four factors: (1) the resistance to abrasion of the floor, (2) the abundance and hardness of the rock fragments frozen into the basal layers of the ice, (3) the speed and duration of flow, and (4) the weight—thickness—of the ice. Thick continental glaciers flowing over weakly coherent rocks cut rapidly; valley glaciers are most effective on cirque floors where the ice is thickest and most heavily armed.

Where abundant ice has been funneled into valleys to great depths, as in the fjords of Norway, Alaska, and New Zealand, it has worn deep troughs, many hundreds of meters below the level of the sea. The seaward ends of fjords generally contain a bedrock sill marking the approximate maximum advance of the ice, where, at the terminus, it was partly melted by the sea water and buoyed up so that it broke into icebergs.

Debris released by glaciers

TILL. That glaciers erode effectively is also proved by the vast amount of debris released at the snout on melting. Hummocky ridges of boulders, sand, and silt, mixed without appreciable sorting or stratification, are piled along the ice front. Such unsorted debris (Fig. 13–20), deposited directly by the ice, is called **till**. The proportion of boulders to fine material in till varies widely. Some till is mainly coarse boulders, but that from thin ice caps eroding shale may be chiefly clay and silt, with only scattered boulders.

Rock fragments in till differ from those in stream and beach deposits. Most pebbles of streams and beaches are rounded, but most in till are subrounded or sharply angular. Some have been crushed by the weight of the overriding glacier; many, especially in valley glaciers, are joint blocks dislodged by freezing and little modified by abrasion. Some fragments are faceted, with nearly flat, grooved, and polished surfaces formed as the boulder scraped along the bedrock floor.

ROCK FLOUR. The glacial rasp produces large amounts of **rock flour** (silt and fine sand) as mentioned in Chapter 5.

The turbulent streams of milky water that

FIGURE 13–20
Till deposited by a valley glacier, West Walker River, Nevada. The largest boulders are nearly half a meter in diameter. (Photo by Eliot Black-welder, Stanford University.)

FIGURE 13–21
Silt-laden stream emerging from an ice tunnel in the front of a glacier, Tanana district, Alaska. (Photo by S. R. Capps, U.S. Geological Survey.)

FIGURE 13–22
Vertical airplane view and explanatory sketch of deposits at the foot of a valley glacier, Alaska. Note how the recessional moraine (black in sketch) has been partly buried by later outwash fans. Note also how the course of the throughgoing stream becomes braided where the glacial outwash enters it. (Photo by U.S. Air Force.)

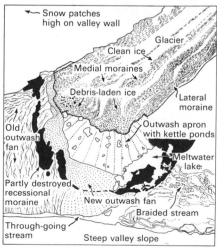

gush from tunnels in the glacier snout (Fig. 13–21) are invariably overloaded, and their braided channels quickly deposit rubble and coarse sand, building up a sloping gravel plain (Fig. 13–22) in front of the glacier. The finer debris goes on to build floodplains or to form bottom deposits in lakes or the sea. Rock flour derived from granodiorite forms great terraces of white silt along many rivers of British Columbia and Alaska.

Rock flour is also widely blown about in late summer when the glacial streams shrink and expose their braided channels to the wind. Unstratified deposits of **loess** (a loam consisting chiefly of silt particles carried by the wind) are widespread near many glaciated areas (Fig. 13–23). Most loess contains innumerable roughly vertical tubules left by the rotting of grass stems and roots. Although only feebly consolidated, loess stands well in nearly vertical banks.

FORMS OF GLACIAL DEPOSITS

The debris dumped by glaciers or by associated streams and lakes is called **glacial drift.** The unstratified material freed directly from the melting ice forms **moraines;** that reworked by streams or in lakes is called **stratified drift.**

Moraines

Most till makes moraines, a term used both for the hills or other topographic forms of a till mass, and for debris upon or within an active glacier. Moraines are generally largest and best developed at the glacier front. If the rates of ice flow and of melting are about equal, so that the ice front remains nearly stationary for a long time, the debris released from the melting ice accumulates in great hummocky ridges. As the ice front often fluctuates with minor climatic changes, however, more than one morainal ridge commonly forms. The farthest advanced is the **terminal**

moraine; those formed during halts in a glacial retreat are **recessional moraines.** Terminal and recessional moraines of valley glaciers are crescent-shaped ridges that curve around the glacier snout and extend up the sides as **lateral moraines** (Fig. 13–24). Small recessional moraines may be almost buried by later outwash as shown in Figure 13–24.

The terminal and recessional moraines of most continental glaciers are broadly lobate in plan and can be followed for many miles except where breached by outwash during the waning phase. (Fig. 13–23). Some debris freed as the ice retreats is strewn as patches of till over the glaciated area (Fig. 13–25). Such irregularly scattered **ground moraine** is not aligned in definite ridges: some is packed into depressions, or plastered around low bedrock hills. Ground moraine is the most widespread deposit of a continental ice sheet. It is generally spotty and thin, but near the

FIGURE 13–23

Relation of loess-covered areas to the terminal moraines of four glacial advances in Europe. (Adapted from R. F. Flint, Glacial Geology and the Pleistocene Epoch, *John Wiley and Sons, 1947, and R. A. Daly,* The Changing World of the Ice Age, *Yale University Press, 1934.)*

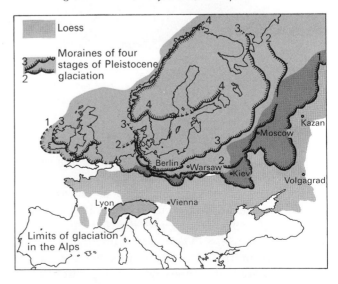

FIGURE 13–24   *Recessional moraines in lower Victoria Dry Valley, South Victoria Land, Ant-*
arctica. The surficial deposits are patterned by frost polygons. A frozen lake lies
against the snout of the glacier. (Photo by U.S. Navy for U.S. Geological
Survey.)

margin of a glaciated area may almost continuously veneer hundreds of square miles.

A later surge of the glacier may override
the ground moraine and mold it into clusters
of hills, each shaped like half an egg, cut
lengthwise. These streamlined hills, called
drumlins, range widely in size, but many are
more than a thousand feet long, three or four

hundred feet wide, and 50 to 150 feet high.
They cluster in scores or hundreds along the
trend of the overridden moraine, each drumlin axis roughly paralleling the direction of
glacial flow (Fig. 13–25). Excavations show
cores of bedrock in some drumlins, but most
are wholly clayey till.

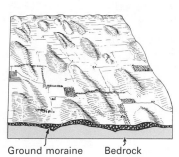

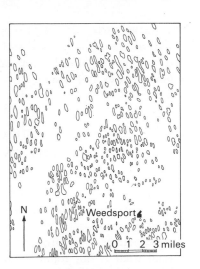

FIGURE 13–25

Map of drumlins and sketch of ground moraine near Weedsport, New York. (From Weedsport quadrangle, New York, U.S. Geological Survey.)

Stratified drift

Glacial meltwater carries huge quantities of gravel, sand, and rock flour, much of which is deposited in alluvial fans just down-valley from the glacier front, but some is carried on to lakes or the sea. The coalescing alluvial fans of many braided streams spread from the margins of continental glaciers and form **outwash plains.** Some outwash plains are pitted by countless undrained holes—most less than a hundred feet across but some a mile or more long and as deep as a hundred feet. (Fig. 13–22). These are **kettles,** each marking the place where a block of ice, stranded during the glacial retreat, was surrounded or buried by outwash gravels. Melting of the ice left the depressions (Fig. 13–26).

Alluvial fans or outwash plains built by overloaded streams during active glaciation are cut into by the no longer overloaded streams after glacial retreat. Their remnants form terraces.

Long ridges of stratified sand and gravel—**eskers**—wind across some areas formerly covered by continental glaciers. Most are less than a hundred feet high and a few hundred feet wide, but may be several miles long. Some merge downstream into outwash fans or abandoned deltas. The eskers must have

FIGURE 13–26

Small kettle lake in outwash gravels of the Baird glacier, Alaska. (Photo by A. F. Buddington, U.S. Geological Survey.)

been built by aggrading streams flowing in tunnels beneath the ice or in crevasses—presumably after the ice became almost stagnant during wasting. The thrust of an active glacier would surely have closed the tunnels or crevasses and scattered the esker into ground moraine.

Many lakes are dammed on one side by glacial ice, and the water extends into crevasses and irregular holes in the wasting glacier. Such lakes are, of course, unstable; they fluctuate in level as advance or retreat of the glacier changes their outlets. Some in Alaska are completely drained nearly every year. Their sediments are thus commonly interlayered with stream deposits and till. Should the glacier melt, patches of these mixed sediments along the ice margins (Fig. 13–8) are left as terraces and flat-topped hills called **kame terraces** and **kames.**

MODIFICATION OF TOPOGRAPHY BY GLACIERS

Topography shaped by glaciers differs conspicuously from that shaped by running water, as is seen in areas recently uncovered by glacial recession.

The polished and grooved bedrock of the glacial floor is not found in normal stream channels. Areas formerly glaciated contain swarms of lakes, ponds, and marshes in rock basins scooped out by the ice. The basins of the Great Lakes, the Finger Lakes of New

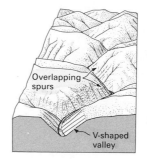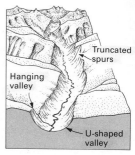

FIGURE 13–27

A hypothetical stream valley and its associated forms before and after being modified by a valley glacier.

York, Lakes Maggiore, Leman, and Lucerne, as well as hundreds of others, were excavated by glacial scour. Depressions dammed by moraines and outwash, or left by the melting

FIGURE 13–28   *A glaciated valley in the Sierra Nevada, showing typical U-shape, faceted spurs, and hanging valley. (Photo by Warren Hamilton, U.S. Geological Survey.)*

of blocks stranded during glacial retreat also impound many lakes and marshes. Streams connecting these lakes are generally ungraded, with many waterfalls and rapids.

The up-glacier sides of most hills and rock knobs overridden by ice are rounded, polished, and grooved; the down-glacier sides are irregularly jagged. The glacial rasp has worn smooth the side on which it impinged but the quarrying and dragging out of joint blocks by the overriding ice has roughened the lee side. Rock knobs so sculptured are called **roches moutonnées** (sheep rocks).

Canyons of mountain streams are V shaped in cross profile, but those of glaciated valleys are characteristically U shaped because of grinding by the glacial rasp. Remnants of the former V shape, cut by a preglacial stream, may be preserved on canyon walls higher than the levels reached by the vanished glacier. Glaciated valleys are also straighter and smoother than the usual V-shaped valley; irregularities on their walls and the spurs between tributary valleys have been worn and quarried away by the ice (Figs. 13–27, 13–28, 13–29). A viscous glacier cannot turn sharp curves as readily as water; because of its mass and stiffness it planes off the irregularities in its channel and facets the ends of the ridge spurs between its tributaries. Thus the valley floor is deepened and widened, transforming an originally crooked and narrow V profile to a straight and wider U.

The long profile of a glaciated valley is commonly interrupted by abrupt steps, above and below which the smooth U-shaped valley may continue with flatter gradients. Several such "cyclopean steps" may appear in a

FIGURE 13–29   *The valley of the Roaring Fork, Colorado, showing hanging valleys, faceted spurs, and a tiny stream wholly out of scale with the width of the valley. (Photo by C. B. Hunt, U.S. Geological Survey.)*

FIGURE 13–30 *Mount Assiniboine, a glacial horn, near Banff, Alberta. Note the many cirques, some with hanging glaciers. (Photo by Alberta Department of Mines and Resources.)*

single valley, alternating with polished rock floors and lake-filled basins.

Unlike stream valleys, most glaciated valleys head in cirques (Fig. 13–10). In recently deglaciated mountains huge semicircular cirques are, in places, so closely spaced that the divides between them have been reduced to knife-edged "combs" (Fig. 13–9), or to triangular "horns" (Fig. 13–30). The Matterhorn is an excellent example.

Stream valleys and glaciated valleys also differ in the junctions of the tributaries to the main stream. In unglaciated stream valleys nearly all tributaries join the main stream at its level. The top of a tributary glacier generally joins the main glacier at grade—though because of the rigidity of a thin ice mass this is not always so—but the floors beneath main glacier and tributary are generally cut to very different depths, depending on the volume and speed of the respective ice streams. A thin tributary glacier, unless favored by less resistant bedrock, cannot keep pace with the scouring and plucking by the larger glacier, so that when the ice melts away the floor of the tributary valley is left hanging high above the floor of the main valley, and its stream plunges in waterfalls or steep rapids to the main valley (Figs. 13–28, 13–29).

Glaciers thus leave unmistakeable marks upon a landscape; such features testify to widespread former glaciation in areas that today have temperate or even tropical climates.

FORMER PERIODS OF GLACIATION

The Iowa farmer, sweltering under the August sun, may doubt that "the present is the key to the past" if told that his fertile soil was formed on deposits left by an ice sheet that once covered most of northern North America. Similarly, the native of the Talchirs in India, resting from the steaming tropical heat on a polished and striated rock ledge, would doubtless think the idea fantastic, though alluring, if told that his perch is the floor of an ancient glacier that once spread over much of India.

Such inferences tax the imagination. Not even geologists accepted the clear-cut evidence until every possible alternative had been found inadequate to explain the facts so clearly recorded in the rocks and in the drainage patterns upon them.

Development of the glacial theory

In most of Scandinavia, southern Canada, Labrador, and parts of the northern United States, soil profiles are either poorly developed or missing. Instead, rounded hilltops expose smoothly polished rock ledges like those beneath existing glaciers. In places the polish and small striations have been weathered off, but where protected by even a thin veneer of till or peat, they may be as fresh and clear as beneath a modern ice sheet (Fig. 4–10).

Boulders—many huge—are randomly strewn over the polished surface (Fig. 13–31). Most of these "erratic" boulders differ from the local bedrock: many in the Iowa fields are of gneiss and granite, though they rest on limestone or shale. No gneiss or granite bedrock is exposed nearby, so the boulders could not have been swept in by floods. In parts of Iowa, sporadic chunks of copper like the ore mined from rock ledges on the Keeweenaw Peninsula, Michigan, or that exposed on Isle Royale in Lake Superior are occasionally found. Boulders of an unusual variety of granite called "rapikivi," found in place only in Finland, are scattered widely over Estonia and even far into Poland. The basalt plateau of eastern Washington is strewn with huge granitic boulders whose nearest outcrops are across the Columbia River and many miles to the north. These boulders must have been transported directly across the Columbia River canyon, which is 1500 to 2000 feet deep. A large nickel deposit in northern Finland was found by tracing scattered ore fragments northward to their bedrock source near Petsamo.

FIGURE 13–31
Glacial boulders resting on a surface polished by a Pleistocene valley glacier, Sierra Nevada, California. (Photo by Eliot Blackwelder, Stanford University.)

The German philosopher-poet Goethe was one of the first to suggest that erratic boulders were dropped by moving ice. In 1832, twenty years later, the German geologist A. Bernhardi followed with a better documented paper. Then two Swiss geologists, Venetz and Charpentier, showed that the erratics so widely distributed over the Swiss plain might have been carried there by former extensions of the present Alpine glaciers. A young Swiss naturalist, J. L. R. Agassiz (1807–1873) was skeptical of their views, but a trip with Charpentier in 1836 to the active glaciers of the Rhone Valley, and to the huge abandoned moraines far below, convinced Agassiz of the reality of the former glacial extensions. He saw that the association of transported blocks with polished and grooved bedrock could not have been produced by floods—only by glacial ice, and soon became the most active protagonist of the idea of widespread glaciation.

But Agassiz, too, met with scepticism. Though he found glacial phenomena in Scotland and Ireland identical with those in Switzerland, his report raised a furore of objections, but when his critics really studied the evidence, many came to share his views.

The Pleistocene glaciations

Agassiz emigrated to America and began the studies of glaciation in New England that have been followed fruitfully by many investigators. Modern maps, summarizing these studies, show in detail the erosional and depositional forms and deposits of the ancient ice sheets. In both North America and Europe, many abandoned moraines have been mapped, lobe by lobe; their distribution is now well known (Figs. 13–23, 13–32). Behind them lie striated rock floors strewn with till and erratic boulders. Innumerable lakes and marshes occupy gouges in the glacier's floor. Debris-dammed older drainage, and kettles half buried in an outwash apron tell of ice action. Outwash fans spread from gaps in the moraines; beyond them are sheets of loess and terraces of silt. All these features stamp the landscapes of central Europe, New York, New England, the Great Lakes country, and the Pacific Northwest with unmistakable glacial imprints.

In mountainous areas, such as Yosemite National Park, the Cascade Mountains, or the Alps, the former valley glaciers are recorded by innumerable cirques and U-shaped

FIGURE 13–32
The distribution of the Pleistocene glaciers in the United States. (After a map by a Committee of the Geological Society of America.)

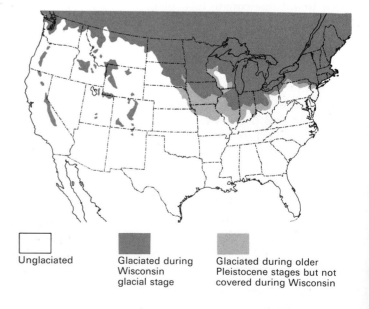

Unglaciated

Glaciated during Wisconsin glacial stage

Glaciated during older Pleistocene stages but not covered during Wisconsin

valleys, by fresh moraines, superb waterfalls tumbling from hanging valleys, clear mountain lakes nestled in rock-scoured basins, and terraces of outwash gravel, sand, and silt extending downstream from the moraines. (Fig. 13–28) .

ADVANCE AND RECESSION OF PLEISTOCENE ICE SHEETS.   At many places in North America and Europe, roadcuts expose two or more different layers of till, one above the other (Fig. 13–33) . The upper layer contains boulders of almost fresh granite and gneiss, some with polished facets and striae. Beneath this, a layer of thoroughly weathered till shows a mature soil profile and grades down into less weathered till. In this lower layer the outlines of boulders can still be recognized but the rocks can be cut with a knife—the feldspars are rotted to clay, and the ferromagnesian minerals are completely decomposed. Only chemically resistant rocks such as quartzite are preserved in this layer (Fig. 13–33) . Such exposures prove that the lower till weathered for a long time before the younger till covered it. In places the B-

FIGURE 13–33
Superposed tills, southwestern Minnesota. In the upper part of the lower till all boulders of granite and gneiss are thoroughly rotted and only weathering-resistant quartzite is still undecomposed; the upper till contains abundant fresh boulders of granite and gneiss.

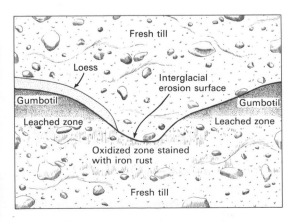

horizon of the weathered till is tough, sticky clay. Such tough, clayey subsoils, whether of glacial or other origin, are popularly called "gumbo." Clay-rich weathered tills are called **gumbotil.**

Moraines mantled by gumbotil, unlike younger, less-weathered moraines, have generally been so eroded as to preserve few, if any, undrained depressions, except where overlain by younger moraines.

Careful study of the superposition and degree of weathering of different glacial deposits has allowed several episodes of Pleistocene ice advance to be recognized: four in North America, six in Europe, and ten or twelve in Iceland. Radiometric and other methods of dating make probable the close time correlation of the last two glaciations in Europe and America; correlations of the earlier episodes are much less clear. Between the ice advances, the climate appears to have been mild and warm, at times warmer than now, as shown by fossils of subtropical plants from stream and marsh deposits between the tills.

DATING PLEISTOCENE DEPOSITS BY VARVED LAKE SEDIMENTS.   As we have seen, lake deposits abound in formerly glaciated regions. Torrents of turbid meltwater pouring into these lakes dropped their coarser sand and silt in deltas; the finest mud settled slowly and spread throughout the lake. Present glacial lakes are deep green, owing to the dispersion of light by the abundant particles of suspended clay.

In winter, the glacial lakes freeze over and small tributary streams may freeze solid. During this quiet period, the suspended clay particles beneath the ice, along with fine algal matter that accumulated during the summer, settle slowly to the bottom to form a dark, fine-grained layer of sediment. By spring, most glacial lakes are nearly clear. Thus the summer layer of deposits is coarser and consists of rock waste only; the winter layer finer and richer in organic matter. Such cycles can be observed in many existing lakes, and cores from holes bored in their bottoms show the characteristic two-fold layering.

These thin laminae of alternating dark and light coarse material, each pair the deposit of a single year, are called **varves,** from a Swedish word meaning "seasonal deposit." The typical pair is only a small fraction of an inch thick (Fig. 13–34), but some are much thicker.

If we find glacial lake sediments exposed in a roadcut, or penetrated by a drill core, and count the varves, we can determine the number of years represented by the deposit. The varves record climatic variations, for example, an exceptionally warm year yields an especially thick and coarse summer layer. By matching sequences of comparable variations in thickness, it is often possible to correlate the upper layers in a southern lake with varves near the bottom of a more northerly, younger lake that lay along the line of ice recession.

Such studies show that the last ice sheet retreated from the site of Stockholm, Sweden, about 9000 years ago, that southern Ontario lay under ice 13,500 years ago, and that about 4300 years elapsed while the ice front retreated from a site near Hartford, Connecticut, to St. Johnsbury, Vermont, a distance of 190 miles.

As mentioned in Chapter 7, radiocarbon (C^{14}) gives us another method of measuring ages during the past 35,000 years. Ages so determined for trees overridden by glaciers are generally, but not invariably, consistent with those from varved sediments.

Drainage changes beyond the limits of glaciation

The drastic climate that buried so much of northern Europe and North America under glacial ice also had striking effects in latitudes not reached by the continental glaciers.

LAKE BONNEVILLE. In Pleistocene time, Nevada and western Utah were not barren semideserts as they are today. Thin bedded clays

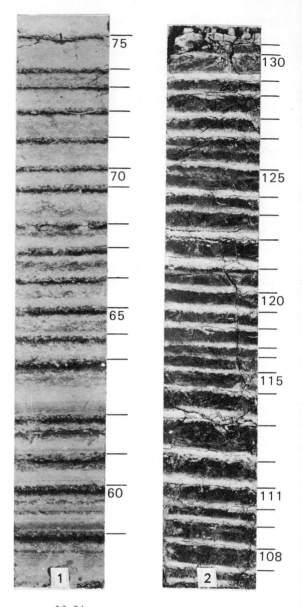

FIGURE 13–34
Varved glacial clay from Steep Rock Lake, Ontario. The two samples are from two drill cores, each 12 inches long. The lines at the edge of the photo show the boundaries of each varve, and some of the varves are numbered. The light-colored laminae are summer deposits; the dark, winter. (Photo by Ernst Antevs.)

with fossils of leaves and of fresh-water animals show that many intermontane valleys contained large freshwater lakes rimmed by

trees and luxuriant grass. The highest wave-
cut shoreline (See Chapter 16) of the largest
of these vanished lakes, called Lake Bonneville, makes a conspicuous horizontal terrace
on the Wasatch Mountain front more than
1000 feet above Great Salt Lake. Lake Bonneville, when filled to this level, overflowed
into the Snake River and thence, by way of
the Columbia, to the sea. The outlet was
over unconsolidated alluvium into which the
torrent quickly eroded a canyon to bedrock,
350 feet below the original divide. This resistant bedrock held the lake at a nearly constant level for a long time, and great deltas
and terraces much more conspicuous than
those at the higher overflow level were built
along the shores. Moraines from valley glaciers in the Wasatch extend to the old shorelines. Some rest on lake sediments and are
themselves cut by beaches. The glaciers were,
therefore, about contemporaneous with the
expansion of the lake.

As the climate became drier, the glaciers
waned, the streams dwindled, and evaporation from the lake began to exceed inflow.
The water gradually fell to lower and lower
levels, recorded in a series of fainter shoreline features carved on the delta fronts and
into the beach deposits of higher lake stands.
Great Salt Lake and the Bonneville salt flats
remain today as the last desiccation pools of
this once vast inland sea (Fig. 13–35).

GREAT LAKES AND MISSOURI VALLEY AREA.   In
the north central United States, the continental glaciers overrode a stream-carved
landscape, damming some pre-existing stream
courses between the ice front and higher land
to the south, and forming many ephemeral
glacial lakes, some of which were destroyed
by further advance of the ice to the divides.
The record of such lakes has been nearly obliterated by the overriding glacier. The present channels of the Missouri and Ohio follow
the approximate edge of the vanished glacier
for many miles and, record glacial blocking
of north-flowing streams, diverting their waters to a course along the margin of the gla-

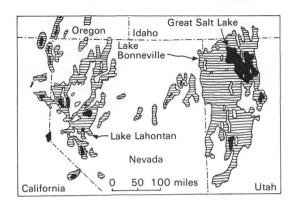

FIGURE 13–35
*Map showing the extent of the great Pleistocene
lakes in the western United States. Present lakes,
in part ephemeral, are in black. (After G. K.
Gilbert and O. E. Meinzer.*

ciers. The Milk and Yellowstone rivers were
not always tributary to the Missouri. They
formerly drained to Hudson's Bay, as shown
by till-filled channels. The present course of
the upper Missouri was cut by water flowing
along the glacial margin. Similar ice-mar-
ginal drainage largely determined the present course of the Ohio.

As the ice front retreated, new glacial lakes
were impounded between the ice and the
higher ground to the south, as preserved
shore features and sediments clearly record.
Drainage changes were many and complex.
Several large glacial lakes and interconnected
river systems formed in succession as the retreating glacial front uncovered lower and
lower outlets. The present Great Lakes are
the last in a long series whose history has
been worked out by glacial geologists.
Though there have been many refinements
through more recent studies, the main elements in the history were worked out more
than 50 years ago.

The evidence of the drainage changes and
abandoned lakes is extensive and convincing.
Abandoned shorelines marked by beach
ridges, wave-cut cliffs, deltas, spits, and bars
stand high above existing lakes. When followed northward, the shorelines generally

end abruptly against a moraine or outwash apron that marks the glacial front against which the lake was dammed. Vast areas enclosed by these old shorelines are covered with varved silts and clays—the deep-water deposits of former glacial lakes.

As shown in Figures 13–36 and 13–37 a series of temporary glacial lakes occupied the southern end of the Lake Michigan basin. They drained by a short stream flowing from the present site of Chicago to the Illinois River and thence to the Mississippi. Simultaneously, a larger glacial lake, called Lake Whittlesey, occupied the expanded basins of Lake Erie and southern Lake Huron. Lake Whittlesey first drained westward across central Michigan into the Michigan basin and thence to the Mississippi, but the ice shrank northward and uncovered a lower outlet across New York via the Mohawk and Hudson rivers (Fig. 13–37). Thereupon Lake Whittlesey shrank greatly, the outlet across Michigan dried up, and huge volumes of meltwater that had formerly flowed to the Gulf of Mexico were diverted to the Atlantic. Still later the ice retreated north of the St. Lawrence; both the Chicago and Mohawk-Hudson outlets were then abandoned and the present outlines of the Great Lakes were established.

As the ice withdrew still farther, an enormous glacial lake, larger than all the Great Lakes combined, developed in the Red River Valley of Manitoba, Minnesota, and North Dakota. This was Lake Agassiz, named for the famous Swiss glaciologist. Its water spilled southward into the Minnesota River, thence to the Mississippi at the present site of St. Paul. With further glacial retreat, Lake Agassiz drained northward to what is now Lake Winnipeg. Its lake sediments form the fertile wheat lands of the Red River Valley.

GRAND COULEE.   The great Columbia River, in eastern Washington, was diverted by ice with striking effects (Figs. 13–38, 13–39). A huge lobe of the ice sheet advanced at right angles upon the westward-flowing river, filled

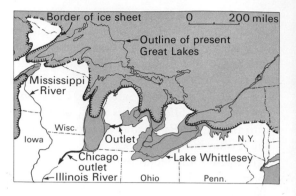

FIGURE 13–36
Meltwater lakes formed during a recessional phase of the Pleistocene ice sheet in the Great Lakes region. The outline of the present lakes and State lines are shown for reference. (After Frank Leverett and F. B. Taylor, 1915; Frank Leverett and F. W. Sardeson, 1932; and W. S. Cooper, 1935.)

FIGURE 13–37
Same as Figure 13–36 at a somewhat later time. (After Frank Leverett and F. B. Taylor, 1915.)

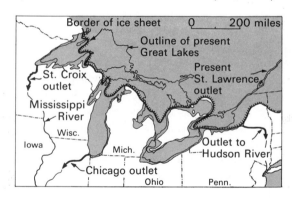

its 2000-foot canyon, blocked the stream, and spread southward upon the Columbia Plateau. Diverted across the plateau, which here slopes southward several feet per mile, the rampant river cascaded across the landscape and, armed with great quantities of outwash gravel and basalt blocks torn from its channels, gashed a plexus of canyons into the plateau. The streams shifted as the ice front changed—as a slight advance blocked a just-formed channel, or a retreat exposed a lower

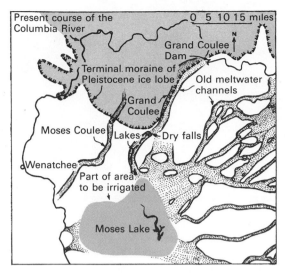

FIGURE 13–38

Map of central Washington, showing Grand Coulee and other features formed by the glacial diversion of the Columbia River. (In part after J. H. Bretz.)

one. Some shifts of the ice front released enormous floods of water from Lake Missoula —a huge glacially dammed lake in the mountain valleys of the northern Rockies a hundred miles east of Spokane. The outlet of the lake, northeast of Spokane, was in a deep narrow canyon whose mouth was repeatedly blocked by the ice front. Rampaging torrents, released by sporadic bursting of the ice dam across this narrow outlet, scoured the plateau surface into a weird complex of interlaced canyons draining to the Snake River. The floods were so deep that the pre-existing shallow valleys hardly diverted the torrents at all—a whole new drainage pattern, perhaps unique on the earth, came into being. Between these great floods the drainage was confined mainly to a single channel, now called the Grand Coulee. It is a great canyon, 500 to 1000 feet deep and 1 to 15 miles wide, cut in the basalt flows of the

FIGURE 13–39   *Dry Falls, a former huge waterfall in the glacially diverted Columbia River. of central Washington. (Courtesy of State of Washington Department of Conservation and Development.)*

Columbia Plateau. Midway was a gigantic waterfall 400 feet high and nearly 3 miles wide, which, during the Pleistocene, must have thundered with the roar of a thousand Niagaras (Fig. 13–39). Today, no water tumbles over Dry Falls: the waning glacier reopened the preglacial canyon and allowed the river to resume its former course.

Recently, man has restored some of the waterflow through Grand Coulee. Across the Columbia at the head of Grand Coulee stands Grand Coulee Dam, part of whose hydroelectric power pumps water from the lake behind the dam into the Coulee, whence it flows southward to irrigate millions of acres of rich but arid land. Grand Coulee Dam is the largest engineering structure ever built in the western hemisphere, yet how puny it appears compared with the ice dam thrust across the river in the same position some 12,000 years ago!

Pre-Pleistocene glaciations

Many ancient sedimentary formations show all the characteristics of till except that they are tightly cemented. They are unsorted debris, contain striated and faceted stones, and are associated with varved shales and slates or with sandstones and conglomerates showing features typical of outwash deposits. Some rest on polished and grooved rock floors. These associated features can only mean that the deposits are glacial. Cemented tills are called **tillites.** Although small bodies of tillite have been found in other older rocks —Ordovician or Silurian in the Hoggar Mountains of the Sahara, and Silurian or early Devonian in the Cape Mountains of South Africa—only two pre-Pleistocene episodes of widespread continental glaciation have yet been recognized. During the late Paleozoic, ice sheets spread widely over India, South Africa, Argentina and southern Brazil, and South Australia. In India, Australia, and South Africa, grooved rock floors beneath the hard tillite may be seen in hundreds of places, (Fig. 13–40) preserved beneath

FIGURE 13–40
Glaciated pavement beneath Late Paleozoic tillite, South Australia. (Photo by Warren Hamilton, U.S. Geological Survey.)

younger sediments. These sediments protected them from weathering and erosion, and the unconsolidated glacial deposits were slowly cemented into rock. Recent erosion has now re-exposed them.

In the late Precambrian, also, glaciers seem to have been widespread. Ancient tillites considered of this age, though precise correlation is still lacking, have been found on every continent except South America.

CAUSES OF GLACIAL CLIMATES

Geologists and climatologists have tried for more than a century to explain the recurrence of continental glaciation. Hypothesis has followed hypothesis, but all seem to explain too little or too much. None can be dignified as a theory, yet they have an interest that justifies brief mention.

Facts to be explained

1. Continental glaciers in Greenland and Antarctica occupy about 10 percent of the total land surface today. At several different times during the Pleistocene they covered an area three times as great.

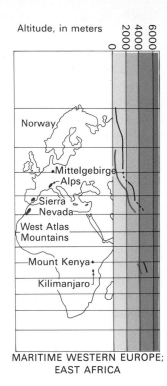

Altitude, in meters

CONTINENTAL AMERICAS

Altitude, in meters

MARITIME WESTERN EUROPE;
EAST AFRICA

FIGURE 13–41
Snowline heights of the present (black line) compared with those of the Pleistocene (brown line). (After G. de Q. Robin, Science Journal, 1966.)

2. During the Pleistocene, climatic zones of the northern hemisphere roughly paralleled their present positions but were displaced southward during the times of greatest glaciation and northward during interglacial episodes. In low latitudes, at least for the two latest episodes, heavy rainfall was contemporaneous with glacial climates at higher latitudes, and the snowlines were lower than at present (Fig. 13–41).

3. Estimates of the duration of the several glacial and interglacial episodes of Pleistocene time do not suggest a periodic recurrence; the climatic fluctuations seem to have been irregular.

4. Evidence of continental glaciation nearly as extensive as that of the Pleistocene is found in Late Paleozoic rocks (about 250 million years old) and in Precambrian rocks (at least 600 million years old), but not in comparable amounts in intermediate strata.

The many suggestions may be grouped roughly into two categories: geologic and astronomic. Some combine elements of both.

Geologic hypotheses

Several attempts to account for glaciation explain the climatic variations by changes in continental elevations, or by changes in oceanic and atmospheric circulation brought about by changes in the shapes of ocean basins or by mountain uplifts. Such explanations are wholly inadequate: there is no evidence whatever that since Pliocene time either the distribution or altitudes of the major land masses have changed significantly. Under these hypotheses, the average size and height of the continents would have had to fluctuate rapidly during the Pleistocene, for we have a clear record in Europe of at least six major glaciations in that epoch, and at least some interglacial climates were much milder than that of the present. There is no record of such vertical oscillations as would be needed to account for these alterations. Furthermore the mountains of today —a relatively nonglacial time—are surely as high as they were during both glacial and interglacial times of the Pleistocene.

Changes in the amount of carbon dioxide

and volcanic dust in the atmosphere might bring about climatic variation, and some suggestions are based on this. Carbon dioxide absorbs—blankets in—some of the heat radiated from the earth's surface. If the air contained more of it, the temperature should rise; if it contained less, the temperature should fall. Quantitatively, however, such changes would be inadequate to produce great climatic variation, especially because simultaneous changes in the amount of water vapor in the air would practically compensate for any variations in carbon dioxide content. Volcanic dust undoubtedly screens out some of the sun's radiation, but there is no evidence that volcanoes were more active in glacial than in interglacial times. Changes in the salinity of sea water, with consequent modification of the ocean currents and their climatic influences, are likely results of glaciation, but they can hardly have brought it about, although it has been suggested that they did.

Geophysical theories, which attribute glaciation to shifts in the position of the continents with respect to the poles, obviously do not explain either the warmer Pleistocene interglacial times or the cooler pluvial and glacial times. A theory of this sort has recently been advanced by the American geophysicists Ewing and Donn, who suggest that the crust is able to slide slowly over the interior of the earth. Continental glaciation of the northern hemisphere, they say, is only possible when the land masses are so placed that there is both an unfrozen ocean at high northern latitudes, to supply water for precipitation farther south, and a broad connection of northern and southern oceans to allow exchange of water between them. An objection to this idea is that the present massive ice cap of Antarctica proves that ice may accumulate to glacial thickness in high latitudes despite the lack of a polar ocean. It is also difficult to accept slippage of the northern continents in such a fluctuating way, for the pattern favorable to glaciation would

have to form at least six times, whereas an unfavorable pattern would have to form in preglacial, interglacial, and postglacial time. Nor could this suggestion account for simultaneous glaciations in both hemispheres. A relatively slight interchange of Arctic and Atlantic water is hard to credit with so great a climatic effect when the far-greater cooling of the sinking Antarctic waters now going on in all the southern oceans has no comparable influence (see Fig. 16–5).

Astronomic hypotheses

These are of three kinds: (1) that the solar system from time to time encounters clouds of cosmic dust, (2) that the earth varies periodically in its distance from the sun and hence in the amount of heat it receives, and (3) that the sun varies in the amount of heat it radiates.

Dark nebulae are known to be partly cosmic dust. Were the solar system to enter such a nebula the dust might either screen out the sun's radiation or blanket-in the earth's radiation to outer space, depending on the size of the particles. There is now no way of testing this hypothesis. The other two suggestions are more amenable to testing.

Three known astronomic factors, periodically affect the earth's relation to the sun: (a) changes in the eccentricity of the earth's orbit, with a period of 92,000 years, (b) changes in the angle between the earth's axis and its path, with a period of about 40,000 years, and (c) changes in the positions of the equinoxes, with a period of about 22,000 years. The simultaneous effect of these variables is to produce periodic changes in the distance between every point on the earth's surface and the sun, and hence in the amount of solar radiation each point receives. This hypothesis was suggested a century ago, and then elaborately worked out by the Yugoslav astronomer M. Milankovitch during the years 1920 to 1938. If such changes had brought about glaciation, the effects on

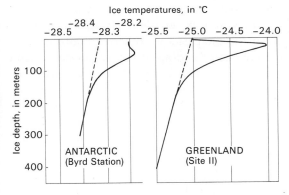

FIGURE 13–42

Ice temperatures measured at depth in drill holes in Antarctic and Greenland ice sheets. Both curves are nearly straight below about 150 meters. The curves between 150 and 60 meters show warming in both hemispheres during the last 40 to 80 years. Above 60 meters the curves show slight cooling in both hemispheres during the last 40 years, approximately. (After G. de Q. Robin, Science Journal, *1966.)*

FIGURE 13–43

Simpson's theory of glaciation based on variations in the sun's radiation and its climatic effects.

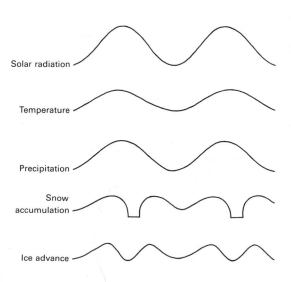

northern and southern hemispheres, though not exactly opposite, would certainly not have been parallel (Fig. 13–42). Furthermore the effect at the equator should be negligible, but the snowline there was affected quite as notably as in high latitudes (Fig. 13–41). Yet we are sure that glaciers have been simultaneously retreating in both hemispheres for some decades, and oceanic sediments from both hemispheres prove that the Pleistocene glaciation was simultaneous in both. Furthermore, as these astronomic cycles are continuous, glaciation should have been regularly repeated every few hundred thousand years throughout geologic time, whereas we must go back to the Permian— more than 225 million years—to find anything comparable with the Pleistocene. These geologic arguments seem conclusively to negate such suggestions. Some meteorologists further contend that temperature changes produced in this way would be far too small to cause glaciation.

Astronomers have shown that the sun's radiation fluctuates, and hence the amount of heat received by the earth. Short-term variations of as much as 3 percent seem well established, and the American astronomer Charles Abbot believes that larger changes may be possible. A British meteorologist, Sir George Simpson, has built an ingenious hypothesis on this idea.

Simpson reasoned that, if solar radiation increased, the air would warm, and cloudiness and precipitation would increase everywhere. More snow would fall, the ice caps would expand, and the greater cloudiness would lessen summer melting. But if the temperature continued to rise, ultimately the ice and snow would melt faster than they were replenished. The glaciers would disappear. At the high point on the radiation curve (Fig. 13–43) the world climate would be milder and wetter than it is today. When radiation began to decrease, the sequence would reverse, ice would first advance, then, as heat became insufficient to supply precipitation, retreat, and finally, when radiation fell to its present value, we would be back to present conditions. Thus, paradoxically, a warming of the air would lead to continental glaciation. On this hypothesis, one rise and fall of radiation would produce two glaciations, separated by a warm, wet, interglacial episode. The climate following the second glaciation would be cold and dry, as it is now. In low latitudes, beyond the limits of the ice, a single long rainy epoch would endure through both the glacial and interglacial episodes. The four Pleistocene glaciations recognized in North America would thus require two cycles of increased solar radiation, separated by a time of "normal" climate like that of today; the six glaciations of Europe would require three cycles.

Simpson's hypothesis appeals to meteorologists since it accounts for the increased precipitation that seems necessary to feed the huge ice sheets. The line at which the mean annual temperature is freezing now lies much nearer the equator than the existing ice sheets, showing that low temperature alone cannot produce glaciation. Increased precipitation, or a different seasonal pattern of precipitation, is needed. With the present configurations of land and sea—essentially those of the Pleistocene—increase in precipitation requires greater evaporation from the sea.

Geologists, however, do not find the hypothesis convincing. The sediments, even in the equatorial ocean, show that the Pleistocene water was cooler. Molluscs now living in higher latitudes lived nearer the equator during the Pleistocene. Furthermore, the relative proportions of the several isotopes of oxygen in their shells (which are known to differ at different water temperatures) show that the equatorial seas as well as those at higher latitudes were then cooler than they now are, instead of being warmer, as Simpson's hypothesis requires.

No hypothesis seems satisfactorily to account for the continental glaciation of the Pleistocene, nor can we say whether the present is simply another interglacial epoch. During the past several decades most glaciers have been receding in both hemispheres and the water released to the sea has raised sea level a few centimeters. If this retreat continued until all land ice was melted, sea level would rise about 65 meters, whereas at the maximum extent of the Pleistocene glaciers it must have stood about 130 meters lower than at present. This is confirmed by the thick alluvium on which the coastal segments of most great rivers flow (Chapter 12). We may then expect either that our coastal cities and low-lying coastal plains will eventually be drowned beneath a shallow sea, or that some centuries hence the sites of Chicago, Copenhagen, and Warsaw may again be overrun by glaciers. From past records, it seems most unlikely that the climate will remain constant for long, but much more work is needed before a well-founded prophecy about the direction of the secular trend is possible.

THE EFFECT OF GLACIAL LOADS ON THE EARTH'S CRUST

As we saw in Chapter 10, strong evidence from deflections of the plumb line and measurements of gravity show that large segments of the earth's crust are virtually in isostatic balance. The great weight of continental ice sheets might be expected to disturb this balance, and, as mentioned in Chapter 8, it clearly did.

Wherever glaciers spilled over or around mountains, some measure of their thickness is possible. In New England, for example, the ice must have been more than 4000 feet thick, for the highest peaks were overridden. In southern Canada, nearer to the source, the ice was certainly much thicker. Precambrian boulders from the Hudson Bay lowlands were carried to elevations of 4500 feet in the Alberta Rockies. Boulders that could

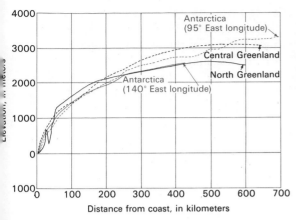

FIGURE 13–44

Similar surface profiles of Greenland and Antarctic ice sheets, showing that despite differences in rate of snow accumulation and rock floors, the surface slopes are systematically related to distance from the glacial front. (After G. de Q. Robin, Science Journal, 1966.)

FIGURE 13–45

Reconstruction of the European ice sheets at their maximum extent. The contours are based on analogy with the slopes of the present Greenland and Antarctic ice sheets. (After G. de Q. Robin, Science Journal, 1966.)

only have come from Sweden were carried over 6000-foot mountains of Norway.

Studies by explosion seismology (Chapter 19) of ice thickness, when plotted against surface slopes of the Greenland and Antarctica ice sheets, show that the ice thickness is systematically related to the distance to the glacier front (Fig. 13–44) Applying this rule to the Fennoscandian ice cap, which spread over most of northern Europe, it is possible to say that at its maximum, this ice cap was more than 3000 meters thick (Fig. 13–45).

The density of ice is only about a third that of ordinary rocks; a load of ice 3000 meters thick would be equivalent to a load of about 1000 meters of rock, and, if spread over a wide area, should have bent the crust downward. Though the high viscosity of subcrustal material might slow the response, if isostasy is really general, the lowering should have been measurable.

The shorelines of ancient glacial lakes and of former extensions of the sea, as in the Baltic, enable us to test the idea. The shores were level when formed. After the ice load

FIGURE 13–46

Postglacial uplift in Fennoscandia. The heavy lines connect points of equal uplift in meters, of the highest strand line of the sea that flooded the area just after the melting of the glacier. (After R. A. Daly, The Changing World of the Ice Age, Yale University Press, 1934.)

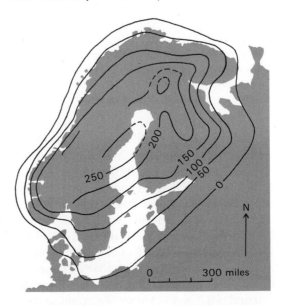

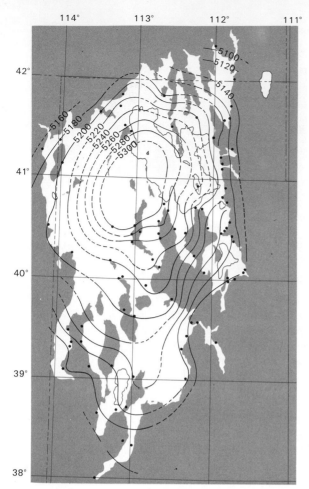

* Point where elevation of shoreline has been determined

▨ Outline of lake at Bonneville shoreline

———— ----- Contour showing present elevation of deformed shoreline
Dashed where inferred, Interval, 20 feet

10   0 10 20 30 miles

FIGURE 13–47
Map showing deformation of the Lake Bonneville shoreline. (After M. D. Crittenden, Jr., Journal of Geophysical Research, *1963.)*

melted, the crust should have tilted in response to the unloading and the shorelines should now rise toward the center of the former ice cap. This is exactly what is found, not only in the Great Lakes region, but in the Baltic (Fig. 13–46), in Labrador, and even in the basin of Lake Bonneville, where the load was only 1000 feet of water, covering an area much smaller than that of the great continental glaciers (Fig. 13–47). The continental shelves of Antarctica stand several

hundred meters lower than most of those of other continents. It has been suggested that this is because of the ice load weighing down formerly normal shelves.

We return to the geologic evidence of isostasy when we discuss the origin of mountains in Chapter 20. Suffice it to say here that the tests of the isostatic principle by glaciers and their meltwaters agree fully with the geodetic evidence on which the theory was based.

THE DURATION OF THE PLEISTOCENE EPOCH

Despite the abundant exposures of Pleistocene deposits and the wealth of stratigraphic information available, one of the most controversial items in geochronology is that of the duration of the Pleistocene epoch. For those who believe that the Milankovitch curve is faithfully followed by climatic variations, the oldest of the four generally recognized glaciations of America took place less than 600,000 years ago. There is indeed some support (in the variations in isotopic abundances of the oxygen present in some Pleistocene fossils) for the occurrence of four relatively cold episodes during this time. The question remains, however, whether these episodes represent the several major glaciations or merely minor fluctuations within one or two of them. Other geochronologists note that the Bishop Tuff, a rhyolitic ash flow along the eastern side of the Sierra Nevada, rests on a till thought to represent the second of the four major glaciations recognized in the midcontinental United States. Consistent measurements of K-Ar ratios in the Bishop Tuff yield an age of 700,000 years. If the correlation with the midcontinent is correct—a doubtful matter —an age of at least a million years would not be unreasonable for the earliest North American glaciation. Radiometric dating has shown that oozes containing ice-rafted pebbles, the oldest glacial sediments in the Bellingshausen Sea, far in the Antarctic are 2.4 m.y. old. But this area is so far south that glacial history there may find no parallel in more temperate latitudes. The data, though interesting, cannot be used to date the glaciation of Patagonia or Kansas.

Though the Pleistocene epoch has come to be thought of as primarily characterized by continental glaciation, it was actually defined by the great English geologist, Charles Lyell, on the basis of certain strata in Italy, far from any glacial deposits—a definition reaffirmed by the International Geological Congress of 1948. The fossil faunas of these beds have been found in similar, but not identical, associations in southern France and northern Italy, where it has been shown that they long antedate the earliest recognized glaciation in the Alps. A similar, somewhat younger, fauna, associated with human fossils in East Africa, has been dated by K-Ar ratios in associated ash beds at about 1.85 m.y. old. On this basis, the Pleistocene began still earlier: the most probable age of the Pliocene-Pleistocene boundary seems to be about 2 million years.

Facts, concepts, terms

Snowfields and glaciers
    Transformation: snow–firn–ice
    Temperate glaciers; polar glaciers
    Nature of glacier flow
    Concurrent brittleness and plasticity of glaciers
Valley glaciers; piedmont glaciers; continental glaciers
Acquisition of rock debris by glaciers
    Frost weathering; avalanching; meltwater shattering; plucking; rasping
    Till; rock flour
Deposits associated with glaciers
    Moraines: lateral; medial; terminal; recessional; ground
    Stratified drift; outwash aprons; kames and eskers; valley trains and silt terraces; deltas; varved clays
    Loess
Topographic forms associated with glaciers
    Cirques; horns; U-shaped valleys; hanging valleys
    Smoothed and grooved rock surfaces
    Lakes and swamps; immature drainage patterns
    Pitted outwash; terraces of silt
    Morainal ridges; drumlin clusters
The Pleistocene glaciations
    Development of the glacial theory
    Evidence of advance and recession
    Evidence of multiple glaciation
        Weathered tills; superposed tills; interbedded interglacial deposits
        Drainage changes
        Evidence of climatic changes from fossils
Pre-Pleistocene periods of glaciation
Cause of glacial climates
Sea level changes due to glaciation
Isostatic response to glacial loading and unloading
The duration of the Pleistocene

Questions

1. What is the evidence that recrystallization takes place in the transformation of snow to firn and ice?
2. Why are most glacial crevasses less than 200 feet deep?
3. Explain the processes by which the head of a valley glacier acquires (a) new snow and ice, (b) rock debris.
4. Explain the processes by which a continental glacier acquires its rock load.
5. Draw a longitudinal profile through a valley glacier and label the following features: cirque, terminal moraine, meltwater tubes, bergschrund, shear banding in ice, snowfield, rasped bedrock, plucked and shattered bedrock.
6. How does rock flour released from a glacier differ from the fine-grained materials formed during weathering?
7. Draw a hypothetical sketch map showing the location of all the following: (a) a lobate terminal moraine; (b) a recessional moraine; (c) pitted outwash; (d) ground moraine; (e) a drumlin cluster; (f) a plain underlain by varved clay; (g) an esker; (h) kame terraces; (i) an abandoned stream course.
8. How can a glacier in contact with sea water lower its bed below sea level?

Suggested readings

Ahlmann, H. W., *Glaciological Research on the North Atlantic Coasts* (Research Series No. 1). London: Royal Geographical Society, 1948.

Charlesworth, J. K., *The Quaternary Era, with Special Reference to its Glaciation* (2 vols.). New York: St. Martin's Press, 1957.

Coleman, A. P., *Ice Ages, Recent and Ancient.* New York: Macmillan, 1926.

Daly, R. A., *The Changing World of the Ice Age.* New Haven: Yale University Press, 1934.

Flint, R. F., *Glacial and Pleistocene Geology.* New York: John Wiley and Sons, 1957.

Gilbert, G. K., *Lake Bonneville* (U.S. Geological Survey, Monograph 1). Washington, D.C., 1890.

Matthes, F. E., *The Geological History of the Yosemite Valley* (U.S. Geological Survey, Professional Paper 160). Washington, D.C.: G.P.O., 1930.

Zeuner, F. E., *Dating the Past, an Introduction to Geochronology.* London: Methuen, 1958.

Scientific American offprints

809. William O. Fields, *Glaciers* (September 1955)

823. Gilbert N. Plass, *Carbon Dioxide and Climate* (July 1959)

834. Edward S. Deevey, Jr., *Living Records of the Ice Age* (May 1949)

835. Ernst J. Öpik, *Climate and the Changing Sun* (June 1958)

843. Harry Wexler, *Volcanoes and World Climate* (April 1952)

849. Walter Orr Roberts, *Sun Clouds and Rain Clouds* (April 1957)

861. Gordon de Q. Robin, *The Ice of the Antarctic* (September 1962)

chapter 14

Ground Water

Where does water in wells come from? Why is water found only a few feet beneath the dry surface soil in many places but not even at several thousand feet in others? When air conditioning was introduced on Long Island, many wells were drilled to obtain cooling water. Some of them soon became salty; in others only salt water was found. Whence came the salt, when the water had been fresh before? The great limestone caverns of Kentucky and Virginia extend for miles—so far that many are still unexplored. What made them? All these questions have ultimately to do with water underground: **ground water.** It fills pores and cracks in soil and rock, comes to the surface in springs, and swells or shrinks the volume of streams by seeping into or out of them through their beds and banks. It also supplies the water to wells.

SOURCE OF GROUND WATER

Surface water has an obvious source—rain and snow—and, as Perrault showed long ago (Chapter 5), this is practically the only source except for a little from volcanic eruptions. Rain and snow also supply virtually all ground water. Most soils and rocks contain voids and openings into which water can seep: tiny pores between the mineral grains, small tubules left by decay of grass roots, larger openings made by burrowing animals, and shrinkage cracks in drying clays. Even well-consolidated rocks are riven by faults, joints, and intergranular openings. Some of the rain water that enters them remains near the surface, absorbed by the soil colloids or held in the smaller voids by capillarity, the force that pulls water up a slender tube and holds it there against the pull of gravity. Some rain water, however, percolates deeper and deeper; it ultimately reaches a zone where all the pores in the rock are completely filled with water. Above this, most openings in soil and rock are open to the air. At still greater depths the pores and cracks are so closed by compaction or so filled with minerals as to be virtually watertight; the rocks beneath this zone are dry, as has been recognized in many deep mines.

THE WATER TABLE

If we sink wells to the water, measure the elevations at which water stands in them (in homogeneous rock), and then contour the surface defined by these measurements, we find we have defined a smooth, even surface, usually gently sloping. This is the **water table.** Because rocks are variably porous, the actual interface between air and water in the rocks is not smooth like the water table, but minutely irregular, for capillarity can pull water higher in a small tube than in a larger one. (The capillary rise in a well even a few inches across is negligible.) Although impossible to measure, the pressure in the water of the capillary zone above the water table must be less than atmospheric, as the capillary force opposes the pull of gravity. The pressure relations are as shown in Table 14–1. Lohman has defined the water table as the surface at which the pressure on the water is precisely atmospheric; below it the pressure is higher; above, in the capillary zone, it is lower. The volume of rock whose pore spaces are completely filled with water includes the thin zone of continuous capillary saturation above the water table; this is the **zone of saturation.** The zone between the zone of saturation and the surface is the **zone of aeration** in which weathering is active (Fig. 14–1). The water table is generally at a depth of only a few feet or a few dozen feet, but in arid regions it may be down hundreds of feet. The water table is at the surface of the ground at the edges of swamps, lakes, streams, and the ocean. The water table is generally a somewhat subdued replica of the surface topography, rising under the hills and sinking under the valleys, but less irregularly than the land surface (Fig. 14–1).

POROSITY AND PERMEABILITY

Porosity is the ratio of pore volume to total volume, expressed as a percentage. Porosities of clastic sediments range as high as 80 or even 90 percent, but most are between 12 and 45 percent, depending on the *shapes* of the grains, their *sorting* and *packing,* and the *degree of cementation* (Fig. 14–2).

Mineral and rock grains vary in shape from thin plates and irregular chips to nearly perfect spheres. The way in which they are

Table 14–1 **Water table and pressure relations in the zones above and below it**

Zone		Pressure relations	Contents
Zone of Aeration	Zone of aeration	Pressure in air is atmospheric Pressure in water is less than atmospheric	Air and discontinuous water in capillary spaces
Zone of Saturation	Zone of continuous capillary saturation	Pressure is less than atmospheric	Water
		— The Water Table, Pressure is Atmospheric —	
	Zone of unconfined ground water	Pressure is greater than atmospheric	Water

SOURCE: Slightly modified from S. W. Lohman, 1965.
NOTE: Compare with Figure 14–2.

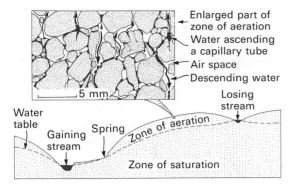

FIGURE 14–1
Cross section showing the water table and its relations to streams and a spring. The greatly enlarged inset shows the movement of water (black) in the zone of aeration.

packed together—that is, whether they are stacked tightly or loosely—greatly affects the porosity. Most sediments are loosely packed when deposited and for a time have high porosity; then burial beneath younger sediments progressively compacts them and cementation (deposition of mineral matter in the pores) further reduces porosity. Uniform spheres, whether one millimeter or 2 meters in diameter, when most tightly packed, have 26 percent porosity. Greater porosities indicate either irregular packing or, more commonly, that the grains are themselves porous.

Of course, shape strongly affects porosity, but the presence of nonspherical grains may either raise or lower the porosity, depending on the packing of adjacent grains.

The capacity of a rock or soil to *hold* water is determined by the porosity, but the capacity to *yield* water to the pump depends more on the pore size than on the total porosity. Not all the water in the pores will flow toward a pumping well. Much is retained as capillary films; rocks with very small pores may retain practically all their water, even though highly porous. This is true of most shales and clays. Laboratory tests indicate that there is a fairly definite minimum pore size—about 0.05 millimeter—through which water flows freely. **Permeability, or hydraulic conductivity,** the capacity of a porous medium to *transmit* a liquid, is therefore the property determining the *yield* of a water-bearing material. A gravel with 20 percent pore space is much more permeable to ground water than a clay with 35 percent.

AQUIFERS AND AQUITARDS

No rock—except perhaps asphalt and related materials—is completely impermeable to water, given a long enough time. But some are so slightly permeable that water scarcely

FIGURE 14–2
Porosity in rocks. A and B: The decrease in porosity due to closer packing of spheres. C: A sand with high porosity due to good sorting. D: A sandstone with low porosity due to poor sorting. E: Low porosity due to cementation. F: Very high porosity due to well-sorted grains that are themselves porous. G: Porous zones between lava flows. H: Limestone rendered porous by solution along joints. I: Massive rock rendered porous by fracturing.

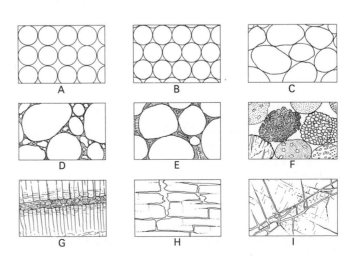

moves through them, even under high pressures. They have been loosely called impermeable, but are more properly called **aquitards** (retarders of water), in contrast to materials that are both permeable and porous and so yield water readily to wells. These are called **aquifers** (bearers of water).

Most aquifers are beds of sand, gravel, sandstone, limestone, or other permeable rock through which most of the flow is intergranular, though some may be along joints. Limestone, though granular, generally has few pores; it transmits water not by intergranular flow but along fractures or openings produced by weathering. Some volcanic ash flows are highly porous, and most lavas readily transmit water through joints, scoria zones, and lava tubes. A few aquifers are narrow sinuous bodies of gravel that fill former stream courses, but these are by no means as common as the popular expression "underground stream" indicates. The only true "underground streams" are those that flow in limestone caves or in lava tubes.

PERCHED WATER

An aquifer may rest on an aquitard that overlies unsaturated but porous material above the normal water table. The water in such an aquifer is **perched.** It is retarded in percolating downward to the normal water table by the less permeable material beneath (Fig. 14–3).

GROUND-WATER MOVEMENT

The water below the water table is not stationary: it flows much like air masses of different heights and densities, moving slowly under the influence of gravity toward an equality of pressure. The high areas of the water table tend to flatten and the low areas to fill up or to discharge water. If not replenished by rain the water table would ultimately flatten out to a level surface; in-

deed in many areas of high permeability within limestone and volcanic terrains the water table has extremely low slopes.

Points of surface discharge, at which the water table intersects the ground surface, are **springs** (Fig. 14–4). Most streams are **gaining streams,** that is, they mark areas of discharge of ground water from storage and lie in troughs in the water table toward which the ground water flows (Fig. 14–1). Streams that flow from well-watered areas into more-arid country (the Nile, Euphrates, and Tigris, for example) lose water by percolation; these are **losing streams,** leaking water to the water table and lying on ridges upon it

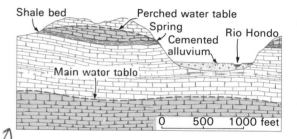

FIGURE 14–3
Cross section of aquifers in porous limestone, water is perched on a shale aquitard, southeast New Mexico. Note that the Rio Hondo, also, is perched above the main water table, on its own caliche-cemented channel sands. (After A. G. Fiedler and S. S. Nye, U.S. Geological Survey.)

FIGURE 14–4
Cross sections showing likely locations (S) for springs.

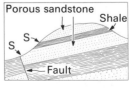
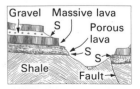
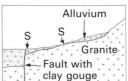
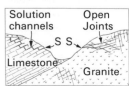

(stream on the right in Fig. 14–1). Irrigation, too, feeds water to the water table; in large areas of irrigated land in the Snake River plains of Idaho the water table is hundreds of feet higher than it was fifty years ago.

The rate and direction of water movement between two points on the water table are determined both by the permeability and the **hydraulic gradient,** the ratio between the *difference of elevation,* or **head** (H), and the distance (L) between the two points measured along the slope of the water table. Most ground-water gradients are low: 0.001 (1 foot per 1000 feet) or 0.01 (10 feet per 1000).

Effect of variations of intake on water levels

For any particular hydraulic conductivity, the hydraulic gradient adjusts itself to the water supply. If discharge into streams and springs is temporarily greater than recharge, the water table flattens. In dry spells the ground-water divides are lowered, reducing the hydraulic head and hence the discharge.

In arid western Texas, eastern New Mexico, and nearby parts of Mexico, the water table is nearly flat and commonly as much as 1000 feet below the surface. Large areas there lack permanent streams, though intermittent ones flow upon perched ground-water bodies or in natural flumes of gravel cemented by caliche (Fig. 14–3), deposited as stream water evaporates under the desert sun.

DARCY'S LAW

The modern concepts of ground-water movement were discovered in the mid-nineteenth century. Almost all ground water moves so slowly that the flow is laminar, rather than turbulent as in most surface streams. Flow lines in laminar flow are smooth, continuous, and traceable. Experiments show that in laminar flow the velocity and discharge vary directly as the hydraulic gradient. This law, fundamental to an understanding of ground-water movement, was discovered in the 1850's by the French hydrologist Henry Darcy while studying the water supply of the city of Dijon.

Darcy's Law states that the rate of movement of water through porous media is proportional to the hydraulic gradient. In simplified form it may be stated:

$$(1) \qquad Q = K\,I\,A$$

where Q = quantity of water moving in a unit time through a unit cross-sectional area A, K = hydraulic conductivity, a measure of the permeability, or ease with which water moves through a porous medium. It is measured in volume transmitted through a unit cross-sectional area per unit of time under an hydraulic gradient, I. (I = unit change in head through unit length of flow path.)

If Q is measured in cubic feet per day, A in square feet, and I in feet of *loss of head per foot of flow distance,* K is measured in feet per day. It is the velocity of flow. Similarly, if all dimensions are in meters, K is in meters per day. In natural aquifers, I is always a very small fraction; few water tables slope more than a few feet per mile.

Darcy's law is used to determine the hydraulic conductivity. If we measure the discharge (Q) of water from a well, and know the area (A) of the openings through which the water moves toward the well, and the difference in elevation between the water in the well and the water table (I) the hydraulic conductivity is the only unknown in Equation 1. Measurements show that some aquifers have hydraulic conductivities several thousand times as great as others. Well yields differ correspondingly.

Rates of ground-water movement

The movement of ground water through uniformly permeable material is shown diagrammatically in Figure 14–5, a section showing both ground-water divides and gaining streams. Some flow lines go much deeper than others, but all ultimately reach the streams.

The velocities of ground-water movement, though low compared to stream velocities, vary greatly, even in different parts of a single water body in uniformly permeable rock, as shown in Figure 14–5.

Mean rates of movement can be calculated from Darcy's law, after the hydraulic conductivity and gradient have been measured. Rates can also be measured directly by introducing dyes or salts in one well and measuring the time until they appear at another. From such tests, O. E. Meinzer, an American authority on ground water, thought the flow—50 feet per year—in the Carrizo sandstone of Texas, to be typical of many aquifers. Movements of 10 to 20 feet per day are sometimes attained in highly permeable materials and velocities as high as 420 feet per day have been measured.

According to Darcy's law, in materials of

low permeability the gradient of the water table increases steeply as recharge is added locally. In highly permeable materials the water table is flatter and hydraulic gradients are very low.

Drawdown by pumping

A pumping well is a point of artificial discharge that disturbs the water table. We have already seen how the water table becomes adjusted to points and lines of natural discharge, such as springs and gaining streams. Similarly, removal of water through a well lowers the water table and produces a **cone of depression** in it, greatly increasing the hydraulic gradient close to the well (Fig. 14–6).

In the example of Figure 14–6, the well pumped water from moderately permeable alluvium in the Platte River valley, Nebraska, where the undisturbed water table sloped eastward 6 or 7 feet per mile. The water table was observed in more than 80 wells arranged in lines about 1200 feet long, radial to the pumping well. The figure shows the cone of depression produced by pumping. The lowering, or **drawdown,** at the well was 22 feet after 48 hours of pumping; at a distance of 250 feet it was 1 foot and at 1200 feet from the well it was barely measureable. Flow lines toward the well must have extended at least this far horizontally, and also for some distance below the level of drawdown (compare with Fig. 14–5).

FIGURE 14–5

Approximate flow pattern of ground water in uniformly permeable material. (After M. K. Hubbert, Journal of Geology, *1940.)*

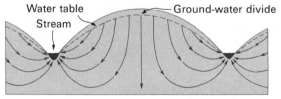

FIGURE 14–6

Cross section (with vertical scale greatly exaggerated) showing the water table before, during, and after pumping from a well. Observation wells are indicated by vertical lines. (After L. K. Wenzel, in Hydrology, *courtesy of Dover Publications.)*

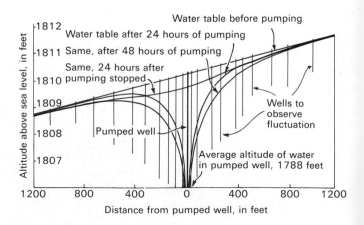

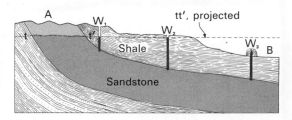

FIGURE 14–7
Cross section showing a series of wells—W_1, W_2, W_s—penetrating a confined aquifer. The water table in the recharge area is t–t'.

CONFINED WATER: ARTESIAN WELLS

An aquifer such as a porous, coarse-grained, loosely compacted sandstone, may be overlain by an aquitard such as shale. If the rocks have been tilted and eroded, the aquifer may crop out in hills or mountains above the surrounding lower country. The water in the aquifer may be partly confined in the lower country where it is deeply covered by shale, and yet be readily recharged in the mountains where it appears at the surface (Fig. 14–7). Water enters the aquifer at A in the recharge area. The water table in the aquifer ($t–t^1$) is higher than the ground surface at B, where the aquifer is confined beneath overlying shale. If a well, W_3, is sunk to this aquifer near B, the confined water will rise under the head of water from the intake area and flow freely without pumping, making this a flowing **artesian well.**

The name "artesian" was originally restricted to flowing wells; it is now applied, however, to any well in which the water rises higher than the top of the aquifer penetrated, such as W_1 and W_2 in Figure 14–7. ("Artesian" is from the old Roman province of Artesium—French, Artois, now mostly in the Department of Pas de Calais, France—where artesian conditions were common.)

Many artesian wells are of great value, furnishing copious supplies of water even in very arid country. Huge artesian supplies are present in the northern Sahara and in the desert of the Artesian Basin of Queensland, Australia. A dramatic example is from semiarid southwestern South Dakota.

The early railroads crossing this region needed much water. In 1905 N. H. Darton of the U.S. Geological Survey, who had just investigated ground-water supplies in the Great Plains, recommended that the Burlington Railroad drill for water in a deeply buried Paleozoic sandstone. His structure sections and maps indicated that at Edgemont, just south of the Black Hills, this probably productive aquifer should be encountered at a depth of about 3000 feet. After nearly three years of old-fashioned churn drilling, a well flowing more than 400,000 gallons a day was completed, within 31 feet of the predicted depth. Forty years later a new well, completed in the same aquifer after fifty days of rotary drilling, flowed about 1,500,000 gallons a day—an unusually large yield, and very valuable in this dry country.

Many Arctic areas furnish interesting evidence of the power of artesian pressures. In the delta of the McKenzie River the permafrost layer is commonly a hundred feet or more thick. As all the pores in it are filled with ice, the permafrost makes an excellent aquitard. Artesian pressures (derived from hydraulic heads at highland recharge areas) in the aquifer beneath the permafrost layer are high enough to punch up the permafrost and the overlying tundra into large blisters called **pingoes,** some of which are scores of feet high and as much as half a mile across. The confined water may then freeze in place to form a huge pancake of ice beneath the hill (Fig. 14–8).

Figure 14–9 illustrates the head conditions in a confined aquifer. Before being discharged from an artesian well, water would have stood in open casings in the well and in the observation wells B and C to the height marked "artesian head before discharge." This is equivalent to the line t–t' projected in Figure 14–7. Well A, which does not penetrate the aquitard, draws its water from a

FIGURE 14–8   *A pingo in the McKenzie delta, Northwest Territories, Canada. (Photo courtesy of Robert F. Leggett, Canadian Research Council.)*

different aquifer and its hydraulic regimen is independent of the artesian system. The load of all the rock between aquifer and surface rests on the top of the aquifer, partly supported by the rocky frame of the aquifer itself and partly by the hydrostatic pressure (artesian head) of water acting on the base of the aquitard. When the well is allowed to flow, the pressure in the aquifer nearby falls, just as it does in the cone of depression

FIGURE 14–9

Diagrammatic section through an artesian well and two observation wells, B and C illustrating head conditions in and near an artesian well before and during discharge. (After S. W. Lohman, 1965.)

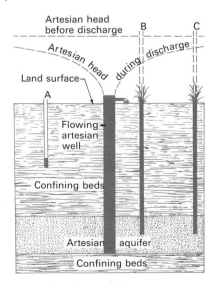

in an unconfined aquifer, but the phenomena are by no means identical, either in speed of response or in area affected. Measurements in wells such as B and C show a declining head toward the discharging well. The load of overlying rocks is there less supported by the artesian head and comes to bear more heavily on the aquifer itself. The aquifer is compressed slightly, some water is squeezed from its pores and moves to the well. In an unconfined aquifer much of the water drains slowly under gravity from the cone of depression; in a confined aquifer no corresponding section is dewatered—there is merely a drop in pressure. In an elastic confined aquifer the pressure drop takes place almost instantaneously; thus, it is felt much more quickly and over a wider area than is the pressure drop in the cone of depression of an unconfined aquifer. Under otherwise similar conditions similar pressure drops in confined aquifers have been recorded over areas several thousand times the area of measureable water-table depression in unconfined aquifers.

EFFECTS OF WATER EXTRACTIONS

The reduction of pressure in confined aquifers in many places has permitted noteworthy compaction of the rocks and dramatic subsidence of the surface. In Mexico City, for example, subsidence of as much as 18 feet followed the pressure reduction in a confined aquifer. Near Los Banos, in the San Joaquin Valley, California, a large area of more than 1200 square miles is subsiding rapidly owing to reduction of pressure in a confined aquifer. As the water pressure lowers, more and more of the weight of the overburden is transferred to grain-to-grain contacts in the weakly consolidated sediments. The pressure packs the grains tighter together as well as compressing them slightly. The subsidence by 1964 was as much as 23 feet, and was then proceeding at 1.4 feet a year. Such changes in ground level obviously must be carefully evaluated for the proposed large irrigation project in this area. Comparable subsidence, reaching as much as 31 feet, has taken place in the Wilmington oil field, Los Angeles County, California, because of lowering pressure in the oil sands and adjacent shales (also under artesian head). As this subsidence is in a highly industrialized area, practically at sea level, great expense has been involved in building dikes, relaying water and sewer lines, and pumping. The subsidence is now being combatted by injection of water into the oil sands at the periphery of the oil field, thereby sustaining the artesian pressure.

Along the hotel "strip" at Las Vegas, Nevada, pumping has lowered the hydraulic head more than a thousand feet, permitting surface subsidence of more than 6 feet. Simi-lar subsidence has taken place in the San Jose area, California, and Houston, Texas. We have already mentioned the cavern collapses at Carletonville, South Africa, brought about by dewatering the dolomite, thereby lessening support of the cavern roofs (Chapter 10).

Continued flow of artesian wells, or pumping from those that do not flow, clearly lowers the head; if continued in excess of recharge, an artesian system may be destroyed, so that, although the aquifer still contains water, it is not full at the site of the discharge well. It has become an unconfined aquifer, hydraulically, even though it is separated from the surface by an efficient aquitard. This has been the fate of many artesian systems that have been over exploited.

DISCHARGE OF GROUND WATER INTO THE OCEAN

Along many coasts, fresh ground water discharges directly through the sea floor for some distance offshore. Moreover, fresh ground water commonly extends far below sea level at the shoreline (Fig. 14–10). The lighter, higher column of fresh water seems to be in static balance with the denser sea water, as though floating within it. A column of sea water 1000 feet high can balance one of fresh water about 1025 feet high. If, therefore, the water table near the shore stands 25 feet above sea level, fresh ground water might theoretically be recovered to a depth of 1000 feet below sea level. This is because, with laminar flow, there is a minimum of mixing of the two fluids at their interface. But such a fresh water body is not static; it is constantly discharging into the sea (Fig. 14–10). The friction of flow through the rock retards the spreading out of the fresh water, but, of course, if it were not constantly replenished by rainfall, the steep interface would soon flatten.

The body of fresh ground water under the volcanic island of Oahu, Hawaii, though

FIGURE 14–10
Cross section showing freshwater flow lines in relation to the contact with underground salt water. (After M. K. Hubbert, Journal of Geology, *1940.)*

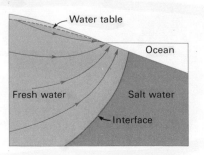

FIGURE 14–11   *Solution-etched limestone surface giving direct access to ground water. Near head of Valentine Creek, Glacier National Park, Montana. (Photo by M. R. Campbell, U.S. Geological Survey.)*

FIGURE 14–12   *A large sink, with alluvial floor, in limestone, Kars region of Yugoslavia. (Photo from Th. Benzinger, Stuttgart.)*

hundreds of feet thick, is thinner than expected from the flotation hypothesis. Furthermore, there is no sharp interface: the fresh water grades into salt through a thick zone of brackish water. Perhaps the thinning of the freshwater body and its mixing with salt water have been caused by intermittent pumping from many large wells. Perhaps, too, the lava contains enough large open channels to permit some turbulent flow and ready mixing of salt and fresh waters.

GROUND WATER IN CARBONATE ROCKS

Rain water, especially the slightly acid ground water of humid regions, effectively dissolves limestone, enlarges cracks and pores, and forms tunnels, irregular passages, and even large caverns along joints and other openings (Fig. 14–11). In places these openings are so extensive that much surface drainage goes underground through **sinks** (Fig. 14–12) and discharges through caves (Fig. 14–13). Sinks and caves, of course, develop very slowly. Water seeping down a crack in limestone enlarges the opening by dissolving some rock; weathering, rainwash, and gravitational collapse of the walls widen it, enabling it to trap more and more surface water, and further dissolve the limestone. The sink thus formed may extend completely through the limestone, discharging into caverns dissolved by waters diverted along an underlying aquitard. In time, the entire bed of limestone becomes honeycombed with interconnected sinks and caverns. Where saturated ground water seeps into the roof of a cave open to the air, it loses part of its carbon dioxide and, in part, evaporates, thus depositing some of its dissolved calcium carbonate as masses of **dripstone** that hang from the roof or rise from the floor in bizarre forms (Fig. 14–14).

The ease of movement of water through cavernous limestone and the flatness of its water table have often been demonstrated

by pumping. At the Los Lamentos mine, about a hundred miles southeast of El Paso, Texas, two years of constant pumping could not lower the water table appreciably, and the rich mineral deposit could not be mined below it. Mines at Eureka, Nevada, Tombstone, Arizona, and many other places have faced the same problem.

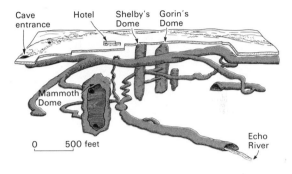

FIGURE 14–13
Diagram showing part of the Mammoth Cave system, Kentucky. (After A. K. Lobeck, Geomorphology, *McGraw-Hill Book Company, 1939.)*

FIGURE 14–14
Dripstone in an Indiana limestone cave. (Photo by Arch Addington.)

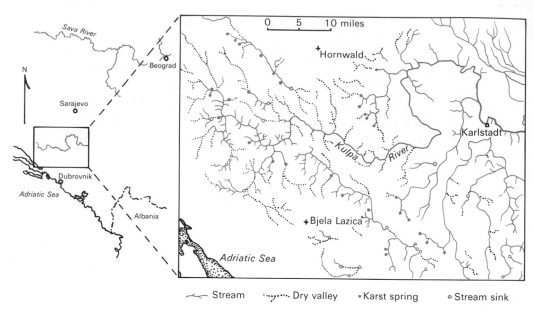

FIGURE 14–15   *Map of part of the Kars region, Yugoslavia. The drainage is partly underground, as shown by stream sinks in small, partly dry valleys, and great springs in larger, deeper valleys. (After N. Krebs, 1928.)*

Karst Topography

Some limestone or dolomite regions have few or no surface streams. The runoff passes underground through sinks and joints, flows through large and small caverns, cascades at intervals to lower levels and finally reaches the water table. Where valleys cut down to the water table, giant springs may gush forth. Such areas of underground drainage are **karst** regions (from the Kars district of the Dinaric Alps in Yugoslavia). Other karst regions are the Causses Plateau of southern France west of the Rhone, parts of the Cumberland Plateau of Kentucky and Tennessee and of the Shenandoah Valley, Virginia. Probably the most spectacular karst country on earth is in the Vogelkop peninsula of New Guinea, where sinks more than a thousand feet deep are so close together that only knife-sharp ridges with precipitate slopes separate them. Their pattern is such as is left by a biscuit cutter in dough.

Karst topography differs from that of an area of normal surface drainage. Instead of a system of slopes closely adjusted to surface streams, a karst region is pockmarked by large and small sinks, some enlarged by weathering, rainwash, and downslope movements (Fig. 14–12). The rivers are mainly fed by large springs. A stream may disappear in a sink in one valley to reappear as a huge spring in a neighboring one (Fig. 14–15).

Karst drainage has influenced men's actions for ages. Crops are poor on the dry plateaus, lush in the well-watered valleys. In southern France great springs that emerge in the Rhone Valley have determined the sites of towns since the time of the Romans.

PIPING, OR PSEUDO-KARST FORMATION.   Sub-surface drainage and the formation of underground caverns are not confined to carbonate rocks. In many arid regions, where the water table is far below the surface, downward-seeping ground water may wash out the finer grains from a weakly consolidated sediment

—in a process resembling that involved in the formation of a clay-rich B-horizon in soils—forming small tubes, or "pipes," that extend farther and farther headward from the gullies into which they empty. This is especially common in areas of "Badlands" (Fig. 14–16), where the pipes may extend for hundreds of feet from the deeper gullies. Collapse of the pipes forms karst-like topography and sinkholes. These pipes, however, do not extend below the water table as do many sinks in true karst regions.

SOLUTION AND CEMENTATION BY GROUND WATER

In general, solution predominates above the water table; deposition and cementation below, though in carbonate rocks solution may go on far below the water table. The extreme effects of solution in carbonate rocks have been described. But these are not the only rocks that dissolve; the dissolved load of all streams include many other elements besides those in calcite and dolomite. In the long lapse of geologic time even minerals, such as quartz, which the chemist considers highly insoluble, dissolve appreciably. Grains of garnet may be pitted and etched, and pyroxene and amphibole completely dissolved from the more permeable parts of a sandstone bed though they are preserved in tightly cemented parts of the same bed. Fossil shells of calcite are commonly leached out of shale and sandstone, leaving open cavities. These may be later filled to form "casts" that faithfully preserve the fossil form. Casts of soluble crystals such as halite or pyrite are also common.

In Chapter 3 we described the cementation of sand to form sandstone. Calcite cements many sandstones, but the reason is somewhat obscure; certainly water far below the water table cannot evaporate and deposit calcite as it does in forming caliche and dripstone above it. Possibly the decreased pressure on bicarbonate-rich ground water as it ap-

proaches the surface allows carbon dioxide to escape and calcite to precipitate. Some sandstones are locally cemented around shell fragments or other nuclei to form ball-like masses called **concretions** (see Fig. 15–14). Experiments show that slow precipitation of any material from solution generally leads to enlarging existing crystals rather than developing new centers of crystallization.

Ground water also deposits many other substances. Silica (as opal, chalcedony, or quartz) and iron oxide (as limonite or hematite) may fill or coat cavities in rocks. Where ground water circulates to depths of 2 or 3 miles, temperatures may be close to the boiling point of water, and many other minerals,

FIGURE 14–16

Top: *Pseudo-karst topography in shale of the Chinle Formation (Triassic), near Round Rock, Arizona. Bottom: Diagram showing inferred subterranean conditions near the Book Cliffs, in Utah. (After G. G. Parker, U.S. Geological Survey.)*

① Shale and sandstone of Cretaceous Mancos Shale
② Tan silt and clay, sandy in places, of Quaternary age
③ Pipe system
④ Block left as natural bridge
⑤ Debris blocks undermined and sapped by pipes
⑥ Flow of ephemeral drainage

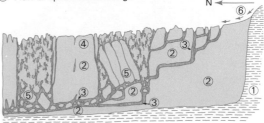

FIGURE 14–17
Steamboat Springs, Nevada, where heated ground water returns to the surface from depth. (Photo by W. D. Johnston, Jr., U. S. Geological Survey.)

such as clays, feldspar, mica, and chlorite may form.

Ground water highly heated at great depths or in contact with magma may return to the surface without losing much of its heat. Some hot springs (Fig. 14–17) so formed are valuable sources of steam power; the Lardarello hot spring area in Italy near Pisa supplies most of the power needed to operate the Italian railway system. Hot springs and steam jets (fumaroles) are also exploited for power in New Zealand, Iceland, and California.

Heated ground water is a powerful solvent of rock material, and when it returns to the

FIGURE 14–18   *Hot Spring terraces of calcium carbonate, Mammoth Hot Springs, Yellowstone National Park. (Photo by Tad Nichols, Tucson, Arizona.)*

surface it deposits much of the material from solution. Thus the geysers of Iceland, Yellowstone Park, and New Zealand build terraces of material precipitated from their heated pools (Fig. 14–18). Some of the terraces are of opaline silica, others of calcite. Algae of various colors may participate in the process of precipitation, and give brilliant coloring to some pools.

WATER WITCHING

Before the nineteenth century men thought that ground water flowed underground in definite rivers just as does surface water; if one were lucky, his well would intersect one of these streams and produce a fine flow of water. A dry or meagerly productive well had failed to intercept a channel. Since none can see beneath the surface, the digging of wells was always uncertain, and in doubt about where to dig for water, many farmers consulted "water witchers" or "dowsers." Such people supposedly possessed supernatural powers that enabled them to discover "underground streams." This belief still persists in some localities. A dowser generally walks about with a tightly held forked stick (Fig. 14–19), which dips violently when he crosses the channel of the supposed underground stream. His success, if any, has no known scientific basis; but his probability of success is high for aquifers are widespread.

COMPOSITION OF GROUND WATER

Ground water beneath swamps, peat bogs, and rain forests is always slightly acid because of the organic acids released from decaying vegetation. Where rain water passes through limestone, or even through decaying rocks that are only moderately calcium-rich, such as granite, it may dissolve enough calcium to become **hard water** ($CaCO_3 + H^+ \rightarrow Ca^{++} + HCO_3^-$). The amount of cal-

FIGURE 14–19
Water witcher or dowser of the sixteenth century. (Styled after old woodcuts.)

cium ion in hard waters in humid regions is only a small fraction of one percent. Such water may also contain fully as much sodium ion, but this is not easily precipitated and ordinarily goes unnoticed.

In arid regions, as we noted in Chapter 4, much water within a few feet of the surface may evaporate after a rain, precipitating relatively insoluble calcium carbonate in the capillary zone just above the water table as crusts of caliche. Complete evaporation will precipitate even carbonates and sulfates of sodium. As sodium-rich ground waters are toxic to plants, such "alkali soils" are nearly useless agriculturally. If such areas are drained, and the alkali waters flushed away by irrigation, they may be reclaimed for agriculture.

Still other ground waters are salty, containing enough sodium chloride to make them undrinkable and injurious to plants. Some salty ground waters are at least partly sea water, infiltrated directly from the ocean, but some salt water in deeply buried marine sedimentary rocks is presumably derived from sea water entrapped during deposition; it is **connate water.** Few connate waters have exactly the composition of present ocean water because of dilution by ground water after burial, concentration by evaporation during burial, addition of salt dissolved from nearby salt beds, and chemical reactions with the enclosing rocks. Salinity generally increases with depth; one cause is that the more saline brines are the denser and displace the fresher water upward.

GROUND WATER SUPPLIES IN THE UNITED STATES

Water is a vital resource. Even in humid western Europe and eastern North America municipal and industrial demands tax all of the available water supplies. The quantity and quality of fresh ground water recoverable is therefore of great economic and social importance. Careful estimates indicate that in the United States the amount of ground water at depths less than .8 kilometer is fully 7000 times the amount in all the freshwater lakes and streams. In almost any area wells will yield some water, but rocks of low porosity yield little, and nonpermeable rocks, even if porous, yield negligible amounts.

Copious supplies of ground water come from unconsolidated Pleistocene and Recent surface formations, from lava flows, and from cavernous limestones. Lesser amounts come from older, partly consolidated, but permeable, sedimentary rocks. The principal unconsolidated aquifers are: (1) alluvial gravels, sands, and glacial outwash; (2) the coarser parts of deltaic and other coastal plain deposits, and (3) sands and silts beneath floodplains.

Interior basins floored with unconsolidated sediments are common in the western third of the United States. In much of this arid to semiarid region, the quantity of ground water fixes definite limits of population. Interior basins normally supply about half the ground water used in the United States. In California alone, several large and productive basins yield more than a third of the groundwater developed in the United States.

Along the Mississippi drainage, glacial-outwash sands and gravels, just south of or interbedded with the relatively less permeable Pleistocene till sheets, grade downstream into river floodplain gravels and sands. Large floodplain aquifers also supply the Great Plains, and permeable coastal plain deposits extend from New Jersey to Texas.

Among more consolidated rocks, good aquifers are: (1) permeable sandstones; (2) well-jointed volcanic rocks; (3) cavernous limestone or dolomite; and, more rarely, (4) fissured crystalline rocks, such as quartzite, gneiss, or granite. Sandstone aquifers supply much ground water in the Mississippi Valley, Texas, and elsewhere. Basalt flows are important aquifers in the Pacific Northwest and Hawaii. In New England, though the glaciofluvial gravels yield much water, even more is derived from fissures in the metamorphic gneisses and schists.

The abundant joints, steam holes, and lava tubes in many volcanic rocks make them almost or quite as permeable as cavernous limestone or dolomite. The most productive springs in the United States are in basalt flows in Idaho. These springs discharge 5000 cubic feet of water per second—two-thirds of the average flow of the Mississippi at St. Paul—into a fifty-mile stretch of the Snake River. Cavernous limestones yield abundantly in Florida, the Cumberland plateau, and the Great Valley of Virginia.

Several highly productive aquifers will be described in the following pages.

Ground water of Long Island, New York

Because it is small and infiltration is easy, Long Island has no large streams. Of the 40 to 50 inches of annual precipitation in west central Long Island, probably 20 percent goes to surface runoff, 40 percent to ground water, and 40 percent to evaporation and transpiration. Lacking adequate local surface supplies, the nearly 5,000,000 inhabitants of Long Island depend on ground water and on surface water piped from the mainland. About 300,000,000 gallons per day is pumped from wells—a little less than is imported from the mainland. Nearly three-fourths of this comes from glacial-outwash sands and gravels; the rest from weakly consolidated Cretaceous sands below.

Among the Cretaceous aquifers, the basal bed is the most productive. This clean quartz sand, 100 to 250 feet thick, is overlain by shale; unconformably above the Cretaceous are Pleistocene sediments as much as 400 feet thick. Moraines form two ridges, one near the northwest shore, the other near the middle of the island. The chief aquifers are outwash plains of sand and gravel between, and south of, the ridges.

In a small area in Brooklyn, the water table in 1903 sloped down from 15 feet to sea level, but by 1943 excessive pumping had lowered it to below sea level. This reversed the hydraulic gradient, and salt water invaded the aquifer. The State of New York now requires that water pumped for cooling and air conditioning be returned after use to the aquifer from which it was withdrawn. By 1946 more than 200 recharge wells were operating in the urban area of Long Island. In the rural areas several very large recharge basins, in which storm and industrial waste are ponded to seep into the ground, have also been built. Total recharge in the summer of 1944 amounted to 60,000,000 gallons a day. The warm recharge water raised the ground-water temperature a few degrees, lessening its value for cooling, but the recharge wells and basins serve their main purpose—the water table no longer falls and saltwater inflow has virtually ceased.

The careful study of withdrawals and recharge in this area has revealed that urbanization has very notable effects on ground-water recharge. One of two adjacent stream valleys was urbanized during the study; the other remained rural. It was shown that the increased roofs and pavements and additional storm sewers cut off at least 2 percent of the ground water recharge in the urbanized area, while the other area was unaffected. The urbanization from Portsmouth, New Hampshire, to Richmond, Virginia, has had a measurable effect on the ground-water recharge of the whole coastal plain.

Ground-water basins in southern California

In semiarid southwestern California, several coastal basins contain alluvial deposits across which intermittent streams flow to the sea, charging the alluvium with ground water on the way (Fig. 14–20). The Santa Ana basin is filled to a depth of 500 to 1200 feet with alluvial fans from the San Gabriel Mountains, which form a compound apron extending almost entirely across the basin. At their heads the fans consist of gravels whose surfaces and bedding slope valleyward as steeply as 9°. Farther out on the fans the gravels grade into and interfinger with sands and silts, and the angle of slope decreases.

FIGURE 14–20
Section across the Santa Ana ground-water basin, California, showing the water-bearing Pleistocene and Recent alluvium and the effect of a fault on the position of the water table. (After California Division of Water Resources Bull. 45, 1934.)

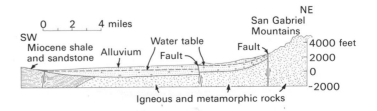

Over parts of the deposits relatively impermeable soils have formed, some of which have been buried by renewed upbuilding of the fans. The permeable gravels and coarse sands between these less permeable soils make up a complex of aquifers. On the lower parts of the fans some of the wells were artesian, the aquifers are confined by clayey soil zones in the fans. The slope of the fans is high enough to supply considerable artesian head. Over-exploitation for three-quarters of a century has been so great that the aquifers are no longer artesian.

Many basins in California are broken by faults so recent that they cut the alluvium. Impermeable clay gouge smeared along some fault surfaces make them effective barriers to ground-water movement. At the fault shown in Figure 14–20 the water table drops 400 feet, making a difference of many dollars in pumping costs on the two sides.

In this populous but arid area, the winter flood water is diverted onto complex spreading grounds of coarse gravel, thus giving it a chance to infiltrate instead of flowing to the sea. These man-made spreading grounds serve the same purpose as the recharge wells and basins on Long Island.

Here, just as in the Long Island example, excessive pumping near the sea had reversed the slope of the water table, allowing incursion of salt water. The threat to the orange groves and truck gardens was met by a system of recharge wells in the coastal zone. Concentrated recharge here has created a ridge in the water table, reversing the slope on the seaward side and halting the salt-water incursion. Such measures are effective where water is as scarce as it is in southern California, but are very costly.

It should be noted, however, that lowering the water level in a basin by pumping is not wholly a misfortune. Surface or subsurface outflow is decreased or even stopped and the water that would have flowed by (if the aquifer had been saturated throughout) becomes available for recharge. Moreover, the cone of depression of the water table in a partly emptied aquifer steepens the hydraulic gradient, so that the aquifer can accept a larger recharge during the rainy season.

Dakota Sandstone artesian aquifer

The great Dakota Sandstone basin is the largest and most-important source of artesian water in the United States, extending over much of the Dakotas, Nebraska, and parts of adjacent states. At least 15,000 wells have been drilled into this Cretaceous sandstone, which is generally somewhat less than 100 feet thick and is overlain by hundreds or even thousands of feet of other strata, mostly relatively impermeable shale. As shown in Figure 14–21, much of the recharge takes place in the upturned zones along the edges of the Black Hills and Rocky Mountains. But the sandstone is not a simple aquifer and recent studies by Frank Swenson of the U.S. Geological Survey have shown that, except near the mountains, much of the recharge is by leakage from the Pahasapa Limestone, a cavernous limestone formation of Carboniferous age beneath the sandstone (Fig. 14–21). The Dakota Sandstone includes a widespread shale bed near the eastern margin of the basin, dividing it into two parts, in which the compositions and pressures of the artesian waters vary independently. Pressure measurements in wells prove

FIGURE 14–21
Section through the Dakota artesian aquifer, from an intake area in the Black Hills of South Dakota to northern Iowa. Vertical scale greatly exaggerated. (After F. A. Swenson and N. H. Darton.)

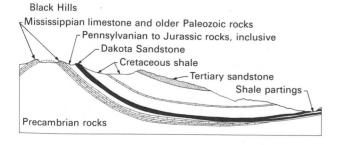

Black Hills
Mississippian limestone and older Paleozoic rocks
Pennsylvanian to Jurassic rocks, inclusive
Dakota Sandstone
Cretaceous shale
Tertiary sandstone
Shale partings
Precambrian rocks

that the flow from both the surface intake area and from the Pahasapa below is locally hindered by less permeable parts of the formation. Because of heavy use, pressures in the aquifer have decreased progressively since the first well was drilled in 1882.

The Dakota Sandstone is not the only productive aquifer in its area. We have already mentioned the deeper Paleozoic sandstone whose depth and productivity were so accurately foretold by Darton.

Water mining on the Llano Estacado

The High Plains of western Texas and eastern New Mexico are formed of Tertiary gravel and sand spread in a great alluvial apron from the southern Rocky Mountains. The canyon of the Canadian River on the north has separated the Llano Estacado from the source area of the gravels, and they now form an isolated mass, resting on an aquitard of Mesozoic shale. The water in the Tertiary gravels is perched. The gravels vary in thickness, but generally are 400 to 600 feet thick. The rainfall is about 20 inches annually, but very little of it sinks into the ground because of high summer temperatures and heavy cultivation. There is, therefore, negligible recharge of the aquifer. The Llano Estacado was virtually unpopulated in 1880, and had fewer than 20,000 people in 1900. Soon afterward, it was found that pumped water permitted production of remarkable crops of cotton, and agriculture increased. Pumpage has increased to the point at which more than 2×10^{12} cubic feet of water are being withdrawn from storage annually, and the prosperous agricultural area now supports a population of about 400,000 people. But the recharge has been estimated to be so slight that, if pumping were to stop today, it would require 4000 years for the water table to return to the position it had prior to pumping. No one can say how long the pumping can continue at present rates, but the water table had fallen more than 100 feet in some areas by the early 1960's, and it is obviously becoming more costly to raise the water from greater and greater depths. As much as 44 percent of the water originally present beneath Lubbock County, Texas, had been withdrawn by January 1962. Eventually it will undoubtedly become uneconomic to deepen the wells, and some farms will be abandoned, thus prolonging the life of the reservoir, so that no one need expect a sudden collapse of the area, but steady decline over the long term seems certain. The water is being mined just as literally as is the coal of Pennsylvania or the copper of Arizona, and just as inevitable is the ultimate exhaustion of the water resource as of the mineral.

ECONOMIC AND LEGAL ASPECTS OF GROUND-WATER USE

Where neither surface water nor ground water suffice to supply everyone's needs, disputes have arisen between individuals, communities, states, and even nations. Many such disputes at the lower levels have been carried to the courts. Applying, but narrowing, the English Common Law rule that the owner of a land surface also owns everything beneath it (a rule not recognized in Roman Law nor in the codes deriving from it), United States courts have held that all the owners of land overlying a ground-water basin jointly own the water of the basin. Water may not be exported without compensation, and water rights are prorated according to acreage. Furthermore the principle of "best use" has been established, as in a dispute between cattlemen wishing to preserve feeble springs and truck gardeners wishing to pump ground water from the same area and put it to more-productive use. In some states—for example, New York and Maryland—permission of state authorities is required for the drilling of large wells, and return of used water to the aquifer may be required. Ground water is an important public commodity, and its use increasingly requires regulation by well-informed officials.

Facts, concepts, terms

Ground water is rain water that fills openings in soil and rock
The water table
   Zone of aeration
   Zone of saturation
Relation of water table to streams, lakes, and marshes
Porosity and hydraulic conductivity
Perched water; confined water
Ground water moves under the influence of gravity
   Hydraulic gradient
   Darcy's Law: $Q = K\,I\,A$
Natural discharge of ground water
   Springs
   Gaining and losing streams
   Discharge into the ocean
   Hot springs
Artificial discharge of ground water
   Cone of depression around pumping wells
   Pressure drop in artesian wells analogous to cone of depression
Solution and precipitation by ground water
   Solution channels, caves, and caverns in carbonate rocks
    Karst topography
    Formation of dripstone
   Slow solution of relatively impermeable minerals
   Cementation of sandstones
Productive aquifers of the United States
   In unconsolidated deposits
   In consolidated but permeable rocks

Questions

1. Draw sketches showing several geologic conditions that could result in the formation of a spring.
2. Draw one well-labeled cross section showing all of the features listed below:
   a) An area of rounded hills with two through-flowing streams: one with a floodplain, the other downcutting far above grade.
   b) Two deep but dry ravines.
   c) The position of the normal water table.
   d) A perched water table.
   e) A swamp.
   f) Two wells of equal depth: one with water, the other dry.
3. A group of large freshwater springs emerge on the sea floor about half a mile off the mountainous coast of Ecuador. Show by a well-labeled diagram how this is possible.
4. Amphibole and garnet grains are abundant in well-cemented concretions from a sandstone, but the remaining, poorly cemented sandstone contains only a few etched grains of these minerals. How do you account for this?
5. Compare the drawdown at the test well near the Platte River (p. 292 with that at the Los Lamentos mine (p. 297), and account for the difference.

6. How can you tell an area of karst topography from the hummocky surface of a large landslide or debris flow?

7. Large springs are common in areas underlain by basalt, but almost nonexistent in areas of granite. Why?

8. How can ground-water basins be artificially recharged from waste water at the surface?

9. If water is neither moving through an aquifer, nor being discharged from it, can there be a hydraulic gradient? Explain, using a diagram.

Suggested readings

Hubbert, M. King, *The Theory of Ground Water Motion.* Journal of Geology, v. 48, 1940, p. 785–944.

Lohman, S. W., *Geology and Artesian Water Supply of the Grand Junction Area, Colorado* (U.S. Geological Survey, Professional Paper 451). Washington, D.C.: G.P.O. 1965.

Meinzer, O. E., *Ground Water in the United States: A Summary* (U.S. Geological Survey, Water Supply Paper 836-D). Washington, D.C.: G.P.O. 1939. [P. 157–229.]

Meinzer, O. E., ed., *Hydrology. Physics of the Earth: No. 9* (National Research Council). New York: Dover Publications, 1942.

Scientific American offprint

818. A. N. Sayre, *Ground Water* (November 1950)

15

Deserts and the Work of the Wind

Deserts are barren because available water does not suffice to support a continuous cover of vegetation. The rugged angular hills, cliffed canyons, and pebble- or sand-covered plains of the desert contrast sharply with the smoothly rounded hills and curving transitional slopes of more humid country (compare Figs. 15–1, 12–35). To a visitor from a well-watered region, the desert at first seems to have been molded by forces different from those of his homeland. The contrasts, however, do not reflect different agencies, merely the differing effects of the same agencies operating under different climatic conditions.

About one-sixth of the lands of the earth are desert. The greatest deserts lie in the Horse Latitudes—the subtropical belts of high atmospheric pressure—where descending air masses are dry, clouds few, precipitation low, and evaporation high (Fig. 15–2). Other deserts lie in the trade-wind belts where the winds have swept long distances over land, with a minimum opportunity to take up moisture. Other great deserts in higher latitudes, such as those of central Asia and parts of western North America, lie in "rain shadows" behind high mountain ranges over which clouds cannot ascend without cooling and precipitating most of their water vapor. Greenland and Antarctica are barren because nearly all the water is in the form of ice, unavailable for plant growth.

CLIMATIC CONTROLS

In most great deserts such as the Sahara, the average rainfall is less than 4 inches per year. A year or even several years may pass without any rainfall at all. But the absolute amount of rainfall does not alone control the amount of vegetation. For example, the annual rainfall (5 or 6 inches) at Point Barrow in northernmost Alaska is nearly as low as that at Yuma, Arizona, yet the ground at Point Barrow is sodden with water and matted with

FIGURE 15–1   *Broad alluvial plains between desert mountains, Salton Desert, California. Belt of small sand dunes in foreground. The straight black line is a railroad. (Air photo by Robert C. Frampton and John S. Shelton, Claremont, California.)*

FIGURE 15–2
Generalized atmospheric circulation.

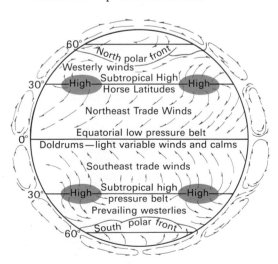

vegetation, whereas at Yuma the soil is parched, and the few plants are highly specialized in drought resistance. The contrast is largely due to the low rate of evaporation in the Arctic, though other factors, among them a high water table perched on permafrost, aid plant growth there.

Some writers divide arid regions into **steppes,** where scattered bushes and short-lived grasses furnish a scanty pasturage, and true deserts, where vegetation is sparse or absent. On this basis, most deserts of North America are steppes. There are, of course, continuous transitions from extreme deserts, through steppes, to humid regions.

FIGURE 15–3   *North Alvord Playa, southeastern Oregon. The irregular dark patches on the white playa surface are wet ground. The straight mountain fronts to the upper left are fault scarps. (Air photo by Richard E. Fuller.)*

INTERIOR DRAINAGE

Only the greatest rivers, like the Nile, Indus, Colorado, and Niger, can persist through deserts to the sea. Most desert streams dwindle by evaporation until the remaining water sinks into the ground or collects in a series of stagnant pools, a salt lake, or an alkali mud flat (Fig. 15–3). The drainage of the desert is only exceptionally integrated into larger and larger tributaries feeding trunk rivers, as in humid regions, and generally consists of many small stream systems, each ending in a closed basin or sinking into a desert plain. Such unintegrated **interior drainage** is characteristic of deserts.

The water table generally lies far deeper in deserts than in humid regions. Rainfall there, as in most humid areas, is greater at high elevations than at low. After a rain, rills and even rushing torrents rise in the desert mountains, but quickly shrink and disappear on the plains below. Yet, although most stream courses are dry except for a few hours or at most a few days a year, effects of stream erosion nearly everywhere dominate the landscape (Fig. 15–4). Barren mountains scarred by stream gullies and sun-baked plains built by stream deposits are characteristic.

Stream deposits are especially conspicuous in deserts (Fig. 15–1). Most desert storms are local, and the streams they generate flow for only a few hours. Most sediment is thus not transported to the sea, as in a humid area, but in a short distance is dumped on alluvial cones at the mouths of mountain canyons. The cones of adjacent canyons grow until they merge to form great alluvial aprons along the mountain bases (Figs. 12–38, 15–5, *top*). These compound alluvial aprons, or **bahadas,** flatten gradually toward the valley floor and merge imperceptibly with it. There the streams, decreased by evaporation and infiltration into the permeable ground, can carry only the finer material. A basin of interior drainage surrounded by such bahada slopes is a **bolson.**

The evaporation of the rains and infiltrated ground water results in deposition of calcium carbonate just below the bahada surface, forming the lime-cemented alluvium called caliche. In some areas, notably Australia and the Kalahari Desert of South Africa, silica is also deposited as opal or quartz, producing a very resistant "armor" at or near the surface of the alluvium. Thus many bahada slopes become plated with well-cemented rocks within a few years.

Bolsons are not filled to overflowing with water as are lake basins in a humid country. The sporadic rain forms only temporary lakes, which evaporate during the dry season, leaving a sun-baked floor of clay, silt, and salt called a **playa** (Fig. 15–2). Some playa lakes may persist for several years after an unusually wet season. Typical playas are the Black Rock Desert of northwest Nevada and the floor of Death Valley. Although Great Salt Lake is perennial and thus not strictly a playa, it fluctuates widely with wet and dry seasons, so that the flat western part of its bed—the Bonneville Salt Flat—has all the features of a true playa. When a playa dries, the dissolved material crystallizes out, depositing halite, various carbonates and sulfates of sodium, and other salts, which coat the "alkali flats" of many arid regions.

FIGURE 15–4 *Wadi Araba, Eastern Desert, Egypt. The dry watercourse of a braided stream. (Photo by Tad Nichols, Tucson, Arizona.)*

EROSIONAL PROCESSES IN DESERTS

Erosional processes in deserts differ from those in humid regions primarily because of the lack of vegetation, which greatly influences minor details of land sculpture, and the intermittent stream flow and general lack of integrated drainage to the sea.

Weathering

Rocks disintegrate and decompose in the desert, though more slowly than in humid regions because of the paucity of moisture and of organic acids in the soil. We have already seen that an Egyptian obelisk moved to New York weathered more in 50 years than it had in 3500 years in Egypt, and that differences in weathering are apparent between Upper Egypt and the slightly less arid Lower Egypt (Chapter 4).

Because weathering is slow and the barren ground is unprotected from rainwash and wind, fine-grained residual soils are rare. The fertile soil of Lower Egypt, flooded annually by the Nile, and that of Iraq, where the alluvium of the Tigris and Euphrates have supported civilization for centuries, was not weathered in place, but in the humid headwater regions. Limestone, which dissolves readily and generally forms lowlands in humid climates, stands in bold ridges in deserts, partly because joint blocks spalled from it dissolve slowly and so protect the slopes, and partly because percolating ground water evaporates near the surface, redeposits its dissolved calcite, and thus seals the openings in the limestone.

Rainsplash and rillwash

Besides the few permanent or intermittent streams and the wind, the principal mechanisms of rock transport in the desert are rainsplash, rillwash, and sheetfloods.

Desert plants are so scattered that their roots bind so little surface material that most of the ground is subjected to the direct impact of pelting raindrops. Even though the mass of an individual drop is slight, on unprotected desert ground it splashes fine fragments of rock and soil into the air, to fall or roll downhill. Anyone who has noticed mud and sand splashed onto a garden path after even a light rain can readily imagine the effects of splash during a heavy hailstorm or rainstorm, when perhaps 2 inches of precipitation falls in a single hour. This is 10 pounds of water to the square foot—nearly 140,000 tons per square mile. Silt, sand, and small chips of rock are battered downhill. During a heavy rain, small rills quickly form. Rainwash coursing down them carries mud, silt, sand, and, as the rills enlarge, even gravel and boulders. The desert streams carry vastly more material than corresponding rills in a humid region, where plant roots bind the soil. Much of this material is left stranded after only a short journey, helping to fill previously eroded channels. Because the water table is low, few desert streams are gaining streams; they are nearly all ephemeral, running dry a few hours after even a heavy downpour. Thus, between storms, newly exposed bedrock is accessible to weathering and sheds new chips and grains into the rill courses so that, if insufficient rain falls to produce a running stream, in a few years the channels may lose their identity by being blocked with boulders and filled with fine debris that rolls down from the walls.

Mudflows and sheetfloods

From time to time—perhaps only once in a decade, or even a century—intense rains pour down in deserts. These are the so-called "cloudbursts," during which several inches of rain may fall in an hour. Most cloudbursts cover only a few square miles; a few miles away, the sky is blue. The torrent from a cloudburst quickly digs gullies in the long-stable slopes, strips off the loose debris, and sweeps away the sediment stranded in former rill channels. Rapidly gaining both volume and load, it races down the canyon as a wall of debris-laden water so charged with mud and sand as to form a turbid fluid far denser than water alone—a viscous muddy sludge capable of buoying up huge blocks and boulders as it rolls downstream. Such a **flash flood,** pouring down Cajon Pass, California, after a cloudburst, overwhelmed a freight train, carried the engine more than a mile down the canyon, and buried it so deeply beneath mud and boulders that it was found only by using a sensitive magnet. Such viscous mudflows may travel completely out of the rain-swept source area before reaching an alluvial fan at the mountain front. There the water sinks into the fan and the mudflow grinds to a halt. Its steep front may be several feet high. Excavations show mudflows to be heterogeneous piles of rock, sand, and clay, almost unsorted by size or shape. They greatly resemble unstratified glacial drift, and some ancient mudflows have been misidentified as tillite.

Loose silt, sand, and rock fragments so abound on desert fans that water flowing over them is soon loaded to capacity. As was pointed out in Chapter 12, it is therefore unable to cut deeply into the surface. Diverted by cobbles, boulders, jams of floating plant fragments, and scattered clumps of vegetation, the water spreads widely in a plexus of small braided channels, or it may cover the whole surface as a film a few inches deep, forming a **sheetflood.** When it sinks in or evaporates, the sheetflood leaves a coating of mud and silt to dry in the desert sun.

Downslope movements

Downslope movements produce somewhat different results in deserts than in humid areas. Although weathering is relatively slow, many joint blocks have weathered so long that they are rotten and fall apart when they tumble from cliffs. Talus piles therefore form only beneath steep cliffs of rock that is not readily weathered, such as quarzite, chert, or limestone. Both steep and gentle slopes may be mantled with fallen boulders and chips, but most of these are only "one boulder thick," with bedrock visible beneath them. The boulders are ultimately swept away by cloudbursts or reduced by slow weathering to grains small enough to be carried away by rills.

Although during cloudbursts runoff is rapid and great, thick masses of water-soaked soil and rock like those responsible for the Gros Ventre slide (Chapter 11) rarely develop in deserts because the storms are brief. In fact, the large ancient landslides and debris flows in Arizona are considered strong evidence of a formerly more humid climate.

Relation of slopes to structure

The lack of soil and vegetation affect desert erosion in still another way. As the loose surface material is not effectively root-bound, it does not creep as a mass. Consequently, changes in steepness and roughness of the surface slopes are not softened and blurred as they are in moist climates. Slope steepness is apparently determined by the size of the joint blocks yielded by the bedrock—steep where blocks are large, gentle where small. Sandstone and shale that break down into small grains have gentle slopes unless masked by boulders rolled down from above. Basalt and quartzite stand in cliffs whose bases are hidden under large talus blocks. Even minor differences in particle size are accurately reflected by changes in slope developed on different rocks (see Figs. 5–14, 9–6). Abrupt changes in slope at the contacts of different rock masses are the rule in the desert, in marked contrast to the blurred and transitional slope changes characteristic of regions of active soil creep (compare Figs. 9–6 and 12–35). In the desert, abrupt transitions link hillsides with valley floors, and the summits are not smoothly rounded off. Steep slopes remain steep; even on wide desert plains iso-

FIGURE 15–5   *Three stages in the erosion of desert mountains.* Top: *Panamint Range, California, showing alluvial fans (bahada slopes) at the foot of a moderately eroded fault block.* Center: *Ibex Mountains, California, showing broad pediment embaying deeply eroded range.* Bottom: *Cima Dome, California, showing a broad graded surface with a few residuals of former large mountains. See Figure 15–6. (Photos by Eliot Blackwelder, Stanford University.)*

lated buttes left after erosion of great volumes of rock rise with characteristic abruptness, their slopes adjusted to the size of the coarse particles weathered from them (Figs. 15–5, *bottom,* 15–7, 15–22, 12–32).

EVOLUTION OF DESERT LAND FORMS

Crustal deformation may disrupt pre-existing drainage in deserts as elsewhere; so, also, may growing alluvial fans, mudflows, volcanic eruptions, or even roof-collapse of limestone caverns. Basins thus formed range from enormous areas like the Caspian and Aral depressions, the Dead Sea trough, or the basin of Great Salt Lake, down to wind-carved hollows a few feet across. In a region of interior drainage the base level of the streams rises as the basin fills. In a humid region base level is stable or slowly sinking. We consider here only the evolution of the closed basins in deserts.

In every closed basin, sediment brought from the uplands builds up the basin floor, raising the base level. Stream gradients flatten toward the basin center and the streams aggrade their courses by depositing alluvial fans. Rainfall is higher in the highlands than in lowlands. As a result, the only gaining streams are there and when they reach the fans they quickly lose water by percolation. Their lessened capacity favors deposition near the fan heads, building them higher. The streams, meanwhile, continue to cut down in the mountains. Eventually the fans build headward into the mountain valleys and aggrade them near the mountain front.

But, of course, the upbuilding of the fans is opposed by the slow weathering of the fan material and its removal by intermittent streams that head, not in the mountains, but on the fans themselves. Feeble as these streams are, they have a strong influence on the landforms developed. A fan can continue to grow only as long as the mountain-fed streams continue to bring more material to it than is removed from the fan; it is obvious that the more the fan grows the greater will be the area of rain attack on the fan. A dynamic equilibrium at which the material brought to the fan is just equalled by that removed to the basin floor is thus approached.

The topography of desert areas where crustal deformation has been fairly recent (as shown by folding or faulting of late Ter-

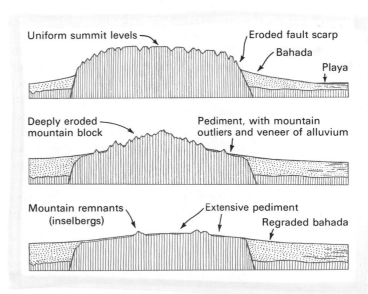

FIGURE 15–6
Diagrammatic sections of the three stages of erosion shown in Figure 15–5.

tiary or Pleistocene deposits) comprises three principal land forms: (1) relatively steep mountain slopes of bare rock and loose fragments, (2) bahada slopes made up of coalescing alluvial fans, and (3) playa floors covered with fine silts, clays, and various salts residual from evaporation (Figs. 15–5, *top,* 15–6, *top*). Such forms abound in Ethiopia, Turkestan, Israel, and the northern Great Basin of the United States (Fig. 15–3).

We have noted that the mountain slopes in deserts are adjusted to the size of the joint blocks or other rock fragments loosened by weathering. The foot of each slope slowly retreats as the bedrock and the surficial fragments weather to sizes that can be moved by streams on the bahada below. Thus the mountain base retreats as does the whole slope above, maintaining a fairly uniform slope. The sharp break between bahada or stream-carved slope and mountain front remains sharp, not rounded off as in humid regions by soil creep (Fig. 15–7).

As the bolson fills and base level rises, the lower parts of the fans are built up while the highlands and upper parts of the fans are still undergoing erosion. Laterally swinging streams emerging from the mountain canyons wear away the spurs of the interstream ridges, and the higher parts of the fans are planed off as the streams wander laterally across them. As the mountain front retreats the bedrock is slowly regraded to slopes virtually identical with those of the alluvial fans, forming a broad, gently sloping surface, called a **pediment,** which is strewn with a thin and discontinuous veneer of gravel in slow transit toward the valley. At such a stage, the desert landscape is composed of four main elements: (1) the mountains, whose slopes are virtually unchanged, (2) the pediment, or planed-off bedrock at whose junction with the mountain there is an abrupt break in slope, (3) the bahada, here composed of old fan deposits, regraded to a lower surface that blends imperceptibly upslope into the pediment and downslope into (4) the playa (Figs. 15–5, *middle,* 15–6, *middle*). This stage of landscape development is widespread in southern Arizona and New Mexico, where deformation has not been quite as recent as in the northern Great Basin.

It is not only time since deformation that determines the relative extent of pediment and bahada, however. If the original depressed areas are small relative to the upland areas, fans will continue to form and pile high against the mountain front. Until the fans are broad and high, erosion of the fans cannot catch up with sediment supply and the dynamic equilibrium necessary for pediment formation is not attained; conversely, broad lowlands and small highlands favor the early formation of extensive pediments.

The ephemeral streams may eventually fill the basin with their deposits and overflow the rim into an adjoining basin, thereby integrating the drainage. As erosion goes on, streams draining to lower basins grow headward just as in humid regions, successively capturing higher basins and ultimately regrading them to lower levels. The main streams thus grow longer and longer, and in time their long profiles become graded throughout, even though the waters of no single storm may flow their entire lengths. This process of drainage integration and regrading of higher basins to lower levels results in the scouring out of older deposits from the higher basins. As the stream level lowers, such materials, like the bedrock of the original topography, are cut to slopes appropriate to the size of their component particles. Because these deposits are generally poorly consolidated and readily eroded, pedi-

FIGURE 15–7   *Erosion in friable sandstone, Coal Canyon, Arizona. Note the abrupt change in slope at the foot of each hill. (Photo by Tad Nichols, Tucson, Arizona.)*

ments develop rapidly across them at the expense of the older bahadas. In this stage of desert erosion, playas are absent (if trunk streams have succeeded in extending through the region to the sea) ; bahadas are much less extensive; mountains have shrunk; and pediments cover most of the area (Figs. 15–5, *bottom*, 15–6, *bottom*) . This is the stage represented in the United States by large parts of southwestern Arizona, where the Gila and Colorado rivers form a slowly lowering base level for the local streams, and where there are no present-day playas (compare Fig. 15–3) . Nevertheless, as shown by drilled wells, much of the area is underlain by thick alluvial fans and playa clays of former interior basins. Pediment surfaces extending across these easily eroded deposits blend indistinguishably into other areas of pediment where only a thin veneer of gravel masks resistant bedrock and from which small mountain masses rise abruptly.

In a still later stage, the mountains, though retaining their steep slopes, have shrunk to small isolated hills that rise abruptly above a rock floor, like islands from the sea (Figs. 15–7, 15–22) . These are **inselbergs** (German for "island mountains") . Presumably, if no structural or climatic change intervened, continued erosion would eventually produce a wide rock plain whose flat surface would be subject primarily to wind erosion. Parts of the Kalahari Desert of southwestern Africa approach this condition, but no large area has been recognized as representing such a hypothetical final stage in desert landscape evolution.

WORK OF THE WIND

The desert land forms just described indicate that water-molded surfaces dominate the landscape. Many people have the impression, perhaps fostered by movies and fictional romances, that deserts are chiefly great wastes of sand dunes. These, they suppose, furnish the chief contrast to a humid landscape. For most deserts this is not true. Yet, because

vegetation is sparse or absent, wind erosion is much more effective in deserts than in humid regions, and locally is a major agent.

Every dry gust of wind wafts dust along a city street. In the open, on hot summer days, dust devils (small whirlwinds) swirl fine debris high above plowed fields. Sporadic tornadoes uproot trees, lift soil, and destroy houses. Dust is in the air everywhere; even in humid regions closed rooms require dusting every few days.

Sorting by the wind

Anyone who allows dry soil to dribble slowly from his hand during a wind notices that some falls almost vertically, but much strings out downwind. Fine dust is carried away completely. By repeated trials, the coarse grains can be rather cleanly winnowed from the fine, even by a gentle breeze, as wheat is winnowed from chaff on primitive threshing floors.

This illustrates a general condition: any object dropped through a fluid, such as air or water, falls at a speed that first increases but eventually becomes constant—the so-called "terminal velocity" of fall for the object. Two forces act on the body: (1) the downward pull of gravity and (2) the resistance of the fluid to its passage. The pull of gravity depends directly on the difference between the mass of the body and that of the fluid it displaces. But the resistance to the movement depends on the viscosity of the fluid, the diameter of the body, and its speed through the fluid. Resistance increases with increasing speed. Thus, gravity, which in a vacuum would produce constant acceleration, is ultimately balanced by the increasing resistance of the viscous fluid; there is no further acceleration, and the speed is constant at the terminal velocity. Experiments show that the terminal velocities of different-sized spheres falling in any fluid vary tremendously. The terminal velocities of particles smaller than about 0.01 millimeter in air vary almost exactly with the square of their

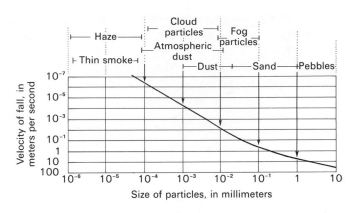

FIGURE 15–8

Graph showing the variation of terminal velocity of fall with grain size of falling particles. (After R. A. Bagnold, The Physics of Blown Sand and Desert Dunes, *William Morrow and Co., 1942.)*

diameters, a relationship, or "law," deduced by Sir G. G. Stokes in 1851. Such particles fall slowly enough to let the air accommodate their passage by laminar flow. The velocities of larger spheres are not as simply related to diameter; their greater size displaces such a volume of air that its inertia becomes important. The air becomes turbulent as they fall through it. Figure 15–8 shows the general relations between size and terminal velocities of particles in air, though flakes and other irregular grains fall more slowly than spherical grains of the same mean diameter. The figure shows that the fine particles in our handful of soil were blown farther than the coarse particles before sinking to the ground because they fell more slowly.

This helps us to understand the transporting power of the wind. Winds are always turbulent; gusts and eddies that swirl in every conceivable direction are superposed on their general motion. Close to the ground the ratio of the speed of upward gusts to the average forward velocity of the wind is extremely variable but averages about 1 to 5. Hence, some particles in the air with terminal velocities lower than $\frac{1}{5}$ of the wind speed will be carried upward by gusts and remain suspended until either they are caught in a downdraft or sink with their ordinary terminal velocity to earth. While in suspension they will, of course, travel along with the wind. Particles with terminal velocities greater than $\frac{1}{5}$ of the wind speed are not wafted aloft. Measurements in dune areas in-

dicate that sand begins to move when the average wind velocity reaches about 5 meters per second (11 miles per hour). If the maximum updrafts have $\frac{1}{5}$ of this speed, or 1 meter per second, we see from the curve of Figure 15–8 that grains of less than about 0.2 millimeters diameter should be winnowed out of surface dunes.

This deduction is amply confirmed by observation of actual dunes. Sieving dune sands through graded screens shows that grains 0.3 millimeter to 0.15 millimeter in diameter greatly predominate. Even the finest dune sands contain almost no grains smaller than 0.08 millimeter.

Wind-blown sand rarely rises more than 6 feet, even in a severe storm, and most moves within a few inches of the ground, as shown by abrasion at the bases of telegraph poles and rock outcrops (Fig. 15–9). The great clouds that blacken the sun in areas like the floodplain of the Nile and the Dust Bowl of Oklahoma, Kansas, and Texas, are clouds of dust, not sand. In sandy deserts away from floodplains the air is generally clear, during even high winds, above a carpet of moving sand only a few feet thick.

Motion of particles with the wind

Sand grains, momentarily carried forward by gusts, strike the ground at a low angle. If the surface is rocky they bounce into the air and travel on in a series of hops. If the surface is loose sand, such a falling grain may

FIGURE 15–9
Fluted and polished Eocene Limestone, sand-blasted by the prevailing winds. Western Desert, Egypt, near Kharga Oasis. (Photo by Tad Nichols, Tucson, Arizona.)

eject others as it "splashes" into the surface; even though a particular grain makes only one jump, it may eject one or more other grains. Even grains too large to be caromed into the air may be pushed along slowly by successive impacts of many smaller grains. The thickness of the layer of sand that creeps downwind depends on wind speed and grain size. If the sand is pebbly, the wind may winnow the sand away, leaving the pebbles to accumulate over the desert surface as a residual layer, one pebble thick, making a so-called **desert pavement** (Figs. 15–10, 15–11).

The more exposed pebbles generally have smooth sandblasted surfaces. Pebbles undermined as the sand blows away from around them may be rolled over by the wind, exposing more sand. When this in turn is blown away, neighboring pebbles are also undermined and overturned, and sandblasted surfaces develop on the new upper sides of the pebbles. In this way pebbles may ultimately acquire several flat facets that meet at sharp angles like those of a Brazil nut, as shown by several pebbles in Figure 15–10. Eventually, wide areas are covered by such deflation armor, one pebble thick (Fig. 15–11).

Similar processes go on in the snowy deserts of Antarctica and Greenland. The hardness of snow increases greatly with decreasing temperature; at −78°C it is 6 on the Mohs scale, the same as that of orthoclase. At some stations in Adelie Land the wind velocity averaged over an entire month is as much as 65 miles per hour, gusting to over 100 miles

FIGURE 15–10
Desert pavement in Death Valley, California. Note how several of the pebbles have been faceted by sandblast. (Photo by Eliot Blackwelder.)

FIGURE 15–11
Deflation armor or desert pavement in the valley of the Little Colorado River, Arizona. (Photo by Tad Nichols, Tucson, Arizona.)

per hour. Drifting snow in the Antarctic is thus a powerful erosive agent, and boulders faceted by snowblast are as common as sand-blasted boulders in a sandy desert (Fig. 15–12).

The surface of a sand dune is so rough that the turbulent wind directly in contact with it whips the most exposed grains aloft in momentary whirls. Where, however, the average diameter of grains is less than about 0.03 millimeters (much below sand size) the result is different: even the most exposed grain projects so slightly above the general surface that it fails to swirl into the air except at very high wind speeds. Dunes never form on a surface composed exclusively of grains as fine as this, and only a high wind can set the grains into motion.

In wind-tunnel experiments, a British military engineer, Brigadier R. A. Bagnold, found that a surface of loose, dry Portland cement was stable, and the air above it dust-less, even though the wind was strong enough to move pebbles $\frac{1}{6}$ inch in diameter. This stability of even-surfaced fine material accounts for the general lack of dust storms on large playas whose surface material is both fine grained and well sorted. Such material is stabilized by the small size of its grains and their strong cohesion when capillary water is present. Only when a playa surface has recently dried up and is covered with curled flakes of dried mud does it yield much dust, even to a strong wind. After these flakes have been blown away (to accumulate as dunes of clay chips to leeward) the playa surface is nearly dust-free unless disturbed by animals or wheels.

Measurements made while sand is drifting show that the wind near the ground moves much less swiftly over loose sand than over a rock floor, even though the velocity at a height of 6 feet is identical in the two localities. A study of grain movements suggests why this is so. Momentarily suspended grains that bounce along the rocky floor are so highly elastic that little energy is needed to keep them rebounding. But more energy is needed to keep similar grains moving over loose sand because they lose momentum on splashing into it and disturbing other grains. Hence, grains that bounce over a rocky floor slow down or stop when they strike loose sand. This peculiar ability of sand dunes to collect grains from intervening barren areas instead of permitting the sand to spread evenly over the entire surface between dunes enables the dunes to grow.

Wind erosion

Unlike streams and glaciers, winds are not confined between banks but blow freely over the whole surface of the earth. Dust clouds raised by the wind may be blown far away

before they settle. This process is called **deflation** (from the Latin, "to blow away"). The only base level for wind erosion is the local water table, and even this may be slowly lowered by evaporation as wider areas are eroded down to the capillary zone.

Most large undrained depressions on the deserts of North America and Asia—those of Death Valley and the Caspian Sea, for example—have been formed by crustal movements rather than erosion. However, in Wyoming, Texas, New Mexico, and Colorado, there are wind-carved hollows hundreds of feet deep and several square miles in area. In the Kalahari Desert of South Africa many shallow "pans" lie below the general surface of the granite bedrock. These are undrained,

FIGURE 15–12   *Snow-blasted boulder, Taylor Dry Valley, Antarctica. (Photo by Warren Hamilton, U.S. Geological Survey.)*

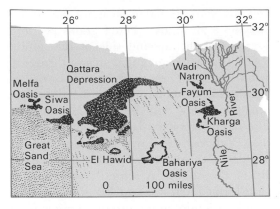

FIGURE 15-13
The large depressions and sand-dune areas of Egypt and Libya. The dark-patterned depressions are below sea level. (After U. S. Air Force Aeronautical Charts.)

FIGURE 15-14
Concretions left on the rim of the Kharga Oasis, Western Desert, Egypt, by the deflation of finer sand grains, not so well cemented. (Photo by Tad Nichols, Tucson, Arizona.)

and hence could not have been formed entirely by running water.

Perhaps the most striking wind-carved depressions make up a chain of oases extending about 400 miles westward from the Nile Delta into the Libyan Desert (Fig. 15-13). Although perhaps started by some other process (ground-water solution, for example), strong evidence shows that the depressions have been enlarged and deepened by the wind.

Their northern margins are steep escarpments, greatly dissected by stream-carved ravines. Some depressions bottom well below sea level; others a few hundred feet above. Their floors rise gradually southeastward and merge with the general level of the desert plain, a few hundred feet above the sea. Long chains of sand dunes, built in part by material blown out of the basins, string out across the southeast slope and beyond the depressions for hundreds of miles.

Flat-lying concretionary sandstone underlies the desert, and there is no evidence that the basins are fault troughs. The dunes to leeward of these depressions show that the wind has been a major factor in transportation, but the water-scoured slopes draining into the depressions show that the wind need have done little actual abrasion of rock. Sand, of appropriate size for wind transportation had already been carried into the basins by rainsplash and rills. The main work of the wind was to carry away material already broken down by weathering and running water. In so doing, it left behind materials too coarse to blow away (Fig. 15-14).

When such basins as these are lowered to the local water table, moist ground and vegetation prevent further downcutting unless the water table itself is simultaneously lowered by evaporation. Many Egyptian oases have springs of fresh water around a central depression filled by a salt marsh or playa whose floor is sealed from the main body of ground water by clay.

Although such large depressions are impressive, they are rare. Most deserts show little sign of deep wind erosion, although, in places grooves a few feet deep and a few hundred feet long have been carved into poorly consolidated sediments. In topographic gaps through which wind armed with sand is funneled, the bedrock may be smoothed, polished, or etched by shallow grooves, testifying to the ability of the wind actually to abrade well-consolidated rocks. The main role of the wind, however, is to remove unconsolidated material from the sandy and silty surfaces of fans and other stream deposits, whose very presence testifies to the dominance of running water in the making of the desert landscape.

SURFACE FORMS OF MOVING SANDS

Small-scale features

As soon as the wind rises to the speed at which sand grains begin to jump, the surface of a dune is bombarded by grains that splash into it and eject some grains they hit. Though the leaping grains differ widely in range and trajectory, most, being approximately the same size, will strike a flat surface at roughly the same angle and with similar momentum.

A surface of sand that is not quite flat is shown in Figure 15–15. A small hollow has developed at B. The paths of the leaping grains are represented by the equally spaced parallel lines. The forward drift of the sand, the aggregate movement of both jumping grains and those hit by them, should be

roughly proportional to the number of grains striking a given area. Fewer grains per unit area strike the upwind side of the hollow (AB) than strike an equal area of the downwind side (BC). More grains will be driven up the slope BC than down the slope AB, and the hollow will deepen. The slope BC also receives more impacts per unit area than a level area of equal size. Grains carried up-slope will, therefore, accumulate at C, on the lip of the hollow. A second slope (CD) is thus formed. On it, as on AB, the grain motion is at a minimum; a second hollow must form farther downwind. In this way the originally flat surface of the sand becomes rippled (Fig. 15–16).

FIGURE 15–16
Wind ripples on the surface of a dune near Newport, Oregon. (Photo by Parke D. Snavely, Jr., U.S. Geological Survey.)

FIGURE 15–15
The beginning of rippling on a sand surface. (After R. A. Bagnold, The Physics of Blown Sand and Desert Dunes, *William Morrow and Co., 1942.)*

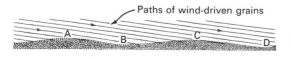

FIGURE 15–17
Uniform transfer of grains and wind-formed ripples. (After R. A. Bagnold, The Physics of Blown Sand and Desert Dunes, *William Morrow and Co., 1942.)*

Once rippling begins, more grains are ejected from slopes facing the wind than from the sheltered slopes, as shown in Figure 15–17. The ripples thus tend to become similar in size and spacing. Furthermore, as their crests rise they enter streams of stronger wind, and the larger and heavier grains tend to linger on them, for the lighter are more readily moved by impact and by gusts. This concentration of coarser grains on the crests is the exact opposite of the way grains are sorted in water-formed ripples: when preserved in consolidated rocks, it helps distinguish rocks deposited by wind from those deposited by water.

Rippling takes place during gentle winds; when wind speed rises (in wind-tunnel experiments, to about three times that needed to start grains moving) the ripples are destroyed, apparently because the difference between the wind speed over crests and hollows becomes negligible. Moreover, if the wind dies away gradually, the hollows tend to fill, because the wind in these protected places is too feeble to maintain them. Hence, winds that slacken slowly may leave a nearly flat, though mildly rippled surface.

Large accumulations of sand

When blowing sand enters an area where either the nature or configuration of the ground or the vegetation interferes with the wind, it accumulates. Two kinds of accumulations are obviously related to topography: **climbing dunes,** where the wind rises over a sharp topographic break (an example is the sea of sand banked against the northeast wall of Panamint Valley, California) , and **falling dunes,** where sand is swept over a cliff and falls into a sheltered hollow. Almost as clearly related to topography are the dunes and sand sheets formed where the wind, after sweeping sand through a topographic gap, diverges across a wide plain with consequent slackening of speed.

Sand also accumulates on wide, flat plains to form great persistent dunes that migrate

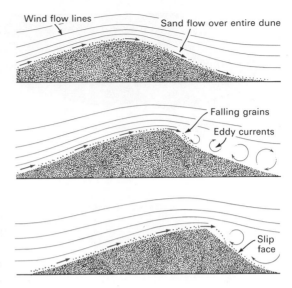

FIGURE 15–18
Evolution of a sand dune with a slip face. (After R. A. Bagnold, The Physics of Blown Sand and Desert Dunes, *William Morrow and Co., 1942.)*

slowly across country for scores or even hundreds of miles. Although the mechanism is complex, we may gain some understanding of dune advance if we consider briefly a few of the factors involved. Among these, vegetation is paramount: other important elements are the effect of sand accumulation itself on the pattern of wind currents and the relation between sand supply and the prevailing winds.

DUNES IN BARREN DESERTS.   Although no desert is entirely without vegetation, in some the plants are so small and widely scattered as to exert only trivial influence on wind speed. Where enough sand accumulates to create a wind shadow the wind speed is obviously greater on the windward than the leeward side (Fig. 15–18) . Sand is then selectively removed from windward and deposited to leeward. When the speed to leeward slackens so much that the average grain in momentary suspension is not carried all the way to the foot of the leeward slope, the sand is deposited in the wind shadow high on the lee-

FIGURE 15–19   *A transverse dune in the White Sands National Monument, New Mexico, showing irregular slip face. (Photo by Tad Nichols, Tucson, Arizona.)*

ward slope. Eventually, the grains pile so high that the slope becomes unstable and the loose pile slides down to form a **slip face,** thus building an even more efficient wind shadow than before (Fig. 15–18).

A slip face is well shown in the foreground of Figure 15–19, where it can be seen to be composed of many small "landslips" extending from top to bottom of the dune.

Dune accumulations a few feet high rise into speedier air streams than flow near their bases, and therefore become increasingly unstable. The wind funnels through any gaps along their crests, counteracting the tendency of grains to roll sidewise into the gaps, and thus a large dune of irregular height that lies across the wind tends to split in two. In deserts of extremely sparse vegetation and constant wind direction many dunes are of the

crescentic variety called **barchans** (Fig. 15–20). The points of the crescent (wings) point downwind, the curving bow faces the wind. Much of the lee face is a slip face. Even during strong winds there is relative quiet in the lee of the dune, so that all the sand swept over the top of the slip face accumulates there until it becomes unstable and slides down into the wind shadow. At the ends of the dunes, on the other hand, sand streams away to leeward in great quantities. The slip face, about two-thirds of the length of the dune, is at right angles to the wind. Since no sand escapes from the slip face, sand arriving from upwind must be deflected around the wings or else the dune will grow larger. If the barchan remains the same size, the sand streams released from its tips must carry away nearly all the sand that reaches the dune from upwind. Consequently the sand streaming from the tips of a barchan often starts a new dune farther to leeward. Field observations indicate that barchans form in areas where the wind direction is almost uniform throughout the year.

In general, the larger a barchan the slower it migrates. A small dune will therefore overtake a larger one downwind; and its wings will enclose a hollow between its slip face and the larger dune, thereby deflecting the local wind and modifying the shape of the dune (Fig. 15–20). Barchan fields can become very complex, especially where vegetation or topography modifies their advance.

Where wind direction varies considerably, barchans are unstable. If the sand comes mainly from one source, so that winds from its direction supply nearly all the sand, but winds from another direction are more powerful, the sand may move very irregularly, and the dunes may be strung out in long chains at an angle to the winds (Fig. 15–21). For these dune chains the name **seif** (from the Arabic word for "sword") has been suggested. Seifs can grow to great size: some in Iran rise more than 700 feet above their bases and are $\frac{3}{4}$ of a mile wide. Individual seif ridges as much as 60 miles long are known, and groups of seifs extend for more than 200 miles in the Western Desert of Egypt. The sand between these ridges is better compacted than that of the dunes and forms the *serir* or hard sand desert, of the Arabs (Fig. 15–22).

DUNES IN CONFLICT WITH VEGETATION.   Even an open vegetative cover greatly influences dune forms. Plants establish themselves more readily in sags in the dunes than on the more active crests, for there they are abraded less by moving sand, and their roots are more likely to reach ground water. Hence **transverse dunes,** at right angles to the wind, do not split up into barchans if plants in the low spots gather and stabilize the sand that would otherwise drift through the sags to form the barchan's wings. Many transverse

FIGURE 15–20   *Barchan dunes near Laguna, New Mexico. The dunes are several hundred feet long. (Photo by Robert C. Frampton and John Shelton, Claremont, California.)*

FIGURE 15–21   *Seif ridges of the Sahara, Africa. (Photo by U.S. Air Force.)*

FIGURE 15–22   *The* serir *or hard sand desert, Kharga Oasis, Western Desert, Egypt.* (*Photo by Tad Nichols, Tucson, Arizona.*)

FIGURE 15–23
From left to right: *Transverse, parabolic, and longitudinal dunes; the arrows indicate a possible transition between the three forms.* (*After J. T. Hack, 1941.*)

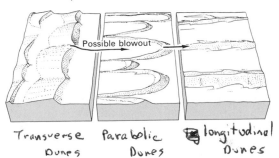

dunes are half a mile or more long and reach heights of 10 or 15 feet before breaking up (Fig. 15–23).

Where vegetation is able to establish itself widely over the sand, however, long transverse dunes do not form; instead, two other varieties predominate; "blowouts," or **parabolic dunes,** and **longitudinal dunes.** The relations between the three forms are shown in Figure 15–23.

Parabolic dunes, some of elongate "hairpin" shapes with the points facing upwind,

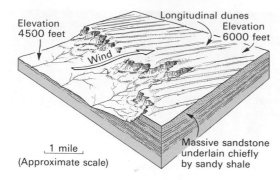

FIGURE 15–24
Longitudinal dunes on the Moenkopi Plateau, Arizona, formed where sand, released by weathering of sandstone cliffs, is drifting across the plateau. (After photo by U.S. Soil Conservation Service.)

instead of downwind as in barchans, form either by blowouts of older stabilized sand or by accumulation of sand downwind from patchy sources. Such a dune may form where sand from a dry stream bed is swept up a ravine in a bordering slope onto a brushy terrace, where it overwhelms the plants in the line of maximum supply. The ravine funnels both wind and sand so that the center of the dune advances faster than the wings (Fig. 15–23). These may lag enough for vegetation to anchor them completely. In extreme cases the lengthening is so great that the dune may be shaped like a hairpin, or even break up into a longitudinal ridge extending directly downwind. Parabolic dunes also form by "blowouts," where excessive cultivation, or trampling by animals, destroys the plant cover and exposes the sand beneath to the action of the wind.

Where the sand supply is spottily distributed or comparatively scanty, and the wind's direction constant, a common form of dune is a long downwind ridge. Such longitudinal dunes also form where climbing dunes reach the top of a cliff and the sand is channeled from notches in the crest (Fig. 15–24). Their formation requires an extremely constant wind direction and is evidently favored by a rather small sand supply and a climate so dry that but little sand motion suffices to overwhelm the sparse vegetation. These are the dominant dune forms in the Navajo country of northeast Arizona, where many are several miles long and as much as thirty feet high. Their pattern is remarkably constant over hundreds of square miles.

SUMMARY OF FACTORS INFLUENCING DUNE SHAPES. We have suggested some of the many factors that influence the formation and shapes of dunes. Others are doubtless involved and much remains to be learned, but three factors seem clearly important: wind speed, sand supply, and vegetation. Abundant sand and strong winds produce transverse dunes in both barren and brushy deserts; where there is less sand and weaker vegetation, barchans and longitudinal dunes predominate. Moderate winds may produce parabolic dunes where vegetation grows rapidly enough partly to anchor the slowest moving parts.

CHARACTERISTICS OF ANCIENT DUNE SANDS

Highway and railroad cuts through dunes show that they differ from other accumulations of sand in several ways. A most conspicuous one is their cross-bedding. The internal stratification of dunes is extremely complex, as suggested by their diverse forms, their slip faces, and their complicated progress as they move downwind. A well-cemented sandstone that preserves these complex cross-bedded patterns is illustrated in Figures 15–25 and 15–26. This particular sandstone, a part of the Navajo Sandstone of Jurassic age, contains other features that suggest its dune origin. Among these are the excellent sorting, wind-carved pebbles, and the frosted, or sandblasted, surfaces of the grains. Frosted

surfaces on sand grains are common in wind-blown but are rare in water-laid sands, both because small grains move faster in wind than in streams and because their effective mass is far higher, since the density of the suspending fluid is much lower. Hence, the impact of windblown grains on one another, though not strong enough to shatter them completely, does tend to pit, or frost, their surfaces, in contrast to those of waterborne sands of the same size. Such features have made it possible to recognize ancient dune sands in geologic formations of many ages.

FIGURE 15–25
Cross-bedding in the Navajo sandstone, Zion Park, Utah. (Photo by Tad Nichols, Tucson, Arizona.)

FIGURE 15–26
Cross-bedded Navajo sandstone. At the holes, sand grains, loosened by solution of the cementing calcite, have been blown away. (Photo by Tad Nichols, Tucson, Arizona.)

LOESS

Great areas of southern Germany, Russia, Turkestan, and China in the Old World (see Fig. 13–23), and of the Mississippi Valley and Columbia Plateau in the New, are blanketed with fine-grained, loosely coherent material called loess. Despite its weak cohesion, loess stands in nearly vertical walls because it contains vertical tubules (left by rotting out of grass roots) and shrinkage joints. These also make it highly permeable to ground water. Many loess-covered areas are very fertile farm lands—for example, the Palouse country of eastern Washington. Some loess deposits in western China are hundreds of feet thick, but elsewhere most are only a few feet thick.

Microscopic studies show that loess is composed of angular particles—mostly less than 0.05 millimeter in diameter—of quartz, feldspar, hornblende, and mica, pieces of fine-grained rocks, and some clay. Most of the grains are fresh or only slightly weathered.

These features suggest that loess is a deposit of dust and silt that settled from the air in grassy country. Most loess lies downwind from areas that were glaciated during the Pleistocene epoch (see Chapter 13), but some deposits are in the lee of deserts. The great loess deposits of China, for example, lie downwind from the Gobi and other deserts, and are probably being added to at the present time, just as dust from the Dust Bowl must, in the middle 1930's, have added to the soil of the more humid lands of the eastern United States. Nigeria has vast loess deposits derived from the Sahara, though much Saharan dust goes on to settle in the Atlantic Ocean (Fig. 17–19).

Facts, concepts, terms

Interrelations between climate, soils, and land slopes
Interior drainage; bahadas; playas
Pediments
Sheetfloods and mudflows
Relation of grain size of weathered particles to desert slopes
Evolution of desert landscapes
Settling velocity and wind sorting
Origin of ripples on sand surfaces
Barchans, seifs; desert pavement; wind-carved pebbles
Dunes in conflict with vegetation; parabolic and longitudinal dunes
Ancient dune sands
Loess

Questions

1. Why are the southwestern slopes of the Hawaiian Islands arid, whereas the northeastern sides receive heavy rainfall?
2. Why do dune sands vary so little in grain size? Why are they generally free from clay?
3. Why does sparse sand on a rock floor accumulate into dunes instead of spreading out uniformly over the whole surface?

4. Draw a cross section through the area shown in Figure 15–1, and label the following features on the section: (*a*) area that is being reduced in height by rainwash and gullying, (*b*) pediment, (*c*) area of stream deposition and braided streams, (*d*) area of active sand dunes, (*e*) area where wind-carved pebbles and desert pavement might be found, (*f*) area from which water might be obtained from wells.

5. Why are pediments not formed in humid regions?

6. Why are windborne sands more likely to be frosted than stream sands?

7. What differences can you find between pediments and stream-cut terraces?

8. The so-called cloudbursts rarely exceed 3 or 4 inches in total rainfall over a period of an hour or two. Heavy rains that last for much longer periods of time are common in humid regions. Explain the cause of the generally more drastic results associated with the desert cloudbursts.

9. Rainfall is higher along the recently uplifted shores of the Baltic Sea than it is along the Italian coast. Why, then, are sand dunes so much more abundant on the North German and Polish coasts than near Naples?

10. The walls of many canyons in the steppes of southeastern Oregon are draped with remnants of debris flows and landslides that are being actively gullied by rillwash from cloudbursts. What does this imply about climatic changes in the area? What additional features would you look for to prove the point?

Suggested readings

Bagnold, R. A., *The Physics of Blown Sand and Desert Dunes*. New York: William Morrow, 1942.

Bryan, Kirk., *Erosion and Sedimentation in the Papago Country, Arizona* (U.S. Geological Survey, Bulletin 730) . Washington, D.C.: G.P.O. 1932.

Denny, Charles S., *Fans and Pediments*. American Journal of Science, v. 265, 1967, p. 81–105.

Gautier, E. F., *Sahara, the Great Desert* (translated by D. F. Mayjew) . New York: Columbia University Press, 1935.

Hack, J. T., *Dunes of the Western Navajo Country*. Geographical Review, v. 31, 1941, p. 240–263.

Hume, W. F., *Geology of Egypt,* Vol. 1. Cairo: Government Press, 1925.

Scientific American offprints

841. Victor P. Starr, *The General Circulation of the Atmosphere* (December 1956)

847. Joanne Starr Malkus, *The Origin of Hurricanes* (August 1957)

chapter **16**

The Oceans

The seas now cover 70.8 percent of the earth, and rocks containing marine fossils or having other characteristics indicating a marine origin crop out over nearly three-fourths of the lands. As most of these outcrops are terminated by erosion surfaces, Steno's reasoning shows that even more of the continental surface has, at one time or another, lain beneath the sea. It therefore seems possible—even probable—that no spot on earth has always been land throughout geologic time.

To interpret the record of the marine rocks we must know something of the sea, of the processes going on in it, of the organisms inhabiting it, and of the widely varying topographic, sedimentational, and ecologic environments that diversify it.

As we saw in Chapter 10, land and sea are very unevenly distributed: the earth can be divided into two hemispheres: one, whose pole is near England, contains four-fifths of all the land; the other, whose pole is near New Zealand, is nearly nine-tenths sea (Fig. 10–3).

CIRCULATION OF THE SEA

Ocean water is about 800 times as dense and several thousand times more viscous than air of the same temperature; its movements, therefore, though complicated and difficult to predict in detail, are sluggish compared to those of the atmosphere. Although ocean waves may move at speeds of scores of miles per hour during storms, the water composing them rarely, if ever, travels more than 5 miles per hour. Until recently it was thought that no ocean current exceeded the 17 mile per hour tidal current in the Moluccas, but eastward-moving currents (the equatorial countercurrents) have been recognized at depths of a few score fathoms beneath the equator in all three oceans. These have speeds as high as 27 miles per hour in the Pacific, 22 miles per hour in the Atlantic, and

11 miles per hour in the Indian Ocean. Most ocean water, though, moves only a mile or two a day, and much appears nearly stagnant.

Currents within the surface layers of the ocean

The large oceanic currents at the surface of the ocean closely resemble the wind patterns. Indeed, wind drag is the chief driving force of currents in the upper layers of the sea. Because of the earth's rotation, any moving fluid tends, in the northern hemisphere to be deflected to the right, in the southern hemisphere to the left—the Coriolis effect. The Trade Winds thus drive the surface water slowly toward the equator, and at the

same time westward, in both hemispheres. Thus is produced a strong **equatorial drift** of westward-moving water—a drift ridden by the famous raft *Kon-Tiki* in its journey from the Peruvian Coast to the mid-Pacific islands. But the westward-moving water of the equatorial drift tends also to diverge both to south and north, leaving an eastward-moving countercurrent between, traveling at the high speed just cited. In this way a continuous upwelling of deeper water is brought about, both along the equator and along the western shores of all the continents (Fig. 16–1).

In the middle latitudes of both hemispheres, westerly winds set up a similar eastward drift. In the southern hemisphere this drift is not interrupted by land masses so

FIGURE 16–1 *The currents of the north and equatorial Atlantic Ocean in February–March. (After H. U. Sverdrup, M. W. Johnson, and R. H. Fleming,* The Oceans. *Copyright 1942 by Prentice-Hall, Inc.)*

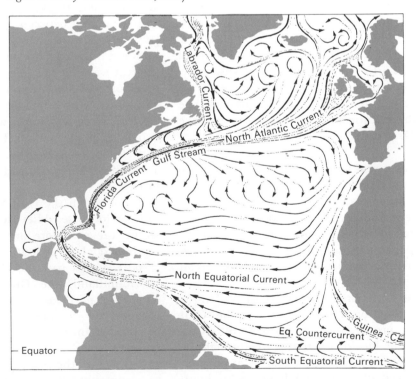

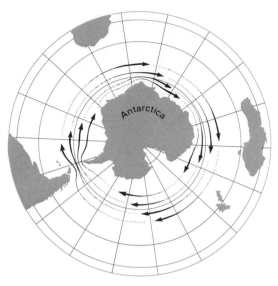

FIGURE 16–2
The West-wind Drift in the Antarctic Seas.

that a continuous **West-wind Drift** rings the Antarctic (Fig. 16–2). In the northern hemisphere a similar drift is obstructed by the continents, which deflect it both north and south. The continents similarly deflect the equatorial currents. In the land-locked basin of the north Atlantic a vast clockwise eddy, of which the well-known Gulf Stream is an important part, is thus established. The South Atlantic and the other oceans have similar systems.

THE GULF STREAM. "There is a river in the sea—the Gulf Stream," said Maury, the great American oceanographer of a century ago. Modern studies confirm his picture of a well-defined stream of warm water, with relatively sharp boundaries, that courses with the speed of a river across thousands of miles of ocean (Fig. 16–1).

The Gulf Stream system consists of three segments: the Florida Current, the Gulf Stream proper, and the North Atlantic Current. The Florida Current pours through the strait between Cuba and Florida at an average speed of nearly 5 kilometers an hour,

carrying between 20 and 40 million cubic meters of water per second, more than a thousand times the normal flow of the Mississippi. The North Equatorial Current, driven by the Trade Winds and deflected northward by the South American landmass, piles water up in the Gulf of Mexico. Precise leveling across Florida shows that the Gulf stands about 17 centimeters (7 inches) higher than the Atlantic; this is, of course, the immediate cause of the Florida Current (Fig. 16–1).

As the Florida Current emerges from the Gulf it is joined by water flowing north along the east coast of Cuba. The combined stream sweeps northeast along the continental shelf, augmented by water from great eddies in the western Atlantic. It reaches its greatest volume off Chesapeake Bay where it has grown to a volume of 70 million cubic meters per second more than 1000 times the average flow of the Mississippi. It varies in width between 50 and 150 kilometers at this latitude and different threads of current move at speeds ranging between 5 and 12 kilometers per hour. The stream sometimes wanders a hundred miles or more off its average course in great wavelike meanders that occasionally break off completely to form large independent eddies. These rapidly interchange large bodies of cold and warm water between the two sides of the stream. The volume varies with the seasons but the current averages about 80 kilometers in width and 500 meters in depth.

Inshore from the Gulf Stream, numerous counterclockwise eddies are thrown off; these set up the nearshore drift that shifts sand southward along Atlantic beaches.

As it sweeps past the Grand Banks near Newfoundland, the Gulf Stream spreads out to the northeast, subdivides, slows, and becomes less definite. Here it is called the North Atlantic Current. Its northern branches trend far into the Norwegian Sea and even into the Arctic Ocean: their warm water notably affects the climate of the British Isles and Scandinavia. Southern branches carry water southward along the European coast to the trade-wind belt, whence it is driven back across the Atlantic in the equatorial drift, completing the circulation.

The deep water circulation

Measurements of temperature and salinity (the concentration of dissolved salts) at various depths show that the deep water is stratified in layers superposed according to density. Warm water is, of course, less dense than cold water of the same salinity; in tropical seas the water is generally less dense than elsewhere. But salinity also affects density—the higher the salinity the higher the density. Salinity is high near the Horse Latitudes, where dry winds suck up moisture but leave most of the dissolved salts behind (Fig. 16–3). Salinity is low in areas of heavy rainfall, and where great rivers dump fresh water into the sea. When sea water freezes, ice excludes nearly all the salt. Consequently the freezing of floe and shelf ice around the Antarctic continent concentrates salt in the cold water beneath.

When surface water sinks it is relatively rich in oxygen dissolved from the air by breaking waves. The very cold water from the stormy Arctic and Antarctic seas sinks quickly to the bottom and spreads widely so that the very bottom water in nearly all the oceans is relatively rich in oxygen. As it slowly mixes with adjacent water masses, the oxygen is gradually depleted by the metabolic activity of marine organisms, and the water becomes richer in carbon dioxide. As we shall see in Chapter 17, this change has a notable effect on oceanic sediments.

Accordingly, measurements of temperature, salinity, and oxygen content at different depths in the sea enable oceanographers to trace movements of water masses from different sources with remarkable accuracy. We describe two examples: the Mediterranean Water and the Antarctic Bottom Water.

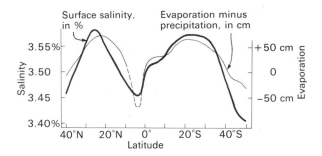

FIGURE 16–3

Graph showing the close correlation between changes of surface salinity and evaporation-minus-precipitation at different latitudes. Note that near the equator, though evaporation is very high, the salinity is kept down by the very heavy precipitation. (After George Wüst.)

THE MEDITERRANEAN DENSITY CURRENT.   The Mediterranean Sea, because of its hot, dry climate, is a huge evaporating pan in which the salinity of surface water increases to about 3.86 percent, 10 percent higher than normal sea water. Thus even though the surface water is relatively warm (about 13°C in winter) its density is such that it sinks to the bottom. At the Strait of Gibraltar, this dense bottom water is out of equilibrium with the less dense, though cooler, water of the adjacent Atlantic; it pours across the rock sill of the Strait in a huge density current that delivers about two million cubic meters of water per second into the Atlantic—a hundred times the average flow of the Mississippi. At the surface, lower density water flows from the Atlantic into the Mediterranean to maintain balance. During World War II, German submarines, with engines turned off to avoid detection, rode into the Mediterranean in the upper current, and out in the lower.

On emerging into the Atlantic, the Mediterranean current flows down the continental slope until it reaches a depth of about 6000 feet. Here it finds water of slightly higher density (but of lower salinity and temperature) over which it spreads in a great flat sheet covering most of the North Atlantic,

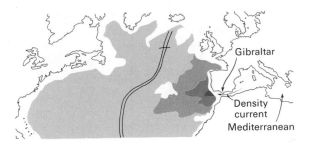

FIGURE 16–4

Salinity of the North Atlantic at depth of 6000 feet. The map is drawn as if all the water above that depth were stripped away. Extremely salty water from the Mediterranean pours through the Straits of Gibraltar and flows down the sloping sea bottom until it encounters water of higher density upon which it spreads as a flat sheet. The successively lighter shades indicate the gradual dilution by mixing with adjacent sheets as the Mediterranean water spreads outward. (After Henry Stommel, "The Anatomy of the Atlantic." Copyright © January 1955 by Scientific American, Inc. All rights reserved.)

gradually mixing with adjacent layers of water that dilute and cool it (Fig. 16–4). At the other end of the Mediterranean, somewhat similar currents flow to and from the Black Sea. In the Black Sea basin precipitation greatly exceeds evaporation so that the salinity is considerably less than that of the Mediterranean. A surface current flows from the Black Sea through the Bosporus while at depth a countercurrent of saline water about half as great flows from the Sea of Marmora to the Black Sea. This current sinks beneath the more brackish water of the Black Sea, forming a stagnant water body which has become virtually depleted in oxygen below a depth of about 150 meters in the center and 250 meters near the shores.

THE ANTARCTIC BOTTOM WATER.   The water around the Antarctic continent is also very dense, but for an entirely different reason. Extensive masses of floe ice along the edges

FIGURE 16–5

The Antarctic Bottom Water, as it would appear if all the water above a depth of 12,000 feet were stripped away. Note how the cold saline water spreads northward, channeled into the western South Atlantic by the Mid-Atlantic Ridge, which rises high above this depth except at the Romanche Trench. The Trench provides a low pass through which the Bottom Water spreads into the eastern Atlantic. The darkest shade indicates the pure Bottom Water; the lighter tones successive stages in its dilution. The Atlantic Ridge is shown only schematically. (After Henry Stommel, "The Anatomy of the Atlantic." Copyright © January 1955 by Scientific American, Inc. All rights reserved.)

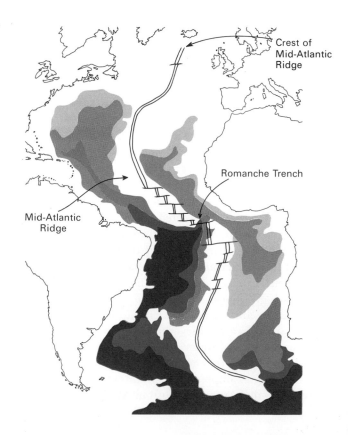

of the continent freeze and thereby increase the salinity of the remaining sea water, because little salt is taken into the ice. Thus, the shelf seas bordering the continent contain a very cold and highly saline water—the densest (1.0274) water in the oceans. This water sinks and flows along the bottom, spreading far to the north in each of the oceans. In the Atlantic, its upper surface is generally about 12,000 feet below sea level. Figure 16–5 shows this deep water mass as it would appear if the overlying water down to 12,000 feet were stripped off. Note how the Mid-Atlantic Ridge (only schematically drawn in the figure) channels the Antarctic bottom water into the western half of the Atlantic basin until it finds a low pass—the Romanche Trench—near the equator through which it can reach the floor of the eastern Atlantic.

TIDES, WAVES, AND CURRENTS

Moving water is a powerful erosional agent both on land and in the sea. Nevertheless, although the major ocean currents move immensely greater volumes of water than all the rivers of the continents, they erode but little. Their energy is largely dissipated in friction with other water masses instead of with the sea floor. Only locally—as over the Blake submarine plateau off the east coast

FIGURE 16–6
The lunar tides. The tidal bulges are greatly exaggerated. (In part after H. U. Sverdrup, M. W. Johnson, and R. H. Fleming. The Oceans. Copyright 1942 by Prentice-Hall, Inc.)

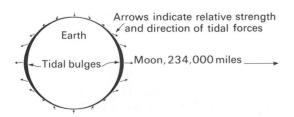

of Florida—does the Gulf Stream extend deep enough to scour the bottom. Here there is little deposition, and perhaps even some erosion at depths of 6000 feet or more. There are a few other areas of current erosion, but the major geologic effect of the great oceanic currents is climatic. It is the smaller but swifter currents caused by winds, tides, storms, or earthquakes, and the turbidity flows of sediment-laden water, that are the efficient agents of erosion and transportation in the sea.

Tides

The ancients knew that the ebb and flow of the tides varied with the phases of the moon. So complex is the real earth as compared with the idealized earth assumed by the astronomers and physicists that no general theory as yet permits tidal forecasts for any point on an ocean. Tides are, of course, predicted with great accuracy for all the principal ports. They are not computed from general theory, however, but from tidal records for many years at the particular port concerned.

Since Newton's time, the forces that produce the tides have been understood much as shown in Figure 16–6. If D is the distance from the center of the earth to that of the moon, M the mass of the moon, and r the radius of the earth, the moon's attraction for a mass, m, at the earth's surface on the side nearest the moon is greater than its attraction for a like mass at the earth's center: $Mm \div (D-r)^2$ is greater than $Mm \div D^2$. Theoretically, if this surficial mass is a fluid, it will bulge upward. Similarly, a mass on the earth's surface directly opposite the moon is attracted less than a like mass at the earth's center: $Mm \div D^2$ is greater than $Mm \div (D+r)^2$. Theoretically, a water mass is "left behind" in a corresponding bulge. At all other points, there is also a difference in the moon's attraction for particles at the surface and for the "average" particles of the earth's body, which can be thought of as concentrated at the earth's center. Hence the earth's gravitation and the attraction of sun and moon cause a force that acts on each particle along a line inclined to that joining the centers of the earth and the moon and sun as illustrated in Figure 16–6. This inclined force can be resolved into vertical and horizontal components. Because the earth rotates with respect to the moon once in 24.84 hours (not 24, because the moon advances eastward in its orbit) , two tidal bulges pass over any given point on the earth's surface during this time.

The sun attracts earth particles just as does the moon, but despite the sun's immensely greater mass, it is so much farther away that its tide-producing force is only 0.46 that of the moon. Twice during the lunar month, at new and full moon, sun and moon lie on a straight line passing through the earth and then their influences are additive. These are times of extreme tides (**spring tides**); at other times their tide-producing forces tend in some degree to neutralize each other. At the moon's first and third quarters their influences are directly opposed and the tides are smallest (**neap tides**). The tidal forces, of course, affect all parts of the earth, not merely the water bodies. The tides in the rocky crust are so infinitesimal, however, because of the rigidity of the rocks, that they can be detected only by extremely sensitive instruments.

Although the simple diagram of Figure 16–6 illustrates the tide-producing forces, it completely fails to explain the vagaries of local tides. For example, many ports have but one tide in a lunar day, in others the high tide lags many hours behind the time the moon passes overhead, in still others the two daily tides are of greatly different heights throughout the lunar cycle. Tides also vary with the seasons, these and many other facts make clear that the tides are not direct responses to the vertical component of the moon's gravitational pull, which is really far too small for effective lifting of the huge water masses involved. It is the horizontal component of the tide-producing force that directly induces the horizontal flow of water masses, which pile up against the land, forming the effective tides. The configuration of the ocean's bottom so strongly influences the direction of flow that tidal currents vary greatly in strength and direction at different ports and, because of seasonal density currents, even at the same point during different seasons.

The principal geologic interest of the tides is in their erosional power. Some tidal currents are prodigious, particularly those in estuaries with converging shores. In the Bay of Fundy, between New Brunswick and Nova Scotia, the vertical tidal range is at times as much as 70 feet; the possibility of harnessing the power of the huge water masses that surge in and out of the bay twice daily has been seriously studied. So far, the cost of the necessary dams and the hourly fluctuations in available power have made the project seem uneconomic. Yet these tidal currents attain speeds of 9 miles per hour during both rise and fall, and have scoured basins in the bottom more than 150 feet deep.

In St. Malo Bay, Brittany, the tidal range is 40 feet and currents reach speeds of 8 miles per hour. Between the Channel Islands and the coast of France currents sometimes reach 12 miles per hour, as they do between the Shetland and Orkney Islands. The speediest tidal currents known are in the Moluccas: about 17 miles per hour. Although the Mediterranean tidal range is only about a foot, the timing of high and low tides at the ends of the Strait of Messina is so different that currents as fast as 6 miles per hour are common there. During storms in the South Pacific, the lagoon of Tuamoto Atoll sometimes becomes so overfilled with water washing over the reef that currents as great as 14 miles per hour develop in its narrow outlet at low tide.

In some rivers high tides may reverse the flow as they rush upstream in breaking waves called **bores.** At spring tide the bore of the Hangchow River is as high as 16 feet, and travels at 16 miles per hour; the bore in the Amazon is comparable, as is that of the Yellow River. The estuary of the Scheldt, although it has a seaward sill less than 10 meters deep, is scoured by the tide to depths of nearly 60 meters. In the very muddy estuary of the Gironde, the reversal of flow at high tide causes sedimentation upstream in and near the harbor of Nantes; at low tide much of the deposit is scoured and carried out to sea. On balance, though, the upstream deposit exceeds the scour, so that Nantes, which was a considerable seaport two centuries ago, is no longer important commercially.

Experiments show that water moving half a mile an hour will transport medium-sized sand grains, and at three miles an hour will carry gravel an inch in diameter. Tidal currents are therefore locally important agents of sediment transport; dredging off the Mull of Galloway, Scotland, proves that coarse gravel moves there at depths of more than 800 feet.

Current meters lowered in the sea indicate that some tidal motion extends to the bottom, even at great depths. In the Romanche Trench through the Mid-Atlantic Ridge, coarse gravel attests the effect of tidal currents; the abrasion of submarine cables where they cross the Ridge (Chapter 5), shows strong currents there, far below the reach of waves. Over the continental shelves tidal currents should be strongest near the edges, for the volume of water moving in and out is there greater in proportion to depth than elsewhere. Perhaps this accounts for the sediments near the outer edge of the shelf being in many places coarser than those nearer land. The stronger currents should winnow out the finer sediment and drop it off the shelf onto the continental slope. Photographic measurements of light transmission by cameras lowered on cables show that the water at depth is slightly cloudy from fine sediment in suspension over most of the continental slopes and, indeed, far out on the continental rise. Tidal currents seem to be active on all submarine ridges, regardless of

depth, for many yield bare rock to the dredge, and nearly all show coarser sediments than adjoining basins or depressions. Tidal currents rushing in and out through offshore bars commonly build submarine deltas, both in the lagoon behind the bars, and offshore.

We thus have evidence that the tidal currents significantly affect the size, sorting, and distribution of sediment over most of the sea floor. But only locally are these currents important in shaping the shore itself; in the actual shore zone waves and wave currents are much more effective.

The great waves that are the tides are caused by the gravitational pull of sun and moon. Two wholly different kinds of waves, neither of them tidal, have unfortunately become popularly known as "tidal waves." One, the seismic sea wave, caused by earthquakes, is considered in Chapter 19; the other is the **sea surge**—a high-water wave caused by prolonged and unusually violent onshore winds.

FIGURE 16–7

A synoptic chart of sea-surface disturbances during the sea surge of January 31 and February 1, 1953, in the North Sea. Disturbance heights are in meters above mean sea level. (After P. Groen and G. W. Groves, in M. N. Hill, ed., The Sea, vol. I, Interscience Publishers, New York, 1962.)

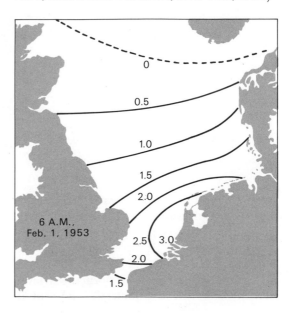

FIGURE 16–8 *Breakers crashing against a headland, Boiler Bay, Oregon. (Photo by Oregon State Highway Department.)*

Such a hurricane-driven water mass overwhelmed Galveston, Texas, in 1900, with great loss of life. A great storm on January 31 and February 1, 1953—probably the greatest in the North Sea since 1571—raised a huge sea surge far above normal sea level (locally as much as 3 meters!) and sent it crashing against the shores (Fig. 16–7). At Lowestoft, England, the waves ate back a 30-foot cliff for 30 feet, and a lower one for 86 feet in less than two days. Three hundred people were drowned in England; in Holland, many miles of dikes were overwhelmed and more than 1800 people perished.

Waves

GEOLOGIC EFFECTIVENESS. Waves and the currents they generate wash every shore on earth. Anyone who has watched the never-ending play of waves on the shore—whether the gentle ripples wafting grains of sand up and down the beach, or the great breakers hurling tons of water against the cliffs (Fig. 16–8)—cannot help being impressed with the power of the sea to mold the shore and to move detritus. Armed with cobbles, pebbles, and sand, the sea saws away at the shore, undercutting cliffs and notching every rock exposed at this level. In weakly consolidated materials erosion is rapid: the sea has eaten back the low cliffs of glacial gravels on the Holderness Coast of Yorkshire at a measured rate of 7 to 15 feet a year for more than a century. Repeated soundings and studies of bottom sediments in many places show that waves also move great quantities of sediment at shallow depths.

The mechanism by which winds produce waves on water is complex. In theory, air friction should not suffice to cause waves until wind speed is 11 to 15 miles per hour, yet winds of only 2½ miles per hour do produce waves. All winds are turbulent: that is, some air particles move much faster, others much slower, than the current as a whole. The corresponding variations in surface pressures and in friction against the water must bring about the first ruffling of the surface.

The motion of the water particles in a wave depends on the wavelength—the distance from crest to crest of successive waves—the wave height, and the depth of the water (Fig. 16–9). Waves on water deep compared to the wavelength (depth greater than one-fourth the wavelength) are called deep-water waves. Their speed is not affected by the depth. The water particles in such waves move in roughly circular orbits but retain the same general position—a floating object rises and falls but does not move forward at anything like the wave's velocity. Indeed, if the water masses actually moved with the

speed of the waves no ocean would be navigable. Surface particles move through orbits whose diameters about equal the wave height (see Fig. 16–10), but the orbits diminish quickly with depth. In waves 330 feet long and 16 feet high—about as large as North Atlantic storms ever generate—traveling about 28 miles an hour, the surface particles move at about 4.4 miles per hour; at a depth of 65 feet, the velocity is only about 1.2 miles per hour, and at 330 feet it is negligible (Fig. 16–10). Because of this quick falling-off of orbital velocity with depth, Vening-Meinesz's submarine (Chapter 10) was stable enough for gravity observations with his relatively crude instruments when submerged less than a hundred feet in moderate seas. But in great swells 1250 feet long and 33 feet high, traveling about 56 miles per hour—such as have been observed in Pacific typhoons—even though the particle velocity at the surface is again only about 4.4 miles

FIGURE 16–9
Schematic diagram of a progressive wave.

FIGURE 16–10
Circular movement of water particles in a deep water wave of small height. Full lines show the position of the water particles at one instant, dashed lines the same particles, ¼ period later. (After U.S. Hydrographic Office, Publ. No. 11.)

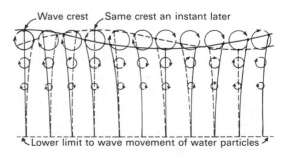

per hour, at 330 feet the orbital motion is still nearly one mile per hour.

Under steady winds, the waves grow in size and speed up to a limit imposed by friction. The maximum storm-wave height ever measured was 70 feet; few attain 50 feet, however. The wind gives waves energy in two ways: by its push against the rising wave crests, and by the friction of the more rapidly moving air against the water surface. The first depends on the difference between wind speed and wave speed: normally wind speed is the greater and the waves are pushed forward. Frictional drag, on the other hand, depends not on the difference between wind speed and wave speed but on the difference between wind speed and that of water particles—rarely more than 4 miles per hour. Thus wave speed and size depend on wind speed, wind duration, the **fetch** (the distance across which the wind blows with the same direction and speed) and, finally, the state of the sea at the time the wind began to blow.

WAVE REFRACTION. When deep-water waves enter shallow water, the bottom interferes with the orbital motion of the water particles, causing the wave to slow and steepen. Normally, this effect becomes notable when the depth is between $\frac{1}{4}$ and $\frac{1}{2}$ of the wavelength; where the water shallows to $\frac{1}{20}$ of the wavelength, the wave speed no longer depends on wavelength, as in deep-water waves, but becomes proportional to the square root of the depth. Most waves begin to "feel bottom" at depths of less than 500 feet, but during exceptional storms waves may extend to depths of 1500 feet. The wave slows down, not because of friction with the bottom but because of internal friction in the water itself. Because the water particles crowded near the bottom can no longer move in circular orbits to fill the wave form, their paths become ellipses, and at the very bottom are reduced to straight lines—the particles move to and fro in the direction of wave advance.

The inshore end of a wave approaching the shore obliquely over a uniformly sloping bottom feels bottom sooner than the offshore parts and therefore slows down sooner. The wave crest then becomes bent, for the offshore part continues to advance as a deep-water wave, with its original speed, after the inshore end has begun to slow and change to a shallow-water wave. Along a straight, evenly sloping coast, waves, no matter what their original angle of approach may have been, tend to be bent (refracted) until the final surge approaches the shore nearly straight on, with its crest nearly parallel to the beach (Fig. 16–11). It is exceptional, along straight coasts, for the obliquity of approach to exceed 10°.

Because the wave energy is carried in paths at right angles to the crest lines, wave refraction modifies its distribution. The energy, uniformly distributed along the wave in deep water, tends to be concentrated against sections of coast where shallow water extends farthest seaward, for the slowing of the waves where they first feel bottom tends to bend the wave toward the shallows. Wave energy is thus concentrated on headlands and dissipated along wider stretches in bays (Fig. 16–12). The waves on headlands thus grow more powerful and higher, those on bay shores weaker and lower, than they would be on a straight coast. This differential attack tends to straighten the shoreline by eroding the headlands and filling the coves with tranported debris.

BREAKERS. When waves reach water so shallow that there is no longer enough water to fill out their wave forms, they steepen and begin to break. They may continue, though, for hundreds of feet without curling over at the crest—the ideal waves for the surf-rider. The wave becomes a wave of translation (in which the wave speed is the same as the water speed) where the water is shallow enough for the wave to curl over and break with a crash, tumbling its water forward onto the

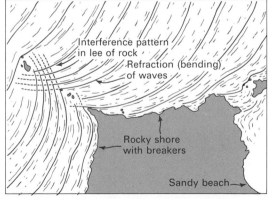

FIGURE 16–11
Vertical air photo and diagram showing bending of the waves (wave refraction) around a point of land. (After U.S. Hydrographic Office, Publ. No. 234.)

beach. This is the **breaker.** Waves break where the still-water depth is between one and two times the wave height. In exceptional places, where the shape of the shore favors convergence of the translation wave, two or even three breaker zones may exist. This is the situation on the Landes of Gascony, but it is very rare.

The energy of the breaker is dissipated in throwing the bottom material violently into

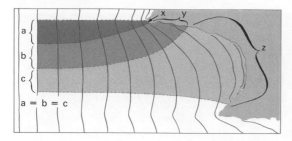

FIGURE 16-12

The distribution of wave energy as conditioned by coastal shape. Each of the equal segments, a, b, c, of the offshore wave has the same amount of energy. The refraction of the waves due to coastal configuration leads to concentration of energy on the headlands and weakening in the re-entrants of the shore. The energy is carried in the direction at right angles to the wave crest at all times. Thus the energy in section a is concentrated at x, that in c is spread over the much greater span, z.

suspension, as any surf swimmer can testify; the concentrated turbulence scours a trough along the breaker line. Some material in suspension is deposited to build bars both seaward and landward of the breaker zone, some is carried landward with the rush of water up the beach, where, in less turbulent water, the detritus is sorted according to size, shape, and density.

WAVE EROSION

Waves erode the shores in three ways: (1) by their impact and hydraulic pressure; (2) by **corrasion,** the sawing and grinding action of the sand, gravel, and cobbles hurled against the cliffs or rolled and dragged across the foreshore; and (3) by solution, a minor process, even along limestone shores.

Hydraulic pressure

Waves contain astounding energy. If we calculate the pressure of even a moderate wave 10 feet high and 100 feet long, we find it capable of exerting a push of 1675 pounds per square foot against an obstruction. Great storms exerted measured pressures of more than 6.6 tons per square foot at Dieppe and Le Havre, France, in 1963.

At Wick, in northern Scotland, such great storm-wave pressures are common. There, as noted in Chapter 5, the waves have broken away masses of concrete weighing as much as 2600 tons from the break-water protecting the harbor. The tremendous wave pressures act not only directly but also by compressing air driven into crevices in the rocks. Such air is compressed enough to pry huge blocks from cliffs exposed to full-wave attack. At Ymuiden, Holland, a seven-ton block in the breakwater was driven a few feet toward the sea, by the compression of air in crevices behind it.

Storm waves wear away weak strata or joint cracks in a cliff and dislodge the blocks between them. Along the joints they tunnel out sea caves, scores or even hundreds of feet long, that may penetrate entirely through small promontories and produce spectacular arches. The roofs of other arches collapse, leaving isolated **stacks** in front of the cliffs (Fig. 16-13).

Corrasion

We have seen that great storm waves can tear huge blocks from the cliffs and hurl them against the shore. Even moderate waves move boulders and cobbles, and feeble ones sand. In a Cornish mine that extends beneath the sea, the menacing grinding of boulders overhead is distinctly heard through a nine-foot rock roof. The shore zone is a veritable grinding mill. At Cape Ann, Massachusetts, angular fragments from granite quarries have become rounded on the beach within a single year. Shakespeare's Cliff, several hundred feet high, a part of the "White Cliffs of Dover," is so rapidly undercut as to produce frequent large landslides. One of these, in 1810, was so great that the vibrations were felt as a strong earthquake at Dover, several

FIGURE 16–13   *Sea caves and sea stack at low tide, near Santa Cruz, California. (Photo by Eliot Blackwelder.)*

FIGURE 16–14
Cliff in rhyolite, undercut by waves. Kindall Head, Moore Island, Maine. (Photo by E. S. Bastin, U.S. Geological Survey.)

miles away. The cliffs of the volcanic island of Krakatau in the Sunda Straits were cut back over 1500 meters in the 45 years between the eruption of 1883 and 1928—an average of more than 30 meters a year. These are spectacular examples of wave erosion in weak rocks, but even the most resistant rocks are impressively notched (Fig. 16–14) .

Nevertheless, despite these examples of important marine erosion, cliff retreat at the shore is a subordinate process when compared with fluvial erosion. Careful estimates by C. K. Wentworth indicated that even in the Trade Wind belt of the Pacific, fluvial erosion in Hawaii is at least 7 times as effective as marine. If this were not generally true, we should find waterfalls along most of the coasts of the world.

Although most wave energy is spent between the breaker line and the shore, corrasion is not confined to that zone. Where wavelengths are great, sediment particles move vigorously at greater depths. Great waves 500 feet long and 22 feet high should theoretically produce speeds of 10 inches per second in water at a depth of 300 feet: enough to move fine sand. When account is taken of tidal and other currents, the bottom water should be agitated enough to keep clay particles in motion to depths of 600 feet—on some coasts to more than 900 feet and in the greatest storms, still deeper. These theoretical conclusions are confirmed by the character of the sediments found by dredging and by the fact that sand is frequently found on the decks of fishing vessels in North Sea storms, even when they are on water several hundred feet deep. One-pound stones have been thrown into lobster pots at depths of 160 feet off Land's End, England, during storms. The depth to which movement of sediment by waves is significant is called **wave base.**

Outside the breaker zone the particles moved by the waves reverse their direction with every wave. But most of the shallow sea floor slopes seaward and, acordingly, a particle moving to and fro on the bottom moves downhill seaward and uphill landward. Since these oscillations are about equal, the sediment tends ultimately to progress downhill —seaward—in response to the pull of gravity. As the motion diminishes with greater depth, coarser particles eventually reach positions where the agitation is too feeble to keep them moving; they come to rest. But finer particles still move, and continue to travel seaward until they, in turn, are sorted out in accordance with their size and density. During all this agitation, the particles of sediment rub against each other and against the bottom. They gradually become smaller and smaller, until they can be moved by successively feebler oscillations. Dragged back and forth with each passing wave, they also wear away the bottom, so that not only the breaker zone, where the wear is much the greatest, but all the coastal zone, to the depth of wave base, is corraded to some degree, though the wear surely falls off rapidly with depth.

Inshore from the breaker zone the situation is somewhat different. Here the shoreward-moving water masses may dash coarse fragments to heights from which the feebler backwash cannot carry them, even though favored by a steep slope. Although as much water must flow away from the shore as toward it, the velocity of a breaking wave is greater than that of the backwash because some of the water percolates into the porous beach materials and returns seaward more slowly than the rest. A **storm beach** of coarse pebbles may thus be built above the reach of the normal waves. Chesil Beach, Dorset, England, has its crest as much as 13 meters above the level of calm water. Such a beach is steep, for coarse material can be moved seaward only on steep slopes; shingle beaches in Morocco have slopes as steep as 31°. Sand beaches of the Pacific Coast of the United States have slopes ranging from as steep as 22° to as low as 1°. The heights and slopes of beach ridges are not constant, but change with the wave patterns and heights. For example, prolonged offshore winds during World War II allowed the shingle ridge at Fécamp, France, to be regraded to a level 7 meters lower. But as with stream profiles, the beach profile fluctuates somewhat from average conditions; normally, onwash and backwash are about balanced at a slope determined by the size of the waves and the grade size and amount of the detritus available.

Solution

As mentioned above, the effects of solution are trivial compared to those of corrasion in the erosion of the shore. Nevertheless, solution is not negligible, for Joly has shown by experiment that rocks such as basalt and obsidian and minerals such as hornblende and orthoclase are from 3 to 14 times as soluble in sea water as in fresh water. In landlocked parts of the Indonesian coast, a corrosion groove, in places several feet deep, has been dissolved at the shoreline in limestones, and even in volcanic rocks. Similiar solution is doubtless prevalent on exposed shores as well, but is there masked by the more conspicuous effects of wave erosion.

THE PROFILE OF EQUILIBRIUM

Partly from wave theory, partly from observed motion of detritus in waves, partly from dredging and sounding, and partly

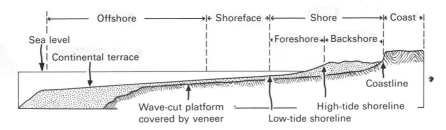

FIGURE 16–15   *Elements of the shore zone and profile of equilibrium. (After D. W. Johnson, Shoreline Processes. John Wiley and Sons, 1919.)*

from study of large dried-up lakes (see Chapter 13, Lake Bonneville) or of uplifted sea-floors (see Fig. 8–12), the concept of the **marine profile of equilibrium** has been developed. This profile is a smooth, sweeping curve, concave upward (Fig. 16–15). It is steep in the breaker zone and flattens quickly seaward. Its slope is adjusted to the average particle size of the detritus moved by the waves at each particular place along it. The slope is just sufficient to keep the material in slow transit toward deep water. Obviously the sea cannot cut into the shore unless the detritus can be moved away from the breaker zone. This demands a seaward slope. As the waves fluctuate in size, the profile is constantly readjusted, flattening and shallowing with feeble waves, steepening and deepening with more powerful ones. But for any coast there should be, theoretically, a general average slope about which the profile fluctuates.

That such profiles are not merely hypothetical is proved by soundings showing that the sea floor near the coast is usually concave upward, despite the complications to be expected because of the worldwide changes in sea level during and since the Pleistocene. The slope and depth of the offshore profile is generally closely adjusted to the fetch and power of the waves. Moreover, such a graded profile can actually be seen on former sea floors (Fig. 8–12), which in many places, have been uplifted to form **marine terraces.** Though now above the reach of the waves, they preserve some or all of the features com-mon to modern coasts: cliffs and cliff notches, stacks and caves, storm beaches, gravel and sand beaches, and a sedimentary veneer resting on a smoothly truncated surface of bedrock whose profile is gently concave upward but retains a general seaward slope. Yet, no actual profile has the perfect idealized seaward slope. Continual changes in wave power, tidal and other currents, and perhaps most important, fluctuations of sea level and slow movements of the earth's crust, constantly interrupt the development of every profile.

WAVE CURRENTS

Even though refracted, most waves break against the shore at a slight angle, so that the swash of the breaking wave has a component of motion parallel to the shore. This produces a current along the beach—the **long-shore drift**—which may consistently flow in one direction or reverse with changes in the wind. Such a drift may be swift, especially if a longshore wind or tidal currents reinforce it. The breaking wave carries sand and gravel obliquely up the beach—the sand grains farther than the gravel. The swash of the retreating wave also has a longshore component. Each particle thus moves in sawtooth-like oscillations down the beach (Fig. 16–16). Marked pebbles made from bricks have been traced along a beach as much as half a mile in a single day; similar movements doubtless occur in the whole zone of the sea

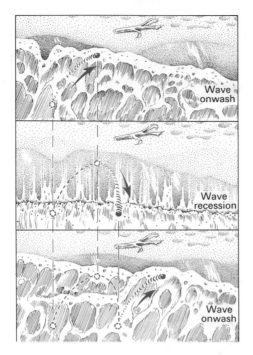

FIGURE 16–16

Longshore drift (to the right) resulting from oblique wash of the waves. Each arcuate segment of the particle's path represents the movement due to one wave.

bottom agitated by the waves. Measurements off Jutland, Denmark, have shown that the longshore drift to depths of 20 meters and for distances of 2 kilometers offshore is virtually equal across the whole zone. Vast amounts of sand are transported parallel to the shore by those longshore currents, and their ability to smooth out irregularities in the shape of the shore is great. At Westport, England, measurements show that the sea is eating into the shore along a 3½ mile stretch at rates between 7½ and 27½ feet per year; the longshore drift is carrying more than 5,000,000 cubic yards of sediment per year away from this eroding shore. The Columbia River discharges silt particles identifiable by their radioactivities (derived from the atomic reactors at Richland, Washington); these enable the sediment to be easily traced offshore. Surveys show that the radioactive silt is moved by currents at rates of 12 to 30 kilometers per year northward along the shelf, and seaward at rates between 2½ and 10 kilometers per year, in water several hundred feet deep.

ARTIFICIAL INTERFERENCE WITH SHORE PROCESSES

The nice adjustment of beach profiles and shore outlines to the average power of waves and currents acting on shore detritus is emphatically shown wherever the shape of a beach has been artificially altered. Even slight obstacles may cause drastic changes. Dredging of sand and gravel offshore is commonly followed by erosion of the shore; the material between the excavation and the shore is swept seaward to fill the hole and restore the original slope. Even more striking effects have followed the building of groins on many bathing beaches. Groins are low walls extending seaward from the high-tide line, built to prevent sand removal by longshore drift. Where they have been successful in holding the fine sand, the beaches farther downdrift, being deprived of their normal supply of traveling sand, have been severely scoured and changed from sandy beaches to gravel or cobble ones. Many parts of the famous Waikiki Beach in Honolulu have been scoured of their sand and become gravelly because of artificial interference with the normal shore drift.

Breakwaters of rock or concrete, built to protect anchorages from storms, may cause beach modification, as at Santa Monica, California (Fig. 16–17). Here a 2000-foot breakwater was built parallel to the shore and about 2000 feet seaward from it, to make a small-boat anchorage. The longshore drift here is generally to the southeast. The breakwater reduced the waves striking the shore behind it, thereby lessening their capacity to keep detritus in suspension; the beach in

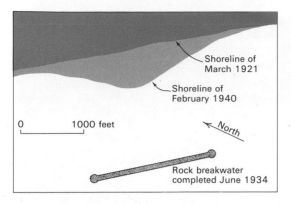

FIGURE 16–17
Map of the Santa Monica beach before and after building of the breakwater. The beach has continued to advance since 1940, but later surveys were not available. Direction of drift is southeastward.

the lee of the breakwater began to build forward. In about six years it advanced more that 500 feet into the sea. The beaches southeast of the breakwater have not been greatly eroded, despite being starved of their normal influx of sand from the northwest; it is noteworthy, however, that great storms cause more damage to the beach southeast of the breakwater than to other nearby parts of the shore.

EROSIONAL AND DEPOSITIONAL FEATURES OF SHORES

The shores of mountainous coasts

The shores of mountainous or hilly coasts are varied. Waves attack exposed promontories, producing cliffs; the debris eroded from them is distributed by longshore drift, producing characteristic shore features—bayhead and baymouth bars, and land-tied islands, spits, and bars.

Wave refraction on bay shores produces currents that tend to sweep material on each side toward the head of the bay, where it accumulates as a bayhead bar (Fig. 16–18). Material carried by longshore drift from eroding headlands tends to continue straight across coastal indentations; a smoothly curved spit may be formed by the debris from a cliffed point from which it springs. Toronto Harbor is in this way protected by a long sandspit growing westward. As spits grow into deeper water, wave refraction and local currents cause their ends to become curved (Fig. 16–18.) Where the outflow from a bay is small, such spits may grow completely across the opening to form a baymouth bar (Fig. 16–19). The lagoon behind may be brackish or fresh and may slowly become a marsh filled by silt from the land or by sand blown inland from the beach.

Islands near the shore, like breakwaters, protect the beach behind from the full force of the sea; the longshore drift cannot effectively carry material behind them. A mainland beach guarded by a nearby island therefore builds out in the same way as the beach at Santa Monica, diverting the longshore currents toward the island to which a spit may extend, tying it to the shore (Fig. 16–20). Many islands become joined to the coast by two spits that enclose a triangular lagoon.

Bottom irregularities may deflect the drift, even on straight coasts, so that the beach

FIGURE 16–18
Sketch of an embayed coast, showing a sandpit springing from a headland, and a bayhead bar which encloses a marsh.

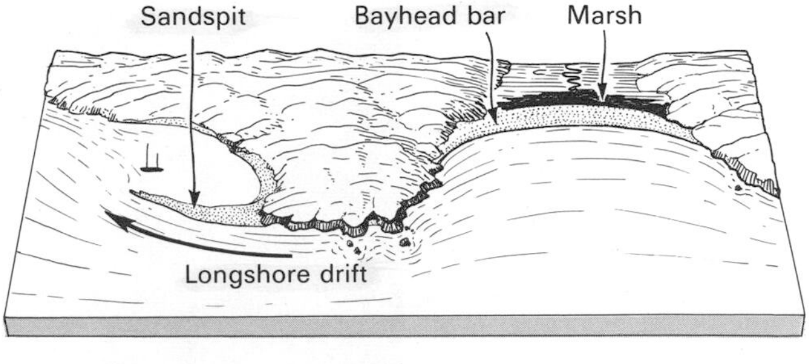

FIGURE 16–19   *Baymouth bar and lagoon, St. Mary's Lake, Glacier National Park. (Photo by Eugene Stebinger, U.S. Geological Survey.)*

FIGURE 16–20   *Land-tied island, Hancock County, Maine. (Photo by E. S. Bastin, U.S. Geological Survey.)*

builds seaward. The amount and coarseness of the detritus available, and the height of the storm waves determine the height of the beach thus formed. As the beach advances, it leaves behind a series of older beach ridges, some perhaps twenty feet high, separated by swales. Perhaps the best known of these is that at the Dungeness, in southeastern England, which has advanced more than a mile into the sea since the time of Elizabeth I—about 6 yards a year.

The shores of plains

Along low-lying coasts like those of the Gulf of Mexico and the southeastern Atlantic States, the wave attack is spread evenly instead of being concentrated upon headlands. The sea deepens so gradually that the waves feel bottom far offshore and the material they stir up is built into an offshore bar, just inland from the zone of the greatest breakers (Fig. 16–21). As wave agitation continually erodes the sea bottom on the seaward side of a bar and slowly moves the detritus seaward, bars must constantly rebuild landward in order to survive if there is a stable sea level. In many places offshore bars have thus been driven landward until they touch the mainland. Then the waves directly attack the land and produce low cliffs. This is the pattern of the shore of northern Florida and southern North Carolina. Part of the material eroded is carried by longshore currents and added to the bar.

The lagoon behind an offshore bar is salty, but rivers may freshen it somewhat. A large river may raise the lagoon level to such a height above the sea—naturally the difference is greatest at low tide—that the bar is broken, forming an inlet through which tidal currents can sweep. Great storm waves also breach bars during hurricanes. Such tidal inlets shift from time to time because of longshore drift; some fill in, and new ones appear. Salt grass grows in the protected lagoon, and as plant debris and silt brought by streams, tidal currents, and winds accumulate, the lagoon gradually changes to a marsh.

The famous beaches of Florida and New Jersey are offshore bars. Even more striking examples are the long sand bars—the Frisches Nehrung and the Kurisches Nehrung—that fringe the southern coast of the Baltic from Danzig to Memel, enclosing an almost-continuous brackish lagoon. Figure 16–22 illustrates a plains shoreline along which some offshore bars enclose lagoons, though others have advanced shoreward to crowd meandering rivers behind them. Magnificent examples of offshore bars fringe the Carolina coast, enclosing Albermarle and Pamlico Sounds and meeting at stormy Cape Hatteras. Their cuspate shape has been attributed to junction of eddies thrown off by the Gulf Stream (Fig. 16–1), but it may partly result from wave refraction by bottom irregularities.

Along plains coasts there is no coarse gravel and the beaches are almost wholly sand. Between tides the beaches dry out and winds may blow the sand inland to form dunes that overrun the country.

FIGURE 16–21
Diagrammatic cross section showing the features of the shore zone of a low-lying coast. The vertical scale is greatly exaggerated.

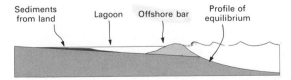

Sediments from land   Lagoon   Offshore bar   Profile of equilibrium

TOPOGRAPHY OF THE SEA FLOOR

In Chapter 5 we described the continental shelves, the slopes, the continental rises and the abyssal plains. There remain several other topographic provinces of interest. The most striking features of Pacific Ocean topography are the great **island arcs** that festoon its northern and western sides. (Fig. 16–23). These include the Aleutian, Kurile, Japanese, Ryukyu, and Philippine Archipelagoes. These island-crowned arcuate ridges separate comparatively shallow seas—the Bering, Okhotsk, Japan, Yellow, and East China Seas—from the Pacific Basin proper. Several comparable arcs branch southward from Japan through the Bonin and Marianas Islands. The seas that border these island chains are not shallow: the Philippine Basin on their shoreward side is as deep as the Pacific.

The Indonesian islands form a comparable

FIGURE 16–22 *The west coast of the Cape York Peninsula, Australia, showing features of a plains coast. The curved white stripe in the upper right is an offshore bar; the ridged beach in the foreground is probably an older offshore bar. Note the curved spit just below the river mouth. (Photo by U.S. Air Force.)*

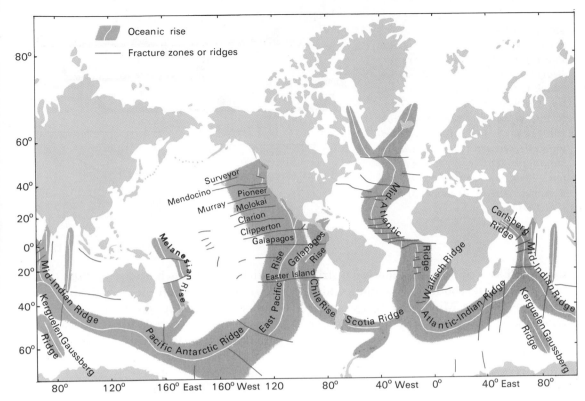

FIGURE 16–23 *Major mid-ocean submarine ridge and rise systems, the island arcs of the northern and western Pacific and Indonesia, and some of the major fracture zones in the ocean floor. (After H. W. Menard, 1965.)*

arc bounding the Indian Ocean on the northeast; the Antilles and Southern Antilles are the only similar features of the Atlantic Basin.

Closely associated with the island arcs are the deepest parts of the ocean basins. Depressions deeper than 7000 meters (23,000 feet) are **deeps.** As noted in Chapter 5, the deepest so far surveyed is the Nero Deep in the Marianas Trench; there are several others in the Pacific more than 10,000 meters deep. In the Atlantic, the deepest trenches are the Puerto Rico Trough, north of that island, and the South Sandwich Trench on the convex side of the Southern Antilles arc, each more than 8000 meters deep.

Perhaps the most dramatic discovery of the recent oceanographic campaigns is that of the longest mountain chain on earth, the Mid-Ocean Ridge, which has been traced continuously from Iceland for more than 40,000 kilometers (more than three-fourths the circumference of the globe!) . The Mid-Atlantic Ridge has been known for nearly a century, since the first trans-Atlantic cable was laid, but it has now been found to occupy the middle third of the Atlantic Basin, with its crest almost precisely in mid-ocean, and to extend continuously—except for linear offsets that must surely be caused by transverse faults—the entire length of the Atlantic, and to the middle of the Indian Ocean, where it splits, one branch trending northwestward as the Carlsberg Ridge to the Gulf of Aden. The other branch, the Mid-Indian Ridge, extends southeastward between Australia and Antarctica into the Pacific-Antarctic Ridge. This is in turn offset

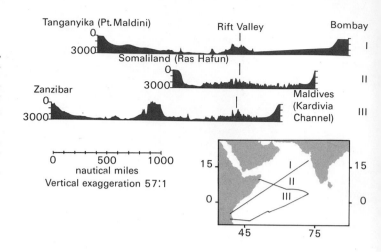

from the East Pacific Rise, a much less striking feature, as it is both broader and less high than most of the Mid-Ocean Ridge and is also located far east of the middle of the Pacific Basin (Fig. 16–23).

For nearly all its length, the Mid-Atlantic Ridge rises almost 3 kilometers above the floor of the Atlantic; much of its crest is less than one kilometer beneath the surface and a few peaks rise as islands above the sea: Iceland, the Azores, Saint Paul's Rocks, Ascension, Saint Helena, Tristan da Cunha, and Bouvet. On the extension into the Indian Ocean lies Prince Edward Island. The Chagos Archipelago and several other atolls rise above the Carlsberg Ridge. For much of its length the Mid-Ocean ridge is marked by step-like topography with longitudinal steps and valleys that strongly suggest faulting. Figure 16–24 shows several cross sections of the Mid-Indian section of the ridge, which like many sections elsewhere, shows a split crest with a valley running along the highest part. This topographic form is much like that of some—but by no means all—segments of the "Rift Valleys" of East Africa (Chapter 20).

Submarine ranges diverge from the Mid-Atlantic Ridge: the Rio Grande Rise and the Walfisch Ridge to west and east respectively, in the South Atlantic. The scale of these features may be appreciated from the fact that the Walfisch Ridge is three times as long as the Alps and rises as high above the ocean floor as the Alps do above sea level.

Within the last decade it has become recognized that the Mid-Atlantic Ridge is offset in many places along nearly east-west lines, by faults that are obviously younger than the so-called "Rift Valleys" and other longitudinal structures. The offsets are such as to leave the Mid-Atlantic Ridge still near the center of the Atlantic Basin even though the shapes of South America and Africa are such as to give the basin a notable reverse bend (Fig. 16–25).

Minor features of the sea floor include the **seamounts,** whose conical shapes are so like those of volcanoes on land that they can hardly be anything else; flat-topped frustums of cones called **guyots,** which we discuss later in this chapter; **abyssal hills,** which are tracts of bottom with smoothly rounded hills a few fathoms to a few hundred fathoms high; and the abyssal plains already mentioned in connection with turbidity currents. Some of the volcanic islands of the western Pacific are surrounded by low cones as much as 200 kilometers in radius that rise a few hundred meters above the sea floor. These have been called **archipelagic aprons,** and attributed to submarine volcanism. The sediments associated with these several provinces are reviewed in Chapter 17.

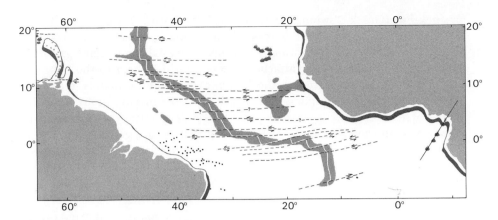

FIGURE 16–25   *Fracture zones in the equatorial Atlantic. Dashed lines are inferred faults, with relative displacements shown by arrows. Dark areas on land are higher than 3000 meters; in oceanic areas, depths of less than 3000 meters. Black circles are seamounts. (After B. C. Heezen, R. D. Gerard, and Marie Tharp,* Philosophical Transactions of the Royal Society, *v. 258, 1965.)*

THE LIFE ZONES OF THE SEA

Life is everywhere in the sea. Photographs from a bathyscaphe at the bottom of the Mariana Deep near the ocean's greatest depths—far below levels to which light penetrates and where the water temperature is only a little above freezing—show living organisms. In fact, fully 300 species of animals, chiefly mollusks, worms, and holothurians (sea cucumbers), have have been dredged from the abyssal ocean floor. Marine environments differ greatly from place to place and so, consequently, do the organisms inhabiting them. A large proportion of all sedimentary rocks are marine; the fossils they contain enable us to infer something of the conditions of their deposition by analogy with associations of similar organisms in the modern seas.

Marine biologists classify the different parts of the sea as shown in Figure 16–26. The two main divisions are the **benthic,** or sea-bottom environment, and the **pelagic,** or open-water environment. Both are divided, at a depth of 200 meters (about the depth of the edge of the continental shelf) into a littoral system landward and a deep-sea sys-

tem seaward. The depth of 200 meters is critical because it is near the limit to which light can penetrate. On the deep-sea floor are neither light nor seasons, and hence no photosynthesis by green plants. The bottom life is confined to scavengers, which live on organisms sinking from above, and to a few bacteria, nearly all of which depend on organic compounds brought to the depths by currents or by sinking.

Marine life, both plant and animal, is classed in three large groups: **benthos** (from Greek, "depth of the sea") or bottom dwell-

FIGURE 16–26

Diagrammatic cross section showing the four major divisions of the life zones of the sea. (After H. U. Sverdrup, M. W. Johnson, and R. H. Fleming, The Oceans. *Copyright 1942 by Prentice-Hall, Inc.)*

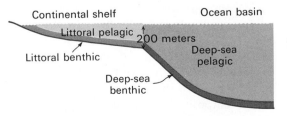

ers; **nekton** (Greek, "swimming") or swimming forms; and **plankton** (Greek, "wandering") or floating and drifting organisms. The benthos includes all the attached, creeping, or burrowing organisms of the bottom: seaweeds and grasses, sponges, barnacles, clams, oysters, corals, bryozoa, worms, lobsters, crabs, and many other animals, among them many species of the minute, single-celled Foraminifera, most of which secrete shells of calcium carbonate. The nekton includes the squids, fishes, seals, whales, and many other animals that are economically important but of little geologic significance. The plankton includes all the surprisingly varied organisms, chiefly microscopic, that float with the ocean currents. Among them are several kinds of diatoms with opaline shells; a group of organisms, the Coccolithophores—of uncertain classification but usually considered algae—which secrete round shells of calcite in thin plates; many individual Foraminifera (though only a few species); and the silica-secreting Radiolaria.

All living things, except for a few bacteria, ultimately depend on **photosynthesis**—the process by which plants utilize radiant energy from the sun to form organic compounds directly from carbon dioxide and water. Plants also require minute amounts of many substances, among them phosphates, nitrogen, iron, and manganese. Variations in the abundance of these in different parts of the sea are reflected in varying densities of plant population and in the abundance and kinds of animals that feed on the plants.

After a planktonic or nektonic organism dies, its body, unless eaten immediately, ultimately sinks, perhaps to feed some scavenger in the depths. During and after sinking, much of the organic matter of the body is decomposed by bacteria. This decomposition uses up oxygen dissolved in the water and releases carbon dioxide to it, thereby, because of the effect of dissolved CO_2 on the solubility of calcite (see Chapter 4), removing shells from the deep-sea sediments.

Decomposition at any depth returns phosphorus, nitrogen, and other nutrient elements to solution, making them once again available for plant growth when water drift brings them to the lighted zone. Deep-water masses ultimately return to the surface by slow mixing or by upwelling. Upwelling of deep water rich in nutrients accounts for the flourishing plant life and the resulting prolific fishing grounds in such parts of the ocean as the Newfoundland Banks and the western coasts of North and South America and Africa.

Remains of marine organisms furnish valuable clues to the depositional environment of a sedimentary rock, whether the organisms constitute a "life association," or whether their dead bodies have been transported from widely differing habitats, finally to be deposited together as a "death assemblage." Obviously the former is the better guide. This aspect of marine life and its significance in geology is discussed more fully in Chapter 17. Here we consider only those organisms whose activities influence the shape of the sea floor and, indeed, of the coasts and islands of much of the world—the assemblages that make up the coral reefs.

CORAL REEFS

Although some species of coral can live in cool water, the reef-building species require water at least as warm as 20°C (68°F), of normal salinity and nearly free from mud. The coral animal, anchored in his limy case, depends on food brought by waves and currents; it therefore thrives best on the windward and offshore sides of reefs. Many species of coral live in reefs, but reef-builders do not grow below a depth of about 150 feet nor much above low-tide level. Because of their narrow depth range, coral reefs are sensitive indices of crustal movement, as noted in Chapter 8.

Although corals—both living animals and broken fragments of their skeletons—form the conspicuous framework of the reefs, algal

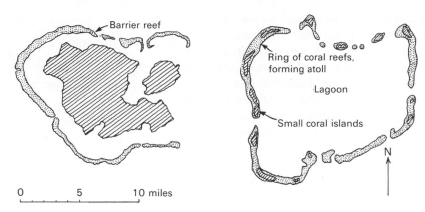

FIGURE 16-27   Left: *the barrier reef of Vanikoro Island, Caroline Archipelago.* Right: *Peros Banhos Atoll, Chagos Archipelago. (After Charles Darwin, 1842.)*

growths bind them together, and hard parts of many other calcareous organisms—mollusks, worms, foraminifera, and a host of others—constitute far more of a reef's bulk than does coral.

Coral reefs have three forms: fringing reefs, barrier reefs, and atolls. **Fringing reefs** are confined to the very border of the land. A few are thousands of feet wide, but most are less than a hundred.

Barrier reefs are separated from the shore by lagoons, some shallow, but some hundreds of feet deep. Many volcanic islands of the Pacific and Indian oceans are ringed by white barrier reefs a short distance offshore (Figs. 16-27, 8-15). The Great Barrier Reef of Australia roughly parallels the Queensland Coast at distances ranging from 25 to nearly 200 miles offshore and extends for 1200 miles south from Torres Strait.

An **atoll** has no central island, only a ringlike reef enclosing a lagoon. The enclosed lagoon is dotted with isolated coral heads, and floored with algal mud and some sand, derived from broken reef fragments hurled into the lagoon by waves.

The origin of atolls

The origin of barrier reefs and atolls has fascinated students ever since the publication of Darwin's *Voyage of the Beagle* more

FIGURE 16-28

Cross section showing three stages in the formation of an atoll, according to the sinking-island hypothesis. (After Charles Darwin, 1839.)

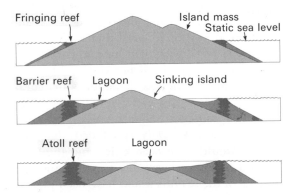

than a century ago. Darwin considered fringing reefs, barrier reefs, and atolls to form a sequence (Fig. 16-28): if an island with a fringing reef subsided, the reef would subside with it, but would also grow upward if growth could keep pace with subsidence, to become a barrier reef, and if subsidence continued until the central island drowned, an atoll. In support of this, it has been pointed out that the shores of many islands with fringing reefs are embayed as they might be if a stream-dissected mountain had sunk slightly. Moreover, the outer slopes of many atolls descend steeply to great depths, and borings on Bikini and Eniwetok atolls and

Daly's Theory

geophysical tests by seismic means (Chapter 19) show that the reef structure extends several thousand feet below the ocean's surface and rests on volcanic rocks. Fossils show the basal part of the Eniwetok reef to be of Eocene age; the basement of the reef has sunk more than 4000 feet in 50 million years.

An alternate hypothesis was suggested by the American geologist R. A. Daly, in 1910. Daly noticed that charts show the lagoons of many barrier reefs and atolls to have remarkably similar and uniform depths, ranging from about 150 to 250 feet. He also noted that some of the higher Hawaiian peaks had been glaciated, presumably during the Pleistocene, and inferred that the water along the shore below must then have been too cool for coral growth. If so, the present fringing reefs of Hawaii must all date from postglacial time. He then estimated the volume of water that must have been locked up in the ice sheets during their greatest expansion. From this he inferred that sea level was then 300 feet lower than now, and that the water must have been not only colder but also siltier, and less favorable for coral growth because the waves would be working on unconsolidated sediments newly exposed to wave attack. Daly concluded that the corals would have been killed and the reefs would not have been able to withstand the attack of the sea but would have been planed off at the lowered sea level. When the ice sheets melted and sea level gradually rose, the surviving corals would find smoothly planed banks to colonize, and would build atolls and barrier reefs on them. Daly's theory does not require subsidence in order to explain lagoons: they now vary in depth because of sedimentation, the smaller being shallower than the larger because their areas are relatively smaller in relation to the reefs over which sediment is washed during storms. Banks and seamounts not colonized by reef-builders since the rise of sea level are simply the planed-off islands of preglacial time (Fig. 16–29).

Daly's theory fails to explain the indented

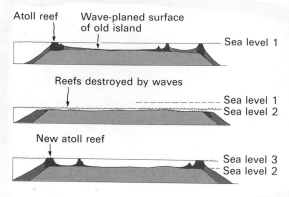

FIGURE 16–29
Cross section showing three stages in the origin of an atoll according to the glacier-control hypothesis. (After R. A. Daly, The Floor of the Ocean. *University of North Carolina Press, 1942.)*

shores of many islands within barrier reefs, for the relief of the valleys and ridges is far greater than can be explained by a mere 300-foot drop in sea level. Furthermore, the coral reefs on the shores of New Guinea are flourishing, even though the Carstenz Range above them is heavily glaciated at the present time.

The drilling on Bikini and Eniwetok atolls has demonstrated that Darwin's subsidence theory is certainly applicable to them and presumably to many other atolls. But Daly's explanation may be applicable to some other fringing reefs and atolls, for certainly not all parts of the ocean floor have had the same history, even since the Pleistocene. Drowned reefs with perfectly preserved atoll shapes have been sounded near the Philippines and greatly elevated reefs abound in Indonesia, Fiji, and Samoa.

Subsidence of great areas of the ocean floor is also proven by the existence of guyots. These flat-topped submerged mountains—shaped like the frustrum of a cone—have yielded basaltic pebbles to the dredge: clearly they are extinct volcanoes, which, apparently, once stood above sea level and were truncated by the waves. Since then they have sunk to various depths, some as great as 3 kilometers. We return to them in Chapter 20.

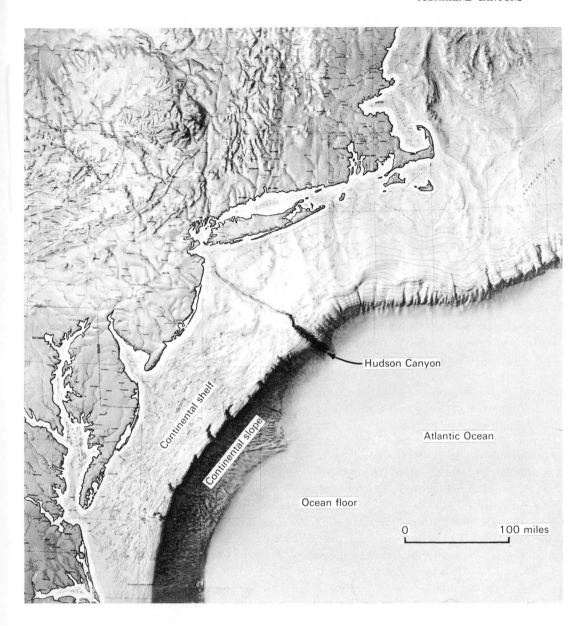

Continental shelf

Continental slope

Hudson Canyon

Atlantic Ocean

Ocean floor

0   100 miles

FIGURE 16–30   *Relief model showing the land and submarine topography of the northeastern United States. Submarine canyons abound on the steep continental slope (partly in shadow). The irregularly ridged submarine topography in the upper right corner is submerged glacial topography. (Courtesy of the Aero Service Corporation, Philadelphia, Pennsylvania.)*

SUBMARINE CANYONS

It was long thought that, except in some small areas of concentrated current action, noteworthy erosion does not operate below wave base. With the advent of sonic sounding, however, it has become evident that most of the continental shelves are dissected by steep-sided canyons and extensive submarine valleys. Figure 16–30 shows many canyons indenting the shelf margin off the northeastern United States. Note that the only river clearly connected with a submarine canyon is the Hudson. This exceptional trench extends from the estuary almost across the shelf before fading out; it reappears as a deep trench in the continental slope, extending clear to the floor of the Atlantic.

Other continental shelves, notably those bordering California, Alaska, and southwestern Europe, are cut by similar gorges. Most submarine canyons are on the continental slope; short and steep, they begin far from shore, except where the shelf is very narrow or interrupted by deep basins, as off southern California. A few canyons are 70 to 150 miles long and 3000 to 5000 feet deeper than the adjacent sea floor, being comparable to the Grand Canyon in size. Among the great submarine canyons are: the Monterey Canyon off California, which heads near (but not at) the mouth of the Salinas River; the Congo Canyon, which extends into the Atlantic from the mouth of the Congo River; and the Nazare Canyon off Portugal, which heads far from any existing river mouth. A smaller, but well-studied example, the La Jolla Canyon off California, heads close to the Scripps Institution of Oceanography, which has studied it intensively.

Monterey Canyon's long profile is shown in Figure 16–31, together with that of the Salinas River. Some irregularities in the submarine profile may represent errors in soundings, but the general form is trustworthy. The average grade of the canyon bottom is almost 4° for the first 40 miles from shore, while that of the lower Salinas River is less than 0.1°. The submarine canyon is probably cut almost entirely in Miocene, Pliocene, and Pleistocene strata, though near its middle, granite has been dredged from one wall. The tributary Carmel Canyon seems to be excavated chiefly in sheared granite. The head of Monterey Canyon is just outside the beach zone, and is apparently cut in late Pleistocene or Recent marine and river deposits.

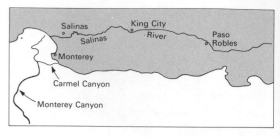

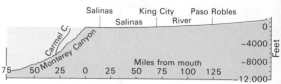

FIGURE 16–31
Map and profile of the Salinas River, the Monterey submarine canyon, and its tributary, Carmel Canyon. The vertical scale is exaggerated 20 times.

In general, submarine canyons are marked by steep gradients, roughly concave long profiles, few tributaries, and heads at depths of a few hundred feet. The relatively small number of canyons whose heads are near the mouths of land rivers include most of the largest ones. Few canyon mouths have been adequately surveyed. Some canyons end in small basins, at various depths below 1200 feet, some at the base of the steep continental slope, 7000 to 11,000 feet below sea level; the Hudson Canyon extends to the very base of the continental slope at an even greater depth. The walls are composed chiefly of young sedimentary rocks, in part fairly well consolidated, as shown by specimens and fossils raised by the dredge. Several submarine canyons end in fan-like cones on the ocean floor, in which channels are sunk for a few scores of meters. Where these channels curve, the outer bank is notably higher than the inner. It seems almost certain that we have here constructional features like the natural levees along river floodplains, built up by the overflow of sediment-bearing currents sweeping down the canyons.

Hypotheses of origin

The many hypotheses advanced to account for submarine canyons belong to two groups, the subaerial and the submarine. The principal subaerial hypothesis is based on the lowering of sea level during the Pleistocene glacial epochs, discussed in Chapter 13. Its validity depends on how much water was removed from the oceans and locked up in glacial ice. Although we are fairly certain of the extent of the Pleistocene glaciers, we are not so certain of their thickness or their precise contemporaneity, so that estimates of the volume of ice vary. As we noted in discussing atolls, Daly estimated that sea level was lowered three hundred feet; borings from which fossils have been obtained in the Mississippi Delta suggest a lowering of about four hundred feet there. Perhaps 5 to 7 percent of the ocean water was locked up in ice at glacial maxima. Surely no conceivable glacial lowering could account for the Hudson Canyon, with its mouth at the very foot of the continental slope. Even though one were to accept the idea of a lowering of the sea to that level, the corollary increase in salinity of the oceans would have left unmistakable records by extinction of numerous species. Yet only a few marine species became extinct in the Pleistocene; the number certainly does not suggest an extreme change in the salinity of the sea. Furthermore, had glacial lowering been so great, one would surely expect to find systematic terraces carved in the sediments of the continental slopes at many places throughout the world. Submarine terraces are believed to exist off Morocco, Angola, and southern California, but they are far from being ubiquitous. If sea level had indeed been lowered many thousands of feet, surely all the great rivers would have cut deep canyons at the present shores. Every river of the world should end in an estuary formed by the drowning of its valley. The Mississippi Valley was indeed about four hundred feet deeper during the Pleistocene, but not several thousand feet deeper, as it would have had to be to account for the depth of the Hudson or Monterey Canyons. The head of La Jolla Canyon shows unmistakable signs of subaerial cutting, but only to a depth of two hundred or three hundred feet below sea level. None of the expected corollaries of a subaerial origin of the deeper parts of any submarine canyon seem to have been found.

The alternative to subaerial origin is obviously that the canyons have been cut under conditions not very different from those of the present, and, in fact, may be deepening now. On this hypothesis the canyons were formed by the erosive action of turbidity currents, described briefly in Chapter 5.

The cable breaks connected with the Grand Banks earthquake (Chapter 5) seem clearly to point to the action of a huge turbidity current or submarine mudflow acting over a wide segment of the continental slope. The motive power of such a current is, of course, gravity, and its force depends on the difference in density between the muddy water and clear sea water at each point along the path. Since this difference in density is much less than the difference between the densities of water and air, a greater slope is needed to produce a given velocity in a submarine channel than is needed to produce it in a land channel of the same size. On the other hand, owing to the incoherence of most underwater sediments, large quantities of the material on the sea floor may be stirred up at one time, and this great volume may more than compensate for the smaller density difference. The speed attained by a large and dense turbidity current may thus be many times greater (as it was off the Grand Banks) than in any known river flood. As mentioned in Chapter 15, desert mudflows carry large boulders in suspension; some marine sedimentary rocks contain similar boulders in a poorly sorted finer matrix—perhaps they, too, were carried in suspension. It is important, of course, to find whether a turbidity current such as seems to have been created by the Grand Banks earthquake could occur in the constricted area of a submarine canyon and thus continue to deepen it once it had started. This question now seems to have been answered.

We have mentioned the historical evidence of subaqueous channeling by turbidity currents in the Lake of Zug (Chapter 11). This flow of 1887 had a mean gradient of 4°, similar to that of many submarine canyons, and much higher than most stream gradients. The largest of the Swiss trenches cuts the delta of the upper Rhone in Lake Leman. It is a few tens of feet deep and clearly the product of a turbidity flow like that of the Lake of Zug.

In a freshwater lake, a turbidity current sinks if its density exceeds 1. In the sea, the density must exceed that of sea water, generally near 1.025. Bottom density currents in the sea are obviously hard to discover in action. Neither that of the Grand Banks nor the one in Tokyo Bay seems to have cut channels. Scuba divers have, however, observed sand flows and streaming of sediment down the submarine canyons at La Jolla, California and Cape San Lucas, Baja California. Longshore currents supply sediment to the canyon heads. We thus know that sediment flows do travel down submarine canyons and it seems reasonable to conclude that once started they should erode effectively and continue to the bottom. Soundings have shown the La Jolla Canyon to deepen suddenly after storms and to shallow in quiet weather, suggesting that storm turbulence triggers the flow. Surveys show that hundreds of thousands of cubic yards of gravel and sand are carried along the shores of Santa Monica Bay, California, from both directions toward the submarine canyon off Redondo. Yet the canyon does not fill up and the shore is not advancing. The sediment must disappear down the canyon somehow —and it can hardly do so except as a turbidity flow. Many other canyons also head where longshore currents converge.

Should we accept the hypothesis that turbidity currents are responsible for most undersea canyons, we would expect to find several of the features that actually exist: steep gradients, canyon heads in water shallow enough to be turbulent, mouths at various levels but mostly at the foot of the continental slope, canyons situated where they can be supplied with unusual amounts of sediment. A large muddy river would be one good source of sediment, the meeting place of two longshore currents another, the outer edge of the continental shelf a third (especially during the Pleistocene times of lowered sea level when abundant debris from melting glaciers was available and storm waves could stir up the unconsolidated sea bottom). Once erosion started, the canyons themselves would furnish additional sediment.

If turbidity currents cut deep submarine canyons, they must deposit submarine deltas or fans, and certainly such fans exist at the bottom of several (Chapter 5). At the mouth of the Hudson Canyon, a broad flat cone extends out onto the ocean floor. Cores show alternating layers of clay and coarser material—sand, silt, and shells. Many fossils are of benthic Foraminifera known to live at shallow depths. The coarse layers show coarser material at their bases, grading up to finer at the tops—graded bedding (Chapter 17)—which suggests sedimentation from a turbidity current. The alternation of coarse layers with the fine clay usual at this depth (nearly 5 kilometers) suggests that the processes responsible for them are sporadic, rather than continuous. Identical graded bedding, some in deposits that contain coarse boulders in a contorted and tumbled sandy and silty matrix, has been found in Cenozoic strata of Italy and California, and is less certainly represented in many other formations of all eras, including the Precambrian.

Although many facts are in accord with the turbidity-current hypothesis of the origin of submarine canyons, we cannot feel completely satisfied. More information is needed.

Can hard rocks be eroded by density currents, as we know unconsolidated sediments can be? How thick is the sedimentary layer off the canyons and what kind of stratification and alternations in kinds of sediment does it show? Do debris fans extend out from all submarine canyons as they do from the Hudson Canyon in the Atlantic and from the Redondo and Monterey Canyons in the Pacific? Many more sonic and seismic surveys, as well as many more long cores from the deep-sea sediments, are needed to answer these questions.

We may, however, conclude this review of oceanic processes with an additional comment on the questions raised by Figure 10–4. Of the two dominant levels of the earth's relief, the higher seems reasonably explained as the level at which streams drop their loads in deltas, and where most of the land-derived sediments of today and of the later parts of the geologic past have accumulated. We do not know enough about the lower of the two great levels, that of the oceanic floor, to be quite sure of its origin. In the large, it is undoubtedly accounted for by the average difference between the densities of continental and oceanic rocks, in accordance with the general scheme of Pratt isostasy. Part, however, of the remarkably featureless abyssal plains are due to the filling in of depressions in an originally rough bottom by sedimentation from turbidity currents and the slow accumulation of volcanic ash and of terrigenous (land-derived) clay, as discussed in the next chapter.

Facts, concepts, terms

Relative areas of ocean and land
Currents in the surface layer of the ocean
    Effects of wind drag
    Equatorial Drift; West-wind Drift
    The Gulf Stream
Deep-water circulation
    Effects of temperature and salinity on density
    Density currents
    Mediterranean density current
    The Antarctic bottom water
Tides
    Tidal currents
    Neap tides; spring tides
    Surges
Waves
    Deep-water waves; shallow-water waves
    Particle motion
Wave growth and speed
Wave refraction; energy distribution in waves
Breakers; turbulence in the breaker zone
Wave erosion
    Hydraulic pressure
    Corrasion
    Wave base
    Motion of sediments
Storm beaches, profile of equilibrium

Wave currents; longshore drift; effects of interference with drift
Coastal topography
    Bayhead and baymouth bars
    Land-tied islands
    Spits
    Offshore bars
Continental shelf; continental slope
Island arcs; deeps; ridges and rises
Banks; seamounts; guyots; abyssal hills; abyssal plains; archipelagic aprons
Marine life zones
    Benthic; pelagic; littoral; deep-sea
    Plankton; nekton
Coral Reefs
    Fringing reefs; barrier reefs; atolls
Origin of atolls
    Darwin Theory
    Daly Theory
Submarine canyons
    Distribution
    Slopes; forms; ends
Subaerial origin of canyons and corollaries thereto
Effect of glacial lowering of sea level
    Turbidity currents

Questions

1. Why are tides in the Mediterranean Sea smaller than those in San Francisco Bay, which also has a narrow connection with the ocean?

2. If the effect of wave refraction is to concentrate attack on headlands, why is a cuspate form of sandspit such as those off Cape Hatteras not destroyed?

3. If a wave 400 feet long has a period of 8 seconds, what is its velocity in feet per second? in miles per hour?

4. Roughly estimate the ratio between the velocity of a storm wave far from land and that of the swiftest ocean current.

5. What would be a reasonable difference in elevation between seaward and landward edges of the rock floor of an erosional marine terrace 2000 feet wide? What is your basis of estimate?

6. The Congo submarine canyon heads in the Congo estuary, which is studded with alluvial islands. The depth of sedimentary fill in the estuary is not known. Draw two long profiles of the base of this fill: (*a*) assuming that the estuary is the slightly emergent head of a canyon formed beneath the sea, and (*b*) assuming that the whole submarine canyon was formed subaerially, but has since been warped below sea level. Explain.

7. At the equator, water on the bottom of both the Pacific and Atlantic is only a few degrees above freezing. What is the source of this cold water and why does it not mix quickly with the warm water at the surface?

8. What probable effects did the waxing and waning of the Pleistocene ice sheets have upon: (*a*) the salinity of the ocean? (*b*) the number of turbidity currents coursing down the continental slopes? (*c*) the circulation through the Straits of Gibraltar?

Suggested readings

Darwin, C. R., in Mather, K. F., and S. L. Mason, *Source Book in Geology*. New York: McGraw-Hill, 1939. [P. 354–357.]

Davis, W. M., *The Coral Reef Problem* (Special Publication 9). New York: American Geographical Society, 1928.

Kuenen, P. H., *Marine Geology*. New York: John Wiley and Sons, 1950.

Scientific American offprints

807. Bruce C. Heezen, *The Origin of Submarine Canyons* (August 1956)

810. Henry Stommel, *The Anatomy of the Atlantic* (January 1955)

813. Walter Munk, *The Circulation of the Oceans* (September 1955)

814. Robert L. Fisher and Roger Revelle, *The Trenches of the Pacific* (November 1955)

828. Willard Bascom, *Ocean Waves* (August 1959)

830. Herbert S. Bailey, Jr., *The Voyage of the "Challenger"* (May 1953)

839. James E. McDonald, *The Coriolis Effect* (May 1952)

845. Willard Bascom, *Beaches* (August 1960)

860. V. G. Kort, *The Antartic Ocean* (September 1962)

chapter

17

Sedimentary Rocks and the Environments of Deposition

Because they cover more than two-thirds of the lands, the sedimentary rocks supply the chief record of earth history, and because fossils are virtually restricted to them, the fullest chronology. In this chapter, we aim to show how the records of geologic processes written in the sedimentary rocks are used in reconstructing past geographies in the drama of earth evolution.

THE VOLUME OF THE SEDIMENTARY ROCKS

Several geologists have estimated the total volume of sedimentary rocks in the earth's crust. Although many sedimentary rocks are obviously reworked from older sediments, nearly all these estimates have been made on the assumption that all the material composing them must be derived ultimately from igneous rocks. The average composition of the igneous rocks of the continents has been computed by several chemists, using many thousand analyses. Although some doubt exists that the sampling has been truly representative, various computations using different approaches agree within narrow limits (Appendix IV).

Many sedimentary rocks of all kinds, both on the continents and on the ocean floor have also been analyzed and their volumes roughly estimated; on the continents from geologic maps, stratigraphic sections, and well records; on the sea floor by geophysical means discussed later. By comparing the average composition of all the sedimentary rocks with that of the average crustal igneous rock, the mass of igneous rock that has been weathered to produce all the sediments can be estimated. Here, because of varying estimates of the composition of the average sedimentary rock, the agreement among different scientists is not nearly as close as among the estimates of the composition of the average igneous rock. The American geochemist

F. W. Clarke estimated in 1924 that the sedimentary rocks represent detritus from the weathering of 1.02×10^{18} metric tons of average igneous rock (equivalent to an earth shell half a mile thick), and that the sedimentary rocks make up about 5 percent of the crust to a depth of 10 miles. The Dutch geologist Kuenen called attention to the large volume of sedimentary rocks that contain unweathered feldspar and other igneous minerals or volcanic ash, and to the greater porosity of sedimentary than of igneous rocks; his volume estimate was three times Clarke's. The Norwegian geologist Goldschmidt suggested that the chemical composition of glacial flour should give a good average composition for the rocks overridden; his analysis of Norwegian glacial silts was strikingly close to Clarke's average igneous rock. Another Norwegian geologist, Tom Barth, has more recently pointed out that many sedimentary rocks are derived in large part from metamorphic terranes and that metamorphic rocks differ chemically from both igneous and sedimentary ones. The striking similarity between Goldschmidt's and Clarke's averages seems to make this criticism unimportant compared with the great uncertainties we are confronted with in estimating sedimentary volumes. In 1964, the American geologists Horn and Adams reached an estimate twice that of Clarke. Others have arrived at somewhat lower figures; the matter still remains uncertain.

Abundance of different rock varieties

Scores of varieties of sedimentary rocks have been described, but more than 99 percent of the total volume is made up of only three: shale (including siltstone), sandstone (including graywacke), and limestone (including dolomite). Different geologists have computed the relative proportions of these as reported in measured stratigraphic sections. The data are poor, for several reasons; many

Table 17–1 **Proportions of sedimentary rocks computed by different geologists**

Rock	Percentages measured in outcrops	Percentages expected under differing assumptions of various authors
Shale	42 to 58	70 to 83
Sandstone	14 to 40	8 to 16
Limestone	18 to 29	5 to 14

silty sandstones and all graywackes, for instance, contain much silt and clay, as do many limestones. The result is that shale is underrepresented in measured sections (Table 17–1). And the measured sections are of stratal *thickness;* they may not closely reflect the *volumes* of rock actually present. When the components to be expected from the weathering of the "average igneous rock" are assigned to the three dominant varieties of sedimentary rock in accordance with the amounts of shale, sandstone, and limestone theoretically to be expected, the proportions are widely different from those actually measured in stratigraphic sections: there should be much less carbonate rock and sandstone and very much more shale (Table 17–1, third column). If we correct the measured values of sandstone for the silt and clay in graywacke, and of limestone for the clay commonly present in them, we still have less shale than even the lowest estimate would lead us to expect. The only way to reconcile the measurements with theory is to postulate that much of the clay produced during weathering has been swept into the deep sea so that it is not represented in the measured stratigraphic sections. As we shall see, intrinsic characteristics of the rocks exposed on the continents—although a few deep-sea deposits are found—show that by far the most were deposited in relatively shallow water, thus supporting this suggestion.

Factors influencing diversity of sediments

Earlier we mentioned many factors that influence the diversity of sediments. These are of three main kinds, operating respectively, (1) in the source area, (2) during transportation, and (3) at the place of deposition.

IN THE SOURCE AREA. Most rocks, on weathering, produce some clay, but no amount of weathering can release clay from a pure quartz sandstone or a pure limestone. Climate, too, is a major control in weathering, as is strikingly shown by the contrast between, say, the frost-riven fragments of fresh granite on an Arctic mountain, the clay-rich soil derived from granite in Virginia, and the high-aluminum laterite, also derived from granite, in a Surinam lowland. Vegetative cover, climatically controlled, influences strongly both disruption of the rocks and the speed and mechanism of erosion. Relief is a major determinant in erosion: for example, virtually unaided downslope movement on a mountain cliff, but solution acting almost alone on a low plain of coral limestone. Relief also influences the maturity of the weathering profile, and thus the completeness of chemical decomposition. Many sedimentary rocks retain characteristics imposed on them at the source. From these we are able to infer much about the area from which they were derived.

DURING TRANSPORTATION. The fragments in a mountain talus pile—angular and unsorted by shape and only slightly coarser on the basal slopes than higher—exemplify material moved by gravity alone. Talus is rarely preserved as consolidated rock, but where it has been, as along the buried mountain slope that underlies the Titus Canyon Formation in the Death Valley region, California, its characteristic angular fragments, trivial sorting and obvious derivation from the bedrock cliff against which it rests leave no doubt as to its origin. Contrast this with the dune sand of the Navajo Sandstone (Figs. 15–25, 15–26), free from clay and other silicates, almost wholly composed of well-rounded, uniformly sized grains of quartz with sparse faceted pebbles and rare lenticles of limestone—a deposit precisely duplicating modern dune regions. Or contrast the mixture of unsorted rock flour, sand, and boulders at a glacier's snout with the organic mud of a tidal flat or the wave-rounded sand and gravel of a coastal spit. These examples, among scores that could be given, show how the agency of transport clearly places its stamp on many sedimentary deposits—the Present is the Key to the Past.

AT THE PLACE OF DEPOSITION. Source area and transport agency thus leave their record, but it is the depositional environment that generally imposes on the sedimentary rocks their most distinctive characteristics. Several books the size of this would be needed to discuss in detail each of the myriad environments and its characteristic sediments: talus cone, moraine, alluvial fan, floodplain, river bar, marsh, reef, dune, grassland, lake, estuary, and all the scores of oceanic environments. We limit ourselves to briefly outlining some of the most significant sedimentary features and suggesting how they may be helpful in deducing the geographies of the past.

STRATIFICATION

The most striking feature of most sedimentary rocks is their stratification, or layering (Figs. 17–1, 17–2, 17–3, 17–4). The stratification gives clues to the origin of the sediments. Layers may be microscopically thin or many scores of feet thick. In coarse clastic rocks, grains of varying size lie in layers, parallel or nearly parallel to the base of the stratum. Slight differences in size and color of the grains from layer to layer emphasize the stratification. In fine clastic rocks grain size

FIGURE 17–1   *Scour-and-fill bedding in Cretaceous strata of the Wasatch Plateau, Utah. A filled stream channel in the alluvial deposits of an ancient coastal plain is seen near the top. (Photo by Warren Hamilton, U.S. Geological Survey.)*

FIGURE 17–2   *Bedding of the volcanic ash of the John Day Formation (Oligocene), near Mitchell, Oregon. Continuous thin beds are ash falls (Chapter 18). The weak and discontinuous layering records intermittent weathering and stream flow between volcanic eruptions. (Photo by Oregon State Highway Department.)*

may seem uniform from one layer to another, but a color-banding, due to slight differences in the content of organic matter or of carbonate may reveal the stratification. Many carbonate rocks show very massive and thick beds; others contain many thin layers of clay or shale. Among the clastic rocks, four varieties of stratification merit discussion because they record significantly different depositional processes. These are: parallel lamination, current bedding, graded bedding, and massive bedding (Fig. 17–5).

Origin of stratification

The word sediment implies settlement from a fluid; but in geology, it generally implies current transport as well. Even though a particle has crystallized on the sea floor, currents must have brought its component ions. Most water currents are turbulent, with different threads ranging widely in velocity and direction. Particles transported by a turbulent current are subject to widely fluctuating forces, although over times of a few

FIGURE 17–3   *Massive limestone reefs in the Horquilla Limestone (Pennsylvanian), Big Hatchet Mountains, New Mexico. Note thin beds at upper right passing into white reef bodies of algal-rich massive limestone. (Photo by Robert A. Zeller, Jr., Hachita, New Mexico.)*

FIGURE 17–4   *Alternating sandstone and shale beds in the Haymond Formation (Pennsylvanian) near Marathon, Texas, a typical flysch deposit. The sandstones characteristically show graded bedding. Note creep to right at right side of picture and to left on left, despite the very low hill slopes. (Photo by Earle F. McBride, University of Texas.)*

FIGURE 17–5

Several varieties of stratification of clastic rocks. A: Current bedding, in which the minor laminae lie at notable angles to the major bedding surfaces; B: Graded bedding, in which the laminations are virtually parallel, with each lamina grading from coarse at the base to fine at the top; C: Parallel lamination, in which thin layers of differing grain size lie virtually parallel; D: Massive bedding, in which no systematic arrangement by grain size is recognizable within individual thick strata.

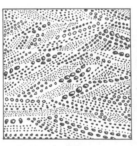

A: Current bedding

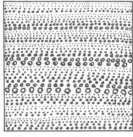

B: Graded bedding

C: Parallel lamination

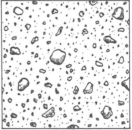

D: Massive bedding

FIGURE 17–6   *Features of sedimentary rocks. A: Thinly laminated sandstone interbedded with a few thicker beds in Coaledo Formation, near Chehalis, Washington. (Photo by Parke D. Snavely, Jr., U.S. Geological Survey.) B: Slump bedding and interbed disturbance due to sliding of unconsolidated sediments. Miocene strata near Dos Pueblos Creek, Santa Barbara County, California. (Photo by M. N. Bramlette, U.S. Geological Survey.) C: Massive bedding in two-foot mudflow on beach at Cape Thompson, Alaska. (Photo by Reuben Kachadoorian, U.S. Geological Survey.) D: Ripple marks on Silurian siltstone, west shore of Moose Island, Maine. (Photo by E. S. Bastin, U.S. Geological Survey.)*

minutes or hours the fluctuations should in general average out. In Chapter 12 we noticed that almost any natural water current is sufficiently turbulent to retain very fine particles in suspension almost indefinitely.

PARALLEL LAMINATION.   Grains larger than about .1 millimeter in diameter, however, are not all carried by a feeble current, even though the current may be turbulent. The size of grain that can be kept in suspension or dragged along the bottom depends on current speed. A mountain torrent can roll great boulders, but as its velocity decreases, so does its competence. Part of the traction load comes to rest and smaller grains become part of the traction rather than of the suspended load; a layer of sediment is thus laid down. If the current continues to slow, finer and finer material is deposited. Such deposition generally alters the bottom configuration, so that the turbulence pattern of a later rapid current will differ from that of the old. The new current may pick up some of the previously deposited material but leave some coarser grains as a uniform thin layer. Of course, if the new current is swifter than the old it may re-entrain the whole deposit and even scour the bottom beneath (Fig. 17–1), but if it does not, the residual layer of the former deposit may be stabilized by the settling of fine particles into the interstices of stranded grains. As we saw from Figure 12–9, such stabilized grains are less readily moved at a particluar current velocity than they would have been during the declining cycle. Thus even a faster current may not suffice to erode the bottom. The resistance of clay-sized particles to re-entrainment is particularly marked, as has been proved in many irrigation canals and other controlled channels. This may explain the parallel lamination so common in shale and fine-grained sandstones. In summary, almost any current that reaches bottom can deposit a sequence of alternating fine and coarse parallel laminae. The moving water sorts out and drops grains of a particular size with each decrease in velocity, thereby producing the common parallel lamination shown in Figures 17–5,C, 17–6,A.

CURRENT BEDDING.   When a sand-laden current slows, as on the inside of a river bend, or in passing from a shallower to a deeper reach of a stream, or at the face of a delta, the sand grains of the traction load are deposited. As the channel becomes constricted, the traction load is carried forward and dropped over the edge of the material earlier deposited. The deposit builds forward with a sloping front, down which the grains tumble and roll. Grains accumulated at the bottom decrease the slope of the embankment until some grains are retained on the slope, building it forward parellel to itself, but at an angle to the water surface. Deposition is also favored by an upstream bottom current that is generated in the lee of the embankment as the main stream loses contact with the bottom (Fig. 17–7). Succeeding increments extend the embankment forward into the slack water, forming a layer of sediment with **foreset bedding**, perhaps only a fraction of an inch thick, if the current is weak, but a score or more feet thick if the current is strong and the slack water deep (Figs. 17–8, 17–9). Each increment of the advancing foreset slopes forward at the angle of sliding friction as modified by the eddies in the lee of the embankment—this may be only a few degrees

FIGURE 17–7
Diagram showing eddy formed in lee of a prograding embankment, with upstream current counter to the traction load sliding down the front. (Modified from A. V. Jopling, Journal of Sedimentary Petrology, v. 35, 1965.)

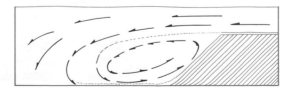

or as much as 40°. A trench cut through such a deposit shows lamination at an angle to the horizon—that is, to the bedding proper. This lamination is called **cross-bedding, cross-lamination,** or **current bedding.**

The process just described is common in shallow streams and in deep marine water, where it resembles dune formation. Whether formed in deep or shallow water, any deposit showing cross-bedding has obviously been laid down from a fluid whose motion extended to the then-existing bottom, upstream from the then-existing face of the embankment. In Chapter 15 we described the distinctive curving cross-bedding of sand dunes (Fig. 15–18). Similar bedding is common in water-laid sands as well, but the two are readily distinguished by the difference in scale: eolian sand dunes show cross-bedding tens or scores of feet high (Figs. 15–25, 15–26), in waterlaid dunes the scale is in inches or at most feet. The grain size of eolian dunes is nearly uniform; that of water-laid dunes may vary widely.

Cross-bedding, then, is often a clue to the sedimentary environment of a deposit displaying it. Fluctuations in current speed and volume may bring about scouring of the sediment to form irregular depressions to be filled by later deposits. Thus **scour-and-fill** structures are commonly associated with cross-bedding (Figs. 17–1, 17–8).

FIGURE 17–8

Scour-and-fill structures and accompanying cross-bedding characteristic of fluvial bedding.

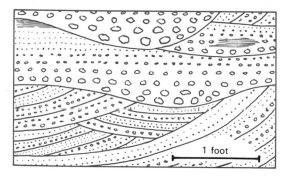

1 foot

FIGURE 17–9   *Current bedding in dolomitic marine sandstone of the Vinini Formation (Ordovician), Cortez Mountains, Nevada. The dark layers at top and bottom are shale.*

1 cm

GRADED BEDDING. Graded bedding consists of layers, each with a sharply marked base on which lie the coarsest grains in the bed (Figs. 17–5,B, 17–4). In each layer this coarsest material grades upward without a break or sudden change of grade size to fine material at the top of the layer, there to be suc- ceeded abruptly by the coarse base of the next higher layer (Fig. 17–10). Such a grading can be readily produced by stirring up sediments of a wide size range in a beaker full of water and allowing it to stand. The coarse fragments fall quickly to the bottom but the finest may remain in suspension for hours. Much finely laminated material is laid down from pulses of such sediment-laden water, and each lamina may show graded bedding. The varves of glacial lakes (Chapter 13) are excellent examples of graded bedding; it is also found in stream backwaters into which freshets overflow; in sheltered bays where storm waves that have entrained much sediment are driven; and in the ocean, even at great depths, where turbidity currents deposit sand covered with fine silt. Graded beds are commonly interbedded with others having regular parallel lamination or showing current bedding. This association is reasonably to be expected, and is shown in Figure 17–4.

Graded bedding is also commonly associated with submarine landslides because these are likely to generate turbidity currents. Sliding of weakly consolidated sediment may be accompanied by gouging (Fig. 17–11) and plowing into the bottom; chunks of mud and sand are twisted and rolled (Fig. 17–13), thin beds are broken and crumpled (Figs. 17–6,B, 17–12), and sandstone dikes may be injected into the underlying beds by the sudden loading. At the same time the landslide may set up strong currents that sort the sediment and produce current bedding. As these currents die away the sediment in the stirred up and turbid water settles out to produce graded bedding. Graded bedding is thus commonly associated with evidence of subaqueous slumping and therefore some geologists consider it a criterion of deep-water deposition. But varved lake sediments and overbank deposits on floodplains are also truly graded and subaqueous slides can form at shallow and intermediate depths as well as in very deep water, as shown by the

FIGURE 17–10

Graded bedding in limestone turbidite from the Dimple Formation (Pennsylvanian), near Marathon, Texas. Note coarser fragments at base, grading almost imperceptibly upward to extremely fine-grained material toward the top. (Photo by Alan Thomsen, Shell Oil Company, Houston, Texas.)

FIGURE 17–11   *Bedding contorted by flowage when soft. The sediment has moved in direction of the bottom of the picture. Scale 6 inches long. Tyee Formation (Eocene), Oregon Coast Range. (Photo by Parke D. Snavely, Jr., U.S. Geological Survey.)*

FIGURE 17–12   *Bedding contorted by submarine slump of unconsolidated sediment of the Dimple Formation (Pennsylvanian), Brewster County, Texas. (Photo by Earle F. McBride, University of Texas.)*

FIGURE 17–13   *Slumping of lake sediments of the Lisan Formation (Pleistocene) in the Dead Sea area, Israel. Presumably the sliding was brought about by differential loading. (Photo by Tad Nichols, Tucson, Arizona.)*

FIGURE 17–14   *Massive-bedded volcanic ash flow, Crater Lake National Park, Oregon. Except near the top of the exposure there is little or no sorting by size. The pinnacles— some 200 feet high—were left standing after rain erosion where scattered, resistant lava fragments served as protecting caps. (Photo by Oregon State Highway Commission.)*

slide in the Lake of Zug, by those in Sagami Bay at the time of the Tokyo earthquake, on the slope below the Grand Banks or at the mouth of the Hudson submarine canyon. A fine example of sliding at relatively shallow depths is illustrated in Figure 17–13. Graded bedding indicates only that, unlike current bedding, it formed where bottom currents were not active enough to sort the sinking sediment. Such currents may have been active at the site before the graded bed was laid down and may recur later, as is shown by common interbedding of graded and current-bedded sandstones. The only unambiguous criterion of a very deep origin for graded bedding is the occurrence of deep benthic fossils in position of growth.

MASSIVE BEDDING.   Strata that show no internal lamination have **massive bedding**; there is no sorting by either grain size or density. Mudflows, whether in the desert or on the slopes of a volcano, may be sufficiently saturated with water to flow, but are too viscous to permit much sorting (Figs. 17–6,C, 17–5,D). Some deposits of volcanic lapilli and ash are also without apparent bedding, doubtless because of the turbulence in the eruptive cloud (Fig. 17–14).

Some well-sorted sediments are also massive. The coarser massive sediments seem to have resulted from redeposition of previously well-sorted sediment; in many of the finer muds any stratification originally present has been destroyed by burrowing organisms, so that only massive bedding remains.

TEXTURES.   The texture (Appendix III) of a rock is commonly a significant clue to the environment of its deposition, as we can readily see by the contrast between unsorted morainal or talus material, poorly sorted and poorly rounded bouldery bed material of a mountain torrent, well-sorted and rounded sands of a desert dune or a bar on a plains coast, and the impalpable mud dredged from a stagnant pond or the deep sea. Even the degree of rounding of the component material

is a clue to its history. Boulders, even of resistant rock, commonly become rounded within a few hundred yards of their source in a mountain stream, but sand grains, with their relatively much greater surface per unit volume, are much less quickly rounded. Among grains of quartz in a poorly sorted sandstone, it is common to find the coarser ones well-rounded and the finer ones angular (Fig. 17–15). Even long wear on a beach may fail to round sand-sized material well—in fact, many geologists think that highly rounded quartz grains are never formed in a single cycle of erosion and deposition, but require reworking from one sandstone to another, perhaps several times. As a sand grain weighs more in air than in water, wind transportation is much more abrasive than water transport; dune sands are therefore generally better rounded than those of streams or beaches.

FIGURE 17–15
Photomicrograph of a thin-section of a sandstone from the Valmy Formation (Ordovician), Shoshone Range, Nevada. Although this sandstone is more than 99 percent quartz, the sorting is very poor; the coarser grains are well rounded, the finer, sharply angular.

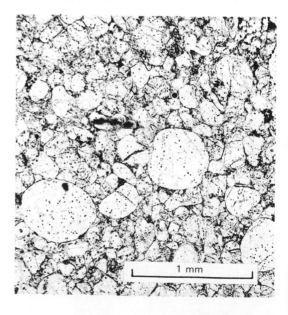

1 mm

TERRESTRIAL SEDIMENTS

Distinguishing features of many terrestrial sediments have already been described and others are treated in later sections: pyroclastic flows (Chapter 18), and coal (Chapter 21). Here we examine some terrestrial deposits with a view to recognizing their ancient analogues among the sedimentary rocks. As we saw in Chapter 12, most rivers fluctuate widely in capacity through the year; the fluctuations are recorded in the alternate scouring of the bed and deposition of gravel, sand, and silt, either in backwaters during floods or over the whole stream bed during flood recession. Coarse stream deposits thus characteristically include scour-and-fill structures, current bedding, local graded bedding, and poorly sorted materials. Alluvial plains have coarser sediments in the channels and wider areas of finer sediment as overbank and meander deposits. When the muds dry on retreat of the overflow, they generally crack into polygonal patterns (Figs. 17–16, 3–3) which are characteristic of clay deposits that are alternately wet and dry. Although such cracks form on tidal flats as well, the intertidal interval is too short to make them as deep as in the Nile floodplain of Figure 17–16. If, as is common, the mud in slack-water areas is somewhat graded, the polygons produced curl upward (Fig. 3–3), for the more silty and sandy lower part of the graded bed contracts less on drying than the more clayey surficial layer. Streams so choked with uniform sand as to be rapidly aggrading form an unusual kind of progressive ripples, each higher rippled layer being advanced slightly downstream with respect to the immediately underlying one (Fig. 17–17) —this structure has been reproduced also in flume experiments.

FIGURE 17–16
Mudcracks on the floodplain of the Nile at Khartoum, Sudan. (Photo by Tad Nichols, Tucson, Arizona.)

FIGURE 17–17   *"Climbing ripple-marked" bedding in alluvium of the Colorado River delta, California. Flume experiments show that climbing ripples form only when the stream is choked with rather well-sorted sand and is rapidly aggrading. (Photo by Tad Nichols, Tucson, Arizona.)*

Such streams as the lower Mississippi, the Amazon, and the Nile carry little coarse sediment; their floodplains are chiefly composed of silt and fine sand—the sand along the channels and the silts and clays in overbank deposits or left by migrating meanders as they sweep across the plain. In fact, Nile silt is so fine that despite annual overflow, it has taken 400 to 500 years to accumulate a foot of alluvium at Memphis.

Sporadic lenses of fine gravel form in the channel of the main stream. Similar deposits, with sinuous lenses of coarser silt, sand, and fine gravel between broad expanses of fine clay and silt are recovered in cores of wells drilled into the floodplain of the lower Mississippi to depths of many hundred feet. At depth they contain Pleistocene fossils: freshwater mollusks and plant remains like those along the present river. Some cores show current bedding and scour-and-fill phenomena, others the even lamination of oxbow lake deposits. Clearly, these deposits are fluvial, undoubtedly those of the ancestral Mississippi. Studies of these cores enabled H. N. Fisk and other Mississippi River Commission geologists to trace the position of a long succession of delta distributaries (Fig. 17–18).

Similar features that remain recognizable in consolidated rocks from many geological systems and on every continent have been interpreted as of fluvial origin. An example is the Arikaree Formation of late Tertiary age, in Wyoming, Colorado, Nebraska, and Kansas. The interpretation of the Arikaree

as the streambed and floodplain deposits of aggrading rivers is supported by its fossils: bones of antelope, camels, and horses, shells of land snails, and pollen of grasses—all of which might be expected on an open floodplain.

Because few lakes are of a size to allow enough fetch for waves to become large, or persistent strong currents to be established, coarse sediments are generally confined to the strand zone and most lake sediments are fine and evenly laminated as is seen, for example, in Figure 17–13, and in the glacial varves of Figure 13–34. Lake sediments can generally be recognized by their fine grain and even bedding, associated deltaic deposits and nonmarine fossils.

We have already described many other terrestrial sediments: loess, sand dunes, talus cones, alluvial fans, and moraines; still others are described in later chapters—we turn now to the less accessible but much more abundant sediments of the sea.

FIGURE 17–18   *The sedimentation pattern of the Mississippi delta. (After H. N. Fisk, E. Mc-Farlan, C. R. Kolb, and L. J. Wilbert, 1954.)*

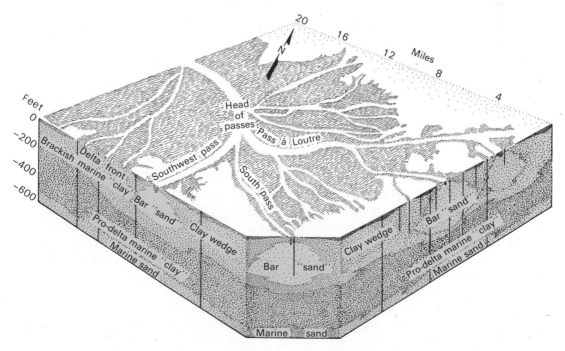

Phytoliths (silica derived from grass fires) and freshwater diatoms in a dust storm of January 17 to 19, 1965, off the west coast of Africa. These land-derived materials abound not only in the dust but also in the deep-sea sediments for many hundred miles from the shore. Pattern indicates abundance of diatoms and opaline silica particles in the dust recovered during the storm by H. M. S. Vidal. (After D. W. Folger, W. H. Burckle, and B. C. Heezen, Science, v. 155, p. 1243–1244, 10 March, 1967. Copyright 1967 by the American Association for the Advancement of Science.)

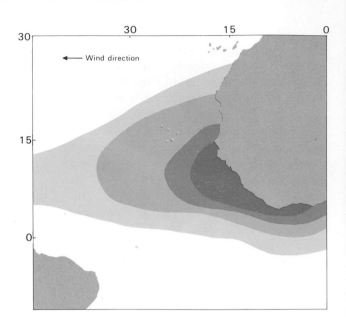

MARINE SEDIMENTS

Sources of marine sediments

Except for a trivial amount of meteoritic dust, the much greater but unmeasurable increment from submarine volcanoes, and an uncertain but probably moderate addition from tidal scour and downslope movements off submarine ridges, the marine sediments are all derived from the lands. Even the material of marine shells, which contribute greatly to marine sediments, was originally leached from terrestrial rocks. Detritus from downslope movement, rivers, glacial erosion, windblown volcanic ash, and desert dust all are carried to the sea, there to mingle with the debris won from the land by the ocean itself in its attack upon the shore.

Every year the rivers sweep about 20 billion tons of rock waste to the sea. More than four-fifths is clastic material in suspension or traction; the rest is dissolved. The fate of the clastic material is clear: sorting begins as soon as the sea is reached. Samples dredged from the sea floor show partly consolidated sediments identical in grain size and mineralogy with the river detritus. Because of contin-

ual wave agitation, stratification and sorting are commonly more pronounced in marine than in river sediments. As is suggested both by the deficiency of shale among the stratified rocks and by the composition of the sediments of the deep oceans, this agitation is generally enough to permit a large share of the finer clays to move off the continental shelf and to the deep sea. This inference has recently been fortified by light-meter measurements of transmitted light at depth in the sea, which have shown water masses cloudy with suspended sediment down the continental shelf and far out into the ocean basins. Windblown dust also is spread far from shore, especially off the desert belts of the earth (Fig. 17–19) but also even off the humid coasts of the north Pacific.

The fate of the dissolved material is not so obvious. Though there are many huge deposits of salt and anhydrite in older strata, these substances seem now to be deposited only in a few small lagoons along some desert coasts, or on the tidal flats such as the Rann of Kutch in westernmost India, which the monsoon annually floods to shallow depths. The rate of deposition of evaporites today is surely vastly lower than during parts of the geologic past. Present river waters hold much higher proportions of silica and calcium than does sea water (Appendix IV) —so much higher that the composition of the sea would change greatly in a geologically short time if these elements were not somehow withdrawn from solution. The withdrawal is chiefly by organisms: much of the calcium and silica brought to the sea in solution is incorporated into the limy and siliceous shells of various plants and animals. Some geologists think that the differing proportions of ancient and modern limestones to their contemporaneous clastic sediments is due to the relatively recent evolution of many planktonic unicellular Foraminifera. These drifting animals now carry much calcium carbonate to the deep sea; before they were evolved (in Cretaceous time), the lime remained on or near the continental shelves, fixed by sessile, rather than by drifting organisms.

Realms of marine sedimentation

Marine strata are by far the most abundant; a core problem in stratigraphy is the recognition of the marine realm in which individual strata were deposited. The first serious oceanographic expedition, that of the *Challenger,* in 1873–1876, showed that sediments are being deposited virtually everywhere in the sea except where currents scour the bottom. But even where depth, exposure, distance to shore, bottom topography, and other obvious features appear identical, the local sediments may vary greatly. Though the great surge of oceonographic research since World War II has answered many questions, we are still far from a thorough understanding of sedimentational regimes of the sea.

The strand zone

The **strand zone** lies along the shore. Its widely varied sediments include those of beaches, deltas, bars, and tidal flats.

BEACHES. Beaches are wave-worked deposits of cobbles, gravels, and sands on and near the shore. During storms, much or all of a beach deposit may be stripped away, or, depending on the set of the waves, it may be piled to heights many feet above its normal level; between storms only a thin surface layer is agitated. On mountainous coasts beaches are short and discontinuous, and may be composed of poorly sorted debris supplied largely by downslope movement and steep streams; but along the coasts of plains, beaches may extend unbroken for scores of miles, and are generally composed of well-sorted sand derived from an older sediment or sedimentary rock that had already been sorted during an earlier cycle of deposition. On coasts of high relief, the beach sands may contain minerals, such as feldspar, supplied by mechanical breakdown of rocks at rates too fast for chemical weathering. In Hawaii whole beaches are composed of grains of olivine, a mineral that weathers readily, derived by wave attack on cones of granulated porphyritic basalt, formed where lava streams entered the sea. On plains coasts, however, where the available sediment is likely to have been at least twice exposed to weathering, the beach sands are rich in the less readily weathered quartz.

Some beaches, particularly in the tropics, are composed largely of shell fragments. Along the Brazilian coast these are being cemented almost as quickly as they form; sea spray dissolves a little calcite from the shells and it re-precipitates below as a cement (Fig. 3–1). Many sand beaches (like stream deposits) contain concentrations of heavy minerals, "black sands," such as magnetite, cassiterite, and zircon that have been sorted out by the waves in accordance with their density. Many such beaches have been mined for rare metals in India, Ceylon, Australia, and elsewhere. At Nome, Alaska, black sands have long been worked for gold, both in the modern beaches, and in ancient raised beaches some miles inland.

Relatively few beach deposits have been

recognized among the consolidated rocks, though there are many raised beaches. Beach deposits are obviously vulnerable to destruction; uplift exposes them to erosion, and submergence to any depth less than wave base subjects them to reworking by waves and tidal currents. Cambrian beaches, with associated sea cliffs and tumbled stacks, have nevertheless been recognized in the Montana Rockies, as have Carboniferous and Jurassic beaches in Great Britain.

DELTAS.   Where a stream enters the sea, the surface slope that provides its current vanishes. If wave action is strong, river and sea water quickly mix, but along quiet coasts the fresh water may float for a while above salt water. The powerful flood of the Amazon spreads widely over the Atlantic and fresh water may be dipped from the surface many miles at sea. If heavily silt-laden, a stream may sink and continue to flow as a turbidity current.

Whether the river water sinks or floats in the sea, the sediment is thus widely distributed over the sea floor. Different rivers differ greatly in grain size of their sediments and all vary seasonally. Some, like the Colorado, carry much coarse sand; they rapidy aggrade their delta plains, producing climbing rippled sand in the channels (Fig. 17–17). Others, like the Amazon, Mississippi, and Rhine carry little except clay, silt, and very fine sand; they aggrade the tops of their deltas only during floods. At the river mouth the coarsest material settles out first and nearest to the channel, followed at greater distances by finer and finer material as seen in the Mississippi delta (Fig. 17–18).

Most streams that enter the sea form deltas, but if the load is small, the coast exposed, or the tidal range large, the detritus may be widely scattered and no delta forms—even so great a river as the Columbia has none, though the Fraser, two hundred miles to the north, empties into a more protected area and has a vigorously growing delta. Deltas furnish much sediment to longshore cur-

rents. In fact, most beach material, including that in spits and longshore bars, is derived either directly or indirectly from stream sediments rather than from coastal bedrock.

Deltas in shallow waters (and especially those with considerable sand) commonly are characterized by foreset, bottomset, and topset bedding (Fig. 12–29). But the great birdfoot delta of the Mississippi, built into the deep Gulf of Mexico, consists of such fine sediment that the slopes of all beds are extremely low, and "foreset bedding" becomes a meaningless term. On either side of the distributaries, coarse silt and sand extend far out into the Gulf as underwater natural levees. Traced landward, these underwater levees continue into the natural levees of the flood plain, and like these, are made of coarser sediments near the channel (Fig. 17–18). Prograding of a delta varies with river discharge and with shifts from one distributary to another; some segments may advance while others retreat under wave attack. As with other plains coasts, offshore bars sheltering tidal lagoons are common. The waves may push the bars inland to the delta front and then rework the stream-laid beds, concentrating the coarser material on the beach and strewing the finer widely over the sea floor. Deltas furnish a good example of the difficulty of geologic classification, for all oceanic deltas contain some truly marine beds, some brackish lagoonal deposits and other truly fluvial beds—all complexly interfingering.

In summary: the coarsest deltaic material comes to rest chiefly on the stream bed or the beaches; finer material forms natural levees and their submarine extensions; the finest sediment is deposited behind the levees or is swept out to sea.

Delta subsidence.—Surveys show that many deltas are sinking, that of the Mississippi as much as eight feet a century in places. This sinking has been attributed to isostatic yielding of the crust to the added load. As with glacial loads some isostatic yielding seems likely, though that of the Mississippi delta seems far too rapid to be explained by this alone. The new, unconsolidated sediments are far less dense than any deeper rocks, and their floor should therefore sink much less than the thickness of the added sediment. Part of the subsidence is almost surely due to compaction of the newly deposited highly porous sediment; part may be due to slow mass flowage of the unconsolidated material seaward; possibly the river is merely being diverted toward an already subsiding area. No one knows the relative importance of these different factors.

Whatever the cause, parts of the delta are being slowly submerged to form tidal lagoons in which fine brackish or marine sediments are accumulating. It is doubtless the submergence of all the periphery of the delta except the natural levees that gives the Mississippi delta its bird-foot form. As distributaries shift, the marine beds may be buried by fluvial, and if subsidence continues, the delta may remain nearly in place rather than prograding. Interbedded marine, fluvial, and brackish water sediments thus may accumulate to great thickness, merging landward into wholly fluvial beds and seaward into wholly marine beds.

Such intimate associations of variable sediments record many ancient deltas. In New York and Pennsylvania, a Devonian delta more than 8,000 feet thick has been recognized, and borings for petroleum indicate that the ancestral Mississippi delta is comparably thick in Louisiana. The structures seen in outcrops or well cores show that each bed of this great thickness formed in relatively shallow water. Clearly, therefore, sinking has been concurrent with deltaic accumulation.

TIDAL-FLAT DEPOSITS.   Tidal-flat deposits accumulate in estuaries of sluggish streams or behind offshore bars. Many are deposited rapidly; at Wihelmshaven and Cuxhaven on the North Sea coast of Germany, 8 to 10 feet of mud may accumulate in a single year, rapidly filling the lagoons behind offshore bars. Some of this mud is brought in by rivers but much is swept in by the tides from the delta of the Rhine. The mud is thickly populated with worms and other organisms which pass the sediment through their digestive tracts and virtually destroy all stratification. Some mud contains so much organic matter that it is used as a fertilizer. Shallows in many tidal lagoons support luxurious plant growth which, by filtering out the sediment, speeds up silting of the lagoons.

Lagoonal deposits, like those of beaches, are rarely preserved in the geologic record. Some Devonian shales of Germany, however, have many features in common with modern lagoonal deposits, and may have formed in a similar environment.

Clay deposition

Clay particles have very large surface areas relative to their weight. The surface ions of the clay crystals have unsatisfied positive charges which attract negatively charged ions such as OH^- from the river water—each particle thus acquires a shell of negatively charged ions. As these negative shells repel each other, the clay particles do not stick together, but remain dispersed. When they enter the sea, these negatively charged ions unite with the abundant ions of Na^+ and Mg^{++} in sea water. Thus neutralized, the clay particles can stick together—they flocculate and form clots or aggregates which sink faster than individual clay flakes.

Much clay may thus settle quickly on entering the sea. Actually, few careful appraisals of this process have been made in nature, though the ideas outlined conform with laboratory experiments. Whether or not coagulation of clay flakes actually does precipitate most clay on entering the sea, sediments dredged many thousands of miles from shore show that some clay particles have been carried throughout the oceans. As discussed later, this should be expected theoretically from the currents involved.

Sediments of the continental shelves

The discussion of marine processes in Chapter 16 emphasized that the marine profile of equilibrium is merely an ideal concept. It applies as a sound generalization for such areas as the northern Gulf of Mexico, the Gulf of Paria, off Somaliland, and in many other places whose bottom topography and modern sediments have been well studied. In these areas, as theory suggests, nearshore deposits of sand grade outward to a mud bottom in deep water. It may be significant that these areas are in places not occupied by the Pleistocene glaciers and several are abundantly supplied with riverborne sediments. Whatever the reason, this systematic arrangement of sedimentary grain size is not found everywhere, although it does appear that the nearshore sea floor is generally concave upward and flattens seaward. Farther offshore, though, the bottom in many areas deviates widely from a smooth ideal profile, and the sediments in transit across the shelf do not everywhere diminish regularly in grain size. Part of the deviations may be explained by the rise of sea level, perhaps 300 to 400 feet, since the melting of the Pleistocene glaciers—a rise so recent that the sea may not yet have had time to adjust its profile to the new level except in areas of heavy sediment contribution or where no morainal deposits were flooded. A well-studied example of a complex pattern of bottom topography and sedimentation is that of the Atlantic continental shelf of the United States.

SEDIMENTS OF THE ATLANTIC CONTINENTAL SHELF. More than 30 years ago it was recognized that the unconsolidated material on the Atlantic continental shelf was by no means systematically sorted. The map (Fig. 17–20) shows the grain-size distribution of material that adhered to the tallow on a sounding lead, as compiled by the U.S. Coast and Geodetic Survey. There is actually more sand than gravel near shore, and the sediments of the outer part of the shelf are in many places coarser than those inshore. Silt and clay, however, are rare on the shelf (at depths less than 600 feet) and are widespread on the continental slope below. The velocities of bottom currents on the shelf almost everywhere exceed those required for erosion and transport of silt and clay, so that most fine sediment bypasses the shelf and drifts down the slope.

Three profiles surveyed across the shelf off

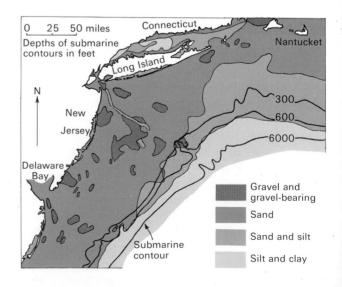

FIGURE 17–20

Size distribution of sediments on the continental shelf off the northeastern United States. (After F. P. Shepard and G. V. Cohee, 1936, from charts of the U.S. Coast and Geodetic Survey.)

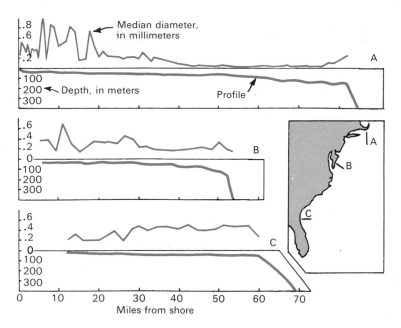

FIGURE 17–21   *The distribution of sediment sizes along three profiles of the Atlantic shelf of the United States. (After H. C. Stetson, 1938.)*

the eastern United States show considerable regional differences in sediment pattern (Fig. 17–21). Above each profile is plotted the median diameter of particles recovered from cores. Profile A, off Cape Cod, shows a sea floor sloping rather regularly except near the shelf edge. Near shore the coarse sediment is very irregularly distributed. This area was glaciated during the Pleistocene and the advancing sea has reworked morainal debris of all sizes. Profile B, off New Jersey, an unglaciated area, shows finer material nearshore than did A, but coarser at depths at which A shows silt. Here, too, grain sizes are irregularly distributed, but more than 25 miles from the coast grain size tends to be finer seaward, except near the shelf edge, where it again coarsens. Silt is lacking here, perhaps because the sea is reworking coastal-plain sedimentary rocks that contain little but sand. Profile C, off Florida, slopes regularly, but here, as in profile B, the material more than 25 miles offshore is consistently coarser than that nearshore. The Gulf Stream sweeps

the outer shelf, and is here swift enough to carry finer sediment off the shelf, across the Blake Plateau at more than 6000 feet depth, and into still greater depths. Photographs of the bottom here show current dunes like those in major rivers and in many places the dredge brings up consolidated rocks, some as old as Cretaceous—the currents are actively eroding the bedrock.

Despite the poor sorting of the sediments, the fact that the profiles are generally smooth indicates considerable reworking of the sediment on the shelf. It is clear from precision profiler records that depressions in the Pleistocene land surface have been largely filled during this reworking (Fig. 17–22).

Sediments of the continental slopes

In places, as off Spain, Brittany, and Ireland, the continental slope is too steep to retain sediment, and barren rock is at the surface. In general, though, the continental slopes are mantled with fine silt and mud

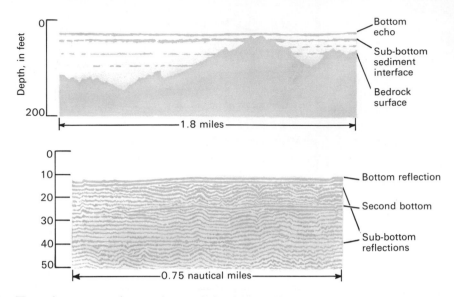

FIGURE 17–22   Top: *A representative continuous reflection profile over an uneven bedrock surface buried in sediment in Long Island Sound, New York. (After W. C. Beckmann, A. C. Roberts, and B. Luskin,* Geophysics, *v. 24, 1959.)* Bottom: *Reflection profile in Vineyard Sound, Massachusetts, showing younger sediments smoothing the irregular surface of the older, somewhat disturbed, beds beneath. (After J. B. Hersey, in* The Sea, *Interscience Publishers, New York, 1963.)*

which the precision profiler shows to lie in strata about parallel to the slope. Locally the continuity of these beds is broken by faulting or slumping.

Sediments of the continental rise

Recent studies by coring and geophysical methods (Chapter 19) reveal the profound influence of deep ocean currents on sedimentation. A southward-trending deep current sweeps along the continental rise bordering the slope off the east coast of the United States and Canada. In many places it lies directly beneath the Gulf Stream and it carries considerable fine clay and silt, as shown by photometric measurements of light absorption. The swiftest part of the current follows the base of the continental slope, and, apparently because of the greater volume of sediment passing a given section in a unit of time, brings more mud, and deposits more along this belt than farther offshore, as

shown by thickness measurements from explosion seismology. This thickening toward the base of the slope is doubtless responsible for the gentle seaward slope of the continental rise (Fig. 17–23).

Even the relatively feeble movement of the Antarctic Bottom water, moving northward around the Bermuda Islands, seems to be governing the deposition of clay and silt on the Bermuda Rise.

Sediments of the Atlantic abyssal plains

Coring of the bottom sediments of the Atlantic abyssal plain to the west of the Mid-Atlantic Ridge has shown thin graded beds, averaging considerably coarser than the sediments of the continental rise. Inasmuch as similar graded beds were found at the surface soon after the great turbidity current from the Grand Banks had swept out onto the abyssal plain, it seems safe to interpret them as due to comparable turbidity currents over a long span of time. Though the Grand Banks current was not confined to submarine canyons, the observed motion of coarse sediments down these, the common existence of low cones at their lower ends, and the pattern of levees across these cones, strongly suggest that most such turbidities were fed onto the ocean floor from submarine canyons. The sedimentation pattern of the Atlantic off the east coast of the United States seems to be much as diagrammed in Figure 17–23.

Sediments of the Indonesian seas

The sediments of the Indonesian Seas are of unusual interest because, as we noted in Chapter 8, many geologists think this is a region of active mountain-making.

The submarine topography of the Indonesian area is highly irregular: it contains barely submerged alluvial plains like that beneath the Java Sea (Chapter 8), partly to completely submerged mountain ridges, and narrow basins such as the Sulu, Flores, Celebes, and Banda Seas, all of which are more than 3 miles deep. More than fifty volcanoes have been active in the region since 1600.

Although the sediments have been studied only in reconnaissance, they have proved most instructive.

When Tamboro, east of Java, erupted violently in 1815 (Chapter 18); the ash was widely strewn by the winds—10 inches fell at a distance of 240 miles. This ash is readily recognized by its distinctive minerals and textures. That benthic organisms effectively mix sediments is shown by the presence of characteristic ash particles at the very surface of the bottom mud more than a century after the eruption—not only in areas of slow deposition but even near the mouths of muddy streams whose annual load of mud should have buried it deeply. Organisms have mixed it with terrestrial clays through several feet of sediment.

Elsewhere in the Indonesian seas, ridge tops at depths of several thousand feet are bare rock, yet fine mud is found at much shallower depths in protected places. Terrigenous mud was cored 300 miles from the nearest land and at depths of 16,000 feet; volcanic muds were found at still greater depths and distances from shore. In the Philippine Trench, 50 miles east of Mindanao,

FIGURE 17–23   *Diagrammatic section of the sedimentation pattern off the east coast of the United States. (Greatly modified from B. C. Heezen, C. D. Hollister, and W. F. Ruddiman, Science, v. 152, p. 502–508, 22 April 1966. Copyright 1966 by the American Association for the Advancement of Science.)*

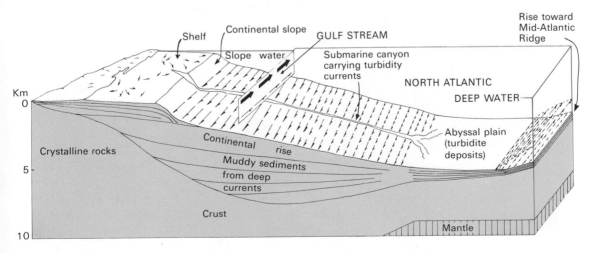

FIGURE 17–24
Directional structures on bedding surfaces of sandstone beds of the Haymond Formation (Pennsylvanian) near Marathon, Texas. Note ripple marks trending from upper right to lower left near center of picture. This is at right angles to the lineation in the direction of current flow—from upper left to lower right—seen on several bedding surfaces. (Photo by Earle F. McBride, University of Texas.)

FIGURE 17–25   *Large boulder at the base of a submarine slide, showing how the soft sediment beneath was squeezed and deformed by the sudden load while still unconsolidated. Tesnus Formation (Mississippian and Pennsylvanian), Marathon region, Texas. (Photo by Alan Thomsen, Shell Oil Company, Houston, Texas.)*

Table 17–2 **Theoretical dispersal of sedimentary particles by currents**

Diameter of particle, in mm	Rate of settling in water at 27° C, in cm per hr	Distances a particle would be transported by a 1 cm-per-hr current while the particle sinks 1000 m,	
		in km	in miles
0.100 (fine sand)	2000	1.8	1.1
0.030 (coarse silt)	180	20	12
0.005 (fine silt)	5	720	430
0.001 (clay)	0.2	18,000	11,000

SOURCE: After Neeb.

silty and clayey sediments were dredged from depths of 33,000 feet. These contain little sand but many larger fragments of metamorphic rock like that exposed on Mindanao. The travel of these coarse sediments across 50 miles of sea floor and to such depths suggests submarine sliding and strong currents that sweep the deep ridges bare, winnow out the fine material, and waft it into quiet basins or off the continental slope. Current speeds as great as one mile an hour at 600 feet and $1/14$ mile an hour at 6500 feet were measured by the *Snellius* on a ridge between two basins.

Some of the coarse sediments now at great depths in this area of high relief have doubtless slid from steep submarine slopes, exposing bare rock at their source and bringing coarse debris to areas whose sediments are normally finer. Many ancient rocks show evidence of such sliding in the mud-galls, load-casts, plastic overfolds, grooved bedding (Fig. 17–24), and sandstone dikes they contain: examples are the Silurian of parts of Wales; the Carboniferous of Texas (Fig. 17–25); the Jurassic of Nevada; the Tertiary of Peru, Ecuador, Italy, Switzerland, and southern California (Fig. 17–6,B). Where the deposition of this type of sediment was soon followed by mountain building (Chapter 20) the interbedded sandstones and shales are called **flysch deposits** (Figs. 17–4, 17–6,B, 17–10, 17–24). They will be further discussed later in this book.

Settling of marine clays

Experiments show that quartz grains of various sizes settle in water at the speeds indicated in Table 17–2. Flakes of clay—with more surface area for a particle of the same mass—settle more slowly. Miss Neeb, a Dutch geologist who studied the *Snellius* collections, computed the distance a current moving only one centimeter per second ($1/44$ mile per hour) would carry quartz grains of different sizes during the time required for them to sink 1000 meters (3300 feet). She assumed laminar flow as the particle sinks, but, of course, turbulence would prolong the time of sinking, and the greater viscosity and density of the water in the cold oceanic depths would slow the particles.

Though the computations neglect flocculation of the clay, which increases deposition, we see that fine silts and clays can be carried almost any distance by currents as strong as those measured, not only in Indonesia but in the Atlantic and Pacific as well. In fact careful studies indicate that the average clay particle may take several centuries to sink to the abyssal floor. Clay settling in a deep marine basin may thus be from a much more distant source than coarser particles in the sediment. Cores from the deep eastern Pacific, collected by the Swedish Deep Sea Expedition of 1947–1948 contain much clay, though the area is more than 2000 miles from the nearest land. Several geologists have

Table 17–3 **Rates of pelagic clay accumulation**

Ocean Area	Rate, in millimeters per thousand years
North Pacific	4 to 7 (Recent)
Pacific, off Mexico	11 (Recent)
Atlantic Continental Rise off Florida	50 to 500 (Recent)
Caribbean southwest of Hispaniola	28 (Pleistocene and Recent)
Argentine Basin	17 to 34 (Recent)
Argentine Basin	60 to 110 (Late Glacial)
Southeastern Pacific	80

pointed out that if the clays are settling far from their sources they should be doing so almost uniformly all over the sea floor in areas of the same depth. Both silica and calcium carbonate are organic deposits that vary with latitude and other geographic factors, but the amount of clay in a deep-sea core should be a measure of the time of its accumulation. Radiometric dating of materials at different depths in deep-sea cores suggests that this—at first plausible—generalization has little merit, doubtless because it neglects the fact that fast currents bring much greater volumes of sediment over a given area than do slow currents of the same sediment content (Fig. 17–23). Some radiometrically measured rates of clay accumulation in the deep sea are given in Table 17–3. It should be noted that several students of marine sedimentation are convinced that not all the clay in deep-sea sediments is detrital; despite its low solubility, they think that some of the Al_2O_3 of the deep-sea clay was in solution in the ocean water and was precipitated in the presence of silica brought in organically.

Still another result of the Indonesian studies is noteworthy. The drowned river plain of the Java Sea (Fig. 8–16) hardly exceeds 200 feet in depth. Bottom muds near Java are chiefly volcanic debris from the nearby island, but farther north the sediments are mainly coarse quartz sand evidently derived from the deeply weathered granite of Borneo and other northerly islands. These coarse sands, are, however, separated from the islands by a belt of much finer, and presumably younger, quartzose sands. Thus they must be either river or residual sands, from the old land surface, that have been little disturbed by the sea that rose after the Pleistocene glaciers melted, a situation such as we inferred for the continental shelf off New England.

COMPARISON OF ANCIENT AND MODERN OFFSHORE SEDIMENTS

At present very little silt and clay is coming to rest on the continental shelves except near such muddy streams as the Hoang Ho, the Mississippi, the Orinoco, and the Nile. Elsewhere clay seems to remain suspended until it drops over the shelf edge into a quiet basin or onto the ocean floor. In many places even sand is swept along by currents to a deep basin. Beyond the immediate beach zone, at least in areas of slow deposition, the grain size of the sediment may or may not diminish regularly with distance from the shore; it is clearly more closely related to the local topography and thus to the current pattern.

The most widespread ancient sediments of Cambrian and younger ages are marine shales, clays, and mudstones, generally containing fossils of shallow-water organisms.

Many can be traced laterally into sandstones in one direction and into limestones in the other, and these rocks also contain fossils of the shallow benthic association. Similar associations among modern sediments are found off the coast of northern Australia, in the Gulf of Mexico, in the southern Carribbean, the Yellow Sea, the South China Sea, and the Persian Gulf. But we know of few marine environments where muds and clays are accumulating in shallow water over great areas, although geologic mapping shows inescapably that they did so accumulate at many times in the geologic past. Perhaps we have fewer shallow seas now than was normal in the geologic past. The Yellow Sea, for example, is smaller but otherwise similar to the huge expanse of shallow water, with a muddy bottom, that in Cretaceous time must have covered the interior of North America from the Arctic to the Gulf of Mexico, and from the present Mississippi-Hudson Bay embayments to the interior of the Rockies. Pending further studies of marine sediments now forming, therefore, our inferences about the conditions under which such huge shale bodies as the North American Cretaceous were formed must rest in large part on the intrinsic character of the rocks and their fossils, rather than upon comparison with any deposits of similar size forming today.

It is easy to infer from the obvious turbidity-current deposits in the Atlantic abyssal plain, that this is an environment in which interbedded turbidite and abyssal clay deposits analogous to those of the Tesnus and Haymond Formations of Texas are forming (Figs. 17–4, 17–10, 17–12, 17–24, 17–25). In these formations graded-bedded sandstones, some with submarine slide interruptions, alternate with clay of probable pelagic origin. The difficulty with this analogy is that, as we shall see in Chapter 20, mountains seem nowhere to have arisen from the deposits of an abyssal plain, but everywhere from more restricted basins of deposition, perhaps more

like the Indonesian basins. Thus, though the abyssal plain deposits of the Atlantic may, indeed, be similar in mineralogy and grain size to many rocks exposed in the mountains, they are almost certainly not to be considered flysch, for that term carries the implication that deposition is almost immediately followed by mountain building. If flysch is being deposited now it must be in the basins of the Indonesian arc or in areas of comparably active crustal deformation.

A few dominantly shaly formations, notably the Repetto Formation (Pliocene) of California, and some others in Timor, Cuba, and elsewhere, contain fossils that indicate water depths of several thousand feet, as do those in basins off the coast of California and in Indonesia. The Repetto basin ultimately filled with sediment, dumped into it from the adjacent higher land. Deposits of the organic oozes and red clay characteristic of the really deep sea, which we describe in the next section, seem exceedingly rare on the continents, although some cherts may represent siliceous ooze and some red shales may possibly represent the deep-sea clay of narrow basins.

Pelagic sediments

Pelagic, or deep-sea sediments cover nearly three-quarters of the ocean bottom, as the *Challenger* discovered. They are of four main varieties, as shown by dredging, distributed in the pattern generalized in Figure 17–26. In addition there are considerable areas of pyroclastic deposits, but their distribution is not yet well known, except in broad outline. Calcareous ooze is most widespread; land-derived sediments are next most abundant, having been widely strewn by turbidity currents and oceanic circulation; siliceous oozes are less in total amount, but locally the most abundant; and the minor sediments formed on the sea floor by precipitation from solution dominate only where

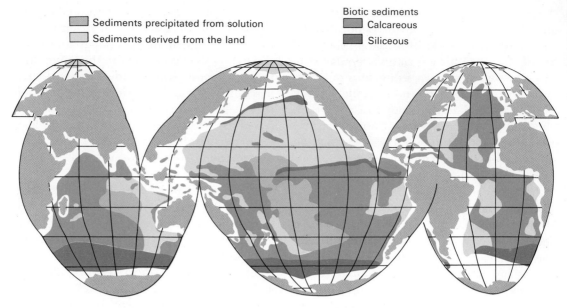

☐ Sediments precipitated from solution
☐ Sediments derived from the land

Biotic sediments
☐ Calcareous
☐ Siliceous

FIGURE 17–26   *Areal distribution of the pelagic sediments. Sediments whose major components have been formed from ions in solution in sea water are less abundant than the sediments derived from the continents. Each variety contains some components characteristic of some of the others. The scale prohibits showing many small areas of distinctive character within broader regions of another variety. (After G. Arrhenius, in* The Sea, *Interscience Publishers, New York, 1963. Use of Goode's interrupted homalosine equal area projection by permission of University of Chicago Press, copyright by the University of Chicago.)*

FIGURE 17–27
Foraminiferal ooze dredged from 450 meters off Central America; enlarged about 15 times. (Courtesy of Patsy J. Smith, U.S. Geological Survey.)

sedimentation of other types is extremely slow—generally on current-swept hills on the ocean floor.

CALCAREOUS OOZE. Calcareous ooze (Fig. 17–27) covers most of the floor of the western Indian Ocean, the Mid-Atlantic Ocean, and much of the equatorial and southern Pacific Ocean. It consists primarily of the calcium carbonate shells of planktonic organisms, chiefly Foraminifera, and coccoliths (calcareous algae), but with lesser amounts of clay, siliceous shells, minute fragments from the disintegration of meteorites in their travel through the air, and minerals crystallized from the ocean waters. Calcareous ooze, the shallowest of the pelagic sediments, seems to be forming where skeletons of calcareous plankton rain down on the ocean floor so abundantly as to mask the terrigenous sediments and oceanic precipitates that are also settling; also faster than the cold deep water can dissolve the minute limy shells.

RED CLAY.   Red clay covers most of the very deep ocean floor. Much is too fine grained to be identified microscopically, but X-ray study has shown the chief minerals to be quartz, mica, several kinds of clay minerals, chlorite, and several of the hydrous aluminum silicate minerals of the zeolite group, all generally stained red by iron rust. Despite the name, not all the "red clay" is really red; some is pinkish and some gray. The oxidation of the iron is due to the fact that the abyssal waters are generally quite rich in oxygen dissolved in the stormy seas at high latitudes where the bottom water sank. Although some of the clay and zeolite minerals are thought to form in place, from ions in solution in the water, most of the pelagic mud was derived as clastic material from the continents—a source consistent with what is known of settling velocities of such fine materials. In fact, though there are no quartz-bearing rocks on the oceanic islands, more than a fourth of the mud of the North Pacific is composed of quartz grains, presumably dropped out of winds in the upper atmosphere as the pattern of distribution does not correspond to either winds of the lower atmosphere or to ocean currents.

Volcanic ash was once considered the chief source of red clay. It contributes, of course, but does not appear to be an adequate source for the great bulk of the material. The clay mineral, kaolinite, seems never to form except on land, whereas chlorite seems to form both in the sea and on land. The distribution of the two minerals in the finest grained oceanic muds offers a strong argument for the dominantly continental source of the pelagic muds, for kaolinite is far more abundant in the equatorial Atlantic (into which many of the greatest rivers empty) than it is either to north or south (Fig. 17–28). Chlorite, abundant in high-latitude soils, also abounds in high-latitude pelagic sediments of this ocean.

The red clays contain some organisms like those in both the calcareous and siliceous oozes and, in fact, intergrade with both these pelagic varieties. Red clay predominates either where calcareous plankton is sparse (in high latitudes) or where the shells of such organisms must sink through vast depths. In sinking, the shells are exposed to solution by waters richer and richer in carbon dioxide produced by the decomposition of organic matter and the metabolism of sea life; at great depths only the thickest shells, or none at all, remain.

SILICEOUS OOZES.   Siliceous oozes are restricted to relatively narrow strips in the North Pacific and equatorial Pacific and to a somewhat broader band in all the southern oceans. There are two varieties: that in the equatorial belt is composed chiefly of the remains of Radiolaria, minute single-celled animals, and that in high latitudes consists chiefly of the shells of single-celled plants, the diatoms. Radiolaria flourish in the nutritous water of the equatorial upwelling, rich in phosphorus and other elements derived from the decay of sinking organisms. The rising water is also cold and rich in carbon dioxide so that most limy shells—which also abound at the surface along with the Radiolaria—dissolve before sinking to the bottom. The Radiolaria thus accumulate so abundantly as to mask other constituents of the ooze. In high latitudes the mixing of deep water with cold surface water and the excessive turbulence due to the prevailing westerlies furnish abundant food for diatoms, which there dominate the plankton.

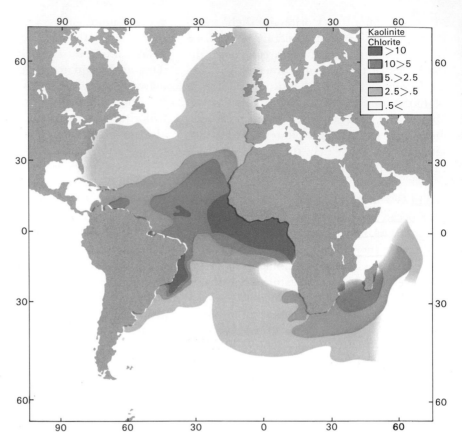

FIGURE 17–28   *Ratio of kaolinite to chlorite in the pelagic sediments of the Atlantic Ocean, as inferred from X-ray studies of the grains less than .002 millimeters in diameter. (Modified from P. E. Biscaye,* Geological Society of America Bulletin, *1965.)*

SEDIMENTS PRECIPITATED FROM SOLUTION. Sediments precipitated from solution are very unevenly distributed in nearly all depths of the sea, but are prominent in topographic positions unfavorable to the accumulation of other sediments.

The most conspicuous are the manganese nodules, which consist largely of oxides and hydrated oxides of manganese, with iron and silica. These are very unevenly strewn over the sea floor, in places practically forming a carpet, elsewhere widely scattered. Enthusiastic oceanographers sometimes contend that these nodules are potential ores of manganese, but it is difficult to see them soon in economic competition with the rich ores of Brazil, South Africa, India, and the USSR. The manganese of these nodules is generally attributed to submarine springs associated with volcanism, but underwater alteration of submarine volcanic rocks may play a more important role. It has already been pointed out that some oceanographers regard some of the pelagic clay as chemical precipitates from the sea water.

Pelagic sediments in the geologic record

Claystones so similar to pelagic red clays (fine grained, iron rich, containing manganese nodules and fragmental fossil Foraminifera and Radiolaria) that some geologists regard them as true deep-sea deposits, have been found in the Alps, in Barbados (West Indies), and Timor (Indonesia). The rocks are so closely associated with coarse sandstone generally considered of shallow-water origin that a deep-sea setting has been questioned repeatedly. The recognition that the coarse clastics might be turbidity-current deposits has favored the deep-sea origin, though it still remains difficult to account for either the lack of heavy terrigenous sedimentation, if the depositional habitat was a narrow basin such as those of the Indonesian seas, or for the development of a mountain range far offshore of a continent (Chapter 20).

The Cretaceous chalk of England and France was once thought to be a consolidated deep-sea ooze, but its fossils are such as lived in littoral waters and most students now think it was deposited in clear water not more than a few hundred feet deep. The Cretaceous rocks of the Caspian region include thick chalks containing coccoliths, like some of those in the calcareous oozes, associated with narrow zones of terrigenous (blue-mud) shales not unlike some deep-sea muds. Shallow-water fossils have not been found. Whether or not these particular beds represent a fossil deep-sea ooze—and geophysical arguments against the possibility are strong (Chapters 19 and 20)—it seems that true pelagic rocks are extremely rare on the continents.

DEPOSITION OF LIMESTONE AND DOLOMITE

Limestones and dolomites make up about 20 percent of the sedimentary rocks. Today, as we have just noted, calcareous ooze covers nearly half the ocean bottom. The pelagic oozes, however, do not resemble most limestones of the continents: most limestones were formed in shallow water as is shown by the coarse clastic texture of some, by the cross-bedding and other indicators of current action of others, and by the shallow-water fossils of nearly all. Among modern shallow-water sediments we find many analogues of these limestones, but few are the modern dolomites compared to the abundant dolomites of the geologic column.

Chemical conditions affecting carbonate deposition

Calcite is among the most soluble of common minerals. Though only slowly soluble in pure water, it dissolves readily in the presence of carbon dioxide (Chapter 4). The solubility of calcium carbonate in sea water is difficult to determine because of the interference of many other ions, and chemists disagree over whether normal sea water is or is not saturated with calcium carbonate at 68°F. All, however, agree that warming sea water, thereby decreasing its carbon dioxide content and, usually, increasing its salinity, favors precipitation of calcium carbonate, whereas decomposition of organic matter, which produces carbon dioxide, increases the solubility. As we have seen, in deep ocean waters calcite shells are commonly dissolved, or at least etched by solution; obviously, these waters are undersaturated.

Life processes modify the carbon dioxide content of the sea and so affect deposition and solution of carbonate. Many organisms secrete shells of calcite and aragonite (a mineral of the same composition but of different crystal form). Photosynthesis by marine plants extracts carbon dioxide from the water, so diminishing the solubility of calcium carbonate that, in the littoral zone of the warm tropical seas the water is practically saturated. Over the shallow Bahama Banks several processes unite to lower the solubility: as water flows over the banks to compensate for the high evaporation, it is warmed, lowering its carbon dioxide content. Photosynthesis by flourishing plants also withdraws CO_2. The abundant bacteria in these shallow carbonate muds include species that combine

FIGURE 17–29   *Fossil reef in the Ellenburger Limestone (Late Cambrian–Early Ordovician), Central Mineral Region, Texas. (Photo by Preston E. Cloud, Jr., University of California, Los Angeles.)*

nitrogen with hydrogen to produce ammonia. Ammonia is weakly alkaline and serves to neutralize some of the free hydrogen ions in the solution, thereby further favoring precipitation of calcium carbonate. (Calcium carbonate is much more soluble in acid than in neutral or alkaline water). These cooperating processes thus bring about saturation, and fine needles of calcium carbonate separate out and settle to the bottom, there to accumulate as limy muds. Of course, these muds also contain fossil remains of the microorganisms from the shallow water above. It seems likely that many fine-grained limestones of the geologic past were formed in

settings similar to this; some, indeed have definite reef forms (Figs. 17–3, 17–29).

Many lime-secreting plants and animals flourish in the littoral zone of the tropical seas. Shells, whole or in fragments, make up many beaches and accumulate in shallow water to be cemented into limestone. Many ancient limestones are also made of fossil fragments and presumably formed in like manner. Calcite recrystallizes so readily in warm water that many microscopic textural features are partly corroded; doubtless many limestones that now show no obvious organic fragments were nevertheless originally composed of shell fragments.

Dolomites

Dolomite, the carbonate of both calcium and magnesium, presents one of the great geologic enigmas. Very few organisms secrete shells with an appreciable content of magnesium carbonate, and in the few that do, the ratio of magnesium carbonate to calcium carbonate falls far short of that in dolomite, in which it is nearly 1 to 1. Nor is inorganic dolomite being deposited in the present seas. Yet dolomite, though extremely rare among Tertiary rocks, is both abundant and widespread among older strata, Precambrian through Mesozoic. Does the Principle of Uniformitarianism fail us here?

Around certain igneous intrusions large volumes of limestone have been altered to dolomite, as shown by their lateral passage, either gradual or abrupt, into unaltered limestone. This dolomite shows definite association with faults and fissures and is clearly a secondary product of the action of ascending hot solutions upon a pre-existing limestone body. No such origin is possible for the great sheets of early Paleozoic dolomite that can be traced for scores or even hundreds of miles, some of them everywhere interbedded with unaltered limestone and shale.

Although no dolomite is being deposited in the present seas, so far as known, there are several places where limestone is being altered to dolomite following its deposition. In the Netherlands West Indies, on Andros Island in the Bahamas, and on wide mud flats on the shores of the Persian Gulf, recent studies have shown that dolomite is forming as a replacement of older aragonite and calcite muds. In each place the topographic setting is similar: the mud flats are just above normal high tide, covered only when exceptional spring tides and onshore winds are favorable. These localities are all in the tropics, with warm climates and high evaporation rates. Experiments in chemical laboratories and field observations in these settings agree in showing that when sea water is evaporated, the first mineral to reach saturation in the increasingly saline remaining water—the bittern—is calcite. After calcite has been precipitating for some time, gypsum ($CaSO_4 \cdot H_2O$) also begins to crystallize. The precipitation of both these calcium-bearing minerals allows the solution to become much enriched with magnesium as compared with calcium. In normal sea water the ratio of magnesium to calcium is about 3 to 1 (Appendix 4, Table 4); considerable evaporation on these mud flats eventually produces a bittern in which the ratio is 30 or 40 to 1—a highly concentrated, magnesium-rich solution. The density of the bittern is high, and it sinks into the underlying mud, there replacing about half of the calcium ions in the carbonate with magnesium ions and thus producing a dolomite with some calcite in solid solution within it. It seems that we here have modern examples that go far to explain the very common association of dolomite with beds of evaporite such as salt, gypsum, or anhydrite.

These examples do not, however, explain the very great deposits of dolomite that are not associated with evaporites, and that, for many miles, are interbedded with quite undolomitized limestone. This aspect of the dolomite problem has puzzled geologists for more than a century. In 1904 the Royal Society Expedition to investigate the atoll problem in the Southwest Pacific drilled a core well on the atoll of Funafuti, in the Ellice Islands. All the material in the well (1200 feet deep) was coral reef rock like that at the surface; it contained coral heads, algal deposits, and shells of many reef-dwelling animals. Although the structures in the reef rock were well preserved, the material at depth was much richer in magnesium than that near the surface, and below about 630 feet was mostly dolomite. It was inferred that part of the calcium in the fossil material had been replaced by magnesium, perhaps from the sea water which, of course, thoroughly soaked the atoll; it was also suggested that the replacement was perhaps from magnesium-rich solutions concentrated by evaporation in the central lagoon of the atoll. Whatever the source of the magnesium, the replacement was very irregular, and undoubtedly due to local conditions, for a hole drilled to 2200 feet on Bikini atoll found neither dolomite nor any significant increase with depth in the magnesium content of the limestone. The lowest beds reached by drilling on Bikini are of Miocene age so the rocks must have remained in virtually continuous contact with sea water for more than 15 m.y. We are thus left with no satisfactory theory for the origin of the extensive dolomites not associated with evaporites. It is true, however, that most of these strata show signs of shallow-water origin, making plausible some former surficial concentrations of magnesium-rich bitterns, even though the gypsum that may originally have been associated with them was later dissolved.

STRATIGRAPHIC SYNTHESES

The Principle of Uniformitarianism is a basic key to an understanding of the past. Were we able to interpret the environmental conditions of each formation and those of nearby correlatives we could construct a segment of ancient geography. The tracing of such successive ancient geographies constitutes the task of **historical geology,** most of which is beyond the scope of this book, but we illustrate the reasoning behind it by three examples, applying some of the data given about environments of deposition in this and preceding chapters to sedimentary rock assemblages. Many economic mineral deposits are limited to specific geologic settings. An understanding of the environment of their origin is often necessary for their intel-

ligent exploitation—the Key to the Past may unlock the door, not only to scientific understanding, but to wealth as well.

The Permian Basin of the American southwest

Permian rocks are widely exposed over the "Permian Basin" of western Texas and southeastern New Mexico—a huge area, rich in petroleum, natural gas, and potash salts. Hundreds of geologists over the past fifty years have reconstructed the Permian geography, aided by many thousand wells and excellent outcrops in this barren region. These studies are summarized in the map of Permian geography of Figure 17–30. The weakly stippled area is approximately the site of the present Delaware Mountains and the Delaware Basin to their east. The Mid-Permian rocks are well exposed in the mountains but are in the subsurface of the basin, where, however, they are cut by many wells and thus known to be fine-grained sandstone and interbedded very dense limestone. The even lamination of both rocks suggests deposition in quiet water. On all sides except the south this sandstone area is bordered by thick, massive beds of limestone, into which the thin limestones of the basin area can be seen to interfinger. Near the zone of interfingering are huge beds of breccia composed of the same kind of highly organic limestone that makes up the thick massive strata. The breccias are at the foot of long sloping layers that rise at angles of 10° to 30° from the level of the thin-bedded limestones for several hundred feet before flattening in dip and merging into thin-bedded, well-laminated limestone, which forms a flat bench nearly surrounding the basin. These massive beds are full of fossils and extend as much as 2500 feet below the topmost of the laminated limestones. These relations are interpreted as follows: the thick massive organic-rich beds constitute a fossil reef that grew on a gently sloping bottom. The breccias are relics of storm-broken reef that rolled down the reef front into the basin, whose thin sandstones and limestones are deep-water strata. The upper set of flat-lying limestones was formed in back-reef quiet-water lagoons (Fig. 17–31). Thus the high sloping curve of the massive reef limestone is considered an original feature of the growing reef, and the amount of the rise is a rough measure of the difference in depth of basin and back-reef lagoons. If so, the difference—1200 feet—indicates that the basin deposits were formed at a depth of about 200 fathoms.

FIGURE 17–30   *The paleogeography of part of Middle Permian time in western Texas and New Mexico. (After P. B. King, 1942, with permission of the American Association of Petroleum Geologists.)*

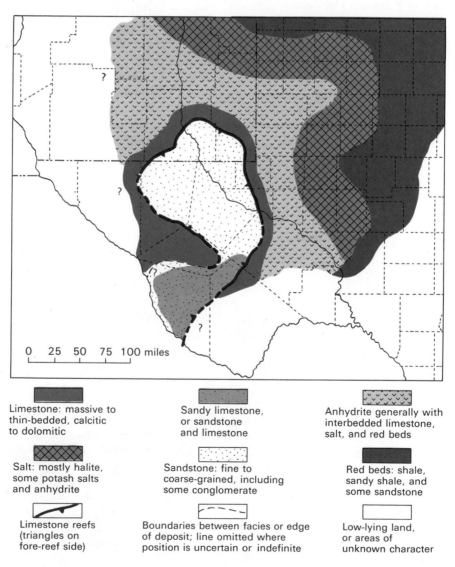

Limestone: massive to thin-bedded, calcitic to dolomitic

Sandy limestone, or sandstone and limestone

Anhydrite generally with interbedded limestone, salt, and red beds

Salt: mostly halite, some potash salts and anhydrite

Sandstone: fine to coarse-grained, including some conglomerate

Red beds: shale, sandy shale, and some sandstone

Limestone reefs (triangles on fore-reef side)

Boundaries between facies or edge of deposit; line omitted where position is uncertain or indefinite

Low-lying land, or areas of unknown character

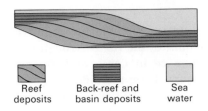

Reef deposits   Back-reef and basin deposits   Sea water

FIGURE 17–31
The relation between reef, back-reef, and basin deposits as interpreted for the Middle Permian rocks of the Permian Basin. (After P. B. King, 1942, with Permission of the American Association of Petroleum Geologists.)

Many corollaries of this interpretation tend to corroborate it: If the reef, whose most conspicuous outcrop is Guadalupe Peak (Fig. 17–32), was a fringing reef bordering the ancient land that nearly surrounded the basin, it explains the fact that to the northwest, north and northeast the back reef limestones in both surface and subsurface become poorer and poorer in fossils and interfinger with beds of anhydrite, salt, and red shale, as might be expected on a low-lying coastal plain in an arid to semiarid climate. Still farther north, in the Texas and Oklahoma Panhandles and northern New Mexico, the limestones give way to red sandstones and shales containing reptilian fossils. These are clearly stream deposits of a semiarid climate. Southward, relations are obscured by overlying Cretaceous rocks but well records suggest that the sand of the deep basin deposits within the reef-rimmed basin was derived from land in what is now the Big Bend country of Trans-Pecos Texas.

Interpretation of this ancient geography has proved to be of the highest economic importance. The highly porous reef limestones are, in some areas, prolific reservoirs of petroleum; the salt deposits are locally rich in potash salts, valuable for fertilizer and chemicals. Understanding the relations and geo-

FIGURE 17–32   *The great reef deposit of Guadalupe Peak, Texas. Oblique aerial view of El Capitan and Guadalupe Peak from the south. Southern Guadalupe Mountains, Culberson County, Texas. (Photo by U.S. Army Air Force, 1938.)*

graphic trends of the several formations is the objective of a fascinating detective game whose prizes have been vast wealth as well as knowledge.

Devonian geography of western Europe

Prominent in the history of geology is the Old Red Sandstone of northern England and Scotland. The British geologist Hugh Miller, a century ago, attracted thousands of amateurs to geology by his reconstructions of the conditions of origin of this formation. As the name implies, the Old Red is chiefly made up of sandstone stained red by iron rust, composed of quartz, much relatively unaltered feldspar, poorly sorted, and with lenses of coarse boulder conglomerate and breccia alongside wedges of fine silt and clay partings. Some of the clay beds contain cubical casts that resemble salt crystals in form. In these and nearby beds many fish skeletons are preserved. These fish had lung-like breathing organs, and are inferred to have resembled the so-called lungfish of modern Australia, which can survive long droughts by burying themselves in moist mud. Also, some of the complexly cross-bedded sandstone with sparse faceted pebbles recalls modern dune sands with desert pavements. Altogether, the current bedding of the coarser layers, the dominance of mechanical over chemical weathering in the source area, the evidence of wind work, of intermittent lakes or playas in which salt was sometimes crystalized, all seem to compel the conclusion that the Old Red is a desert deposit on an old Devonian continent. It records conditions like those that prevail today in the Mohave Desert or in western China.

To the south, in northern Devonshire, a few beds of this typical red sandstone are interlayered with coarse sandstone, shale, and thin limestone that contain marine fossils; still farther south the red sandstone disappears by lensing out into a succession of marine shale and fossiliferous limestone. This

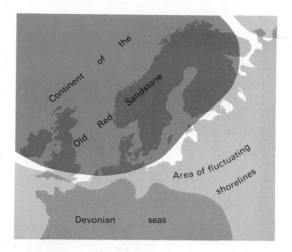

FIGURE 17–33
The Old Red Continent and its bordering seas. (After Maurice Gignoux, Stratigraphic Geology, *W. H. Freeman and Company, San Francisco. Copyright 1955.)*

is the type area of the Devonian System, and one of the early triumphs of systematic stratigraphic studies was the recognition that these marine beds correlate with the rocks of arid continental origin—the Old Red Sandstone —farther north. Between them there must have been a shoreline; the lenses of interfingering red terrestrial sandstone and gray marine rocks show that its position fluctuated from time to time across a belt some scores of miles wide.

The Old Red Sandstone is found in the Hebrides, and similar rocks, with the same kinds of fish and plant fossils, are also present in southern Norway. In the Ardennes of Belgium, in Czechoslovakia and in Poland interfingering marine and continental Devonian rocks like those of Britain are also well known; they extend across the Leningrad region to the White Sea. In the Alps to the south, the Devonian strata are wholly marine (Fig. 17–33). Across the Atlantic, the Devonian rocks of New Brunswick strongly resemble the Old Red Sandstone; to the northwest they interfinger with marine beds just south of the St. Lawrence estuary. The Catskill Formation of New York (Upper Devonian), several thousand feet thick, consists of similar red sandstones and shales with primitive amphibian, fish, and plant fossils. West of the Catskills these beds interfinger with black marine shales and eventually disappear in a wholly marine section. Rocks resembling the Old Red in composition, color, and faunas are also present in parts of Green-land. Many geologists think that these relations mean that a Devonian continent extended from the White Sea to New Brunswick, across the present site of the North Atlantic, but the same evidence can be taken to show general aridity of distinctly separated lands bordering the sea. So much of the pertinent record is lost, by erosion or by burial beneath younger rocks or the sea, that absolute proof of either hypothesis is lacking.

FIGURE 17–34   *An old mudflow, part of the San Onofre Breccia. (Photo by Wright M. Pierce.)*

A Miocene geography in California

Another ancient geography inferred from stratigraphy is that of the San Joaquin Hills southeast of Los Angeles, California. A large area here is underlain by a thick diatomaceous shale, the Monterey Shale, which contains, besides the myriads of diatoms, many Foraminifera and in some sandy interbeds, fossil mollusks that establish its marine origin. The very thin and evenly laminated strata testify to either deep water or a sheltered position, for they show little or no sign of bottom disturbance, either by animal burrowing or waves. The shales pass northeastward into thick, poorly sorted sandstones containing material that might have been derived from older granitic rocks nearby to the north and east. A few of these coarser beds extend well out into the diatomaceous shale area and suggest by their molluskan fossils and cross-bedding, that they are old beach deposits. Some interfinger, near the center of the hills, with a very unusual rock,

the San Onofre Breccia, made up almost wholly of the debris of glaucophane schist and related metamorphic rocks. (Glaucophane is an amphibole of very distinctive optical properties, readily recognized under the microscope.) In the breccia are great boulders and angular blocks many feet across (Fig. 17–34). Nearly all the recognizable fragments are of glaucophane schist, and the interstices are filled with a glaucophane-rich silt. Although the breccia interfingers with marine rocks toward its northeastern limits, it does not itself contain marine fossils. It is poorly, or not at all, sorted and though locally bedded, most of it is massive. Much of it seems to be mudflow breccia, perhaps a gigantic debris flow that glided out into a protected seaway.

A most significant feature of the breccia is the composition of its materials. To the east and northeast there are no glaucophane schists (and as noted, they are readily recognized) closer than Wales, Corsica, and the Alps, but such rock is well exposed to the

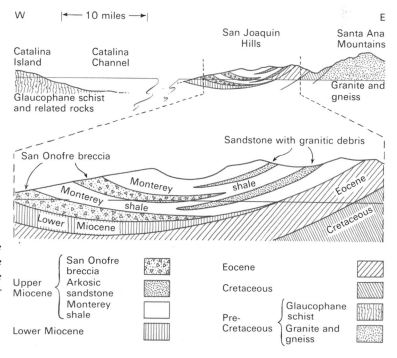

FIGURE 17–35
Map and sections showing the relations of the San Onofre Breccia to the Monterey Shale of southern California. (After A. O. Woodford.)

west on Palos Verdes Peninsula and, across an arm of the Pacific, on Catalina Island. The San Onofre Breccia unquestionably came from a land mass to the southwest that is now almost wholly buried beneath the ocean (Fig. 17–35). In the San Joaquin Hills then, we see deposits of a northwesterly trending depositional trough supplied by sediments from both northeast and southwest. The trough was an arm of the sea, bordered on the southwest by a highland that shed coarse mudflows. Perhaps the climate was semiarid: not only do mudflows suggest this, but there is almost no clay in the diatomaceous shale of the Monterey. Did the pau-

city of streams on a semiarid landscape hamper sorting of debris on the northeast side of the basin as well as on the other? Critical exposures are lacking to evaluate this suggestion.

The former highlands to the southwest are all but buried beneath the Pacific, with only local remnants still visible on the islands. We are not simply dealing here with a Miocene flooding of the continental margin, but with a series of more complex earth movements: some areas rose high above the sea and have since sunk far below, as shown by soundings, while other areas close by went through the opposite movements.

Facts, concepts, terms

Volume of sedimentary rocks
Source of sedimentary rocks
Abundance of different varieties
Factors influencing sediment diversity
    Processes in source area
    Transportation processes
    Depositional processes
Stratification
    Causes of stratification
    Parallel lamination
    Current bedding
    Graded bedding
    Massive bedding
    Textures
    Rounding of sand grains
Terrestrial sediments
    Stream deposits
    Gravel-filled channels; scour-and-fill; current bedding; sorting
    Features of aggrading streams
    Alluvial sediments of fine grain
    Lake deposits
Marine sediments
    Sources
    Fate of the clastic river load
    Fate of the dissolved river load
Realms of marine sedimentation
    The strand zone
        Beaches

Questions

1. Why is the systematic distribution of sediments in lakes not paralleled by that in the ocean?
2. Assuming that turbidity currents build fan-like deposits on the ocean floor at the mouths of submarine canyons, how would you expect the form of such a deposit to differ from that of a normal fan? How would its composition and internal structure differ?
3. Why are dune sands generally better sorted than water-laid sediments of the same average grain size?
4. If relief in the source area is an important factor in sedimentation, how would you expect the marine sediments off California to compare with those off Texas?
5. How would you expect first-cycle sandstones to differ from reworked sandstones?
6. The St. Lawrence carries much more water to the sea than the Colorado. Why does it end in an almost unsedimented estuary whereas the Colorado has been building a huge delta since Pleistocene time?
7. Aside from the temperature control of the life cycle of reef corals, would you expect greater, less, or similar proportions of calcium-carbonate deposits and noncarbonate deposits in arctic or tropical waters? Why?

8. How would you expect graded bedding formed by a steadily weakening current to differ from that formed by settling of a turbid flow?
9. Why does the paucity of clay in the San Onofre Breccia suggest an arid landscape?

Suggested readings

Gignoux, Maurice, *Stratigraphic Geology*. San Francisco: W. H. Freeman and Company, 1955. [Chapter 1.]

Kuenen, P. H., *Marine Geology*. New York: John Wiley and Sons, 1950.

Marr, J. E., *Deposition of the Sedimentary Rocks*. Cambridge: Cambridge University Press, 1929.

Shepard, F. P., *Submarine Geology*. New York: Harper and Bros., 1948.

Society of Economic Paleontologists and Mineralogists, *The Filling of the Marathon Geosyncline*. Publication 64–9, 1964.

18

Igneous Activity and Metamorphism

Igneous rocks, as we saw in Chapter 3, solidify from molten magmas generated deep within the earth. The **volcanic rocks** have been erupted to the surface; the **plutonic rocks** solidify underground and are revealed only when unroofed by erosion or penetrated by wells or mines.

Metamorphic rocks are products of changes, chiefly by recrystallization and plastic flow, in other solid rocks, brought about by heat, pressure, and chemically active fluids; each new association of minerals and textures in such rocks records a fascinating history of events that took place deep within the earth, could we but learn to read it aright.

We begin our study with the easily accessible volcanic rocks. In Chapter 3 we emphasized the dramatic effect of Desmarest's proof that volcanoes were once active in central France, far from any erupting volcano of today; he thereby put an end to Werner's theory of worldwide geologic formations precipitated from a primeval ocean.

VOLCANOES

Volcanoes are mountains or hills (Fig. 18–1) made by materials erupted from the earth's interior through a central vent, or, more commonly, a group of vents and fissures. The material pours forth as liquid **lava** or else is violently ejected as **pyroclastic debris**—fragments of liquid froth, glass shards, and bits of already solid rock. Every active volcano also gives off **volatiles**, chiefly water vapor, and often in astounding amounts. From Vesuvius, in 1906, vast quantities of steam, virtually unaccompanied by lava, roared from the crater as from a gigantic steam boiler. For more than a dozen hours it escaped with enough violence to carry small fragments to heights of hundreds of meters.

FIGURE 18–1   Mount Hood, a composite volcano. (Photo by Oregon State Highway Commission.)

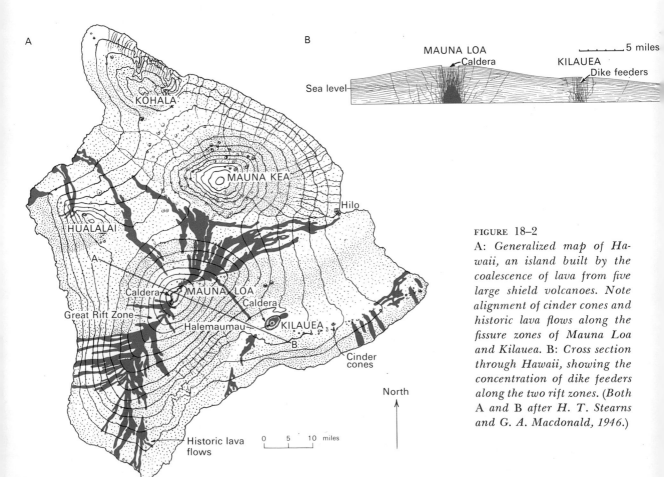

FIGURE 18–2

A: *Generalized map of Hawaii, an island built by the coalescence of lava from five large shield volcanoes. Note alignment of cinder cones and historic lava flows along the fissure zones of Mauna Loa and Kilauea. B: Cross section through Hawaii, showing the concentration of dike feeders along the two rift zones. (Both A and B after H. T. Stearns and G. A. Macdonald, 1946.)*

Shield volcanoes

Shield volcanoes (Fig. 18–2), unlike many others (Fig. 18–1), slope gently, generally 2° to 4° on their lower slopes, steepening to 5° or more near their summits. Thin interlacing streams of lava are their chief components. Some lava wells from the central crater, but most breaks out through numerous fissures on the flanks of the cone (Fig. 18–2). Explosive activity is confined mostly to lava fountains (Fig. 18–3). Most shield volcanoes are composed of basalt, though a few are of andesite. Some contain small bodies of rhyolite or obsidian, either as intrusive masses or as flows and pyroclastics.

At the summit of many shield volcanoes are small cone-shaped **craters,** but others have much larger basins in or near their tops which are called **calderas.** Most calderas are 2 to 9 miles in diameter; craters are smaller, generally less than 2000 feet across. Calderas are steep-walled, flat-floored, and generally contain several small volcanoes within them.

FIGURE 18–3
Lava fountains, 300 feet high, play above the feeding fissure of a flank eruption. Kilauea Volcano, Hawaii, September 23, 1961. (Photo from J. G. Moore, U.S. Geological Survey)

Although calderas tend to be roughly circular or elliptical in gross form, many are very irregular with rhomboidal or squarish indentations in their walls. Craters are formed by the blasting out of material from the volcanic conduit by rising volcanic gases, and it was formerly thought that calderas were similarly formed—the products of gigantic explosions during which the volcano literally "blew its top" and scattered great blocks of broken rock far and wide. Some large explosion pits have indeed been blasted out by mighty explosions, as noted in the discussion of Tamboro and Krakatau volcanoes later in the chapter, but nearly all calderas that have been geologically mapped prove to be due to downfaulting of parts of the volcanic cone. Such collapse may be sudden and catastrophic, caused by withdrawal of support for the upper part of the volcano by draining out of underlying magma during eruptions from fissures or other vents low on the flanks of the cone (as described later in this chapter for Mount Katmai's caldera), or the subsidence may occur slowly and gradually during growth of the volcano by settling of angular fault blocks loosened from time to time during the gradual rise of the underlying magma into innumerable dikes beneath the volcanic edifice (Fig. 18–2,B). In addition to the larger calderas, smaller areas of subsidence called **pit craters,** also punctuate the Hawaiian "rift zones" of faults and dikes (Figs. 18–4, 18–5).

Although their slopes are gentle, shield volcanoes are the world's highest and bulkiest volcanoes. The Hawaiian Islands are composed of overlapping volcanoes, some rising more than 13,000 feet above the sea. As the nearby Pacific floor is more than 15,000 feet deep, some of these volcanic accumulations are more than 28,000 feet high (Fig. 18–6).

The summit of Mauna Loa, over 13,000 feet above the sea, contains a caldera 2 miles across and about 1000 feet deep (Fig. 18–4). At times this caldera contains a lava pool, fluctuating in size and height, and occasion-

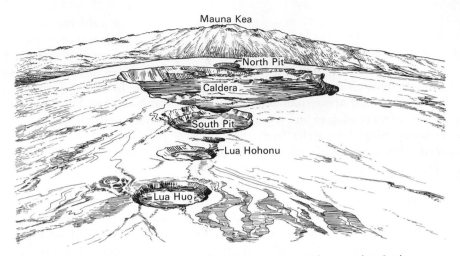

FIGURE 18–4 *Sketch of the caldera at the summit of Mauna Loa. The associated pit craters extend along the rift zone of dikes and fissures. (After H. T. Stearns and G. A. Macdonald, 1946.)*

FIGURE 18–5 *Kilauea caldera, Halemaumau, and associated features. (After H. T. Stearns and G. A. Macdonald, 1946.)*

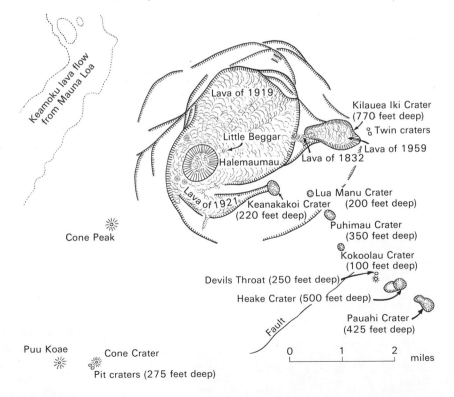

FIGURE 18–6   *Profile of Hawaii. (After H. T. Stearns and G. A. Macdonald, 1946.)*

ally spilling thin lava flows over the caldera floor, or crusting over and appearing dormant. On the southeastern slope of Mauna Loa, about 20 miles from its summit and 9000 feet lower, a second volcano, Kilauea, holds a caldera about 1½ miles across (Fig. 18–5). A deep pit (Halemaumau) within this caldera formerly contained a similar lava pool, frequently active within historic time. While active the lava pool would partly crust over, but many such crusts were broken up and engulfed by slow convection currents within the lava lake. Gases—largely water vapor—rose almost continuously, at times escaping violently in lava fountains (Fig. 18–3). In 1924 the lava sank out of sight, leaving a deep hole in the bottom of the pit into which ground water poured, causing a violent steam explosion as it contacted lava deep in the hole. The lava later reappeared and crusted over. Halemaumau has been alternatively active and quiescent since.

As the lava in Mauna Loa stands nearly 9000 feet higher than that in Halemaumau, the two lava columns cannot be directly connected; if they were, the lava in Mauna Loa would drain down and spill out of Kilauea.

FISSURE ERUPTIONS ON THE FLANKS OF SHIELD VOLCANOES. Within historic times many lava flows have been added to Mauna Loa (Fig. 18–2,A), and some have broken out from Kilauea. These emerged, not from the Mauna Loa and Kilauea lava pools (as must often have happened during prehistoric time) but from fissures, some opening at the top, but others low on the flanks of the shields. Most flows came from a northeast-trending zone of roughly parallel cracks—

the Great Rift Zone—that crosses the top of the Mauna Loa shield (Fig. 18–2,B). Some flows were small; others, such as that of 1855, contain several billion cubic feet of rock. Although only historic and other recent fissure flows can be easily traced to visible sources, the main bulk of large shield volcanoes must have been slowly built up from thousands of such lava streams. Confirming this inference, the deeply eroded shield volcanoes on Oahu and Kauai expose innumerable dike feeders.

CINDER CONES AND PARASITIC CONES. Small **cinder cones** (Fig. 18–7), which are steep-sided accumulations of pyroclastic debris (chiefly bombs and lapilli, see Appendix III) heaped around a central vent, abound in most volcanic regions. Many form on the flanks of shield volcanoes, built up along the fissures as the underlying dikes were congealing. Others are found above dikes not obviously connected with shield volcanoes (Fig. 18–8), and still others show no association with dikes (Fig. 18–9). Most cinder cones are less than a mile across and from 50 to 500 feet high, but some—Paricutin (Fig. 18–9), for example—are much larger and may give rise to extensive lava fields at the base.

Cinder cones and other minor volcanoes that occur on the flanks or in the calderas of larger volcanoes are **parasitic cones**. Many dot the surfaces of Mauna Loa and Kilauea. Mount Newberry, a large shield volcano in central Oregon, is embellished by more than 100 parasitic cones. Larger parasitic cones of lava or of mixtures of lava and pyroclastic products commonly form near the summits of shield volcanoes, particularly along the caldera rims and on their floors (Fig. 18–10).

FIGURE 18–7   *Cinder cone, with lava flow at its base. Lava Butte, Oregon. (Photo by H. A. Coombs, University of Washington.)*

FIGURE 18–8   *Cinder cones aligned along a fissure, Cascade Mountains, Oregon. Snow-capped Mount Jefferson, a large composite volcano, rises in the distant right. (Photo by Oregon Department of Geology and Mineral Industries.)*

FIGURE 18–9
Paricutin Volcano, Mexico, a large cinder cone in eruption (July, 1945). Lava emerging from the base of the cone has covered the village of San Juan until only the church steeple projects above the black basalt. (Photo by Tad Nichols, Tucson, Arizona.)

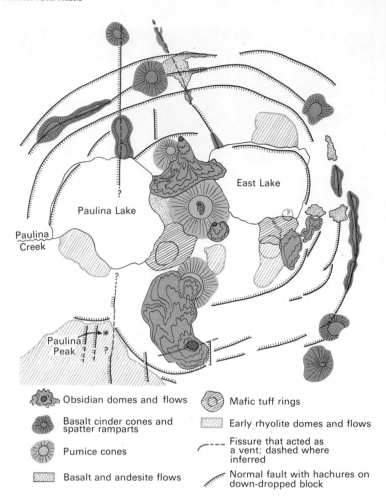

FIGURE 18–10

Newberry caldera, central Oregon. Note the parasitic cones, obsidian flows, and spatter ramparts associated with faults and fissures. (After M. W. Higgins and A. C. Waters, 1967.)

East Lake

Paulina Lake

Paulina Creek

Paulina Peak

Obsidian domes and flows

Basalt cinder cones and spatter ramparts

Pumice cones

Basalt and andesite flows

Mafic tuff rings

Early rhyolite domes and flows

Fissure that acted as a vent; dashed where inferred

Normal fault with hachures on down-dropped block

FIGURE 18–11

Geologic map of an eroded volcanic complex, probably the roots of a former shield volcano and caldera. Slieve Gullion, Ireland. (After J. E. Richey, 1932.)

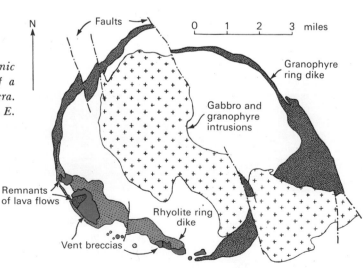

N

Faults

0   1   2   3   miles

Granophyre ring dike

Gabbro and granophyre intrusions

Remnants of lava flows

Rhyolite ring dike

Vent breccias

RING DIKES AND RIM VOLCANOES.   As the top of a volcano subsides to form a caldera, the underlying magma may rise along a roughly circular fault bounding the downsunken block, to form, on solidifying, an arcuate or circular dike—a **ring dike** (Fig. 18–11) . Lava from the ring dike may well out and flood the caldera floor, but more commonly it reaches the surface through parasitic rim volcanoes spaced at intervals along the arcuate dike. In this way a ring dike generally becomes mantled under its own parasitic volcanoes until they have been removed by deep erosion (compare Figs. 18–10, 18–11) .

At Askja volcano in Iceland, an irregular-shaped caldera about 4½ miles across is rimmed by several volcanoes built along the fractures bounding the downdropped blocks. These volcanoes partly buried the caldera floor and walls under basalt flows and scoria. Knebel, a younger and smaller caldera, then subsided along part of the older caldera rim. Another example is Newberry caldera of central Oregon, 5 miles long and 4 miles wide, bounded by a mixture of straight and crescentic faults (Fig. 18–10) from which basalt spattered to build small cinder cones and low ramparts along the fissures. Rhyolite magma burst out through other fissures to spread downslope in sticky obsidian flows or to froth and explode into pumice lapilli and glass shards. Several pumice cones also were built on the floor of the caldera (Fig. 18–10) , and the surrounding country for many miles was dusted with a coating of volcanic ash and shreds of pumice.

A deeply eroded volcanic complex such as Slieve Gullion in Ireland (Fig. 18–11) exposes the deeper structure of a shield volcano with a few ring dikes and rim volcanoes. At Slieve Gullion only a few patches of surface lava have survived erosion, and these only because they collapsed into the caldera. A huge ring dike of granophyre (a rock of rhyolitic composition but coarser grain) defines the margin of the old caldera; it encircles a downdropped block of basement rock about 7 miles across. Large irregular intrusions of gabbro riddle the downdropped block; perhaps they are solidified parts of the former basaltic magma chamber from which fissures branched upward to feed the long-vanished volcano. A second ring dike of aphanitic rhyolite clings closely to the first one for about one-fifth of the circumference. In several places along one side of the larger ring dike, pipe-like masses of breccia shattered by explosions cut upward through the dike or grade into it along their edges— obviously the roots of parasitic rim volcanoes. Erosion has destroyed all evidence of these volcanoes except for their feeding pipes, filled with breccia.

Composite volcanoes

Composite volcanoes, also called **stratovolcanoes,** differ from shield volcanoes chiefly in their strong explosive activity. The beautiful steep-sided cones of snow-capped Mount Rainier in Washington, (Fig. 18–12) , Fujisan in Japan, Mount Hood in Oregon (Fig. 18–1) , Vesuvius in Italy, and Popocatepetl in Mexico have been built by an alternation of lava outpourings and of violent explosions that heaped pyroclastic fragments about the vent. In most composite volcanoes pyroclastic debris alternates irregularly, and in about equal volumes, with tongues of lava; Mount Rainier is mostly flows of viscous lava; other composite cones are great chaotic piles of pyroclastic rock with relatively little lava. A graceful steep-sided cone, such as Cotapaxi, Fujisan, or Hood, appears at first to have little in common with a low flat-topped lava shield like Mauna Loa. Yet radial dikes and fissure feeders are common to both. Calderas may form by subsidence, either along faults and ring fractures as in many shield volcanoes, or by the piecemeal crumbling and sinking of a mountaintop as is inferred to have happened at Crater Lake, Oregon (Figs. 18–13, 18–14) . Some shield volcanoes have become composite when quiet

FIGURE 18–12   *Mount Rainier, Washington, a glacier-scarred composite volcano. Three other large composite volcanoes rise above the dissected platform of the Cascade Range in the distance: Mount Adams, 48 miles from Mount Rainier at the left, Mount Saint Helens, 43 miles away at the extreme right, and Mount Hood, 100 miles away in Oregon, near the center of the photo, just to the left of Mount Rainier. (Photo by H. Miller Cowling, Spokane, Washington.)*

outwelling of lava gave way to strong explosions. Others, such as Mount Newberry, Oregon, built up steep-sided cones of rhyolitic and andesitic debris, later overtopped by a huge shield of basalt, which was, in turn, invaded by parasitic cones of basalt, obsidian, and pumice (Fig. 18–10).

Varieties of explosive activity

TAMBORO AND KRAKATAU.   The strongest volcanic explosions known have occurred in long-dormant composite volcanoes. Many appeared extinct, not having erupted within historic times; of several the cones had been largely eroded away. Most strongly explosive volcanoes are andesitic, though many contain basalt and dacite also.

In April, 1815, a tremendous explosion decapitated Tamboro, an Indonesian volcano. Thirty-six cubic miles of molten lava and solid rock were shattered into fragments and blown high in the air, scattering pyroclastic debris thickly over an area more than 400 miles across. The mountain lost 4100 feet in height, and a crater 7 miles in diameter—as big as most calderas—was formed. The large number of people killed could not be closely estimated.

Krakatau, an island in the Sunda Strait between Java and Sumatra, exploded violently in 1883, blowing about a cubic mile of shattered rock high in the air. A large composite volcano had collapsed here in prehistoric time, leaving only an arc of islands to mark the rim of its caldera. Later eruptions raised several parasitic cones above the sea; the largest, the rim volcano Krakatau, to a height of more than 2600 feet. Then, in 1883, after emitting steam and dust, the volcano demolished nearly its whole edifice and blasted a hole 1000 feet deep on the site of its former cone. The eruption cloud rose 17 miles into the stratosphere and rained millions of tons of broken rock, dust, and pumice over the sea. Chunks of rock as much as

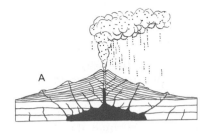

FIGURE 18–13

The evolution of the caldera at Crater Lake, Oregon. A: Early eruption cloud from the summit of former Mount Mazama. B: Great pumice eruptions and pyroclastic flows, with the mountaintop beginning to founder. C: Caldera resulting from collapse of mountaintop into magma chamber nearly complete; eruptions diminishing. D: Formation of lake and crystallization of underground magma after minor eruptions into the lake. (Modified from Howel Williams, 1942.)

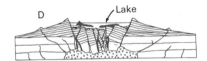

FIGURE 18–14

Crater Lake, Oregon, occupying the caldera formed by the subsidence of the top of the vanished former "Mount Mazama" (see also Fig. 18–13). Mount Scott, a parasitic volcano, rises across the lake. Only the top of Wizard Island, a cone formed after subsidence was complete, projects above the caldera rim in the right-center of the photograph. (Photo by Oregon State Highway Commission.)

15 feet in diameter were hurled to distances of more than 15 miles, and fine ash was wafted over the whole earth by the jet streams of the upper atmosphere to cause brilliant sunsets for several years.

Few people lived within the killing range of Krakatau's eruption cloud, but the surge of water and mud as the volcano tore loose from more than 1000 feet below the sea sent a gigantic wave—as high as 100 feet—against the low coasts of Java and Sumatra, killing more than thirty thousand people and destroying everything in its path.

MONT PELÉE.   In 1902 Mont Pelée, on the island of Martinique, was vigorously active over several months. Fortunately much of this activity was observed by the great French geologist A. Lacroix. During strong explosions immense columns of dust, rock fragments, and red hot pumice lapilli shot from the volcano to great heights, boiling, eddying, slowing down, and then swelling into a terrifying black mushroom-shaped cloud of seething particles high above the mountain crest. As gravity overcame the upward explosive force, the hot fragments tumbled back, picking up speed as they fell, and bounding out laterally when they hit the sloping sides of the volcano. Once on the ground the seething, turbulent mass cascaded into the ravines on the slope of the volcano, followed them downslope and spread over the lowlands as a pyroclastic flow. On May 8, 1902 one of these pyroclastic flows roared out of a gulch on the side of Mont Pelée at more than 60 miles per hour, followed a river valley to the seashore, and engulfed the port of St. Pierre. Of the 28,000

inhabitants only one man, imprisoned in an underground dungeon, survived the searing blast.

Following the eruptions at Mont Pelée, glassy lava, too viscous to spread laterally, punched up through the floor of the crater and rose slowly over a period of months into a gigantic **spine** high above the volcano (Fig. 18–15). During its rise minor steam blasts broke out at the base of the spine, weakening the rock until eventually most of it came tumbling down. Such spines, or slightly less viscous **domes** are characteristic of waning activity at composite volcanoes. They may rise through the crater, as at Mont Pelée, or punch through the lower flanks, as did the Showa-Shin-zan dome at Usu-Yama volcano, Japan in 1944. This dome pushed up through wooded ground and a cultivated field, lifting and heaving the broken rock and soil aside, and finally emerging as a steaming mass of practically solid rock.

KATMAI, AND THE ASH FLOW FROM NOVA-RUPTA.   Glassy lava is generally so highly charged with gases that instead of rising as a viscous dome or solid spine it froths into bits of pumice and glass shards as it approaches the surface. If the frothing is violently explosive, seething eruption clouds like those at Mont Pelée form, but during some eruptions the gas-charged lava boils more quietly from the vent, bubbling out with minor explosions into a pumiceous froth that breaks into sticky glass shards and small lapilli of pumice. These broken bubbles and bits of frothy lava pour over the lip of the vent and flow downslope in hot, highly mobile **pyroclastic flows.** Some are still so

FIGURE 18–15
Four stages in the eruption of Mount Pelée, Martinique. (After A. Lacroix, 1904.)

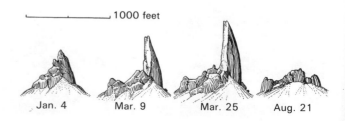

1000 feet

Jan. 4   Mar. 9   Mar. 25   Aug. 21

hot when they come to rest that the particles of softened glass weld together again, forming a rock called **welded tuff,** that superficially resembles obsidian or rhyolite (see Appendix III and Fig. 18–16). C. N. Fenner, an American geologist, first comprehensively described this kind of deposit in his account of the ash flow that filled, and gave name to, the Valley of Ten Thousand Smokes near Mount Katmai in southwestern Alaska.

FIGURE 18–16 *Pyroclastic deposits of Pliocene age, Cove Palisades, Oregon. The two thick medium-gray beds are welded tuffs; the thinner and lighter-gray beds are ash falls composed of sharp, unwelded glass shards, the much darker beds are chiefly stream gravels and sands. (Photo by the Oregon State Highway Commission.)*

FIGURE 18–17   *The downstream end of the pyroclastic flow in the Valley of Ten Thousand Smokes, Alaska. (Photo by A. C. Waters.)*

FIGURE 18–18   *Sketch map showing the pyroclastic deposit in the Valley of Ten Thousand Smokes in relation to Novarupta, Katmai, and Trident volcanoes.*

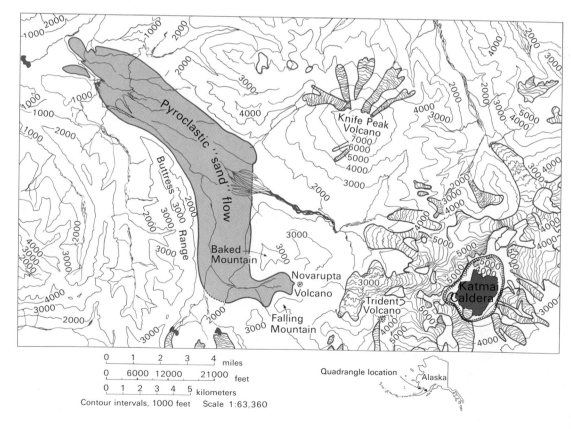

In 1912 Mount Katmai, not previously known to be active, was reported to have exploded with great violence. Its steep-sided but deeply eroded cone had become a shattered irregular hole 2 miles long and 1½ miles wide, from which a huge dust cloud was emitted. Simultaneously, 7 miles west of Katmai and 4200 feet lower in elevation, a great sheet of pumice, glass shards, and rock fragments spread over the lightly forested and marshy floor of a formerly glaciated valley, forming a pyroclastic deposit 14 miles long, 1 to 3 miles wide, and, along the axis of the valley, 40 to more than 100 feet thick (Figs. 18–17, 18–18). Two years later scientific expeditions reached the valley; the scientist-explorers were particularly impressed by the thousands of fumaroles emitting steam and sulfurous vapors from cracks in the already compacted ash flow. Their photographs and descriptions of this isolated area made it famous as "The Valley of Ten Thousand Smokes."

Where did this pyroclastic deposit—about ⅙ cubic mile in total volume—come from? At first Katmai was the suspected source, but only a relatively thin dusting of ash covered the country between it and the head of the Valley of Ten Thousand Smokes. Moreover, the coarse blocks to be expected near a newly formed Katmai "crater" are missing and the other valleys radiating from Mount Katmai are not filled with such deposits.

At the head of the sand flow, a small pumice cone, Novarupta Volcano (Fig. 18–18), contains a small dome of pumiceous obsidian in its throat. This obsidian was still very hot and steaming when the explorers reached the valley. The hills for a few miles around Novarupta are thickly dusted with pumice pellets and glass shards. Could the sand flow have come from Novarupta? The first visitors rejected this, mainly because the conduit beneath could not be more than about 200 feet across—seemingly too small to supply the large volume. Also, why is the sand flow distributed along a crooked valley floor instead of radiating in all directions like an ash-fall

blanket? They concluded that the pyroclastic debris had welled up through many dikes in the valley floor marked by the lines of fumaroles in the pyroclastic deposit.

Since 1914 several changes furnish new evidence helpful in interpreting the deposit. First, both the temperature and the amount of gas emitted from the fumaroles have decreased at an astonishing rate. Within 2 to 3 years after the first examination, more than half of the fumaroles were gone, and in less than 10 years, nearly all. "The Valley of Ten Thousand Smokes" is now a complete misnomer! Only the throat of Novarupta still emits a few steam jets. Glacier-fed streams have cut deep box canyons along the sides, and, in some places, along the axis of the pyroclastic deposit, revealing that many fissures along which fumaroles had risen do not penetrate the underlying rock, thus seriously weakening the theory that the deposit erupted through dikes cutting the valley floor. Furthermore, the pumice in the deposit is petrographically identical (except for being more frothy) with the pumiceous obsidian of the Novarupta dome, and both show an intimate mixing of two magmas, one of obsidian frothed to a light-colored pumice, the other a dark andesitic glass.

Today it seems not unreasonable that the sand flow came from Novarupta, perhaps emerging with only enough explosive force to froth the pumice into broken glass shards. Unlike Pelée's explosive projection of a high eruption cloud, the sand flow seems to have seethed and spilled out like violently boiling porridge, and flowed like a river down the winding valley as a spattery emulsion of gas and viscous glassy fragments—a river whose "high-water mark" can still be recognized along the lower stretches of the valley a few feet above the top of the deposit.

As the red-hot ash spread over the swampy tundra, the swamp water flashed into steam, which escaped from fumaroles for years, perhaps cooling the deposit so that it did not weld except in a few such places as next to a dry cliff.

Can the pouring of this hot pyroclastic flow from Novarupta be connected with the formation of the hole in the top of Katmai? Katmai, and Trident volcano, its presently active parasitic cone near Novarupta, are of andesitic composition. Had an andesitic magma beneath Katmai broken into the obsidian magma chamber beneath Novarupta, the much higher hydraulic pressure of the Katmai magma would have forced it to drain into the lower Novarupta chamber, thus forcing the Novarupta magma to the surface. Here the lowered pressure would permit rapid frothing into a pyroclastic flow. Mingling of the two magmas beneath Novarupta would account for the mixed obsidian- and-andesite pumice in both the sand flow and in the Novarupta dome. Drainage of the Katmai magma chamber could account for the collapse of Katmai's summit into the cavity as a series of rock falls whose dust clouds were mistaken by distant observers for volcanic eruptions from the peak.

In the last 30 years welded and unwelded tuffs deposited by pyroclastic flows have been widely recognized. They cover thousands of square miles in the Great Basin province of the United States and Mexico and are widespread in New Zealand, Indonesia, Turkey, and many other areas. They are increasingly being recognized—in rocks of all ages—back to the early Precambrian—as probable explosive equivalents of near-surface granitic plutons. Indeed, volcanic deposits formed throughout geologic time by the kind of eruptions just postulated for the Novarupta pyroclastic flow and by the more explosive Peléean glowing avalanches are probably second only to those of flood basalts in total volume.

FLOOD BASALTS

In some of the world's most extensive volcanic areas true volcanoes are rare or absent. Instead, great sheets of lava have welled out through fissures not connected with volcanic cones. Such **flood basalts,** also called **plateau basalts,** cover vast areas in the northwestern United States, Siberia, western India, the Parana basin of South America, and that part of the North Atlanic which includes Iceland, southeast Greenland, northern Ireland, and the Hebrides. Old flood basalts are found in Michigan, Quebec, Virginia, and many other areas.

FIGURE 18–19   *Flows of flood basalt near Vantage, Washington. The cliff is 1100 feet high. (Photo by the Washington Department of Conservation and Development.)*

FIGURE 18–20
Underwater photo of pillow lavas on the sea floor off Hawaii. Note starfish relaxing on a small pillow near center, bottom edge of photo. (Photo by James G. Moore.)

FIGURE 18–21
Pillow lavas of Miocene age. Roadcut near Ellensburg, Washington. The lava, flowing from the left, entered a shallow lake. Light-colored mud squirted up between the pillows from the lake bottom. Length of view, 12 feet. (Photo by A. C. Waters.)

The Columbia River Basalts, of Miocene age, cover approximately 150,000 square miles on the Columbia River plateau of eastern Washington (Fig. 18–19), northern Oregon, and western Idaho. The Eocene basalts of western Washington and Oregon are even more voluminous. Hundreds of dikes of basalt and dolerite, marking the fissures through which these lavas rose, are grouped in a few great dike swarms. Individual flows fed from the dike swarms have spread more than 100 miles from their source. Such floods of basaltic lava, piled up flow upon flow to thicknesses of thousands of feet, are the most extensive of all volcanic deposits.

Pillow lavas and palagonite tuffs

Basaltic flows, in Samoa, on entering the sea have been observed to subdivide into irregularly rounded and ellipsoidal masses, from several inches to a few feet across, which resemble a stack of pillows. Underwater photographs of the sea floor off the Mauna Loa rift zone show that recent submarine eruptions off Hawaii are in this pillow form (Fig. 18–20). Such pillow lavas are interstratified with marine sedimentary rocks in many parts of the world, and are particularly abundant in thick geosynclinal accumulations (Chapter 20). Pillow lavas are common on the mid-ocean ridges and smaller rises, island archipelagoes, and seamounts. Indeed basalt is the prevailing igneous rock of the oceans.

Pillow lavas, however, are not confined to the ocean floor. The Miocene basalts of the Columbia River plateau contain many pillow lavas, but the fossils in the associated sediments show that these flows entered shallow freshwater lakes, filling them with pillows and glass breccia (Fig. 18–21).

Associated with nearly all pillow basalts are varying amounts of glass breccia, generally hydrated in the course of time to a yellowish rock called palagonite tuff (Fig. 18–

FIGURE 18–22

Palagonite tuff and palagonite breccia of Miocene age near Boiler Bay, Oregon. Note the isolated large pillow enclosed in the thick bed of breccia near the upper right corner. (Photo by Parke D. Snavely, Jr., U.S. Geological Survey.)

FIGURE 18–23

Altered pillow breccia, Siletz basalt (Eocene), western Oregon. Isolated large pillows are enclosed in a matrix of broken pillows, fragments of pillow rinds, and altered palagonite breccia. Note how the cavity fillings of alteration minerals (white carbonate and zeolites) bring out details of the chill and vesicular zones within the pillows. (Photo by Parke D. Snavely, Jr., U.S. Geological Survey.)

FIGURE 18–24

Pillow lava, western Oregon. Deep-water pillows, packed tightly together, with little granular breccia between. (Photo by Parke D. Snavely, Jr., U.S. Geological Survey.)

22). Mixtures of pillows and palagonite are also common (Fig. 18–23). Slight differences in temperature, viscosity, rate of flow, and depth of water into which the magma is extruded probably determine whether the liquid lava will, on contact with water, granulate into small fragments of glass, or segment into large tightly packed pillows (Fig. 18–24).

In time the thick rinds of chilled glass on pillows and the finely granulated glass of the breccias absorb water and slowly hydrate into yellowish palagonite. This mineraloid is inherently unstable as well: in rocks older than Mid-Cenozoic it has generally broken down into black or greenish-gray mixtures of clay minerals, zeolites, carbonate, chlorite, and other minerals (Fig. 18–23). Such dark-colored clay-rich rocks are often mistaken for mudstones, "argillites," and "mudstone conglomerates." Much fresh and altered palagonite has been misidentified in oceanographic work.

Explosive eruptions on contact with water

The formation of pillow lavas and palagonite tuffs generally results in only moderate explosive activity, but under some circumstances the meeting of magma with water may result in violent steam explosions.

Some historic flows on Hawaii, upon entering the sea, did not plunge under water in pillow lavas, but instead fragmented into small and large fragments of frothy glass which accumulated in piles of debris at the shoreline. Because the light-weight small particles are quickly removed by the waves, these **littoral cones** would only rarely be preserved in the geologic record.

Phreatic explosions (from the Greek word for "well") are much more vigorous. They may develop when magma, or even hot but solid lava comes in contact with water, as in underground aquifers, beneath permafrost or glaciers, in thick delta or alluvial deposits, or even beneath open marshes, lakes, and seas (Fig. 18–26). A few representative eruptions may be mentioned:

TAAL VOLCANO. Situated within Lake Taal, which fills a probable volcanic caldera in southwest Luzon, is Volcano Island, a cone about 5 kilometers in diameter. It has been intermittently active since at least the sixteenth century. A violent eruption through its central crater in 1911 destroyed all life on the island, killing more than 1300 people. The volcano did not erupt again until 1965, when, over a period of three days, a series of flank eruptions blew a hole 150 meters deep above the level of the sea, and an unknown additional depth below sea level, in the southwest side of Volcano Island. The eruptions plastered an area of about 60 square kilometers with a coating of mud (Fig. 18–25) and ash more than 125 centimeters thick. One hundred and eighty-nine people lost their lives during these eruptions. James G. Moore, an American volcanologist, was sent to the island, and gave the following summary of events:

The main phreatic explosions, which were preceded by ejection of basaltic spatter, opened a new crater 1.7 kilometers long and 0.8 kilometer wide. . . . The clouds that formed during the explosive eruption rose to heights of 15 to 21 kilometers and deposited fine ash as far as 80 kilometers west of the vent. At the base of the main explosion column, flat, turbulent clouds spread radially, with hurricane violence, transporting ash, mud, lapilli, and blocks. The horizontally moving, debris-laden clouds sandblasted trees, coated the blast-side of trees and houses with mud [Fig. 18–26], and deposited coarse ejecta with dune-type bedding in a zone roughly 4 kilometers in all directions from the explosion crater.

. . . the exploding gases at the explosion center first vent vertically and then . . . push out a wall of brecciated roof and crater material. After the wall is overturned . . . outward expanding gases rush over . . . the crater lip and tear ejecta from it. . . . In an underwater blast, the crater lip is represented by a large solitary wave, which breaks and forms spray jets. . . . (the) surge cloud (then) moves outward as a density flow, taking advantage of topographic irregularities.

FIGURE 18–25

Cross section of a palm tree plastered by many thin layers of mud during the 1965 eruption of Taal Volcano, Philippines. (Drawn from a photograph by James G. Moore, U.S. Geological Survey.)

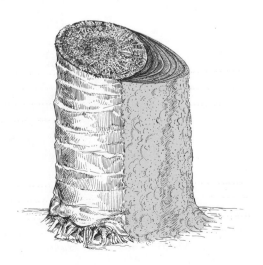

FIGURE 18–26   *Underwater eruption, Capelinhos volcano, the Azores. (Photo by U.S. Air Force.)*

ANAK KRAKATAU.   That submarine volcanic activity was going on within the submerged crater of Krakatau became clear in 1927—forty-four years after the catastrophic eruption of 1883. In 1928 Anak Krakatau ("Child of Krakatau") finally appeared above the surface, and has been intermittently active since. First to appear above water was a breached ring of fragmental volcanic glass about ½ kilometer in diameter. Within it a boiling pool of sea water emitted great jets of steam and ash. In a few years the top of a volcanic cone took form, but its main bulk was underwater. From the still submerged vent came violent vertical and horizontal bursts of steam and ash which steadily added to the height of the surrounding ring of glassy particles (Fig. 18–27). Thus when it first rose from the sea, Anak, like the new volcano Surtsey, which started with underwater eruptions 35 kilometers off the coast of Iceland in 1963, had a much larger crater with more gently sloping flanks than do cinder cones on land. As long as water had access to the vents the strong horizontal blasts kept the craters broad and flat floored. As such cones grow to greater heights above the water, the broad craters begin to fill with lapilli, bombs, and lava, as is now happening at Surtsey. Thus underwater volcanoes deposit thinner and more continuous beds of glassy but less vesicular fragments than do volcanic cones built on land.

Maar volcanoes and tuff rings

Eruptions from Taal, Anak Krakatau, Surtsey, and other underwater volcanoes give insight into the probable origin of **maar volcanoes, and of puzzling circular accumulations of volcanic tuff and breccia called tuff rings.**

The name *maar* comes from the small circular lakes in the Eifel volcanic district of Germany. These lakes, most about 2 kilometers in diameter, evidently fill the craters of formerly active volcanoes. Unlike most crater lakes, however, they lie not at the sum-

FIGURE 18–27

Anak Krakatau, in the crater formed by the 1883 eruption of Krakatau, as it appeared in 1931. Anak first built up as an underwater volcano, coming to the surface as a tuff ring in 1927. (Drawn from a photograph.)

mits of large cones, but in pits blasted out of the bedrock floor, and surrounded by only low rims composed of a mixture of broken sedimentary bedrock fragments and volcanic debris. The lakes filling the Eifel maars prevent effective observation of the crater walls. In certain desert areas, however, where copious supplies of ground water lie at depth, numerous maars can be more closely examined (Fig. 18–28).

In the desert of central Oregon is a typical maar volcano with the descriptive name of Hole in the Ground (Fig. 18–29). It is a circular pit, 5000 feet across and 425 feet deep. The original pit was much deeper; it has been partly filled by lake deposits, ash falls from neighboring volcanoes, and debris from the steep crater walls. A thin blanket of ejecta, in most places less than 100 feet thick,

FIGURE 18–28   *Crater Elegante, a dry maar in the Sonora Desert, Mexico. The crater is about 4500 feet across and 796 feet deep, with its lowest point 200 feet below sea level. The walls are chiefly basalt flows, but fragments of underlying permeable sediments are common in the thin graded beds that form the 150-foot thick ejecta blanket on the crater rim. (Photo U.S. Geological Survey, by permission of the Government of Mexico.)*

FIGURE 18–29   *Hole in the Ground, a maar-type crater in central Oregon.*

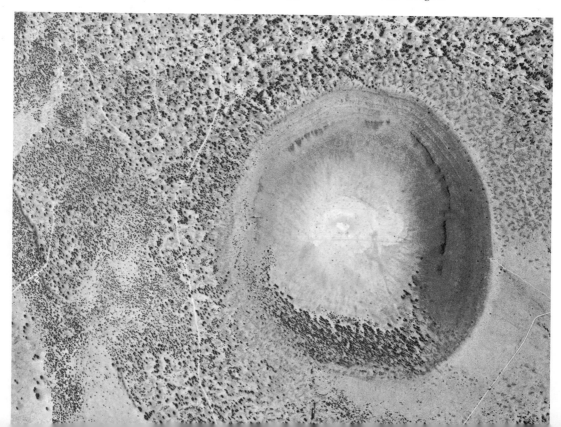

drapes over the crater rim and thins outward into faint dune-like ridges of fine volcanic sand about a mile from the crater rim. Clustered in the ejecta, mostly within a few hundred feet of the rim, are great blocks of rock as thick as 15 feet. Some have been rifted from the basalt flows exposed on the crater walls, but others are of distinctive porphyritic basalt, black rhyolite, and welded tuff not seen in the crater walls. Obviously, these blocks were blown up from beneath the present crater floor. Mixed with this debris in the ejecta blanket is a matrix of chilled volcanic particles ranging downward to fine silt. A crude grading and stratification divides the ejecta into layers, mostly between 2 inches and one foot thick. This demonstrates that the ejecta blanket was not formed in one grand explosive event, but resulted from many bursts of steam surging out of the hole.

Hole in the Ground undoubtedly formed when hot magma rose along a fissure and encountered abundant ground water. At the time it was formed a large Pleistocene lake of the same vintage as Lake Bonneville (see Chapter 13) occupied the desert basin to the southeast; its ancient shorelines are clearly visible only a mile south and east of the crater. Highly permeable basalt flows form part of the walls of Hole in the Ground, and underlie the crater at depth, readily supplying large quantities of ground water to the fissure through which the basalt rose.

East of Hole in the Ground are three other places where lava erupted along the trend of the same fissure. The most easterly is Fort Rock, a large tuff ring of palagonite tuff and breccia (Fig. 18–30). The deep Pleistocene lake in which the Fort Rock tuff ring was built has completely evaporated, leaving a sage-covered plain. As the lake subsided waves eroded away the gently dipping outer slopes of the tuff ring, leaving a high cliff on three sides, and completely breaching the crater on its southeast side (Fig. 18–30). On these cliffs, and on the inner slopes of the tuff ring, can be seen the record of thousands of surges of hot water and chilled glass particles.

Peléean-type eruptions underwater

What happens when a submarine explosion takes place comparable to those which produced the Peléean cloud that destroyed

FIGURE 18–30   *Fort Rock, an eroded tuff ring in central Oregon. The ring, originally composed of granulated bits of glass, was formed by the underwater eruption of basalt into a Pleistocene lake. The outer, gently sloping original sides of the ring, similar to those of present-day Anak and Surtsey, have been heavily eroded by the waves as the lake slowly evaporated. A cliff of cemented palagonite breccia remains above the dry floor of the former lake. (Photo by Oregon State Highway Commission.)*

Saint Pierre? That such explosions do take place under water is shown by abundant bedded tuff-breccia of granulated and partly vesiculated lapilli of andesitic and dacitic composition in many geosynclinal accumulations (Chapter 20). Most such tuff-breccias show a subtle density grading; the vesiculated fragments are abundant toward the top, and denser lava fragments near the base. Also many thin graded beds, from a few millimeters to several centimeters thick, lie between thick major tuff-breccias. R. S. Fiske, an American geologist, studied such deposits

in Washington and Japan. He attributed them to submarine eruptions of Peléean type, spread outward from the vents by underwater turbidity currents as indicated in Figure 18–31.

MYOJIN REEF UNDERWATER VOLCANO. At least one underwater eruption of the kind Fiske postulated has occurred in recent years. At Myojin Reef, on the Mariana arc about 400 kilometers south of Tokyo, submarine eruptions were observed from many ships during several months in 1952. Some burst through the sea surface in broad turbulently churning eruption clouds with strong horizontal blasts. Many were of great violence: one on September 24, 1952, engulfed the Japanese research ship Kaiyomaru with the loss of all on board, 31 scientists and crewmen. Very likely the tremendous eruption of Krakatau in 1883 sent turbidity flows of volcanic detritus coursing outward from its underwater vent in addition to raining the great mass of glass shards over the surrounding sea and islands.

FIGURE 18–31

Inferred sequence of events in the course of a Peléean-type underwater eruption. (After R. S. Fiske, U.S. Geological Survey.)

A: Beginning of eruption

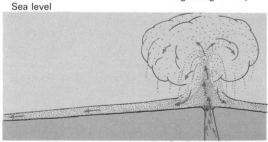

B: Climax of eruption

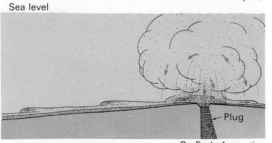

C: End of eruption

INTRUSIVE IGNEOUS MASSES

Masses of magma underground are necessary to supply the lava and pyroclastic volcanic products. We turn now to the root zones of the volcanoes and to other igneous masses, large and small, that never reached the surface but congealed underground within the crust.

Shallow intrusive masses

PLUGS AND STOCKS. A mass of igneous rock solidified at shallow depth in a vertical pipe-like conduit immediately beneath a volcano is a **volcanic plug** or **neck**. Most are a few hundred feet in diameter, but some are well over a mile.

Most plugs are composed of porphyritic rock, perhaps medium-grained in the center

FIGURE 18–32 *Devil's Tower, Wyoming, probably a volcanic plug, but perhaps part of a roofed intrusive. (Photo by N. H. Darton, U.S. Geological Survey.)*

of the plug, but chilled to glass or aphanitic rock at the borders. Some are wholly glassy; these may once have fed seething pyroclastic flows, domes, or spines. Many contain explosion breccia in their upper parts. As might be expected from observed volcanoes, many plugs are composite, consisting of several kinds of rock differing in texture or composition, and emplaced at different times.

Most plugs are nearly vertical, but some flare outward in depth and pass into larger masses a few miles across, called **stocks.** Not all stocks, however, show a connection with volcanoes; many never reached the surface.

Most plugs resist erosion better than the surrounding rock and are left standing as steep-sided buttes above the surrounding country (Fig. 18–32). More than 150 plugs mark the sites of extinct volcanoes in northwestern New Mexico and adjacent parts of Arizona (Fig. 18–33). An area of less than 150 square miles near Neuffen, Germany, contains over 100 plugs. Most steep-sided buttes in the Midland Valley of Scotland and in the John Day basin of Oregon mark the feeders of former volcanoes.

DIKE SWARMS. Dikes are among the most common intrusive igneous forms. In many regions they form **dike swarms,** some of which are obviously related to volcanoes; among these are the buried linear dike swarm that must be inferred from the rift zone of Mauna Loa (Fig. 18–2,B), and the radial swarms that surround many dissected volcanic plugs. Some large dolerite dike swarms such as those in central and northwestern Oregon fed flood basalts; others fed sill complexes.

A great series of dolerite dikes in western Scotland and northern Ireland clusters thickly near the major volcanic centers of Skye, Mull, Arran, Mourne, and Slieve Gullion. Many of them, however, such as the 110-mile-long Cleveland dike of northern England, extend much too far to be considered parasitic dikes fed laterally from volcanic stocks or plugs. The map in Fig. 18–34 permits only a few of the largest dikes to be shown; for each line on it there are scores or even hundreds of dikes cropping out.

Similar swarms of dolerite dikes cut rocks of widely diverse ages and structures, yet huge areas of the earth's crust show none. Only in places have fissures riven deeply enough into the crust to tap a source of basaltic magma. Through these fissures vast masses of molten rock have risen to or near the surface.

SILL SWARMS. In many areas of flat-lying sedimentary rocks magma has been squirted between the beds to form flat, pancake-like bodies called sills (Chapter 3). Sills, like dikes, differ greatly in size, composition, and association with other igneous masses. Dolerite sills are the most common.

In South Africa, the Karoo dolerites, a swarm of hundreds upon hundreds of dolerite sills, range from a few feet to over a thousand feet thick; they nearly equal the Columbia River flood basalts in aggregate volume. Other sill swarms, like those of Mount Rainier (Fig. 18–35), are fine-grained granitic rocks, and appear to be offshoots of much larger granitic bodies at depth.

FIGURE 18–33   *Volcanic plug, northeastern Arizona. The man is standing on one of the dikes that radiate from the plug. The once overlying volcano has been completely eroded away. (Photo by Warren Hamilton, U.S. Geological Survey.)*

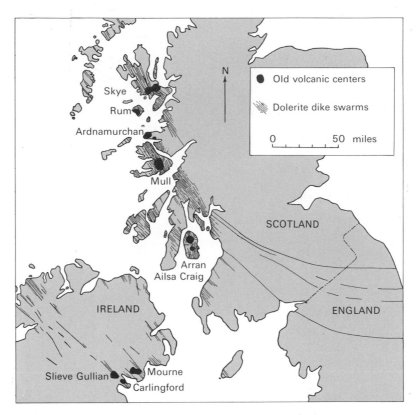

FIGURE 18–34   *The dolerite dike swarms and eroded volcanic centers of Scotland and adjacent parts of England and Ireland. (After J. E. Richey, H. H. Thomas, and others, Geological Survey of Great Britain.)*

FIGURE 18–35   *Cross sections showing a sill swarm (Tdi) of fine-grained granitic rocks, reinjected by the pluton from which they were fed at an earlier stage of its development. A final outburst of granitic magma to the surface fed a large pyroclastic flow (Tv). Mount Rainier National Park, Washington. (From R. S. Fiske, C. A. Hopson, and A. C. Waters, 1963.)*

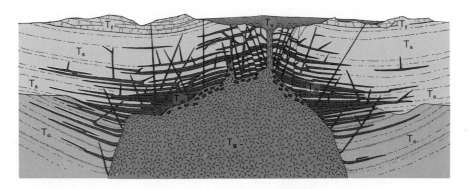

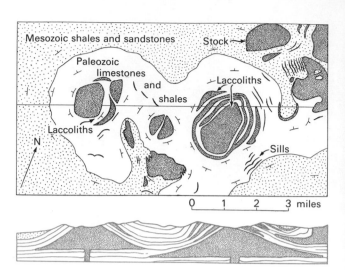

FIGURE 18–36
Map and cross section of a group of laccoliths and stocks in the Judith Mountains, Montana. (After W. H. Weed and L. V. Pirsson, U.S. Geological Survey.)

LACCOLITHS. Magma may spread sill-like between sedimentary layers and concurrently lift the roof rock into a dome, thereby forming an underground magma body with a flat floor (where the strata are horizontal) and an arched roof. Congealing, the magma produces a laccolith (Fig. 18–36). Laccoliths are seldom more than a few miles across. Like lavas from a volcano, they tend to cluster radially about a central stock which evidently fed them. Some sill-like or tongue-like feeders connecting laccoliths with the parent stock can be seen at the present level of erosion in Figure 18–37.

DIFFERENTIATED SILLS AND LACCOLITHS. The Palisades that face across the Hudson toward New York are the eroded edge of a dolerite sill locally more than 900 feet thick. This huge mass is not uniform dolerite from top to bottom but consists of layers of differing composition. Along its base and locally at its top, olivine phenocrysts are scattered through a zone of fine-grained rock. The central part of the sill is coarser grained and contains no olivine; in it pyroxene is abundant in the lower portion, but less so upward. Just above the fine-grained basal zone, a layer 10 to 20 feet thick contains about 25 percent olivine crystals (Fig. 18–38).

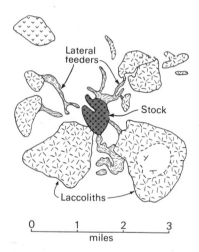

FIGURE 18–37
The Middle Mountain stock in the La Sal Mountains, Utah, showing three large laccoliths and several smaller intrusive bodies that were fed laterally from the stock. Some of the connecting feeders between stock and laccoliths are visible. (After C. B. Hunt, U.S. Geological Survey, 1958.)

If the olivine in this enriched layer were uniformly distributed throughout the sill, the entire mass would have the same chemical composition as the fine-grained border zone. From this we infer that the fine-grained rocks at bottom and top are chilled zones, quenched magma as it came in contact with

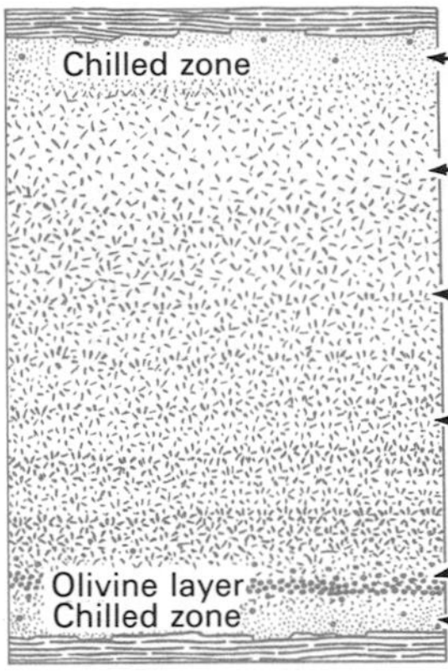

FIGURE 18–38
Diagrammatic section of the Palisades sill, New Jersey, showing the vertical variation in texture and mineral composition. (After Frederick Walker, 1940.)

Chilled zone ← 1% olivine, 50% pyroxene, 47% plagioclase

← no olivine, 30% pyroxene, 65% plagioclase

← no olivine, 33% pyroxene, 61% plagioclase

← no olivine, 40% pyroxene, 53% plagioclase

Olivine layer ← 25% olivine, 38% pyroxene, 35% plagioclase
Chilled zone ← 1% olivine, 50% pyroxene, 47% plagioclase

cooler rocks. Evidently, during the slow cooling of the remaining central part of the sill, early formed and relatively dense olivine crystals had time to sink through the molten mass and accumulate at the top of the basal chilled zone. Such a settling of dense crystals is **differentiation by crystal settling.** Differentiation includes any process whereby a once-homogeneous and uniform magma comes to yield rocks of divergent compositions upon solidifying. Crystal settling—gravitative differentiation such as we see has happened in the Palisade sill—doubtless goes on in some volcanic plugs and stocks as well as in sills. The more siliceous obsidian that rises as spines and domical protrusions into volcanic throats that had formerly erupted only denser basalt or andesite may represent only the last liquid residue of a magma mass from which the typically basaltic minerals had crystallized and sunk to lower levels. Or the still-molten obsidian magma may be forced upward by crustal movements, or pushed out as a new rise of magma from depth squeezes it out from the mesh of earlier-crystallized denser crystals.

Deep intrusive masses or plutons

Many sills, dikes, and particularly some of the very large intrusive masses called lopoliths and batholiths were doubtless intruded at much greater depths than the shallow forms just described. In general, intrusions that are coarse grained and show little chilling at contacts are inferred to have cooled slowly against hot wall rocks and thus at considerable depth. When such intrusions are mingled concordantly with metamorphic rocks this conclusion is still more likely. All these large bodies are called plutons, whatever their shape, known or unknown, or their composition. We now discuss two varieties.

LOPOLITHS.   Many deep intrusive masses are highly differentiated layered complexes of sill or saucer-like form. One kind, the **lopolith** (from the Greek words for "basin" and "stone"), is shaped like the bowl of a spoon —both floor and roof of the magma chamber sag downward. The Duluth lopolith, a huge mass of gabbro that crops out on either side of the west end of Lake Superior, apparently continues beneath the western part of the lake as a thick, spoon-shaped mass about 150 miles wide, perhaps 10 miles thick, and probably containing 50,000 cubic miles of rock. Lopoliths differ from sills and laccoliths in their enormously greater size and in their downsagging floors. Such large structures, however, must be composite; it seems incredible that such enormous bodies of magma could have been emplaced in a single magmatic surge.

Most lopoliths, some large and deep sills, and even a few small floored intrusive masses are marvelously differentiated into many small sheets and bands of contrasting mineral composition (Figs. 18–39, 21–11). In the Bushveldt complex—a huge lopolith, or more likely, a plexus of lopoliths, in South Africa—and in the Stillwater complex of Montana, this banding is so striking that when viewed from a distance outcrops of the igneous rock resemble thin-bedded sedimentary rocks.

How the layering in stratiform complexes is formed has been much debated. Since the denser rocks are generally near the base and the less dense at the top, crystal settling under gravity probably plays a significant part, as it did in the Palisade sill. But the hundreds of thin layers of alternating light and heavy minerals are not easily explained by crystal settling alone (see Figs. 18–39, 21–11).

FIGURE 18–39

Layering in a gabbro sill produced by alternating concentrations of the minerals plagioclase (light) and pyroxene (dark). Oregon Coast Mountains. (Photo by Parke D. Snavely, Jr., U.S. Geological Survey.)

Perhaps fluctuating convection currents within the slowly cooling magma helped sort out the sinking crystals, just as fluctuating water currents produce stratification, and repetitions of layers with different degrees of sorting in the deposits of surface streams.

One small stratiform mass of gabbro, the Skaergaard intrusion of Greenland, forms a tilted cone with apex downward. Its strikingly layered structure is well exposed on the walls of the deep Greenland fjords. The stratiform layers bank against the wall-rock contacts, and in places show structures that resemble the cross-bedding and channeling of stream deposits. From these features the English geologists L. R. Wager and W. A. Deer concluded that as the mass began to fill with crystals, convection currents sweeping slowly across the floor sorted the accumulating crystals into thin layers. Sill-like and lopolithic masses in Quebec, Alaska, Newfoundland, and California show similar features. Valuable ores of platinum, chromium, nickel, and cobalt have been concentrated in certain thin layers of stratiform complexes (Fig. 21–11).

Batholiths

The largest plutons are great bodies of granite and granodiorite exposed in the cores of many major mountain ranges and over vast areas in the ancient shields.

Granodiorite and related quartz-bearing rocks extend as overlapping plutons in a belt at least 1000 miles long and 20 to 150 miles wide along the Coast Mountains of British Columbia (Fig. 18–40). Canyon walls reveal up to 7000 feet of uniform granodiorite without any visible bottom. Other huge granitic masses are exposed in the Sierra Nevada and in the Patagonian Andes (Fig. 18–40). Granitic masses of various sizes—some rounded in plan, some elongated, and some irregular—form intricate patterns with the metamorphic rocks that underlie most of eastern Canada, Scandinavia, and Brazil.

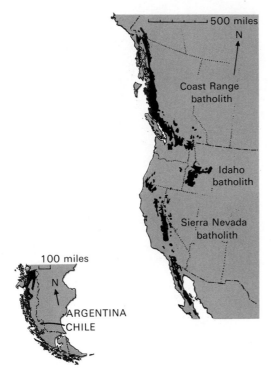

FIGURE 18–40

Large granitic intrusives (black) *of western North America* (right), *and the Patagonian batholith* (left). (*After geologic maps of North and South America, Geological Society of America.*)

Granitic plutons having an area of more than 40 square miles have been called **batholiths,** if their area is less they are **stocks.** In most definitions batholiths are said to flare outward with depth and to be "bottomless" in contrast to intrusions with a recognizable floor, such as lopoliths and laccoliths. But they are, of course, not bottomless, though many are clearly many miles thick. Although anything resembling a floor can rarely be seen in the field, indirect evidence suggests, and, indeed, proves that batholiths end within the crust, possibly tapering downward like the root of a tooth, or a tree with short stubby roots, or even grading into other rocks through their rounded or flat bottoms. Isostatic, thermal, and seismic evidence for this conclusion is given in Chapters 19 and 20. From surface exposures alone it is impossible to infer the form of an igneous mass at depths of 2 to 20 miles. Because of the uncertainty regarding the shape of the lower parts of large granitic masses many geologists prefer to use the noncommital term pluton instead of batholith.

CONTACT RELATIONS OF PLUTONS. Granitic plutons show varied structural relations to their roofs and walls. Some break across the bedding, folds, and other structures of the surrounding wall rocks (Fig. 18–41). Obviously these acted as liquids, engulfing numerous fragments of wall rock and penetrating their walls in large and small dikes (Fig. 3–10). In places small injections so abound that the contact area becomes a transitional zone of "injection gneiss" consisting of intimately interpenetrating masses of granite and metamorphic rock in small layers, bands, dikelets, and irregular masses.

In other areas the metamorphic wall rocks bend concordantly around the pluton instead of being cut off by it. The granite itself may also show a marked flow banding, or even a gneissic structure parallel with its walls, along which it may be streaked out, granulated, and even partly recrystallized. The structural pattern in many areas (Fig. 18–43) indicates that both pluton and wall rock have undergone slow laminar flow as pasty masses of only slightly differing viscosity. Such structural relations suggest that the pluton was injected into wall rocks nearly as

FIGURE 18–41

Map of cross-cutting batholiths (black) *in the Pyrenees. The lines are fold trends. (After R. A. Daly,* Igneous Rocks and the Depths of the Earth, *McGraw-Hill Book Co., 1933.*)

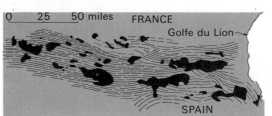

hot as the magma itself. Perhaps the magma had almost completely crystallized, and moved into place as a pasty mass of crystals and liquid, dragging the softened wall rocks with it. Or perhaps the intrusive was itself an intimate mixture of older metamorphic rock and new liquid material which had been formed by partial melting of the more fusible constituents of the metamorphic rocks just before the mixture was forced upward.

These complex small-scale mixtures of granite and wall rocks are called **migmatites** ("mixed rocks") (Fig. 18–42). Migmatites abound in many areas, chiefly in those of older rocks (more deeply eroded). They make up 26 percent of the surface rocks of Finland. They are puzzling rocks: do they represent an intimate soaking of schists and other metamorphic rocks by granitic magma that was injected in concordant layers along the foliation, and in tongues and dikes that cross-cut it? Or are they mixtures of the most readily fusible constituents of the metamorphic rocks being squeezed out of the more recalcitrant matrix? Or does the granitic fraction of the rock arise through partial replacement of the metamorphic rock by granitic minerals, just as we know that fossils can be replaced by silica or garnet? Or are all these processes acting in conjunction? These are most difficult questions, and clearcut answers cannot always be given, though in one place or another each process seems to have operated.

Some plutons show no definite contact with the wall rock; instead the granite fades gradually into metamorphic rocks. Although the metamorphic rock is thoroughly recrystallized, in places it may still retain clear relics of undoubted sedimentary or volcanic structures. Metamorphosed sedimentary rocks, when traced toward some granitic masses, begin to lose their typical foliation and other structural features; potassium feldspar and other minerals typical of granite begin to appear within them, first in small isolated crystals, then in increasingly abundant clots, until, finally only granitic min-

FIGURE 18–42
Migmatite, Clear Creek Canyon, Colorado. Note the complex folds and the intimate interpenetrations (mixing) of the light-colored granitic and the dark-colored schistose rocks. (Photo by Warren Hamilton, U.S. Geological Survey.)

erals are present, and only a vague streakiness gives a hint of the former metamorphic foliation. Some granites contain nebulous patterns that resemble stratification, outlines of pebbles, and other structures found in sedimentary rocks. Still other granites enclose frail unbroken layers of metamorphic marble and quartzite that could not have withstood forcible intrusion of magma without breaking up in the manner shown in Figure 3–10. Such structural features suggest that in some places former sedimentary rocks have been transformed to granite by slow recrystallization and replacement in the solid state, and that metamorphosed limestone and sand-

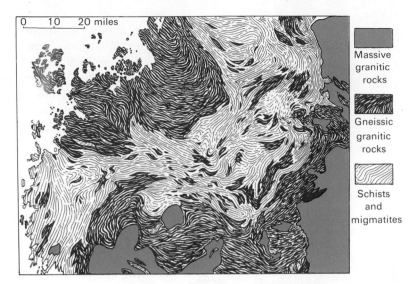

0   10   20 miles

Massive
granitic
rocks

Gneissic
granitic
rocks

Schists
and
migmatites

FIGURE 18–43   *Concordant batholiths and migmatites in southern Finland. The lined patterns indicate the strike of foliation in the gneissic granites, schists, and migmatites. (After Martti Saksela, 1935.)*

stone beds were the least susceptible to such replacement. Thus some granites appear to be products of metamorphic transformation, others are unquestionably igneous, and still others appear to be products of partial fusion in zones of migmatization (Fig. 18–43). But how can we discriminate between the different modes of origin? Many geologists consider that all transitions exist—that recrystallized sedimentary and volcanic rocks can be partly melted deep within the earth's crust, and the magma thus formed may either solidify into migmatites in place or be squeezed upward toward the surface, dragging the softened and partly melted wall rocks along with it, and finally slowly freeing itself from them as it rises into cracks and shatter zones in the colder and more brittle rocks above. In this view all the varying structural features shown by batholiths may be interpreted according to the depth of cover under which they were emplaced. Strongly discordant bodies with many dikes and sills extending out from them would characterize the shallower zones; with greater depth these would pass into concordant bodies sur-

rounded by broad zones of foliated metamorphic rocks; and finally, at great depths, into migmatites from which the partly melted granitic fractions have been forming and escaping upward (Fig. 18–44).

SPACE AND TIME RELATIONS.   The distribution of batholiths in space and time has significance in this problem of origin. Granite has not been found on any of the isolated Pacific Islands, and it probably is not present beneath them, since fragments of granite are not found in the ejecta from volcanoes on these islands. Further, the travel time of earthquake waves across the Pacific Basin (Chapter 19) is such that there can be no significant amount of granite or granodiorite underneath this ocean. Except for the granite of the Seychelles Islands in the Indian Ocean and of Iceland in the Atlantic, quartz-bearing plutons appear to be confined almost entirely to the continents, although basalt occurs in both continental and oceanic areas. Most large masses of granite apparently form in the root zones of mountain belts (Chapters 19 and 20) and appear at the surface

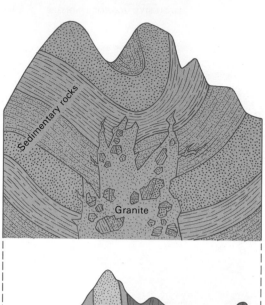

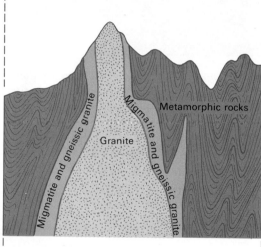

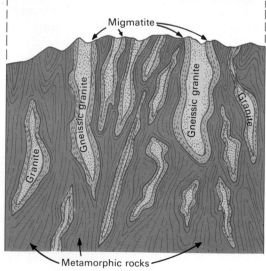

FIGURE 18–44
Hypothetical relations of plutons at three levels in the crust.

mainly, but not exclusively, in the cores of deeply eroded mountains, or in the sites of former mountains now eroded away. The few finer grained rocks of granitic composition that have injected plateaus, such as those of Iceland, Utah, and New Mexico are puzzling exceptions to the generalization that most plutons are related to mountain building. We return to this in Chapters 19 and 20.

PHYSICAL CHEMISTRY OF MAGMATIC CRYSTALLIZATION

For more than a century geologists have tried to duplicate the processes that go on in crystallizing magmas. Because high temperatures are needed to melt rocks, and because most rocks are highly complex, containing several solid-solution minerals of variable composition, such experiments have proved very difficult. The Norwegian geologist J. H. L. Vogt made the first great step forward during the 1890's by experimenting with artificial melts chosen to resemble blast-furnace slags, whose chemistry was fairly well known. His results were so encouraging that in 1904 the Carnegie Institution of Washington founded a Geophysical Laboratory in Washington, D.C., to begin a long-range, systematic attack on the physical chemistry of magmas. They began by studying artificial melts uncontaminated by the great number of subordinate elements invariably found in natural rocks. Their studies of even these simplified chemical systems have thrown much light on the history of igneous magmas. The late N. L. Bowen of this laboratory eventually developed a comprehensive and widely accepted theory of the evolution of igneous rocks.

Bowen's theory

Here we can, of course, present only a simplified statement of Bowen's ideas: because basalt appears in all geologic ages and structural settings, in ocean basins, continents, mountains, and plateaus, he thought

FIGURE 18–45

Schistose, gneissic, amphibolitic, and granitic rocks in complex structural relations, near Riggins, Idaho. (Photo by Warren Hamilton, U.S. Geological Survey.)

basaltic magma was the parent of all igneous rocks, and all the diverse varieties had arisen through crystallization differentiation. The great diversity of the igneous rocks has come about through the separation of early crystallized minerals from the parent basaltic magma during its cooling and by the accumulation of these early formed minerals in a different part of the magma chamber. Crystal settling by gravity, a process suggested by the olivine-rich ledge in the Palisades sill, Bowen thought very important; a second mechanism for separating solid from still-liquid fractions of the magma he thought to be **filter-pressing,** in which a spongy mass of partly crystallized magma is squeezed by crustal deformation, crushing the solid minerals together and squeezing out the still molten fraction of the magma as water is squeezed from a sponge. Such a process can be readily visualized as operating at depth in a mountain range as it is being formed, and one possible example of squeezing out is roughly illustrated in Figure 18–45.

By painstaking laboratory experiments, Bowen and his colleagues worked out the order of crystallization of the many common igneous minerals—that is, the order in which the different minerals begin to crystallize during the freezing of basaltic magma. These studies included not only those in which no early formed crystals were separated from the rest of the magma, but also many in which the earlier formed minerals were removed at various stages of magmatic consolidation. The order of crystallization worked out (if early crystal crops are successively removed during the cooling of the originally basaltic magma) —the Bowen Reaction Series—is shown below. Each horizontal line except the first represents the minerals formed if most of the earlier formed minerals are removed, and the magma remaining can react chemically with the few remaining.

Bowen Reaction Series

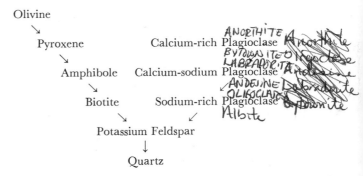

Olivine and calcium-rich plagioclase are the first minerals to crystallize in abundance from a basaltic melt low in silica. Unless removed by crystal-settling or filter-pressing, much of the olivine reacts at somewhat lower temperature with the surrounding liquid to produce pyroxene, and the calcium-rich plagioclase similarly reacts to produce a plagioclase richer in sodium. If none of these crystals are removed from the melt, and the reactions go on unimpeded, the whole mass will solidify to a mixture of plagioclase, pyroxene, and a little olivine—the characteristic minerals of basalt. A slightly more siliceous melt might have all its early formed olivine react to pyroxene; this would produce an olivine-free basalt, a relatively common rock.

If, however, the olivine or calcic plagioclase, or both, are separated from the melt, such reactions between crystals and liquid cannot go on. Olivine contains relatively more magnesium and relatively less silicon than the melt as a whole; similarly, calcic plagioclase contains relatively more calcium and less sodium and silica than the melt. If they are separated, then, the remaining liquid is relatively impoverished in magnesium and calcium and relatively enriched in silicon, sodium, potassium, and iron as compared with the original melt. Its composition is no longer basaltic but andesitic. With no more crystals separating, the liquid crystallizes to a diorite (if deep underground) or to an andesitic lava (if ejected to the surface).

But if the next crop of crystals—now pyroxene and calcium-sodium plagioclase—are removed about as fast as they form, so that they are unavailable for further reactions with the liquid, the residual magma continues to change in composition, ultimately reaching that of a siliceous, alkali-rich rhyolite. Only 10 percent or less of the original basaltic magma can be thus extracted as a rhyolitic liquid; the rest accumulates as peridotite, olivine-rich gabbro, diorite, and similar rocks on the floor of the magma chamber.

By this simple mechanism Bowen explained the great diversity of the igneous rocks. Some field relationships strongly support the reality of the scheme: for example, olivine rocks are common near the floors of thick sills, and quartz-bearing rocks at their tops; small rhyolite eruptives are common in large basaltic and andesitic volcanoes. The theory accounts for these small siliceous masses as the last residual liquids remaining after crystallization differentiation had removed the early formed minerals. Stratiform lopoliths may well have been formed by accumulation of the early crystallizing minerals

into sheets and layers so closely packed that the remaining magma was squeezed out and was unable to react with the crystals.

Objections to Bowen's theory

But not all the evidence is favorable. Although the theory is adequate to explain differentiated sills, stratiform complexes, and some composite volcanoes, it is not generally accepted as accounting for the origin of the great granitic and granodioritic plutons. It is hard to believe that these huge bodies represent only 5 or 10 percent of the original magma from which they were derived. The "room problem," that of providing space in the crust for such huge masses, not to mention the space needed for the vastly greater amounts of basaltic magma that would be needed as parents for such gigantic plutons as those of British Columbia or Idaho and California, is staggering (Fig. 18–40). The relative rarity of intermediate rocks such as diorite (according to the theory these should be far more abundant than granite) is a persuasive argument against its general validity.

The contacts of various plutons also suggest processes other than crystallization differentiation; in places, replacement, partial melting and assimilation, or merely recrystallization of wall rock have each played an important role in the development of large granitic plutons.

The virtual restriction of granite and granodiorite to the continents and their absence from the Pacific Islands, which are composed of basalt that did not differentiate to granite, also oppose the theory. Still more notable is the association of most batholiths in Cambrian and younger masses with the axial regions of mountain ranges, where they are closely associated with the zones of maximum metamorphic intensity. In the low-lying Precambrian areas, too, the structures of the associated wall rocks show that the plutons occupy former mountain chains, now leveled by erosion. Yet basalt, its supposed parent, is erupted in every kind of structural setting, and the greatest flood basalts—those of the Columbia, Parana, and Deccan plateaus—are in no way connected with either batholiths or fold mountains (Chapter 20).

METAMORPHIC ROCKS

Metamorphic rocks generally appear in the cores of mountain ranges and are the chief components of the ancient shields (Chapter 20). Deep drilling also shows that they underlie large parts of the continental plates, and as we saw in Chapter 17, they make up, together with associated plutonic rocks, about 85 percent of the earth's crust to a depth of 10 miles.

In Chapter 3 we noted that slate and certain other metamorphic rocks grade locally into only slightly altered sedimentary rocks. Slate must therefore have been formed by the recrystallization and growth of new minerals that replaced those formerly present in shale. Moreover, relic structures such as stratification could not have survived if the growth of the new minerals had not taken place in the solid state, without melting of the rock. Most original textures and structures such as fossils and stratification in sedimentary rocks, or the porphyritic and scoriaceous textures of lavas are obliterated during metamorphism. All too often, with such tell-tale features obliterated, we face a bewildering assemblage of highly folded, sheared and veined crystalline rocks that vary in appearance and generally contain a diverse assemblage of unfamiliar minerals (Fig. 18–45). How does one read the record of such puzzling rocks? No fossils remain to guide us, and the Law of Superposition is surely not reliable in rocks so strongly deformed. Here is a challenge, indeed!

Even the Uniformitarian Principle can help us only indirectly; metamorphism goes on deep within the earth; we cannot observe it in operation. But, as we mentioned in Chapter 3, recently invented machines can duplicate the pressures prevailing at depths of 50 miles or more, and the temperatures both above and below those at which rocks melt. Even though other variables such as geologic time, nonuniform pressures, and changing heterogeneous compositions cannot be duplicated, we do have crude experimental approaches to metamorphic conditions.

But the ultimate test of all geologic experimentation and theory lies in the field. What light has field mapping brought to the problems of metamorphism?

The "Basement Complex"

Up to the 1890's little progress had been made in the understanding of metamorphic rocks. Geologists had recognized their complexity, and that they were derived from other rocks, but their sequence in time, their stratigraphic order, and even significant clues to their parental rocks had puzzled the most competent. On most geologic maps all metamorphic rocks and most plutonic igneous rocks as well had been grouped under a single color as the "Basement Complex," even though on the same map unmetamorphosed sedimentary formations might be subdivided into many small units, based on minor differences in lithology and fossil content. Since the metamorphic rocks generally underlay the fossiliferous rocks and since their disturbed and recrystallized appearance (Figs. 18–46, 18–48) gave an impression of great age, they were nearly all assigned to the Precambrian, even though the fossiliferous rocks that rested upon them might be eras younger than the Cambrian. Early Scottish geologists called such rocks the "Old Boy."

Some geologists, however, were not willing to concede defeat by the "Old Boy." To them the wonderful diversity of the metamorphic rocks, the vast complexity of their textures and structures, and their unusual mineral assemblages were an irresistable challenge.

Successful discrimination between stratification and foliation in slate (Chapter 3), and the recognition that many coarse-grained foliated rocks rich in feldspar, such as those shown in Figure 18–47, are not igneous granites but the recrystallized products of old sedimentary and volcanic rocks, stimulated these observers to more careful field observations, and to the search for principles that would unify and unravel the history recorded in these enigmatic mineral assemblages and structures.

Soon it was found that rocks that had been assigned to the Precambrian because of their metamorphic attributes could in some places be traced laterally over a distance of many

FIGURE 18–46

Intricately folded marble and quartzite formed by intense shearing and recrystallization of former beds of limestone and chert. Big Maria Mountains, southeastern California. The original sedimentary rocks were of Permian age; their unmetamorphosed fossiliferous equivalents are exposed in the Grand Canyon, 150 miles to the northeast. (Photo by Warren Hamilton, U.S. Geological Survey.)

FIGURE 18–47

Coarse-grained feldspathic gneisses alternating with thin layers of amphibolite. Note local contortion and faulting. (Photo by Sidney Paige, U.S. Geological Survey.)

FIGURE 18–48

Contorted chlorite schist and phyllite. Note the complex folds and the broken and scattered fragments. How can we tell whether the disrupted layering is a former sedimentary stratification or a new structure caused by metamorphic processes? Mount Lydenia, Alaska. (Photo by J. C. Reed, U.S. Geological Survey.)

miles and be found to intergrade with unmetamorphosed fossiliferous rocks of Paleozoic (Fig. 18–46) or even Mesozoic age. Geologists then began to look much more carefully into the nature of the variations, both lithological and structural, and to map them in detail. Are the crumpled and shredded layers shown in Figure 18–48 remnants of sedimentary beds like those shown in Figure 18–46, or were they formed by the segregation of certain constituents during the process of metamorphism? **Metamorphic differentiation** involves the segregation of contrasting layers or blebs of minerals by local migration of their constituents during metamorphism.

Mineral zoning and isograds

Perhaps the earliest unifying principle in the understanding of metamorphism came from field studies in the highlands of Scotland by the British geologist George Barrow. He noted that the metamorphic rocks bordering granite bodies in the Grampian Highlands are generally coarse grained and rich in feldspar whereas those farther away are finer grained and more micaceous. Still farther out, some preserve relic structures such as stratification and rare, badly deformed fossils. Looking more closely at the minerals of the metamorphic rocks, Barrow noted that the feldspar-rich gneisses and coarse schists near the plutons contain many needle-like crystals of *sillimanite* (Al_2SiO_5) . A little farther away the schists contain blades of *kyanite,* a mineral of the same composition as sillimanite, but of different crystal structure. Still farther from the plutons, cross-shaped twin crystals of *staurolite* are prominent in the schists. Barrow found this sequence virtually the same completely around the plutons—he demonstrated a crude but definite **mineral zoning** around the centers of maximum metamorphic intensity. The zoning is more or less independent of the composition of the metamorphic rocks so can not be attributed to original chemical differences such as are common between adjacent sedimentary strata. *The zoning, instead, must record the intensity of the metamorphic processes.*

The British petrologist Alfred Harker showed that this mineral zoning could be analyzed in more detail by careful petrographic work. One of the garnets, *almandine,* characterizes a zone of schist outside the staurolite zone and still farther out, in a broad belt of finer grained schists that grades into phyllites, a *biotite zone* can be recognized. Still farther out the rocks are chloritic phyllites and slates, the *chlorite zone.* Apparently decreasing temperature outward from the plutonic center controlled the mineral phases developed in the original parent shales.

Still another British petrologist, C. E. Tilley, proposed in 1925 that the *first appearance* of one of these key minerals: chlorite, biotite, almandine, staurolite, kyanite, and sillimanite, as one approaches the plutonic center, records the place where a definite temperature, necessary for the stability of that particular mineral, had been attained. He thought that a line on a map connecting these points of first appearance is an **isograd** —a line of equal temperature in the earth at the time of the metamorphism.

Physical factors that affect metamorphism

Significant and important as were these new concepts, mapping has since shown them to be oversimplified: Many factors other than temperature also influence mineral formation during metamorphism. Not all of these are fully understood, yet certain broad generalizations are already possible:

1. We know that changing pressure affects the equilibrium of a chemical system and must therefore influence metamorphic mineral reactions. Chemists have shown that

higher pressures favor the growth of denser minerals, but laboratory tests on metamorphic minerals are few.

2. Grain size is an important factor in the speed of chemical reaction. Field observations show that a coarse-grained rock, such as granite, may undergo almost intact a metamorphic environment that has brought about complete recrystallization of fine-grained rhyolite and tuff, which had been deposited unconformably on the granite. The chemical compositions of the rocks are identical, but the greater surface area relative to bulk of the minerals in the finer grained rocks rendered them more susceptible to chemical reactions.

3. Difference in grain size also affects susceptibility to shearing and plastic flow, factors very important in metamorphism. Tuff is more easily deformed than granite, but if a granite is subjected to pressures great enough to shear and pulverize it, not only does it become more mobile, but the areas of contact between the various minerals are greatly increased, reaction between them is speeded, and the shearing also releases frictional heat. All these factors facilitate flowage, recrystallization, and metamorphic differentiation between minerals. The rock illustrated in Figure 18–49 has thus been formed from granite. The matrix of this rock consists of streaky layers and blebs of fine-grained recrystallized feldspar, quartz, biotite and chlorite, but the augen (German, "eyes") of microcline, though cracked and milled on their edges and with tails drawn out in the foliation, have survived complete crushing and recrystallization. These record the original coarse grain of the granite before it metamorphosed into gneiss. Clearly, the mechanical stirring during this shearing constantly brought new surfaces into contact and promoted metamorphic reactions, but the strong microcline resisted shearing so well as largely to survive.

4. The chemical composition of a rock determines the possible metamorphic min-

FIGURE 18–49
Augen gneiss, near Tonasket, Washington. Granite has been crushed to powder and simultaneously completely recrystallized except for the eye-shaped fragments (augen) of resistant microcline.

erals that may form in it. Obviously no mineral can form unless the chemical elements composing it are available, however favorable the temperature and pressure. Most of the rocks studied by Barrow, Harker, and Tilley were derived originally from clay shale and siltstone. Besides one or more of the six minerals defining isograds, each rock also contains much mica and quartz, and, near the plutonic centers, potassium feldspar. But a basaltic lava interbedded with such shales and metamorphosed with them forms a wholly different mineral suite. Micas, quartz, and potassium feldspar are absent or nearly so; the dominant minerals produced by metamorphism are chlorite, epidote, amphiboles, pyroxenes, magnesian garnet, and sphene.

5. Water is also an important variable. Many metamorphic minerals are hydrous, chlorite, mica, amphibole, epidote, and many others; moreover, even many anhydrous minerals form readily only in the presence of water.

Metamorphic facies

In 1921, Pentti Eskola, a brilliant Finnish geologist, emphasized the point that several kinds of metamorphic rocks, though differing markedly in mineral composition and texture, all have the same chemical composition as basalt. Most of them contain no relic features allying them to basalt; evidently recrystallization has wiped out all original characteristics. Because of their chemical identity, however, Eskola considered them surely derived from either basalt or its plutonic equivalents, gabbro or dolerite, under metamorphic conditions so intense as to destroy the original textures. He proposed, therefore, that because each mineral assemblage records the intensity of metamorphism, metamorphic rocks of the same chemical composition can be classified into distinct metamorphic facies, each characterized by a unique mineral assemblage. *Each metamorphic facies must represent a special metamorphic environment—a definite range of temperature and pressure—wherein this particular assemblage of minerals is stable.* If metamorphic intensity increases, some formerly stable minerals recrystallize into new assemblages characterizing the newer, more intense metamorphic conditions.

Among the metamorphic equivalents of basalt Eskola recognized four very common metamorphic facies, which, with their characterizing minerals, are listed in Table 18–1. Additional work in the last 40 years has added a few more facies and has shown that it is possible to equate these facies, based on basalt, with those based on the metamorphism of shale, graywacke, and other rocks.

Recent laboratory studies

Eskola's work focused attention on the stability relations of different minerals. If we knew the exact conditions of pressure, temperature, and chemical environment under which a given metamorphic mineral formed, we could use this mineral as a geologic thermometer and pressure gage. But unfortunately we are a long way from this happy objective.

Metamorphic minerals are notably difficult to synthesize in the laboratory. Van't Hoff's classic experiments with the easily handled Stassfurt salts (Chapter 3), and the pitfalls attending their interpretation may be recalled. V. M. Goldschmidt, a Norwegian geochemist, made many significant investigations of the much more difficult silicate minerals between 1911 and 1940. He threw considerable light on the stability of some of the anhydrous minerals in the metamorphic aureoles surrounding certain intrusive masses in Norway. But many metamorphic minerals are hydrous silicates, and nearly all attempts to "grow" them and determine their

Table 18–1 **The metamorphic facies equivalent to basalt in chemical composition**

Rock and facies	Mineral composition
Original rock	
Basalt, gabbro, dolerite	pyroxene, plagioclase, minor olivine and magnetite
Metamorphic facies	
Greenschist	chlorite, albite, epidote
Amphibolite	amphibole, plagioclase
Pyroxene granulite	plagioclase, pyroxene (augite, hypersthene, or both)
Eclogite	Sodic pyroxene, magnesian garnet

SOURCE: After Pentti Eskola, 1921.

conditions of stability in the laboratory failed until, in the late 1940's, O. F. Tuttle, an American geologist, succeeded in making a "hydrothermal bomb" in which water vapor and other volatile substances could be held in contact with silicate powders at high temperatures and pressures. Since then geochemists have successfully synthesized most mineral groups, and have determined the stability relations of many simple mineral assemblages.

In recent years, too, we have learned how to determine the age of the abundant mica so common in metamorphic rocks by potassium-argon analysis (Chapter 7).

Despite all these advances, the detailed stratigraphy of metamorphic terrains often eludes us. Potassium-argon dating gives only the time of metamorphism; we still have no measure of the date when the original sediment or volcanic rock was formed, perhaps millions of years before the metamorphism recorded by the mica.

Thus, although the bastions of his citadel are constantly being undermined by closely integrated laboratory and field attacks, the "Old Boy" still retains many a secret. Our knowledge of the conditions of metamorphism also increases as we gain new understanding of two other complex and controversial subjects: the origin of earthquakes and of mountain ranges. These problems are the themes of our next two chapters.

Facts, concepts, terms

Volcanic rocks

Shield volcanoes

Fissure eruptions, rift zones, cinder cones, parasitic volcanoes

Calderas, ring dikes

Lava pools, lava fountains

Composite Volcanoes

Explosive activity

Explosion products, blocks, bombs, pumice lapilli, glass shards

Eruption clouds, pyroclastic flows, ash falls, welded tuffs

Spines and domical protrusions

Mudflows

Flood basalts, dike swarms

Pillow lava, pillow breccia, glass breccia, palagonite tuff

Maar volcanoes

Phreatic eruptions, tuff cones, explosive submarine eruptions

Plutons

Lopoliths

Stratiform complexes, layered differentiates

Batholiths

Contact relations of plutons

Space and time relations

Migmatites, concordant batholiths, replacement masses

Physical chemistry of magmatic crystallization

Bowen's theory, the reaction series, crystallization differentiation, gravitative settling, filter-pressing

Objections to Bowen's theory
Volume problem, lack of intermediate products in suitable quantity, absence of granite from areas of huge basaltic accumulations
Metamorphic Rocks
Wide distribution
"Basement complex," diverse ages of metamorphism
Mineral zoning, isograds
Physical factors affecting metamorphism, shearing, grain size, plastic flow
Chemical factors, contrasts between shale and basaltic metamorphic products, water and its influence
Metamorphic facies, laboratory research
Dating metamorphism by radiometry
Association of plutons with zones of maximum metamorphic intensity.

Questions

1. Why are cinder cones more likely to develop along a dike after the dike has fed lava flows and is in process of congealing than when the dike first breaks through to the surface?

2. How can you distinguish a deposit of welded tuff from a flow or domical protrusion of flow-banded rhyolite?

3. Obsidian from a Japanese volcano has a specific gravity of 2.60, pumice lapilli from the same volcano floats two-thirds submerged in water. Approximately what volume of ejected pumice would be required to account for the formation at the top of this volcano of a caldera 4 miles in diameter and with an average depth of 1000 feet? (Assume that the caldera was the result of piecemeal subsidence by lack of support after the pumice lapilli had been ejected from a magma chamber directly beneath the site of the caldera).

4. Draw cross-section diagrams of the following igneous bodies: (*a*) a basalt flow, (*b*) a ring dike, (*c*) a differentiated sill, (*d*) a laccolith fed from a stock, (*e*) a concordant batholith.

5. Draw a sketch or a geologic map showing a portion of the edge of a discordant batholith. Show and label the following typical features: (*a*) a discordant contact, (*b*) inclusions, (*c*) a series of dolerite sills that are older than the batholith, (*d*) a rhyolite dike that is younger than the batholith, (*e*) a series of sedimentary rocks that are older than the batholith, (*f*) a welded tuff younger than the batholith.

6. Explain the process of differentiation by crystal settling in an igneous mass.

7. What is the evidence that some granites are of metamorphic origin?

8. How could you tell that a granite body had been injected into cold rocks rather than into a zone of high metamorphic intensity where the wall rocks were nearly as hot as the granite?

9. Why is it more difficult to make synthetic metamorphic minerals in the laboratory than it is to make evaporite minerals?

10. Many greenschists, composed of chlorite, epidote, and albite show well-developed pillow structures. Would you expect these to be associated with chlorite-bearing mica schists typical of the Barrow-Harker-Tilley chlorite zone, or with highly feldspathic sillimanite-bearing gneisses. Why?

11. Assuming the chlorite schist to be in contact with the sillimanite gneiss, what inference can you draw regarding the nature of the contact?
12. Why is an isograd not a true measure of metamorphic temperature?

Suggested readings

Buddington, A. F., *Granite Emplacement with Special Reference to North America.* Geological Society of America Bulletin, v. 70, 1959, p. 671–748.

Bullard, F. M., *Volcanoes.* Austin: University of Texas Press, 1962, 441 p.

Eaton, J. P., and K. J. Murata, *How Volcanoes Grow.* Science, v. 132, No. 3432, 1960, p. 925–938.

Hunt, C. B., *Structural and Igneous Geology of the La Sal Mountains, Utah* (U.S. Geological Survey, Professional Paper 294–I.) Washington, D.C.: G.P.O., 1958. [p. 305–364.]

Macdonald, G. A., and D. K. Hubbard, *Volcanoes of Hawaii National Park.* Hawaii Nature Notes, v. 4, 1951, 43 p.

Read, H. H., *The Granite Controversy.* London and New York: Interscience Publishers, 1957

Shelton, J. S., *Geology Illustrated.* San Francisco: W. H. Freeman and Company, 1966, 434 p.

Tuttle, O. F., and N. L. Bowen, *Origin of Granite in the Light of Experimental Studies.* Geological Society of America Memoir 74, 1958.

Tyrrell, G. W., *Volcanoes.* London: T. Butterworth, 1931.

Scientific American offprints

819. O. Frank Tuttle, *The Origin of Granite* (April 1955)
822. Howel Williams, *Volcanoes* (November 1951)
854. Edwin Roedder, *Ancient Fluids in Crystals* (October 1962)

19

Earthquakes and the Earth's Interior

EFFECTS OF EARTHQUAKES

In the early morning of November 1, 1755, All Saint's Day, the churches of Lisbon were thronged with worshippers. Suddenly the ground thundered forth a terrifying roar and began to heave and writhe in horrible, jarring shocks that seemed endless. The roofs and arches of the great stone churches crumbled, crushing hundreds beneath them. Most of the buildings in the city crashed in rubble. Within six minutes, when the awful quaking stopped, thousands had perished, and thousands more lay trapped beneath the wreckage. The sea withdrew, exposing the bar at the harbor mouth, then rushed in as a wall of water 50 feet high, drowning hundreds who had taken refuge on the open wharves, and destroying ships, docks, and nearly everything in its path. A shorter shock of great intensity cascaded slides of rock from the mountains onto the city, raising dust clouds so dense that many thought a volcanic eruption had begun. A third shock struck two hours later. Fires completed the destruction: by nightfall 60,000 people of a population of 235,000 had perished, and thousands of the survivors were crippled, maimed, or mad from terror.

Rivers as far away as Lübeck, Germany (1400 miles), rose or fell several feet. Loch Lomond, 1200 miles away, was thrown into waves two feet high. Though possibly reinforced by a nearly simultaneous but independent shock farther south, the earthquake wrecked, with great loss of life, the cities of Fez and Mequinez in Morocco, 400 miles from Lisbon, as well as scores of other towns in Spain and North Africa. The quake (or quakes, if the doubtful separate southern shock really occurred) affected an area at least five times that of the United States.

The Good Friday Earthquake of 1964 which wreaked havoc over much of southern Alaska has already been mentioned in connection with the downslope movements triggered by it (Chapter 11). It is also of interest for the widespread deformation of the crust that accompanied the quake. Surveys of changes in shorelines following the earthquake show that nearly every spot in Prince William Sound southeast of a line extending from Port Nellie Juan to Valdez was uplifted; and that nearly every spot northwest of this line sank. The maximum uplift measured—more than 30 feet—was on Montague Island; the maximum subsidence measured (but probably not the true maximum) was 6 feet on a line through Whittier roughly parallel to the line of no change (Fig. 19–1).

No doubt these changes of level extended for considerable distances inland, but comparably precise measurements could not be there be made. For the most part the changes in level along Prince William Sound were not abrupt, but in places, as on Montague Island, clear-cut normal faults of displacements as high as 4 to 5 meters were found (Fig. 19–1).

The Good Friday earthquake of 1964 was only one of many that have wracked southern Alaska; one on September 10, 1899, centering at Yakutat Bay, is distinguished as having accompanied the greatest vertical dis-

FIGURE 19–1   *Level changes brought about during the 1964 Alaska Earthquake in Prince William Sound. Contour interval 2 feet between −6 feet and +10 feet; 10 feet between +10 and +30 feet. (After George Plafker, 1965.)*

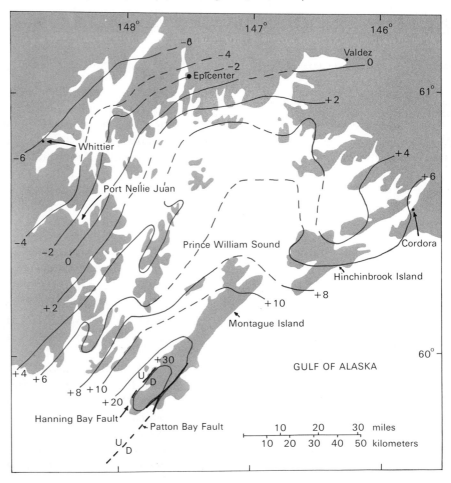

placement of any yet studied. Barnacles and boring clams, marking the old strand zone, were lifted more than 47 feet above the sea in some places; other areas nearby were lowered. The Yakutat Bay earthquake affected the coastal glaciers drastically: Muir Glacier, more than a hundred miles from Yakutat Bay, was so severely shaken that great icebergs broke away, and the glacier wasted back at abnormal speed. Near Yakutat Bay, however, though many bergs also broke free, so many avalanches were shaken down onto the glacier heads from the towering St. Elias Range as to drive the glaciers vigorously forward, some many hundreds of yards in less than 10 months. Even stagnant parts of the Malaspina Glacier (Fig. 13–11), so long inactive that a dense forest had grown in the debris-strewn ice, resumed motion and tossed its surface into a wild confusion of tilted and overturned trees, crevasses, hummocks, and pinnacles.

Lisbon and southern Alaska are mountainous. Most earthquakes originate in regions of high relief, either terrestrial or submarine, but some great earthquakes have taken place in areas of low relief. Among these was the great Indian earthquake of 1819 in Kutch, at the mouth of the Indus. During it a huge lowland was flooded by the sea, while a scarp to the north, the "Allah Bund" or "Dam of Allah"—80 kilometers long, was raised as much as 6 meters.

Among the most notable of lowland earthquakes was that of December 11, 1811, near New Madrid, Missouri, on the banks of the Mississippi. At 2 A.M. the quake threw people from their beds; in a few seconds many of their log cabins had toppled, and over thousands of acres, sand, mud, and water gushed out of cracks in the earth, burying many of the cleared fields. The undercut alluvial banks along miles of the Mississippi meanders caved off into the stream; islands sank, others rose; boats were swamped or hurled ashore. During the next 15 months an unusually persistent series of minor aftershocks

continued. Thousands were felt, along with two severe quakes comparable with the first. Square miles of land rose, draining former swamps, and a huge tract nearly 150 miles long and 35 miles wide sank—in places as much as 10 feet—to form new lakes and swamps. Reelfoot Lake, so formed, is several miles across. The great shocks stopped pendulum clocks and rang church bells as far away as Boston and cracked plaster in Virginia. Had this earthquake come a century later the loss of life would have been appalling, but in those pioneer days few were endangered.

Many other major earthquakes may be cited. One struck eastern Sicily and the Calabrian coast across the Straits of Messina on December 28, 1908, destroying the cities of Messina and Reggio, killing about 100,000 people, and leaving the coast at Messina submerged more than 2 feet below its former level. Two great earthquakes rocked Kansu, in western China, one in December 1920, the other in May 1927; each was reported to have killed about 100,000 people, chiefly by the collapse of dwellings dug in weakly consolidated loess. Two great earthquakes jolted Assam, India, one in 1897 which raised a scarp 35 feet high and destroyed buildings in Calcutta, 200 miles away; the other, on August 15, 1950, stripped soil and trees from a landscape 12,000 square miles in extent, and catapulted an estimated 60 billion cubic yards of rock and soil into the valleys, damming even the major rivers (Fig. 8–1). When the Brahmaputra overtopped its landslide dam, it changed to a slurry of 30 percent silt and clay, and raced at speeds estimated at 50 miles an hour down its valley. During a great earthquake in Mongolia on December 4, 1957, an oblique-slip reverse fault, more than 150 miles long and as much as 30 feet high, broke the surface with such violence that riders were thrown off their camels as far as 20 feet, sheep rolled "like balls" down the hills, and houses almost 200 miles away were destroyed; a month later travel was still almost impossible because of persistent avalanches and landslides. On February 29, 1960, an earthquake flattened hotels and other multi-story buildings in the resort town of Agadir, Morocco, and killed one-third of its inhabitants. More than 1000 lives were lost in the southern Chile earthquake of May 22, 1960. The Wellington earthquake of 1855, and the Hawkes Bay earthquake of 1931, in New Zealand, were each accompanied by land tilting and uplift of 6 to 10 feet. A quake on the plain of the Hoang Ho in the sixteenth century is reported to have killed more than 800,000 people—almost certainly the greatest catastrophe in history.

The San Francisco earthquake

The San Francisco earthquake is of special interest, for many of our present ideas about earthquakes are derived from its study. At a little after 5 A.M. on April 19, 1906, a great earthquake struck San Francisco. Many buildings were wrecked, especially those on marshy or filled ground, but many built on solid rock were little damaged. Hundreds of people were killed or injured, pavements broken, gas and water mains and electric power lines torn apart. Hundreds of fires sprang up, and raged out of control for days—the firemen helpless because of the broken water mains. Though the loss of life could only be estimated, it probably exceeded 700. Material losses exceeded $400,-000,000, mostly from the fire. San Francisco suffered most, but Santa Rosa, Palo Alto, San Jose, and many other towns, some more than a hundred miles away, were severely damaged.

A great fault zone—the San Andreas rift—cuts obliquely across the California Coast Ranges for more than 600 miles, from the ocean at Point Arena on the north, past San Francisco, and thence far to the southeast, where it is finally lost in the alluvium of the Colorado Desert. During the earthquake, the ground was rent open along this fault from Point Arena to San Juan Bautista, more than 270 miles (Fig. 19–2); movement was everywhere nearly horizontal, with the ground on the west side moving northward in relation to that on the east: a right-lateral fault. The greatest displacement—21 feet as measured by the offset of a road—took place about 30 miles northwest of San Francisco. The displacement diminished both to north and south, though not regularly. Locally, especially toward the north, slight vertical displacements took place, but nowhere more than 3 feet.

The San Andreas rift had been recognized as a fault zone for many years before the 1906 earthquake. Not only are geologic formations cut off and the rocks much sheared and crushed along it, but it is also conspicuous in the landscape—marked for much of its course by parallel valleys and ridges. Some streams bend abruptly—nearly all to the right—as they reach it, and follow it for scores or hundreds of feet before resuming their original trends. Small ponds are strung out along it, some on steep slopes—strikingly anomalous features in arid southern California. In 1857 a strong earthquake shook the country along a segment of the San Andreas rift in the Tehachapi Mountains, far south of the 1906 break. It, too, was accompanied by right-lateral movement of the fault. Several earthquakes along parts of this zone to the south accompanied horizontal right-lateral displacements. Figure 19–3 shows an example of such an offset that occurred in December, 1940, in an orange grove in the Imperial Valley about a mile north of the Mexican border.

CAUSES OF EARTHQUAKES

No one knows the ultimate cause of earthquakes. It seems certain that the immediate cause is the sudden movement of rock masses along faults, for such movements would be adequate to cause the shaking, and fault dis-

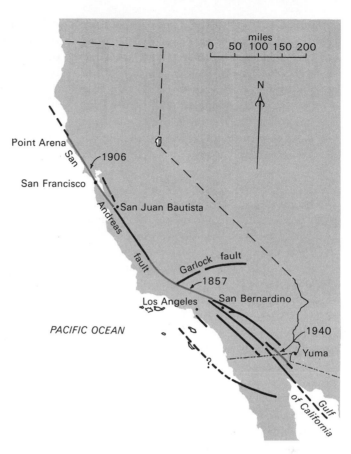

FIGURE 19-2

The San Andreas and associated fault zones in California and northern Mexico. Brown lines show where the surface of the ground was broken during historic earthquakes. (After Clarence R. Allen, 1957.)

FIGURE 19-3

Orange grove in Imperial Valley, California, displaced in December, 1940. About one mile south, the horizontal slip was almost 15 feet. (U.S. Army photo, courtesy E. Marliave.)

placement has been observed during many quakes. Most earthquakes, however, are unattended by visible fault displacement, though such displacement may have taken place below the surface. Every fault is of finite length and beyond the last point of rupture disappears: in 1906 no movement was measured on the San Andreas fault south of San Juan Bautista. Similarly variable displacements of individual faults are seen in mines where many faults die out before reaching the surface. Although the correlation between fault displacement and maximum intensity of shaking is clear, details of the relationships are not. In 1906 buildings a few hundred yards from the San Andreas fault were not greatly damaged except where boggy ground rendered them particularly susceptible. Many oil wells in the Los Angeles basin have been cut off by faults during

earthquakes, even though there was no surface sign of slipping, establishing that faulting is associated with some quakes where no
surface displacement can be found. Because
of such observations, nearly all seismologists
now agree that major earthquakes arise from
movement on faults, even when no movement is discernible at the ground surface.

Elastic-rebound theory

The fault motion accompanying the San
Francisco earthquake was chiefly horizontal,
and therefore was not directly due to gravity. The region is not volcanic—and even if
it were, no known volcanic eruption has
shown energy remotely comparable to that
expended in moving thousands of cubic
miles of rock for many feet along a break
270 miles long. What, then was the immediate source of this prodigious energy?

The American geologist H. F. Reid suggested an answer. Most crustal movements
are slow. Though the fault displacement was
sudden, the energy released had probably
been slowly accumulating as elastic strain as
the rocks west of the fault slowly drifted
northward relative to those on the east.
Slipping along the fault was long delayed by
the cohesion of the rocks across it. The strain
accumulated slowly, just as energy is stored
elastically when we bend a bow. Ultimately,
however, it reached a critical value, the fric-

tion along the fault plane was overcome, and
the two sides of the fault "snapped past each
other," as a bow snaps and breaks if we bend
it too far.

Reid's analysis of the precise triangulation
surveys by the U.S. Coast and Geodetic Survey in 1851–1865, 1874–1892, and after the
earthquake, in 1906–1907, strongly supported this idea. Though the first survey was
less accurate than the later ones, its data are
consistent with theirs. If the stations called
Diablo and Moncho, both 35 miles east of
the rift, are considered not to have moved,
then a comparison of their positions with the
computed positions of points near the San
Andreas rift show large systematic movements with respect to Diablo and Mocho
during the interval between the last two surveys. Reid grouped the data according to the
average distance of the several stations from
the fault. His results are shown in Table
19–1.

The relations may be visualized from Figure 19–4. Let us assume a time when there
was no elastic strain in the rocks of the region; the line AOC represents a line then
crossing the fault at right angles. As the regional distortion began the point A moved
slowly north to A' and the point C south to
C'. Because the fault did not slip during this
time, the formerly straight line through O
became strongly bent. Just before the earthquake, point A had advanced still farther,

Table 19–1 **Average displacement of points between surveys of 1874–1892 and 1906–1907, relative to the Diablo-Mocho line considered as fixed in position**

Group	Number of Stations in group	Average distance from fault of stations in group, in miles		Displacement, in feet	
		East	West	Northward	Southward
A	1	4	...	...	1.9
B	3	2.6	...	...	2.8
C	10	.9	...	...	5.1
D	12	...	1.2	9.7	...
E	7	...	3.6	7.8	...
F	1	...	23	5.8	...

FIGURE 19–4
Diagrammatic map showing how the 1906 offset along the San Andreas fault is explained by the elastic-rebound theory. (After H. F. Reid, 1911.)

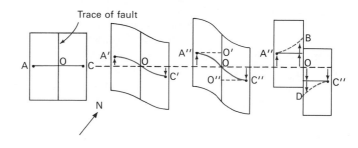
Trace of fault

N

to A″, and point C to C″, these distance being such that the total A–A″ and C–C″ amounted, on the average, to 14.8 feet. (The greatest advance was 21 feet.) Then the stored elastic force overcame the friction along the fault: the strain was relieved with explosive violence. A″O straightened out to A″O′ and C″O″. It is clear that the lines such as A″O′ and C″O″, which had been straight just before, would be bent during faulting into curves A″B and C″D, identical with A″O and C″O but bent oppositely. When the fault slipped Reid assumed that the elastic strain (bending of the rocks without rupture) was almost completely released; the fault movement represents only the "elastic rebound" of the rocks from strain slowly accumulated before. The data in Table 19–1 conform to the pattern of lines like A″B and C″D, lending strong support to the theory.

Since 1907 the Coast and Geodetic Survey has made further systematic resurveys of the same triangulation points; these confirm a continued northward displacement of stations west of the Diablo—Mocho reference line. The movement seems to go on at a rate of about 2 inches a year. If we assume, though, of course, there is no sound basis for such a simple assumption, that when this displacement reaches that prior to the 1906 earthquake another will take place, about a century must still elapse. Such a prediction is valueless, for we cannot be sure that the same displacement will renew the faulting, nor that another nearly parallel fault, or even folding of the rocks, might not relieve the strain instead. But the existence of the

movement strongly supports the "elastic-rebound" theory, and suggests that if sufficiently refined methods of measuring and analyzing earth strains can be developed, it may ultimately be feasible to predict earthquakes accurately.

Seismic sea waves

The great wave that overwhelmed Lisbon was doubtless caused by displacement of the sea floor to the west, perhaps caused by submarine slides. The dramatic changes that Tokyo and Grand Banks earthquakes made on the sea floor have already been mentioned in Chapters 5 and 8. These effects were chiefly due to slides in unconsolidated sediments and turbidity flows. Few earthquakes on land are accompanied by very large fault displacements, and this is presumably true of submarine earthquakes also, for few of them are accompanied by such large waves as those that wrought havoc at Lisbon. Nevertheless, continuously recording tide gages do reveal many large waves, presumably set up by earthquakes or their accompanying slides, that would otherwise go unnoticed.

Waves caused by earthquakes are called **seismic sea waves** or **tsunamis** (Japanese). In many, as at Lisbon, the first movement is a withdrawal of water followed, after an interval measured in minutes, by a great inrush of the sea. Some seismic sea waves are truly gigantic: perhaps the greatest on record is one 210 feet high that broke on the south tip of Kamchatka in 1737. During the Alaska earthquake of 1964 a tsunami in Valdez Arm deposited debris 170 feet above sea level and threw barnacle-covered boulders weighing nearly a ton to heights 88 feet above low water. Even the small Kenai Lake, only 20 miles long, developed standing waves whose interference caused flooding at one end to heights of 70 feet. Most of the loss of life during the Chilean earthquake of 1960 was caused by tsunamis. A tsunami 93 feet high struck the city of Miyako, Japan, in 1896; still another, in 1868, carried the U.S.S. *Watersee* far inland from its anchorage off the Chilean coast and left it high and dry. Waves from an earthquake off Peru were 8 feet high as they reached Japanese tide gages 10,300 miles from their source. These heights depend very largely on configuration of the shores; in the open ocean the waves are never noticed by ships. The speed of the waves depends only on the depth of water: it is often 400 or 450 miles per hour in the Pacific, but much less in the shallower Atlantic. Damage and loss of life from tsunamis in Hawaii have been great enough that coastal warnings are now broadcast when the possibility of seismic sea waves is indicated by seismograph records of earthquakes.

EARTHQUAKE WAVES AND THEIR TRANSMISSION

If we break a bat while hitting a baseball, our hands are stung by the vibrations transmitted through the wood. In the same way, when two huge blocks of rock slip past each other along a fault, elastic vibrations are set up and transmitted through the earth in all directions. The nature of these vibrations may be seen from Figure 19–5, *left*.

If we imagine that the point P in the figure is a particle within a uniform mass of perfectly elastic rock, and that it is pressed to the right, toward P′, by some outside force, we can see that the material on its right is compressed, while that on its left expands. Since the rock is assumed to be perfectly elastic, these changes in volume mean that potential energy is stored up in it, and that the compressed material tends to return to its original volume and the rarified material to contract. Let us now consider the movement of a line, APB, through P. If the point P is moved to P′ by an external force, the line must bend to some position such as

FIGURE 19–5   Left: *The distortion of line* AB *during the passage of compressional waves at right angles to* AB. Right: *The effect of compressional and distortional waves on the grouping of a series of equally spaced points. Note how the compressional wave affects their spacing in the direction of propagation, whereas the distortional wave offsets them as it passes from left to right. (After J. B. Macelwane, When the Earth Quakes, Bruce Publishing Co., 1947.)*

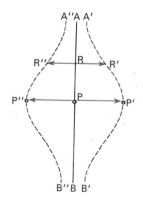

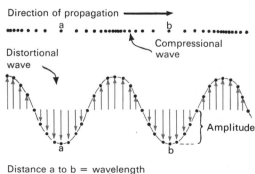

A'P'B', thereby setting up a distortion, or shear, in the line. The nearer each point on the line APB is to P the farther it tends to slip, parallel to PP', from its original position, as the line becomes A'P'B'. Thus there is differential shear between P and R for P-P' is larger than R-R', etc. This means that some energy is also stored up by distortion that can be released in shear.

Now let the outside force be removed. The point P' will not simply return to its original position P, but will have a momentum (like a pendulum) that will carry it on past P to a point such as P''. The part of the rock to its left will now be compressed and that to the right rarified; the direction of the shearing tendency will also have been reversed. At P'', the kinetic energy that carried the point past the center will have been transformed again to potential energy; the point will again oscillate back through P to P'. The distance between P' and P'' is the amplitude of the oscillation.

Of course, rocks are not perfectly elastic. In nature some energy is consumed as frictional heat, so that each oscillation is less than the preceding one. Still, the principle involved is not affected. If we consider the effects of the vibrations of a particle of rock at P on all other particles surrounding it, and of these, in turn, on their neighbors, we see that two types of waves, one compressional and the other a shear wave, must emanate from the point and spread through the surrounding rock in all directions.

In the *compressional wave,* the particles vibrate back and forth in the line of wave progress as alternate pulses of compression and rarefaction through the rock. It is thus like a sound wave in air. This wave is called the **P wave** (primary wave). The other wave, the *shear wave,* is transverse; that is, the particles vibrate at right angles to the direction of wave progress (Fig. 19–5, *right*). This is called the **S wave** (secondary). The particle motion in the S wave is like that set up

in a loosely hanging rope when one end is given a sharp flip. Each particle of the rope moves virtually at right angles to the length of the rope, but the wave travels from one end of the rope to the other. These transverse vibrations are not the visible ground waves seen at the surface during some strong earthquakes; their wavelengths are measured in miles and their speeds in thousands of feet per second, far too long and too fast for the human eye to see.

From the theory of elasticity we know that the compressional waves in an ideal elastic solid travel at speeds that vary directly as the resistance of the solid to compression and shear and inversely as its density.* The speed of shear waves varies directly with resistance to shear and inversely with density. In rocks of the same density, the more rigid and incompressible the rock the faster both waves travel. In two equally rigid and incompressible rocks, on the other hand, the speed is greater in the less dense rock. As can be seen from the formulas, the compressional (P wave) travels faster than the shear wave (S wave).

The elastic properties of rocks—the incompressibility and rigidity—can be measured in the laboratory. Assuming that the wave theories are correct, we can also compute them from the measured speeds of waves made in the earth by exploding dynamite (artificial earthquakes). In a dynamite explosion, we know the exact point at which

---

* The formulas are:

$$\text{Velocity of } P \text{ wave} = \sqrt{\frac{K + 4/3\mu}{\rho}}$$

$$\text{Velocity of } S \text{ wave} = \sqrt{\frac{\mu}{\rho}}$$

in which K = bulk modulus (a measure of incompressibility or resistance to change in volume); μ = modulus of rigidity (a measure of resistance to shear or change of shape); and ρ = density. It is assumed that the medium is isotropic and "perfectly" elastic.

the "earthquake" occurred, and hence can accurately measure distance from the source. With precise chronometers, we can also time the explosion and measure the travel time of waves to various detectors to less than $\frac{1}{1000}$ second. Wave velocities and elastic properties determined by these measurements fail to agree exactly with those made in the same rocks in the laboratory, but the deviations are generally not great and are thought to come in part from imperfect sampling and errors in measurement, but mainly from inhomogeneity of the rocks in nature. When we think of all the faults, bedding surfaces, joints, gneissic structures, slaty cleavages, and other deviations from uniformity of rocks, this explanation of the discrepancies seems entirely reasonable. Rocks in the accessible part of the earth are certainly far from being ideal homogeneous solids. Another difficulty in using the seismic properties to infer the composition of the rocks through which the waves have traveled is that some rocks of widely differing mineral content have very similar elastic properties.

The P and S waves travel in all directions from their origin through the elastic body of the earth. In an isotropic medium (that is, one whose properties are identical in all directions) waves travel in straight lines, but when they pass from one rock into another with differing elastic properties—say from limestone into shale—they are bent or refracted like water waves that cross a shoaling beach diagonally (Chapter 16). They may also be reflected at such a boundary, just as light is reflected from a mirror or sound echoes from a cliff. (The P wave is indeed a sound wave in rock.) Furthermore, when either a P or S wave strikes a sharp boundary—a **discontinuity** in the elastic properties of rocks along its path—it sets up new waves. The new waves generated at the discontinuity include new compressional and new shear waves set in motion by each of the original P and S waves, that is, two new S waves and two new P waves. Besides these, there

are formed several kinds of "surface waves," so-called because they travel along, or at least close to, the discontinuity. Such waves are set up at the surface of the earth, where the discontinuity consists of the contact between rock and atmosphere or water, and even within the earth at such boundaries as geologic contacts, if, as is usual, the rocks on either side have different elastic properties.

The surface waves set up at these discontinuities travel much more slowly than either the P or S waves and are far more complex: they are called long, or **L waves.** They travel along the earth's surface, and the disturbance they produce diminishes with depth in the earth.

From this outline, it is obvious that earthquake waves are extremely complex. Because they are generally felt only near the source, delicate instruments are needed for recording them effectively at long distances. We briefly discuss these instruments, called seismographs, before going on to the deductions they enable us to make about the structure of the earth.

SEISMOGRAPHS

To record earthquake vibrations it is necessary to establish a point as nearly independent of the earth as possible. We all know that we can knock the bottom book out of a pile laid on a table so quickly that the books above are hardly disturbed and fall almost vertically, without tipping over. The inertia (tendency to resist acceleration) of the upper books prevents them from moving with the bottom book. The seismograph is an instrument designed to measure the ground displacement with respect to a mass that, like the upper books, is as independent as possible from the ground surface upon which it rests. A seismograph is so constructed that, when the earth moves under the impulse of an earthquake wave, as little motion as possible is transmitted to the main mass of the seismograph. If, then, we can measure the displacement between the ground and the seismograph mass, we thereby measure the ground motion during the earthquake.

This problem has been attacked in many ingenious ways: masses have been supported by springs; long pendulums have been suspended from high structures (so that their time of swing would be great compared with that of earth vibrations); but for many years the most widely used mechanism has been the so-called **horizontal pendulum.** In this device (Fig. 19–6), a pendulum consisting of a heavy weight at the end of a boom is held by a wire fastened to a supporting pillar. The weight thus tends to remain in its position of rest as the support vibrates during an earthquake. Either by a delicate pen attached to the pendulum weight, or by a beam of light reflected from a mirror on the pendulum to a motor-driven strip of photographic paper the relative motion of the pendulum and its foundation is recorded. Such a seismograph measures only the horizontal component of motion at right angles to the length of the pendulum; to record all horizontal movements completely, two such pendulums are needed, usually with one supported so that the boom is north-south, the other east-west. Still a third device, a mass suspended by springs, for measuring vertical movements, is necessary to describe fully the local earth motion. Time is marked automatically on the records, or seismograms, usually by an electric clock suitably linked to the device that moves the record, so that the time each vibration reached the seismograph can be determined very accurately.

Inferences from seismograph records

By comparing seismograph records of the same earthquake at different stations, and of different earthquakes at the same station, seismologists are able to recognize the various kinds of waves that elastic theory predicts. In general, a seismogram shows several different kinds of waves, each related to a definite wave path through the earth. For example, in the seismograms shown in Figure 19–7, the points indicating the arrival of the P, S, and L waves, are labeled. The arrival of a reflected compressional wave, PP and of a reflected shear wave, SS, are also indicated (see also Fig. 19–10). Note that the onset of the surface waves (L waves) renders the seismogram much more complex than it is during earlier phases of the record.

REFRACTION AND REFLECTION AT DEPTH. By tabulating the **travel times** of the waves from an earthquake of known source and by iden-

FIGURE 19–6
Diagrammatic sketch of a horizontal pendulum seismograph. Modern instruments are much more complex than the model illustrated, but the principle involved is identical.

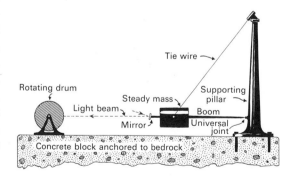

FIGURE 19–7
Seismogram, with letters indicating the arrival of the various earthquake waves. (After L. D. Leet, Practical Seismology and Seismic Prospecting, Appleton-Century-Crofts, 1938.)

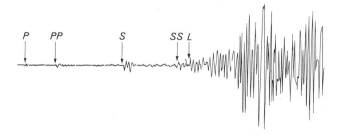

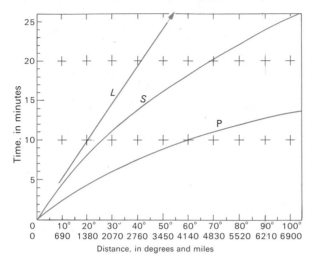

FIGURE 19–8

Average time-distance curves for the three principle earthquake waves. (Data from H. Jeffreys, 1959.)

tifying the various wave groups on the seismograph records at many stations, **time-distance tables** have been made. When the distances from the source (in degrees of the earth's circumference) are plotted against travel time, we have a **time-distance curve** (Fig. 19–8). It is significant that the curves for the P and S waves are concave toward the axis of distance: that is, the greater the distance of travel, the faster the apparent speed of the waves. From this we infer that the waves travel faster as they penetrate deeper within the earth, for the increase in speed with increasing distance is greater than would be expected if we considered only the difference between the surface distance (arc) and straight-line distance (chord) to be the explanation. For the L wave, which travels along the surface, the time-distance curve is a straight line (Fig. 19–8); its travel time is directly proportional to its arc distance from the source.

Because of their increase in speed with distance, it is evident that the P and S waves do not travel along the surface, but through the body of the earth, and the deeper their

paths the greater their speeds. From this it follows that their paths of travel are curved, just as light rays are curved by lenses (Fig. 19–9). This accounts for the fact that at points far from the source, the waves emerge at the surface at higher angles than they would if they followed straight lines. When they strike the surface, they are reflected back and proceed again in curved paths. A whole train of reflected waves recorded on seismograms at distant stations, as shown in Figure 19–10, is thus explained.

We know from the earth's mass and dimensions that its average density is about 5.52, whereas the average density of the surface rocks is only about half as great. The material making up the earth's interior must therefore be far denser than that at the surface. As the formulas for wave speed show, if only the density of the rocks increased with depth and their other properties remained unchanged, the waves should actually travel more slowly as they go deeper. Since they speed up, we see that the elastic properties—rigidity and incompressibility—must increase with depth even more than the density. We return to this important point later in this chapter, but before doing so let us see what other information the seismograms reveal.

EPICENTRAL DISTANCE.   The sharply pulselike records on seismograms suggest that most earthquakes begin in a very small area, even though many miles of fault may ultimately be active, as in the San Francisco earthquake. The Chilean earthquake of 1960 was well recorded. It began at one point from which the rupture traveled more than 1200 kilometers at a speed of 3.5 kilometers per second. The point at which the first movements seem to occur is called the **focus**. The point on the surface directly above the focus is called the **epicenter** (Greek, "above the center") (Fig. 19–11).

The time lag between the P and S waves shown on a seismogram enables us to read the "epicentral distance" (the distance from the station to the epicenter) from the time-distance curves. This distance is measured in degrees of arc of the earth's curvature. (Modern instruments are so accurate that account must be taken of the earth's ellipticity in making these measurements.) If we draw a circle on a globe, using the seismograph station as the center and the epicentral distance as the radius, we know that the

shock must have occurred somewhere on the periphery of this circle. If we have adequate records from at least three stations, the epicenter can be found: it is the point at which the three circles drawn about the three stations intersect (Fig. 19–12). In fact, it is sometimes possible to estimate closely both direction and distance from a single station by observing the direction of first movement and the relative amplitudes of the waves recorded on the vertical and two horizontal records. As the time-distance curves for all stations more than a few degrees distant from the epicenter are virtually the same, regardless of the direction of approach of the seismic wave, the earth must everywhere be nearly homogeneous (or else similarly variable) at any particular depth greater than a few score miles. If it differed appreciably from place to place the travel times should vary regionally as, indeed, they do for nearby earthquakes which travel only in relatively shallow zones of the crust.

ISOSEISMAL LINES. We ordinarily have no quantitative way of measuring the force of tremors near the most intensely shaken area.

FIGURE 19–9
The bending of rays of earthquake waves caused by the increase of wave velocity with depth. The rays must always progress in the direction at right angles to any small segment of the wave front. Only six of the infinite number of wave paths emanating from the source are shown.

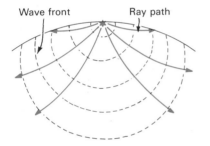

FIGURE 19–10
Section through a part of the earth, showing the paths of a few of the many earthquake waves and the records they leave on the seismograms at four stations. Note the reflected waves, PP, PPP, etc. The time scale of all the seismograms is the same. (After A. Sieberg, Erdbebenkunde, *G. Fischer, 1923.)*

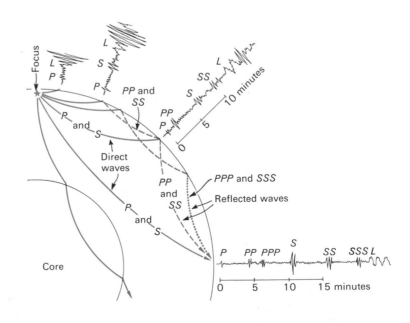

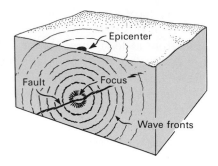

FIGURE 19-11
Diagram showing the positions of the focus and epicenter of an earthquake caused by local deep-seated movement on an inclined fault.

FIGURE 19-12
Locating an epicenter in northwest Utah from seismograms recorded in Seattle, Berkeley, and Livingston.

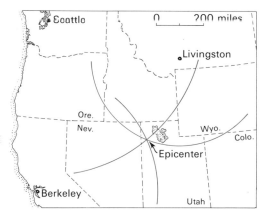

We must rely on qualitative information such as the destruction caused or the perceptibility of the shock to persons. Many "scales of intensity" have been suggested by students of earthquakes, but most are highly influenced by the past experiences of persons interviewed, the methods used in questioning them, the density of population, the nature of the ground, and the quality of building construction in an area. Most scales now in use are modified from one proposed by the Italian seismologist Mercalli: the one most widely used in America is the "Modified Mercalli," scale (1956).

Modified Mercalli Intensity Scale (1956)
(Modified from Don Tocher, 1964)

I. Not felt.

II. Felt by persons at rest, especially on upper floors, or similarly favorable places.

III. Felt indoors, but may not be recognized as an earthquake. Vibrations resemble those from a passing light truck.

IV. Felt indoors like the vibrations from a passing heavy truck or the jolts of a heavy ball striking the walls. Hanging objects swing; standing objects rock; windows, dishes, doors rattle; glasses clink; walls and frames may creak.

V. Felt outdoors. Sleepers awaken; liquids move and some spill; small unstable objects move or fall; doors swing; shutters and pictures move; pendulum clocks stop or change rate.

VI. Felt by all. Many run outdoors in fright; people walk unsteadily; windows, dishes, glassware break; knicknacks, books, dishes fall from shelves, pictures from walls; furniture moves or overturns; weak plaster and poor masonry cracks; small church and school bells ring; trees, bushes, shake visibly and rustle.

VII. Noticed by automobile drivers. Walkers have difficulty keeping balance; weak chimneys break at roof lines; furniture breaks; poor masonry cracks; plaster, loose bricks, stones, tiles, cornices, fall; small slides and caving develop along sand and gravel banks; water becomes turbid with mud; large bells ring; concrete irrigation ditches are damaged.

VIII. Affects steering of motor cars. Damage to good unbraced masonry, with partial collapse; some damage to good, somewhat reinforced masonry but none to masonry reinforced against horizontal stresses; walls of stucco and some of masonry fall; chimneys, factory stacks, monuments, towers, and elevated tanks twist and fall; frame houses move on foundations if not bolted down; loose panel walls thrown out; decayed piling breaks off; branches break from trees; flow and temperature of springs and wells change; wet ground and steep slopes crack.

IX. Causes general panic. Poor masonry destroyed; good unbraced masonry heavily damaged; reinforced masonry seriously damaged; general damage to foundations; frame structures, if not bolted, shifted off foundations; frame cracks; serious damage to reservoirs; underground pipes break; alluvial areas crack conspicuously, ejecting sand and mud; earthquake fountains and sand craters develop.

X. Destroys most masonry and frame structures. Some well-built wooden structures and bridges destroyed; serious damage to dams, dikes, embankments; large landslides; water is thrown on banks of canals, rivers, lakes; sand and mud shift horizontally on beaches and flat land; rails bend slightly.

XI. Puts underground pipelines completely out of service. Rails bend greatly.

XII. Distorts lines of sight and level. Damage nearly total; large rock masses displaced; objects thrown into the air.

Local factors vary too much for these estimates of intensity to be either quantitatively accurate or directly comparable for different localities. Nevertheless, much information valuable to engineers, insurance underwriters, civic planners, and others can be derived from a systematic study of intensity distribution. In the United States, immediately after a destructive earthquake, the Coast and Geodetic Survey sends, to persons in the area affected, postcards containing lists of characteristic earthquake effects and asks them to check items according to their experience of the shock. When the returned cards are tabulated by locality, a map showing the intensities according to the Modified Mercalli scale can be compiled.

Lines drawn on such a map through points of equal intensity are called **isoseismal lines** (Fig. 19–13). The isoseismals generally lie in rough ovals about a center which either coincides with the position of the epicenter as determined from seismograph records or is close to it. The fact that the instrumentally determined epicenter commonly does not quite coincide with the "field epicenter" may

be accounted for by differences in soils and near-surface geology. Differences in underlying rocks not only influence the distribution of earthquake damage and therefore the isoseismals, but also affect the speed of elastic waves to nearby seismographs and thus affect the instrumental records. A complex pattern of damage characterized the San Francisco earthquake because in the affected area hills of strong rock alternate abruptly with small basins filled with unconsolidated muds and silts.

EARTHQUAKE MAGNITUDE.   For a quantitative comparison of the sizes of earthquakes, intensity is not very useful. Because intensity is only a measure of the strength of ground shaking in a restricted locality, it varies considerably from place to place for a single

FIGURE 19–13
Isoseimals of the Charleston earthquake, 1886. The fine dashed lines (called coseismals) connect points where the earthquake struck at the same time; the heavy numerals indicate their actual arrival times. (After C. E. Dutton, U.S. Geological Survey.)

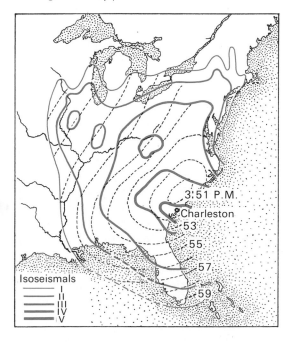

earthquake, diminishing from a maximum (epicentral intensity) to zero as distance from the epicenter increases. Even epicentral intensity is strongly dependent on the nature of the ground in the epicentral region and on focal depth; it is thus a poor measure of the intrinsic size of an earthquake.

A more useful scale for expressing the size of earthquakes was developed by the American seismologist, C. F. Richter. His scale, called earthquake **magnitude,** is based on the amplitude of the largest horizontal trace written by a standard seismograph located 100 kilometers from the epicenter of an earthquake with normal focal depth. Empirical tables and graphs that express the manner in which this maximum horizontal trace amplitude varies with distance and focal depth permit seismologists to calculate the magnitude of any earthquake recorded at any distance by any of a wide variety of seismographs. Although the agreement between magnitudes computed for a given earthquake from the records of a number of seismographs is far from perfect, the range in size of recorded earthquakes is so tremendous that even a rough estimate of an earthquake's magnitude is extremely useful.

Semi-empirical studies by a number of seismologists have led to several estimates of the relationship between earthquake energy and magnitude: for a one unit increase in magnitude, the energy released by an earthquake increases between 30 and 60 times. Thus between 25,000 and 200,000 shocks of magnitude 5 are required to release as much energy as a single shock of magnitude 8.

The San Francisco earthquake of 1906 had a magnitude of 8.25; the Tokyo earthquake of 1923 one of 8.1. The highest magnitudes yet determined by this method are those of an earthquake in Columbia in 1906 and one in Assam, India, in 1950, both approximately 8.6. Horizontal acceleration during the Assam quake was half that of gravity so that material on a slope of 60° became wholly unsupported and the support, even on gentle slopes was much reduced—hence the prodigious landsliding on south-facing slopes (Fig. 8–1). The Alaska earthquake of 1964 had a magnitude variously estimated as 8.4 to 8.6 and was thus at least twice as energetic as the San Francisco earthquake of 1906. A magnitude of 2 corresponds to a shallow shock barely perceptible near the epicenter; a magnitude of 7 is usually considered as the lower limit of a major destructive earthquake, although smaller earthquakes have wrought great destruction in areas where buildings are poorly designed to withstand them. Magnitude is always reported in Arabic numerals; intensity in Roman.

DEPTH OF FOCUS.   In comparison with their travel times to distances of several tens of kilometers, the first waves that reach the epicenter from an earthquake focus at depth within the earth are retarded relative to those from a near-surface source. This phenomenon provides the data that seismologists use to calculate the focal depth of an earthquake.

Most earthquakes have focal depths between 2 and 20 miles. If the depth of focus is less than 5 miles, the earthquake is rarely felt for any great distance, though it may be strong at the epicenter. Such shallow earthquakes are common near volcanoes, especially just before and during eruptions, and thus were formerly grouped as a separate class whose origin was supposedly different from that of "normal," or tectonic earthquakes. Their seismographic records, however, are identical with those of normal shocks; so they are now thought to originate in the same way, by faulting, even though the forces involved may result from the bursting of a magma chamber rather than from tectonic movements.

DEEP-FOCUS EARTHQUAKES.   About 4 percent of recorded earthquakes differ from normal ones in having small if any L waves recorded, and also in arriving at distant stations sooner than the normal time-distance curves would suggest. They seem to have taken a short-cut from their origin. Furthermore, when the isoseismals for such earthquakes are drawn, they form very erratic patterns, and reveal a very gradual decrease of intensity with increasing distance, in notable contrast with the fairly systematic arrangement of the isoseismals and rapid decrease of intensity with increasing distances of most earthquakes (Fig. 19–14). This combination of features is taken as qualitative evidence that the focus of such a shock lies much deeper than that of most earthquakes. The focal depths determined for some shocks are as great as 700 kilometers. Because isostatic yielding of the crust is thought to inhibit strain accumulation at depths so great, it has been suggested that these shocks are due, not to shear, but to some mysterious explosions—perhaps explosive changes in mineral phases owing to the high pressures. But this seems unlikely. If they were explosive volume changes, the first *P* motion at *all* stations should be either toward the focus, if the change were a collapse, or away from it, if the change were expansive. The seismograph records, though, except for the anomalies already mentioned, are identical with those of earthquakes known to be connected with faulting: as many begin with rarification as with compression. A further argument for their fault origin is their systematic relation to known faults as shown in Figure 19–15. We have, then, a further clue to conditions at great depth in the earth: the rocks to depths as great as one-eighth of the earth's radius are strong enough in at least some regions to accumulate elastic strain until they fault like those at shallow depths in the crust.

Practically all of the really deep-focus earthquakes—deeper than 300 kilometers—have their epicenters in the island arcs of the Pacific or in the Andean chain of South America. A single focus at a depth of 640 kilometers (380 miles) under southeastern Spain shows that they are not restricted to the Pacific, however. None have been re-corded from beneath North America, although the Charleston earthquake, which took place before it was possible to determine depth, may have had a deep focus.

When the focal depths of the earthquakes along an island arc are plotted on a vertical section at right angles to the trend of the arc, some strikingly systematic associations are found. The deepest shocks invariably origi-

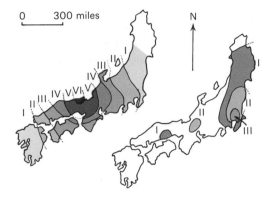

FIGURE 19–14

Maps of Japan, showing the arrangement of isoseismals of the normal North Tazima earthquake (left), and of the deep-focus earthquake of March 29, 1928 (right). (After Wadati, redrawn from J. B. Macelwane, When the Earth Quakes, Bruce Publishing Co., 1947).

FIGURE 19–15

Cross section of the outer earth, at right angles to the Kurile Islands arc, showing the foci of deep earthquakes. There is no vertical exaggeration. (After H. H. Hess, 1948.)

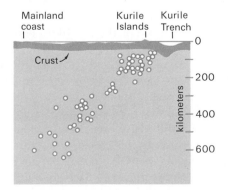

nate farther within the concave side of the arc, and the foci are all close to a plane that intersects the sea floor at the boundary of arc and foredeep (Fig. 19–15). In South America, too, the foci of the deeper shocks are farther from the Pacific than those of the shallow ones.

This pattern is a strong argument against the "explosive phase-change" origin of the deep quakes and has suggested to some geologists that the shocks arise on thrust faults along which the island arcs and South America are overriding the floor of the Pacific. The systematic distribution of the foci on planes dipping away from the Pacific Basin may support this idea, and the directions of the first motion recorded on seismograms at variously situated stations are also consistent with the hypothesis.

DISTRIBUTION OF EARTHQUAKES. Seismologists estimate that every year more than a million earthquakes shake the earth strongly enough to be felt (M = 2), although only a very few are strong enough to be recorded at any considerable distance from their sources. It has been estimated that about 220 great shocks (M>7.75) and about 1200 other strong earthquakes (M = 7.0 to 7.7) occur per century. Figure 19–16 shows the distribution of epicenters of earthquakes of magnitude 7 or greater between 1904 and 1946. Small shallow shocks (M = 5 or less) apparently occur nearly everywhere over the earth, but the larger shocks do not. The crust of the earth seems to include several large blocks, notably the central part of the Pacific Basin (except the neighborhoods of the Hawaiian Islands and other island chains) and most of the shield areas of the continents, that have few large earthquakes. (It must not be forgotten, however, that the Charleston and Mississippi Valley earthquakes, both with foci in the continental plates, must also have been powerful, though instruments were not available to measure them.) Between these relatively stable blocks are linear zones of major seismic activity.

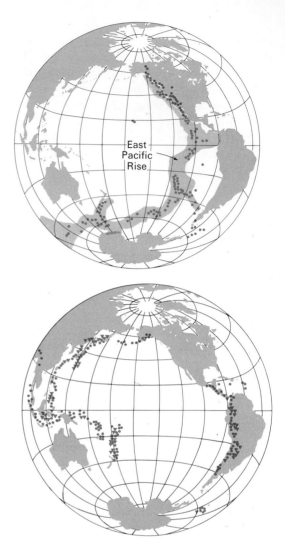

FIGURE 19–16

The Circumpacific Belt. Top: *Distribution of shallow earthquakes (depth of focus less than 60 kilometers) between 1904 and 1946 of magnitude 7 or greater. These shocks release 85 percent of all earthquake energy.* Bottom: *Distribution of deep-focus earthquakes (▼ = depth of focus more than 300 kilometers) and of intermediate-focus earthquakes (● = depth of focus between 60 and 300 kilometers) of magnitude 7 or greater. The intermediate-focus shocks release about 12 percent, the deep-focus shocks about 3 percent of all earthquake energy. Time covered by record: 1905 to 1946. (Modified slightly from R. W. Girdler,* Geophysical Journal of the Royal Astronomical Society, *1964.)*

These include:

1. The *Circumpacific belt* of young mountains, including the branches through the Antilles and through the island arcs south of Japan. Here occur about 80 percent of all shocks with focal depths less than 60 kilometers.
2. The *Mediterranean* and *trans-Himalayan* zone, in which nearly all other large shallow shocks occur.
3. The *Mid-Atlantic* and *Mid-Indian ridges,* along which there are many shallow shocks but few of large magnitude.
4. The *Hawaiian Islands* and *African Rift Valleys,* where there is moderate activity.

The deep-focus shocks are still more closely localized: 90 percent of those whose foci lie between 60 and 300 kilometers, and all but a very few at depths of more than 300 kilometers, are in the Circumpacific belt.

THE CRUST OF THE EARTH

The Yugoslav seismologist Mohorovičić in 1909 found certain features in seismograms indicating that the continental segments of the outer part of the earth have a layered structure. He saw that earthquakes less than about 800 kilometers (495 miles) from a recording station gave records of two compressional and two shear waves instead of one of each. By comparing travel times to more distant stations, the smaller pair could be identified as the normal P and S waves long known on records of distant shocks. The larger pair traveled more slowly but seemed to have started earlier. They were, therefore, received first at nearby stations (up to about 100 miles) but lagged farther and farther behind P and S as the distance from the source increased, finally becoming unrecognizable 450 to 600 miles from the source. Mohorovičić showed that this could be explained on the assumption that the earth has a layered structure, with an outer layer —the crust—in which speeds are relatively slow, that rests on the deeper body of the

earth—the mantle—in which speeds are higher. A shock originating in the crust sends waves directly to a nearby station. These waves are powerful and arrive before other waves that penetrate the mantle—even though the waves travel faster in the mantle. But at more distant stations the waves that penetrate the mantle travel fast enough there to more than make up for the time lost traveling from the focus down through the crust to reach the mantle. Hence they overtake the waves whose whole travel is in the crust and arrive first at distant stations.

Although our knowledge of the rocks beneath the earth's crust is wholly indirect, there can be no doubt that this surface, called a **discontinuity,** is a fundamental feature of earth structure. Nearly everywhere there is a definite physical difference between the crust above and the mantle below. This particular discontinuity is called the **Mohorovičić or "M" Discontinuity;** it marks the base of the crust of the earth.

The continental crust

With the increasing use of explosion seismology—the creation of artificial earthquakes by detonation of large charges of explosives—our knowledge of the elastic properties and thickness of the crust and of the elastic properties of the upper mantle has expanded rapidly. Instead of the crust's being, as was formerly thought, of fairly uniform thickness—say 35 kilometers under the lowlands and perhaps as much as 60 kilometers under the mountains—as might be expected from the Airy hypothesis of isostasy (Chapter 10), its thickness and elastic properties vary quite widely and abruptly from region to region of the United States as is shown in Figure 19–17.

Crustal thickness—the depth to the M Discontinuity—can be measured by explosion seismology to within about 10 percent. Within these limits, then, the map shows that crustal thickness at sea level varies greatly from place to place, ranging from about 20

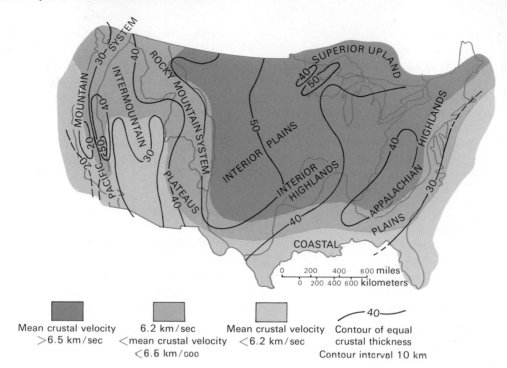

FIGURE 19–17   *Map showing mean crustal thickness and mean velocity of P waves within the crust of the United States. (After L. C. Pakiser and J. Steinhart, 1964.)*

FIGURE 19–18   *Speed of P_n (the compressional wave immediately beneath the M Discontinuity) in the United States. (After Eugene Herrin and James Taggart, Seismological Society of America Bulletin, 1962.)*

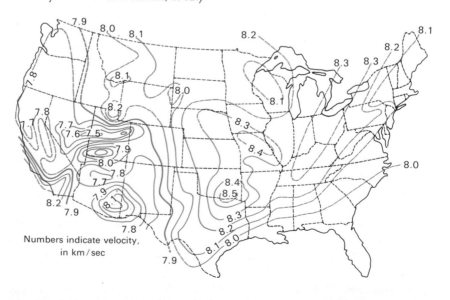

kilometers in California to more than 30 kilometers along the Gulf of Mexico and near the Atlantic. Crustal thickness is not simply related to altitude: in much of the intermountain plateaus and the Great Basin the crust is less than 30 kilometers thick—in the Great Valley of California only about 20 kilometers—and in some mountainous regions it is thinner than at sea level in Texas. Some mountains have roots but others do not: the Sierra Nevada has a root more than 50 kilometers deep, but the southern Rocky Mountains have the same crustal thickness as Kansas and the crust beneath the northern Rockies is thinner than that beneath the Interior Plains to the east. In the Southwest there are places where crustal thickness changes abruptly—the M Discontinuity slopes as much as 30 or 40°.

Mean crustal velocity of the P waves is also greatly variable, from less than 6.2 kilometers per second to more than 6.5 kilometers per second; it is high where the crust is thick and low where it is thin. We noted in Chapter 10 the remarkable correlation between topography and negative Bougeur gravity anomalies in the western United States, and we now see that this corresponds only in part to there being a thicker crust beneath highlands than elsewhere—in general it must mean that the crust of the mountainous regions is actually less dense—not merely thicker—than that beneath lowlands. Thus isostatic compensation is accomplished only in part by the Airy mechanism, and in part by that of Pratt; it must involve density variations not only of the crust, but of the upper mantle as well.

That the upper mantle also varies notably from region to region is indicated by the wide variation in the velocity of P_n—the compressional wave in the mantle immediately below the M Discontinuity—as shown in Figure 19–18. The range is from less than 7.5 kilometers per second near the Utah-Nevada border to more than 8.5 kilometers per second beneath southern Oklahoma.

This range—more than 15 percent of the lowest figure—is so great that it must be considered in establishing local time-distance curves for individual seismograph stations. Such regional variation in the elastic properties of the upper mantle must reflect real differences in the composition of the upper mantle rocks from place to place. In a rough way the speed of P_n is low where the continental crust is thin and high where it is thick, though the correlation is far from perfect.

Of what is the crust composed? From geologic, seismic, and gravity studies we know that in parts of the earth the sedimentary rocks are as thick as 15 kilometers (9 miles). These, however, are only narrow zones, treated more fully in Chapter 20. Over the crust as a whole the sedimentary layer is rather thin; it is estimated that in North America it averages only .8 kilometer (about half a mile) for all Cambrian and younger rocks and less than 2 kilometers for all sedimentary rocks including the Precambrian. The difference between this thickness and that expectable from the volume of igneous rocks decomposed, as discussed in Chapter 17, is accounted for by the metamorphosis of large volumes of sedimentary rocks into gneiss and schist. These form a large part of the upper crust beneath the sedimentary skin.

We have just seen that the crust is far from homogeneous, either in thickness or elastic properties, when studied in detail. This should not be surprising, for wherever the basement rocks upon which the sedimentary cover rests have been exposed, as in the great shields of all the continents, we find highly varied gneisses, schists, marbles, and plutonic rocks of many kinds, all in the most diverse structural arrangements and with complex changes of trend from place to place. The surprising thing, in view of this complexity of the basement rocks, is that average elastic properties of the crust in Europe, Japan, and North America are nearly the same, so that roughly the same time-distance curves are applicable in each place. The average velocities of the seismic waves in the upper part of the crust are quite similar to those expected in granite, whose elastic properties have been determined in the laboratory. Granite and gneiss of roughly the same composition are indeed the dominant rocks in the exposed parts of the continental basement. Despite the great local variability, it is not surprising that the average rock of the upper part of the continental crust has elastic properties like those of granite, for most consist mainly of minerals rich in silicon and aluminum as are those of granite. Laboratory studies show that a major control of elastic properties in solids is the mean atomic weight of the elements composing them. Following a suggestion of the Austrian geologist E. Suess, geologists call the material of the upper part of the crust by the coined name **sial** (si for silicon, al for aluminum).

Since earthquake speeds increase with depth even within the crust, it is commonly thought that the material constituting the crust must change in average composition toward the base. Thus the crust consists of two more or less distinct layers (and where there are sedimentary rocks at the surface, of three). The lower part of the crust differs from sial. It was formerly thought that there was a rather sharp break between sial and the lower crust, and in certain places there is—a so-called **Conrad Discontinuity**—but recent studies seem to indicate a general transition rather than an abrupt boundary. The wave speeds in the lower part of the crust, though variable, are close to those expected if the rock is of basaltic or somewhat more siliceous composition. As basalt is widespread in the outer part of the earth and because the seismic velocities deep in the crust are those appropriate to rocks of basaltic composition, the lower part of the crust has been referred to as the *basaltic layer*. Suess suggested that, since magnesium is a prominent constituent of basalt, the material should be referred to as **sima** (si for silicon, ma for magnesium).

As noted in Appendix IV, Table 2, the crust as a whole is less siliceous and richer in iron, magnesium, and aluminum than the average of the exposed rocks. As we mentioned earlier, the rocks immediately below the Mohorovičić Discontinuity constitute the "lower layer" or **mantle.** Recent seismic-explosion experiments in central North America, central Europe, and in the Soviet Union have found evidence of sharp discontinuities within the upper mantle to depths as great as 150 to 250 kilometers. These discontinuities appear to mark boundaries of, or features within, a region of depressed wave velocities that has been detected over large sections of the continents. This is the **Low Velocity Zone** and seems to be a locus of magma generation and of isostatic adjustment. The rock whose elastic properties seem most nearly comparable to those of the mantle is garnet peridotite, perhaps a variety especially rich in olivine. Other rocks, such as garnet pyroxenite, or less probably, eclogite, also meet the elastic requirements. We must, however, maintain a lively skepticism as to the exact composition of all rocks below the zone of observation, and refrain from taking a positive position about a pyroxenite or a peridotite layer. Perhaps the great pressures at this depth may so change the physical state of other rocks that their elastic properties come to resemble those of garnet peridotite.

The crust beneath the oceans

The crust beneath the oceans differs from that beneath the continents. The evidence is both from isostasy (see Chapter 10) and seismology. The seismologic evidence is of three kinds, two from natural earthquakes and a third from explosion seismology.

The earthquake evidence was first to be interpreted. The higher the angle at which a wave strikes the surface, the greater the proportion of wave energy reflected back into the earth; it is at a maximum for waves striking at right angles. The significant feature in crustal studies is that two earthquake waves of equal epicentral distance, one of which has been reflected from a continental surface and the other from the bottom of the ocean differ greatly in intensity. If the crustal structure were the same, waves generated by shocks of equal magnitude should have about equal amplitudes in both environments, but the oceanic reflection is weaker. This difference suggests that the waves strike the ocean bottom at smaller angles than they do the surface of the continents as might be expected if the crust beneath the ocean lacked a sial layer (Fig. 19–19). Because of their slowing down as they pass through the continental sial, the waves are refracted and strike the surface at a higher angle than would waves of the same epicentral distance where such a layer is absent. Waves reflected from continental surfaces do carry more energy than those reflected from the ocean floors, therefore sial is probably thin or absent beneath the oceans.

The surface waves (*L* waves) tell a similar story. The speeds of surface waves, unlike those that pass through the body of the earth, vary with wavelength. This means that we can tell something about how the elastic properties of materials beneath the surface vary with depth. As a very crude rule of thumb, a surface wave of a given wavelength travels at a speed that depends on the elastic properties of a layer about as thick as the wave is long: a wave with a length of 3 kilometers travels at a rate determined by the elastic properties of the material within 3 kilometers of the surface; one with a wavelength of 200 kilometers travels at a rate determined by the elastic properties of all the rocks from the surface to a depth of about 200 kilometers. In detail the dependence of surface-wave velocity on the "velocity-depth-profile" is quite complex, but mathematical methods provide an adequate means of establishing this dependence.

Surface waves of short wavelengths travel at different speeds in different parts of the

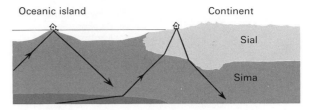

FIGURE 19–19

Angles of incidence of earthquake waves arriving beneath ocean basins and continents. (After B. Gutenburg, Internal Constitution of the Earth, *courtesy Dover Publications.)*

crust. The speeds of short wavelength transverse surface waves (Love waves) across segments of the Pacific floor, for example, are higher than across other areas, both oceanic and, especially, continental. But longer wavelength surface waves of this type, whose speed is more dependent on the properties of deeper material, travel at nearly the same speed across both continents and ocean basins. The American seismologist Beno Gutenberg showed that these facts are consistent with the absence of sial beneath the ocean floor.

In the years since World War II, it has been found that shock waves emanating from an explosion under water can be transmitted from the water into the bottom, there to be refracted or reflected precisely like earthquake waves (Fig. 19–20). Sensitive pressure devices towed astern enable the waves emerging from the bottom to be recorded, and the records can be analyzed like seismograms. The timing of the direct water wave from the explosion enables the distance between shotpoint and receivers to be determined accurately; timing of waves that are reflected or refracted through the ocean floor permits the elastic properties of the suboceanic crust to be determined. In this way, it has been shown that all the ocean floors are underlain, immediately beneath the pelagic sediments, by material whose elastic properties are like those of the continental sima. It forms a layer only about 5 kilometers thick above the Mo-

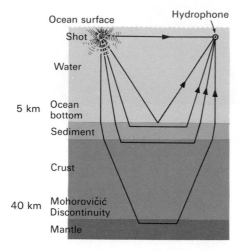

FIGURE 19–20
Refraction and reflection paths for oceanic seismic measurements. (After Ewing and Press, Structure of the Earth's Crust, *Handbuch der Physik, Springer, 1956.)*

horovičić Discontinuity. The Mohorovičić Discontinuity thus generally lies only 10 to 12 kilometers beneath the sea surface, in contrast to its much greater depth beneath the continents.

But the oceanic crust is by no means uniform everywhere. Although the average crust may be represented somewhat as shown in Figure 19–21, seismic sections in the southern Gulf of California are considerably thinner, on the East Pacific Rise still thinner, and on the Mid-Atlantic Ridge there is no sharp discontinuity referable to the Mohorovičić interface; instead, immediately beneath the supposed sediments ($P = 5.1$ kilometers per second) the velocity of presumably basic intrusive rock ($P = 7.2$ kilometers per second) seems to increase imperceptibly downward into velocities characteristic of normal mantle material.

FIGURE 19–21   *Seismic cross section of oceans and seas. Numbers correspond to velocities of P waves from explosions. Oceanographic seismologists generally interpret the velocities as follows:*

1.8 to 2.5 kilometers per second, unconsolidated sediment;
3.8 to 5.4 kilometers per second, consolidated sedimentary rock;
6.5 to 6.9 kilometers per second, basaltic lava;
7.1 to 7.5 kilometers per second, basic intrusive rock;
More than 7.7 kilometers per second, garnet pyroxenite or peridotite
(Data from Drake and others, 1964; Ewing and Ewing, 1959; Raitt, 1956; Phillips, 1964; and Menard, 1967.)

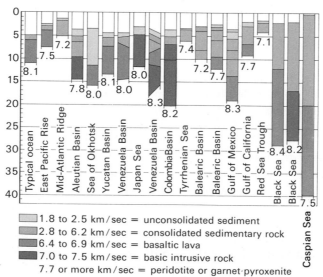

Crust transitional from continent to ocean

The great contrast between the crustal structures of continents and ocean basins renders the transitional zone between them highly significant. The continents stand high above the ocean floor and naturally tend to yield under long term stress and spread laterally over the oceanic crust. Furthermore, as the land is eroded and the sea receives the load, the land tends to rise and the sea floor to sink in response to isostasy, bringing about a landward movement of material at depth. Accordingly, much work has been done on the crustal structure of the continental shelves and slope in the years since World War II.

Off Cape Hatteras the continental crust begins to thin at the shoreline and within about 80 kilometers has thinned to a normal oceanic section by elimination of sial. Near Cape May the thinning begins more than 100 kilometers inland but is much more gradual; a normal oceanic crust is not found until 200 kilometers offshore (Fig. 20–27). South of Woods Hole, Massachusetts the thinning does not begin until about 100 kilometers offshore and is not complete until about 350 kilometers offshore.

The American oceanographer H. W. Menard has pointed out that although over most of the ocean floor sediment is not much more than 1 kilometer thick, in many seas behind island arcs sediments are much thicker and in areas like the Gulf of Mexico and the Black Sea, into which great rivers flow, they are thicker yet, so that even though the material beneath the sediment and basaltic lavas still has the seismic properties of the suboceanic mantle, the crust above it approaches continental thickness and composition (Fig. 19–21). He proposed the possibility that these segments of the sea are in process of being converted from ocean to continent as many segments appear to have been converted in the geologic past (Fig. 19–22). In Chapter 20 we note that continental areas that supplied the sediments that now form the Alps and the Appalachians now lie beneath the Ligurian Sea and the Atlantic, respectively, and approach oceanic crust in their seismic properties. Perhaps island arcs represent the converse conversion of ocean to continent.

FIGURE 19–22

A sequence of Mediterranean crustal segments arranged in order of their approach toward continental thicknesses of sial. (From H. W. Menard, Science, v. 157, p. 923–924, 25 Aug. 1967. Copyright 1967 by the American Association for the Advancement of Science.)

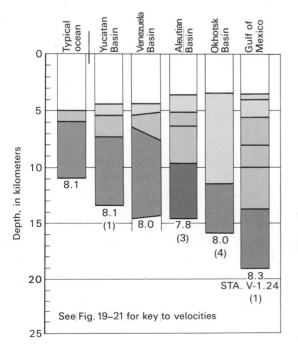

THE DEEP INTERIOR

The increase in speed of earthquake waves with depth within the mantle indicates that rigidity and incompressibility of the deeper rocks increase more or less steadily downward beneath the low-velocity zone. The increased speed cannot be due to lower density of the deeper rocks, for we know from measurements reviewed later in this chapter that the density of the earth as a whole (5.52) is far higher than that of surface rocks (2.2 to about 3.2). Furthermore, the approach of large surface blocks to isostatic balance implies that they are virtually floating on a substatum that must have a higher density.

Except for the low-velocity zone, elasticity continues to increase with depth faster than density for a long way below the Mohorovičić Discontinuity. It then changes abruptly. P waves emerging at about 102° to 104° epicentral distance have followed a curved path whose deepest part lies about 2900 kilometers (1740 miles) beneath the surface. Within a short distance beyond this, however, both P and S waves suddenly fade out. The S cannot be detected beyond this zone (except those reflected from discontinuities), and the P wave is found only by sensitive seismographs. But at epicentral distances of about 143°, a powerful P wave reappears. The travel time for this P wave is much slower, however, than would be expected from the normal time-distance curves (Fig. 19–23).

If this deep-penetrating P wave had traveled through the center of the earth at the speed it had at a depth of 2900 kilometers, it should arrive on the opposite side of the earth about 16 minutes after the earthquake. Instead, it arrives 20 minutes after. The delay can only mean that the speed through the central core of the earth is far less than in the mantle above the core. Moreover, if the speed is lower in the core than in the mantle above, we see a reason for the weak records between epicentral distances of 102° and 143°—the so-called **shadow zone.** A medium

in which speed is low bends the wave paths toward its thickest part, just as a reading glass bends the light rays to a focus in line with its thickest part, because the speed of light is less in glass than in air. Thus the central part of the earth acts like a huge converging lens for the seismic waves. This is the basis for the interpretation indicated in Figure 19–24, which shows the earth with a central **core,** whose radius is about 3400 kilometers (2100 miles) surrounded by the *mantle* that extends from the core boundary to the Mohorovičić Discontinuity at the base of the *crust.*

Figure 19–24 shows how the slower velocities in the core explain both the shadow zone and the extraordinary strength of the wave at 143°, for here are focused waves that impinge upon a considerable segment of the core. The abruptness of the core boundary— the Gutenberg-Wiechert Discontinuity—is strikingly shown by Canadian records of a South Pacific earthquake. At Toronto (epicentral distance 141°) only a very faint record was made, but at Ottawa, only 2° farther from the epicenter, the P wave was very strong. (In Fig. 19–24, the shadow zone embraces the surface between 12°S and 53°S, that is, the belt between 102° and 143° from the North Pole, the assumed earthquake origin.)

Beyond an epicentral distance of 103°, the S waves, if present at all, are very faint. Although some seismologists believe they may be present but so weak and obscured by

FIGURE 19–23

Graph of velocity of the P *wave in the interior of the earth, as related to the depth of its penetration. (After B. Gutenberg,* Internal Constitution of the Earth, *courtesy of Dover Publications.)*

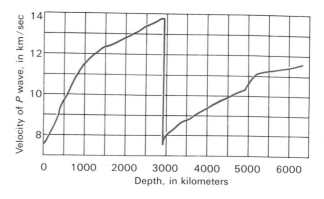

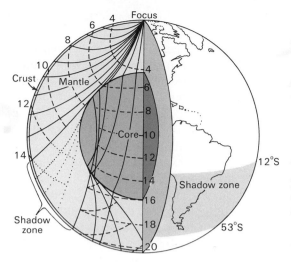

FIGURE 19–24

The shadow zone of an earthquake originating near the North Pole. The cutout shows the effect of the core on the pattern of wave paths and wave fronts. The numbers are the travel time in minutes for each of the paths shown. (After B. Gutenburg, Internal Constitution of the Earth, *1928, courtesy of Dover Publications.)*

various reflected waves that they cannot be identified, the consensus of experts is that *S* waves are not transmitted through the core. This means that the core has practically no rigidity and as an absence of rigidity is characteristic of all fluids, most seismologists commonly refer to the core as liquid. A Danish seismologist, Miss E. Lehman, has adduced evidence, however, that the central part of the core, extending from a depth of about 5000 kilometers to the earth's center at 6350 kilometers, differs from the outer core and appears to be rigid, thus solid instead of liquid.

A MODEL OF THE EARTH

Study of seismologic records has thus led to a postulated model of the earth that seems to fit nearly all the known data. This model has a central core, whose inner part is solid with a radius of about 1300 kilometers; the outer

part presumably is liquid, though highly viscous, and extends to a radial distance of 3400 kilometers—locus of the sharp Gutenberg-Wiechert Discontinuity between core and mantle. The mantle may contain some discontinuities, but none appears to be as sharp or as widespread geographically as the Gutenberg-Wiechert or Mohorovičić Discontinuities. The mantle is bounded at its outer surface by the well-defined Mohorovičić Discontinuity. This discontinuity marks the base of the crust, a fundamental feature of the earth's structure. The part of the crust beneath the continents consists of different materials than that beneath the oceans. The continental crust—about 30 to 40 kilometers (18 to 25 miles) thick on the average— grades upward from sima to sial, with perhaps the lower two-thirds sima. The sial is blanketed by sedimentary rocks to an average depth of about .8 kilometer (½ mile) . In the oceanic crust the layer of sial is either entirely lacking or is thin and patchy. The sima is also thin, so that the Mohorovičić discontinuity lies at a depth of only 10 or 12 kilometers below the ocean's surface—approximately a third of its average depth beneath the continents.

Other clues to the Earth's Interior

What other information can we glean about the mysterious depths of the earth? The evidence from earthquake waves confirms our earlier inference that the continents stand high above the ocean basins because they are underlain by less dense rocks— they are huge rafts of more granitic material resting on somewhat denser rocks; the oceanic crust, below a thin veneer of sediment, seems to consist largely of basalt. Both these crustal segments are "floating" on the still denser material of the mantle, which lies beneath the Mohorovičić Discontinuity.

Although the velocity of *P* waves increases with depth in the crust, and nearly everywhere abruptly increases further at the Mohorovičić Discontinuity, it generally does not continue to increase steadily with depth in the upper mantle. It is difficult to obtain detailed information about lower velocity zones beneath zones of higher velocity, for they reveal themselves only indirectly by the *absence of records* at expected distances and times, but it nevertheless seems now well established that between depths of about 60 and 250 kilometers the velocities of both *P* and *S* waves are generally, but not everywhere, somewhat less than they are immediately below the M Discontinuity. This is the Low-Velocity Zone previously mentioned. We return to it in the next chapter.

From the speeds of seismic waves compared with elastic properties of rocks tested in the laboratory under conditions of high pressure, we can infer tentatively that the upper part of the mantle probably consists of rock like garnet peridotite or garnet pyroxenite. But of what are the lower mantle and core composed?

Below the Low Velocity Zone, the increase in earthquake speeds downward through the deeper mantle seems fairly regular. The pressure within the earth increases tremendously with depth; any reasonable estimates of density distribution within the mantle indicate pressures of many million pounds per square inch at the core boundary. In the laboratory, rocks become more rigid and incompressible the higher the pressure; perhaps the entire mantle is composed of something close to garnet pyroxenite mineralogically, the greater elasticity at depth being brought about by the great confining pressure rather than by a chemical difference. But for many reasons it seems clear that the core must be chemically different from the mantle. What is it?

Of course we do not know—such depths are inaccessible and we must reason wholly from analogies. Most astronomers consider meteorites to be fragments of asteroids (Chapter 22)—and thus samples of planetary material. Among the meteorites are many composed of metallic nickel and iron.

Because the core does not transmit transverse waves it is thought to be liquid; because of the earth's magnetic field (as explained later in this chapter) it is thought to be conducting and therefore metallic. Though the pressures at these depths are far beyond laboratory attainment, theoretical physicists have concluded that the measured speed of the *P* wave through the core is compatible with what might be expected of a molten alloy of nickel and iron, with perhaps a little metallic silicon. The mantle thus floats on the core as slag, rich in silicates, floats on molten iron in a blast furnace. The central solid core is probably crystallized nickel-iron like the metallic meteorites. How do these deductions check with what we know of the distribution of density within the earth?

Weighing the earth

Strictly speaking, it is impossible to weigh the earth, for weight is defined as the gravitational pull of the earth on a mass. As was pointed out in Chapter 10, the weight of a mass varies with its distance from the earth's center. When we speak of weighing the earth, then, we are really speaking of determining its total mass. This problem has been approached in many ingenious ways, but all depend upon comparing the attraction of the earth to that of a known mass. One of the most readily visualized experiments—though far from the most accurate—was that performed by von Jolly of Munich, in 1878.

Von Jolly mounted a balance on a support at the top of a high tower, with the usual scale pans under the beam (Fig. 19–25). Another pair of scale pans was suspended by wires from these, about 70 feet below. Four glass globes—A, B, C, D—were prepared of equal weight and volume. A and B were each filled with 5 kilograms (11 pounds) of mercury, C and D were left empty. A and B were put in the upper pair of pans and C and D in the lower and a balance was made. Then A and C, on the same balance arm but at different levels, were interchanged, thus bringing the mercury in A a measured distance closer to the earth. The increased attraction of the earth on the mass of mercury was measured by making a new balance; it turned out to be 31 milligrams (about 0.0007 pound).

Von Jolly now placed a lead sphere close beneath one of the lower pans and repeated the measurements; this time A gained 0.59 milligram more than it had before, because of the attraction of the lead sphere. The centers of the lead sphere and the mercury globe were 57 centimeters (about 2 feet) apart. If then, the lead sphere at a distance of 57 centimeters exerted a pull of 0.59 milligram on the mercury and the earth at an effective distance equal to its radius—about 637,000,000 centimeters—exerted a pull of 5 kilograms or 5,000,000 milligrams, the mass of the earth could be easily compared with that of the lead sphere. Von Jolly's result was about 6,100 billion billion metric tons

FIGURE 19–25
Von Jolly's method of "weighing the earth." (After J. H. Poynting, The Earth, G. P. Putnam's Sons, 1913.)

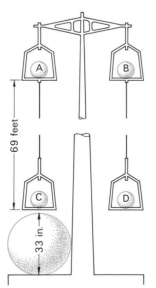

$(6.1 \times 10^{21}$ metric tons) —a figure so large as to be incomprehensible. A metric ton is about 10 percent heavier than an avoirdupois ton. When Von Jolly divided this figure by the volume of the earth he concluded that the mean density of the earth is 5.69, that is, 5.69 times that of an equal volume of water. More accurate methods, too complex for discussion here, but embodying the same principle, give a figure of 5.516 as the best value to date.

Now the average density of the accessible rocks is about 2.8 and very few minerals are as dense as 5.5. Obviously rock density is much greater at depth than at the surface, and in fact the deeper parts must be denser than most natural substances we know.

Since the earth shells below the Low-Velocity Zone appear to be concentric and homogeneous, as shown by the similarity of time–distance curves in many parts of the globe, any assumptions we make about density at differing depths imply assumptions as to the rotational inertia of the earth. Rotational inertia is a measure of the tendency of a rotating body to persist in its rotation against a braking action of any kind—such as, in the case of the earth, the tides. Each particle of matter in a rotating body contributes to the rotational inertia in proportion to its mass and its distance from the center of rotation. (When a spinning skater pulls in his arms, he speeds up his spin; when he throws them out he slows up, for the product of mass times velocity must be the same in the two postures.) When, therefore, we assume a particular density for the matter at a distance of, say, 3000 kilometers from the center of the earth, we can compute the rotational inertia of that material. Estimates of the density distribution within the earth can thus be checked by their agreement or disagreement with the earth's rotational inertia measured astronomically.

The Australian K. E. Bullen and the American Francis Birch have made most careful studies of this matter, taking into ac-

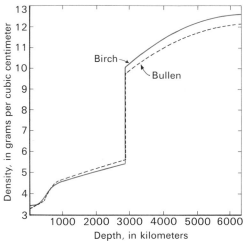

FIGURE 19–26

Density at various depths in the earth. (After K. E. Bullen and Francis Birch; redrawn from Francis Birch, Journal of Geophysical Research, *1964.)*

count both seismic data and inertia as computed from assumed density distributions (Fig. 19–26). Their data indicate that the density of material at the center of the earth can hardly be less than 12 (higher than that of lead at the surface) and may be as high as 13.2, though densities as high as 13.5 are most unlikely. At the Gutenberg-Wiechert Discontinuity the density can hardly be less than 9.6 or greater than 10.1—both higher than those of iron (7.9) or nickel (8.6) at the earth's surface.

Such a density distribution is consistent with that to be expected if the mantle were composed of garnet pyroxenite of chemical composition similar to that of stony meteorites, and if the outer core were made of molten iron and nickel in the proportions found in some metallic meteorites. The densities, although higher than these materials would have at the surface, could be brought about by high pressure alone. The Gutenberg-Wiechert core boundary must be a fundamental discontinuity at which a great change in chemical composition can be inferred, but it is possible that some iron-

nickel alloy is scattered through the lower mantle in the solid rather than liquid state. If the amount of such alloy diminishes upward, so that the upper part is near garnet pyroxenite in composition, and if the pyroxenite gives way abruptly at the M Discontinuity to intermediate rock beneath the continents, and to basalt beneath the oceans, there would be reasonable accordance between our inferences regarding the origins of the igneous rocks (Chapter 18) and the geophysical data.

TEMPERATURE WITHIN THE EARTH

Every well or mine shaft sunk into the ground proves that the temperature of the rocks increases downward. The rate of increase varies greatly from place to place: in the hot spring and geyser area of Yellowstone Park drill holes have reached temperatures of several hundred degrees Centigrade within a few hundred feet. Wells in the plains of Hungary show temperatures increasing as rapidly as 1°C in as little as 7 meters—a rate that would reach the boiling point of water in less than 600 meters. Yet in the Transvaal gold mines of South Africa the temperature increase is so gradual that mining can go on at depths of more than 3000 meters, though only with elaborate refrigeration of the ventilating air. The average rate of increase is about 1°C in 100 meters. However variable the rate, the universal increase in temperature with depth over the earth shows that the earth is losing heat to outer space, for heat flows only from bodies of higher temperature to those of lower.

The amount of heat lost depends on two factors: the rate of temperature increase with depth—the **temperature gradient**—and the amount of heat transmitted through a surface of one square centimeter in one second, under a thermal gradient of 1°C per centimeter—the **thermal conductivity** of the rocks. Both gradient and conductivity depend on rock properties and structure, for heat can be refracted by differences in rock conductivities just as light is. The gradient is also disturbed in many places by seasonal and longer-term temperature changes and by ground-water movements, rock structure, and the topography. Accordingly, we have relatively few reliable measurements of heat flow from the continents.

Strangely enough, it is much simpler to measure heat flow accurately on the sea floor than on the land. The sea-floor measurement is made by sinking a probe into the sediment to a depth of 5 to 20 feet. The probe has sensitive temperature sensors arranged along its length so that the temperature difference (often 0.1°C), and hence the thermal gradient can be measured. A core of sediment collected alongside at the same time enables the conductivity of the mud to be estimated from the water content of the core or measured more accurately by physical means. As the temperature of most places on the deep-sea floor is virtually constant, and has been for a very long time, the heat flow determined is commonly more reliable than that measured on land. We have nearly ten times as many good measures of heat flow from the sea as from the continents, though, of

course, many continental measurements are of very high quality. The state of our knowledge in 1965 is summarized on Table 19–2.

Although there are some measurements in each of these provinces that deviate widely from the averages given, and the data for some areas is sparse, the averages are not far from the most common measurements—the modes. The data show that on the continents heat flow is generally lowest in the Precambrian shields, which have been tectonically inactive and exceptionally deeply eroded for more than 600 m.y. It is intermediate in the continental plates and Paleozoic mountains and highest in areas of post-Paleozoic tectonic activity. Near the young rhyolite intrusions of the Imperial Valley, California, for example, a heat flow of 7 microcalories per square centimeter per second has been measured. Though samples are few, the oceanic trenches seem to show the lowest submarine heat flow, perhaps because of recent sedimentation. Narrow median zones along the mid-ocean ridges are the highest, equaling readings in the young continental mountains. We return to this significant localization in Chapter 20.

It was formerly thought that the loss of heat to outer space necessarily implies a cooling of the earth; since the discovery that radioactivity releases large amounts of heat,

Table 19–2 **Mean heat flow from various geologic provinces**

Province	Microcalories */ cm /sec
Precambrian shields	0.92 ± 0.17
Areas of mountains formed during Paleozoic time	1.23 ± 0.4
Areas of the continental plates	1.54 ± 0.38
Areas of mountains formed during post-Paleozoic time	1.92 ± 0.49
Oceanic trenches	0.99 ± 0.61
Deep ocean basins	1.28 ± 0.53
Mid-oceanic ridges	1.82 ± 1.56
Mean for the whole earth	1.5 ± 0.15

SOURCE: Data from W. H. D. Lee and S. Uyeda, 1965.

* A calorie is the amount of heat required to raise the temperature of one gram of water from 15° to 16° Centigrade; one microcalorie is one-millionth of a calorie.

it has been necessary to examine the question of whether the radiogenic heat is greater than the loss to outer space. Is the earth cooling or heating?

The three radioactive elements whose disintegration contributes most to the earth's heat budget are uranium, thorium, and potassium. Sampling of a wide variety of crustal rocks shows that these elements are far from uniformly distributed; all are strongly concentrated in the more siliceous rocks. One group of measurements on large composite samples shows that the average uranium content increases from 0.000109 percent in basalt to 0.000442 percent in siliceous granites, roughly parallel to the increase in silica content. Potassium in this composite group of samples behaves in the same way, increasing from 1.07 percent in basalts to 3.70 percent in granites. Most rocks contain three or four times as much thorium as uranium; it also is concentrated in the siliceous rocks.

Even the least radiogenic surface rocks—the ultrabasic dunite, peridotite, and pyroxenite group—contain so much radioactivity that it is clear that if the whole earth below the crust were composed of them, the earth would be molten. It is obvious that the existence of the solid mantle demands that the radioactivity be concentrated in the outer part of the globe. The average granite produces so much radiogenic heat that a layer only about 13 kilometers (8 miles) thick encircling the globe would supply all the heat being lost to outer space. But we have seen that, with trivial exceptions, the granites are confined to the continents, and indeed, to the shallow part of the continental crust. Yet the heat flow from the ocean basins is about the same as that from the Paleozoic mountain chains and far higher than that from the shields. The heat flow from the continents must be in very large part supplied by the crust; the thin and poorly radioactive basalts of the ocean floor cannot possibly suffice to supply the comparable heat flow;

most of the heat passing through the ocean floor clearly must come from the mantle—impressive evidence that the mantle beneath the oceans must differ fundamentally from that beneath the continents.

More than 40 years ago the great Norwegian geochemist V. M. Goldschmidt pointed out that the enrichment of the radioactive elements in the siliceous rocks is readily explained by the fact that their ionic radii are such as not to be accommodated in the crystal lattices of the early crystallizing iron- and magnesium-rich minerals. They remain in the magma and accompany the later fractions of the differentiation series, being concentrated in the higher parts of plutons and corresponding shallow parts of the earth's crust—they are presumably virtually absent from all zones of the earth below the uppermost part of the mantle.

Although the upward concentration of the radioactive elements is chiefly through magmatic differentiation, a smaller but significant part is contributed by hydrothermal solutions. This is shown by the fact that the average metamorphic rock of the granulite facies—the highest metamorphic grade and therefore probably the deepest crustal levels we can sample—shows only 0.000015 percent thorium and 0.000006 percent uranium, whereas the shallow granitic bodies and lower-grade metamorphic rocks contain 12 times as much thorium and 3 times as much uranium. The ratio of thorium and uranium to potassium is also many times higher in the shallow zones. The transfer of the radioactive elements from the metamorphic rocks must be largely by movement of fluids and ions, for these rocks were not melted. Thus we may understand the lower heat flow from the Precambrian shields, which, despite the large areas of granitic rocks they expose, have surely been much more deeply eroded than most of the crust. Therefore their original shallow zones, presumably enriched in radioactivity, have been eroded away.

The distributions of radioactivity and of

siliceous rocks thus greatly fortify the suggestion that the continents are the results of magmatic differentiation that allowed the more siliceous and more highly radioactive fractions of the upper mantle to rise while the more basic and earlier crystallized, less radioactive fraction remained behind. We conclude that the mantle beneath the continents is differentiated whereas that beneath the ocean is much less so.

A continental example of the problem of heat source is from the Sierra Nevada. The total heat flow from the high eastern part of the Sierra, overlying a 50-kilometer root, identified seismically, can be supplied by a mere 15-kilometer thickness of the local rock, a granite. Gravity measurements show that the granite does not extend so deep, but it is sure that the rocks of the deeper root are not wholly free from radioactivity, unless upward concentration of radioactivity has been extreme (see below). It is difficult to avoid the conclusion that here the deeper rocks are heating up. On the western slope of the Sierra, somewhat older granitic rocks show a heat flow only half as high as that to the east, but the local rocks are also much less radioactive: they would have to be 30 kilometers thick to supply all the heat. These relations can be interpreted to mean that the older granitic rocks of the western slope have been more deeply eroded than those along the crest, and their originally more radioactive higher portions have been removed.

No laboratory experiments have been able to affect the rate of radioactive disintegration, even at the highest attainable pressures, which approach those that must prevail at depths of several hundred kilometers. We must therefore assume that unless the upward concentration of radioactive elements has been remarkably efficient, the earth must be becoming not cooler, but warmer. Any heat in excess of that conducted to the surface, however, has not been sufficient to liquefy any large volume of the mantle, except perhaps in the low-velocity plastic layer just

below the M Discontinuity. Transmitted shear waves show that nearly all the mantle is solid and rigid under short term stresses, even though it does yield plastically under long-term loads, as shown by isostasy. Nevertheless, seismograms of some Japanese earthquakes recorded in Kamchatka, behind an active volcanic chain, record no S waves. This implies considerable liquid in the upper mantle, filling magma chambers beneath the volcanic chain. Magma bodies are also known beneath Hawaii, where seismic evidence shows that the Kilauea magma rises from at least 45 kilometers below the M Discontinuity. Perhaps these magma pockets form because of localized radioactivity, which would explain the relatively high radioactivity of surficial lava and granitic masses high in the crust. Or, perhaps, release of pressure along active faults lowers the melting point, permitting the rocks to melt. Partial melting of a garnet pyroxenite (Chapter 20) in the mantle would selectively concentrate the radioactive elements upward. The magma so formed rises through the more basic mantle rocks and becomes a part of the crust because it is a heat source and is also less dense. It now seems probable that the only large molten bodies above the Gutenberg-Wiechert core boundary are in the Low Velocity Zone of the upper mantle.

What the temperature may be at the core boundary and below is, of course, uncertain, but Sir Francis Simon, a British expert on solid state physics, has computed a temperature of 3900°C ± 200° at the boundary of the inner core, and about 4100°C at the center of the earth. These figures justify an estimate of about 3000°C at the Gutenberg-Wiechert Discontinuity, a figure consistent with seismic data and elasticity theory.

A strong argument that the relatively steep temperature gradient in the crust does not extend far into the mantle is given by the associations of diamonds in the sporadic volcanic vents that contain them. The diamonds are invariably accompanied by garnet pyrox-

Dynamo Theory

enites, eclogites, and other basic rocks in fragments of all sizes. Laboratory experiments indicate that these rocks could only be stable at considerable depths, estimated at 150 kilometers, at least, well down in the mantle. The temperature at the source area, if it were indeed this deep, could not have exceeded 1100°C, for at a higher temperature the diamonds would have been converted to graphite. Since many lavas on eruption have higher temperatures than this, yet came from shallower depths, we have strong additional evidence that molten pockets are only locally present in the upper mantle.

THE EARTH'S MAGNETIC FIELD

The compass needle has been used in navigation for nearly a thousand years, but it was not until 1600 that Sir William Gilbert, Queen Elizabeth's physician, noted that the earth is a huge magnet, with its poles near the geographic poles. From the magnetic poles emanate magnetic lines of force so that the north-seeking pole of a freely suspended magnet is inclined downward in the northern hemisphere, is horizontal at the magnetic equator, and is inclined upward in the southern hemisphere, and tends to lie in the plane of the meridian. Gilbert knew that this is an oversimplified picture and that the needle does not behave so regularly. The German mathematician Gauss showed in 1835 that the main elements of the earth's magnetism are internal; atmospheric electricity modifies the field only slightly. But the cause of the phenomenon remained a puzzle that deepened with the discovery by French scientist Pierre Curie in 1895 that all magnetic substances lose their magnetism on heating above a certain temperature, named the **Curie point,** which differs in different substances. No mineral has a Curie point higher than 800°C, a temperature reached at depths of about 30 or 35 kilometers nearly everywhere in the crust. The most important

magnetic mineral, magnetite, has a Curie point at 578°C. This seemed to eliminate any deep-seated source of the magnetic field, and the measured magnetic properties of observable rocks are wholly inadequate to produce the observed field in the thin earth shell above the Curie depth. The puzzle had no satisfactory answer until, as has so often happened in the history of science, the same solution was independently proposed in 1954 and 1955 by E. C. Bullard, a British geophysicist, and W. M. Elsasser, an American.

Their theory—that of a self-exciting dynamo—attributes the magnetic field to fluid motion in the outer core of the earth, assumed to be molten iron, a conducting but nonmagnetic substance. Motion of the conductor generates a magnetic field, thus a source of energy is required to keep the fluid in motion. For a time, this source was thought to be radioactivity, but more recent analyses of metallic meteorites supposedly analogous in composition with the earth's core, indicate too little radioactivity to supply the energy needed. If, however, the inner core of solid metal is slowly growing by crystallization from the overlying melt, the heat given off on freezing—the latent heat of crystallization—would be adequate to maintain the convection that produces the observed field. This theory has thus far met all the tests suggested, though, of course, all evidence is indirect. The argument can be reversed and used to indicate a molten core of conducting but nonmagnetic material such as molten nickel-iron because of the existence of the magnetic field.

Because of the earth's rotation, the convection currents in the core are dragged in the direction of spin; the field produced tends to be symmetrical about the geographic axis of the earth. The symmetry is, however, by no means perfect: the main part of the magnetic field is such as would be produced by a powerful short magnet at the earth's center, aligned not parallel to the axis, but tilted at 11.5° along the meridian of 70°W.

This is the so-called **axial dipole field.** This main field is, however, modified by a transient field that migrates slowly westward, thought to be produced by eddies in the convecting core. The result is that the magnetic poles are more than 500 miles from the poles of the axial dipole field—the north magnetic pole at 74° 54′N, 101°W, the south magnetic pole at 70°S 148°E—thus more than 15° and 20°, respectively, from the geographic poles. The northern pole is in slow motion, perhaps at the rate of about 5 miles a year; the southern has moved 480 miles between 1910 and 1960. A line connecting them misses the center of the earth by many hundred miles.

The field is far from constant, either in orientation or strength. For example, the compass needle at London has swung through an arc of more than 36° in the last 400 years, and is now swinging back again. At Cape Town the change has been even greater. The inclination of the local fields also fluctuates notably. Furthermore, the strength of the field has been diminishing about .05 percent per year since adequate measurements began in 1830.

Although the earth's magnetic field is relatively weak, it is sufficient to magnetize many rocks, both igneous and sedimentary. When a magma or a lava flow cools, its magnetic minerals crystallize, and as the temperature drops below the Curie point, they become magnetized parallel to the local magnetic field. (Some minerals or mineral pairs are magnetized precisely opposite to the local field, but these can be recognized by their internal structure and by their magnetic behavior in laboratory tests; they are so rare that we do not consider them further.) Metamorphic rocks behave in the same way as igneous, if their temperature during metamorphism rises above the Curie points of their magnetic minerals; thus the rocks in the contact aureole of a pluton are magnetised parallel to those of the pluton itself. Magnetic minerals carried into a sedimentary basin tend to align themselves parallel to the local field also, and enough do in most sandstones to record the local field. By collecting carefully oriented specimens and determining the alignment of their magnetic fields with regard to azimuth and inclination to the horizon, students have been able to trace the orientation and location of the magnetic poles of the earth far into the geologic past, thus throwing light on several fundamental geologic problems.

At present the earth's magnetic field shows marked local deviations from a field symmetric about the magnetic poles. If we assume that the north-seeking pole of a compass needle points directly at the north magnetic pole, and that the inclination of its needle is a measure of its distance from the pole, and we then plot the location of the inferred north magnetic pole from observations at the many magnetic observatories in the international

FIGURE 19–27

Positions of the virtual magnetic pole assuming that the compass needle at each magnetic observatory of the worldwide network points directly toward the north magnetic pole and that the inclination of the needle is a measure of the polar distance from the observatory. The wide scatter and deviations from the actual position of the north pole shows the local deviations from an ideal dipolar field. (After R. R. Doell and Allan Cox, 1961.)

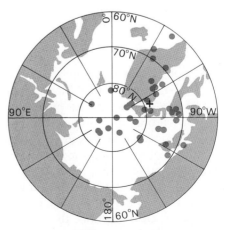

+ Present pole

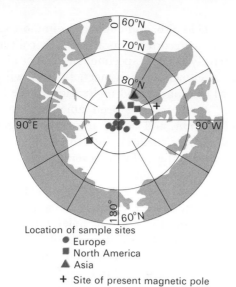

Location of sample sites
● Europe
■ North America
▲ Asia
+ Site of present magnetic pole

FIGURE 19–28

Recent and late Pleistocene (present to 500,000 years ago) virtual magnetic poles. Equal area projection. (After R. R. Doell and Allan Cox, 1961.)

network, we would obtain the large scatter of inferred poles shown in Figure 19–27. While the "center of gravity" of these inferred "virtual poles" is not far from the true magnetic pole, the scatter is over an angular distance of more than 30°. Inasmuch as the deduced magnetic pole found from the magnetism of one lava flow or a sedimentary stratum corresponds to just one of the "virtual poles" in Figure 19–27, one would hardly think this is a good method for locating either the magnetic or the geographic pole.

When, however, instead of using an instantaneous picture of the magnetic field, as in Figure 19–27, we use a field averaged over a considerable time span, the picture is quite different. Figure 19–28 shows the pattern of magnetic poles determined by the same method as before, using the magnetic alignments determined in several series of lava flows and sedimentary rocks younger than ½ m.y., from widely separated parts of the earth. This clearly shows that during the past half-million years the *average* position of the magnetic pole has been very much closer

to the geographic pole than it is at present. This is what would be expected if the dynamo theory of earth magnetism is correct, and is indeed a strong argument in its favor, tending to show that the present displaced and asymmetric position of the poles is due to transient variations which average out over an extended but uncertain time span into a field symmetrical about the geographic axis. Studies of magnetic directions in datable rock sequences representing a time span estimated as 10,000 to 100,000 years can thus give us a clue as to the positions of the magnetic and, less precisely, the geographic poles at various times in the past. We return to this in Chapter 20.

Reversals of the earth's magnetic field

We have already mentioned the rare development of a precisely reversed magnetism due to certain mineral associations; but many rocks that do not have these mineral associations and are in all other respects identical to normally magnetized rocks show reverse magnetization also. The Japanese geophysicist Matuyama first recognized in 1929 that many Pleistocene volcanic rocks are reversely magnetized. Since the development of the potassium-argon method of dating rocks the polarity of relatively young rocks that can be closely dated has been intensively studied. This work has demonstrated that there have been prolonged epochs during which the field has been the same as it now is, alternating with comparably long epochs during which the field has been reversed, as shown by like polarities of contemporaneous rocks from widely scattered localities.

The several longer epochs of constant polarity have been named for the several geophysicists who have contributed to this study: the youngest, the Brunhes normal epoch, extends from about .7 m.y. ago to the present; the preceding Matuyama reversed epoch extended from 2.5 m.y. to .7 m.y., though it was apparently interrupted very briefly by the Jaramillo and Olduvai "events"

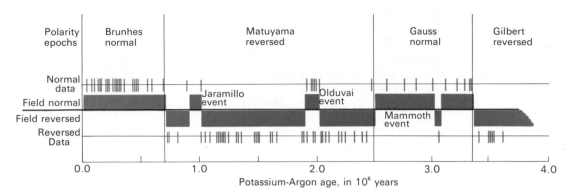

FIGURE 19–29   *Time scale for reversals of the earth's magnetic field. The observed magnetic polarities and the potassium-argon ages of volcanic rocks are shown by vertical lines. (After Allan Cox and G. B. Dalrymple, 1967.)*

of normal polarity. Before the Matuyama epoch was the Gauss normal epoch, between 3.36 and 2.5 m.y., interrupted by the brief and somewhat uncertain Mammoth event of reversed polarity. Beyond the Gauss normal epoch was the Gilbert reversed epoch, but because the precision of the potassium-argon method is not adequate to distinguish small time intervals at these distant times, the tracing of older polarity epochs is virtually impossible with present techniques. The data are summarized in Figure 19–29.

It was pointed out above that the strength of the earth's field has been diminishing for the past 135 years; perhaps it will diminish to zero at some time in the future and then reverse its polarity. Reversals are not in conflict with the dynamo theory of origin of the earth's field; they merely require a differential motion between mantle and core opposite to that now prevailing, though a mechanism to bring this about seems not yet to have been suggested. A careful study by the American scientists Allan Cox and G. B. Dalrymple indicates that the time involved in the reversals they have established is somewhere between 1600 and 21,000 years, with a best estimate of 4600 years.

Facts, concepts, terms

What are earthquakes?
Elastic-rebound theory
Elastic strain shown by triangulation
Seismic sea waves or tsunamis
Earthquake waves, P, S, and L
Seismographs and seismograms
Time-distance curves
Epicentral distance
Isoseismal lines
Modified Mercalli intensity scale
Earthquake magnitudes—Richter scale
Deep-focus earthquakes
Distribution of earthquakes

Mohorovičić Discontinuity
The crust of the earth
Sial and sima
Mantle and core
Gutenberg-Wiechert Discontinuity
Weighing the earth
Inferred composition of the earth's interior
Temperature gradient
Causes of high temperature
Differentiation within the earth
The magnetic field
Field reversals

Questions

1. During many Central American earthquakes, well-built masonry buildings have been destroyed, while bamboo huts nearby were undamaged. Can you suggest a reason?

2. The Bouguer anomalies for the Alps (see Chapter 10) suggest a greater thickness of light rocks beneath the mountains than beneath the lowlands to the north. What would this suggest regarding the heat flow to be expected in the two areas?

3. During the San Francisco earthquake the porch was sheared off a house and moved more than 10 feet by movement on the fault; the house's brick chimney, just a few feet from the fault, was not knocked over. Well-built structures 4 miles from the rift were demolished. What factors can you suggest to account for these different results?

4. Why is the Mohorovičić discontinuity of greater importance than any discontinuity within the crust?

5. What does the elastic-rebound theory suggest concerning the distribution of changes in elevation near a fault line while strain is accumulating preparatory to a vertical displacement?

6. Assume that a mountain range with an average height of 10,000 feet is buoyed up isotatically by a "mountain root." The average density of the range and root is 2.7, that of the substratum 3.3. If this mountain range lost an average thickness of 1500 feet by erosion, how high would it have to rise to restore isostatic equilibrium?

Suggested readings

American Iron and Steel Institute, *The Agadir, Morocco, Earthquake of February 29, 1960*. New York: The Institute, 1961.

Florenzov, N. A., and V. P. Solonenko, *The Gobi-Altai Earthquake*. Washington, D.C.: U.S. Coast and Geodetic Survey, 1965. [A translation of a Russian book published by Akademii Nauk U.S.S.R.]

Gutenberg, Beno, and C. F. Richter, *Seismicity of the Earth*, 2d ed. Princeton, N.J.: Princeton University Press, 1954.

Iacopi, Robert, *Earthquake Country*. Menlo Park, Calif.: Lane Book Company, 1964.

Macelwane, J. B., *When the Earth Quakes*. Milwaukee: Bruce Publishing Company, 1947.

U.S. Geological Survey, *The Alaska Earthquake* (Professional Papers 541 and 542). Washington D.C.: G.P.O., 1965–1967. 2 vols.

Scientific American offprints

804. K. E. Bullen, *The Interior of the Earth* (September 1955)

825. Walter M. Elsasser, *The Earth as a Dynamo* (May 1958)

827. Jack Oliver, *Long Earthquake Waves* (March 1959)

829. Joseph Bernstein, *Tsunamis* (August 1954)

855. Don L. Anderson, *The Plastic Layer of the Earth's Mantle* (July 1962)

20

Mountains

Almost any conspicuous high land is popularly called a mountain; geologists, however, distinguish mountains from plateaus: **Mountains** are elevated areas underlain by structurally disturbed rocks or by lavas and tuffs erupted from central volcanoes. Land masses perhaps higher or more rugged but underlain by low-dipping sedimentary or volcanic rocks are **plateaus.** Thus the Colorado and Ethiopian plateaus, even where intricately dissected by canyons thousands of feet deep, (Fig. 5–14) are not mountain ranges to geologists, though many of their canyon walls are almost unscalable. Relief is considerably greater than in the Appalachians or Urals but these lesser uplands are true mountains in the structural sense.

Mountains are of several kinds: some, like the Alps, Appalachians, Urals and Rockies are linear belts of greatly distorted strata— **fold mountains**—the only kind considered in much geologic writing, as these are most numerous and include the greatest ranges. Others, like the Cascades, are linear belts of volcanoes standing upon a basement which in places is the eroded core of an older fold mountain, elsewhere an actively folding range (Chapter 9), and in still other places a gently tilted plateau. Still others, like the so-called Basin Ranges of western North America, consist of huge blocks of rock separated by faults of great vertical displacement. The rocks of the fault blocks may be either highly distorted, as in fold mountains, or almost flat lying, as in plateaus, but the terrain is nonetheless considered mountainous because of the abundant fault disturbances, even though an individual block alone might be called a plateau. Yet other highlands, the Adirondacks and those of Labrador, for example, are composed of severely distorted rocks but their trends are nearly independent of the rock structure, whereas most fold ranges trend parallel to their internal structures. It is clear that the most recent elevation of such mountains as the Adirondacks, those of Scandinavia, and of Labrador is but little related to their internal structures.

Most of the greatest ranges are fold mountains, and we begin our study with them.

FOLD MOUNTAINS

Geosynclines

In 1859, the great American geologist James Hall noted that the folded strata of the Appalachians are both much thicker and more siliceous, in every system, than the correlative flat-lying strata of the Interior Lowland to the northwest. Comparable differences between mountain and lowland strata are general over the earth. In the Alps, Himalayas, Urals, Andes, and the Cordilleran system of North America, strata as thick as 10 or even 15 kilometers have been measured, although correlative rocks of the adjacent continental plates do not average more than a kilometer in thickness.

The rocks of these great ranges are sedimentary, volcanic, and in the core of the range, commonly, though by no means invariably, metamorphic and plutonic. Fossils are nearly all of shallow-water organisms. Many rainprints, mudcracks, salt-crystal casts, and other features indicate that the sediments were deposited in shallow water, and some beds, such as the coals of Pennsylvania, are even land-laid. Hall pointed out that shallow-water deposits recur time after time through 40,000 feet of Appalachian strata.

Though a few strata in the Alps, West Indies, and Timor have been thought to be original deep-sea oozes, their close association with shallow-water strata make this uncertain; in any case their volume is trivial. The huge thicknesses of mountain strata are not the fillings of ocean deeps, even though they are thick enough to overfill any existing deep. Hall emphasized the only possible conclusion: *the crust was slowly sinking at about the same rate that the sediment accumulated;* the surface of the sediment was never far above or below sea level during all the long time of their accumulation. With the recognition of turbidites among mountain strata, several geologists have suggested that deep oceanic sediments are more abundant than had been thought. Many turbidites are interbedded with pillow lavas containing scoria and amygdules, which show that bubbles were present in the lava as it was erupted. Bubbles could not form under the water pressures of abyssal depths, however, so we must conclude that these turbidites, though obviously deposited below wave base, formed at depths of several hundreds rather than several thousands of meters.

A trough formed by downwarping and concurrently filled with sediments is a **geosyncline,** and the pile of strata filling it a **geosynclinal prism** (Fig. 20–1) . Nearly all the fold mountains are formed from geosynclinal rocks.

Many of the Cambrian rocks of the Appalachian geosyncline show by their current features that they were derived from the continental plate to the northwest, but comparable features in Ordovician through Devonian strata, together with the thickening and coarsening of the clastic beds of these systems for hundreds of miles along the strike show that the bulk of the sediment of the

FIGURE 20–1

The thickening of strata from the Interior Lowland into the Appalachian Geosyncline. (After A. W. Grabau, 1924.)

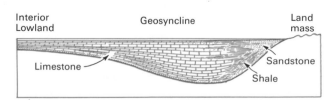

Interior Lowland   Geosyncline   Land mass

Limestone   Sandstone

Shale

pre-Carboniferous Appalachian geosyncline was derived from a land to the southeast, the area of the present Piedmont, Coastal Plain, or Continental Shelf. Such relations are common in other geosynclines; much Alpine sediment came from areas now 8000 feet beneath the Ligurian Sea; some of the Indonesian strata from areas now at a depth of 24,000 feet.

Each of the geosynclines studied shows similar relations: (1) a foreland, comparable to the Interior Lowland for the Appalachians, (2) the geosyncline itself, with its thick prism of sediment, and (3) a mountainous hinterland, from which most of the sedimentary fill was derived. Because extensive erosion was required to produce the great volume of geosynclinal fill, most stratified rocks have been eroded from the hinterlands and we know little about these complex source areas. The relative coarseness of many geosynclinal strata as compared with most modern deltas suggests that most hinterlands were mountain chains of high relief paralleling the geosyncline; the mountain we now study that rose from the geosyncline is a

second-generation product! Many old hinterlands are buried beneath younger strata and several we know to be drowned beneath the sea. The significance of these features will be discussed later in this chapter; we pass now to the structure of fold mountains.

Fold-mountain structure

The rocks of fold mountains are far more deformed than those of the continental plates; we now review some representative structural details.

THE APPALACHIANS.   The folded and faulted Appalachian rocks emerge from beneath the Alabama coastal plain and extend 1500 miles northeastward in a sinuous belt to Newfoundland, where they disappear in the Atlantic. Most individual faults and folds roughly parallel the trend of the belt and persist for many miles, so that geologic cross sections spaced several miles apart generally resemble their neighbors recognizably. Along the northwest side of the central Appalachians the folds are open, becoming increas-

FIGURE 20–2   *The two upper sections are the left and right halves of an idealized section across the Appalachians, showing the increase in deformation toward the southeast. (After W. B. Rogers, 1843.) The bottom sketch is an idealized section showing the repetition of Cambrian beds by thrust faults on which they have moved over the Ordovician beds beneath. The rocks labeled C1, C2 and C3 are all of virtually the same age. Their piling one on top of the other, and the outlying representatives of two of these sequences to the northwest can only be explained by a shoving together of the rocks by lateral compression.*

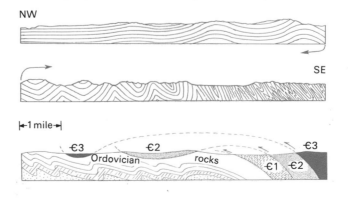

ingly tight and with steeper limbs toward the southeast. The most northwesterly anticlines are merely asymmetrical, with the northwest limbs the steeper, but farther southeast, the folds are overturned and both limbs dip southeast (Fig. 20–2). In the southeast, too, thrust faults have repeated beds of Cambrian age as many as five times: Figure 20–2, *bottom,* shows three such faults. At the northwest, the rocks are unmetamorphosed, but metamorphism increases toward the southeast and the rocks change into slates, schists, and gneisses, injected by granite plutons. Plutons are common, but not invariably present, in the most intensely folded cores of other mountain ranges, thus suggesting

deeper erosion in the areas of more intense deformation than in the less disturbed forelands.

In West Virginia and to the south, part of the folded belt is locally thrust several miles northwestward over the foreland. These great thrusts, some of which have themselves been folded, were first inferred from the outcrop pattern; they were proved by oil wells drilled through the upper plate into younger strata beneath the faults. At the latitude of Knoxville as many as six large and several smaller thrust faults have been recognized (Fig. 20–3). Great thrust faults also mark the northwest border of the folded belt in the Hudson-Champlain Valley in New York and

FIGURE 20–3   *Geologic map and section of the southern Appalachian region. The cross section (top) shows how the Ordovician rocks (not distinguished on the map) have been repeated eight times by thrust faults. The vertical scale of the section is greatly exaggerated, so that the faults appear to dip steeply; actually most have dips of less than 30°. (The map is after U.S. Geological Survey, Geologic Map of the United States, 1933. The section is based in part on other maps of the Knoxville region and is largely diagrammatic.)*

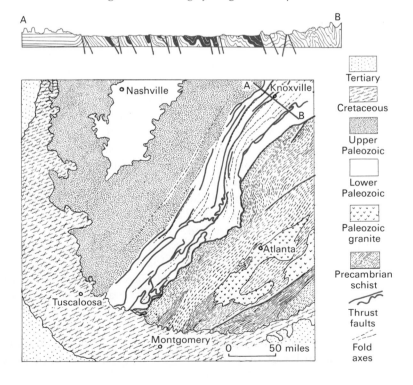

Vermont. Most thrusts bring older rock over younger, but some Appalachian thrusts have rocks of the same age both above and below. They are, however, of wholly different facies; the lower plate is largely carbonate rocks and the upper metamorphosed siliceous clastics. Thus, strata of identical age in the two plates were deposited far enough apart so that their depositional conditions were wholly different; later they were juxtaposed by thrusting, requiring travel of the rocks a minimum of several miles to bring them together. The Roberts Mountain thrust fault in Nevada, of early Mississippian age, has telescoped such contrasting facies deposits in areas formerly 60 miles apart, and probably more. Such transport is difficult to visualize but is demonstrated by the consistent facies contrast of the rocks of the two plates wherever exposed in eroded folds over this great width.

Crustal shortening.—A series of symmetrical anticlines and synclines can be pictured as forming in either of two ways: by differential uplift of the anticlinal areas and sinking of the synclines or by compression of the strata laterally so that they wrinkle like a pile of blankets on a table when it is pushed from one side. But in the Appalachians most folds are systematically asymmetric; they lean to the northwest, and the thrust faults consistently carry their upper plates northwestward with respect to the lower. Vertical movements cannot explain this; it demands lateral compression. If we measure the length of the beds along all the convolutions normal to the fold axes in the least deformed part of the Appalachians in Pennsylvania and compare this with the width of the folded belt, we find that points originally 81 miles apart have been brought 15 miles closer—this part of the earth's crust has been shortened 18 percent. This figure for the shortening does not include that due to thrust faults farther southeast. In the southern Appalachians half a dozen thrust faults in a single cross section each demand several miles of overriding—

there the shortening must have been far greater.

Parts of the Appalachian system were deformed in Ordovician time, other parts in Devonian. Apparently the latest folding involved Permian rocks, but the folds had been deeply eroded prior to the Late Triassic; the culmination seems to have been late in the Permian.

As further examples of mountain structure we cite some elements of the complex deformation of the Alps, a range more intensively studied by geologists than any other.

THE ALPS.   The Alps are part of the gigantic mountain system that stretches from the Pyrenees across southern Europe and Asia through the Himalayas to the island arcs of Indonesia. Like the Appalachians, the Alps rose from a great geosyncline, but it was filled chiefly with Mesozoic and early Cenozoic rocks rather than Paleozoic. Also, the latest of a long series of deformational episodes that affected the Alps was of Miocene age through most of the range. The foreland lies to the north, where relatively thin Mesozoic rocks unconformably blanket considerably deformed older rocks. Within the Alps the Mesozoic and Cenozoic rocks differ markedly from those of the foreland and are far thicker; their source, as shown by facies developments and current markings lay in a hinterland to the south.

A much simplified map of the Alps is shown in Figure 20–4. As our interest is in principles only, and not in the vastly complex details, we consider only the western Alps, which are representative of much of the range.

The Jura Mountains rise from a plateau north of the Alps, exposing chiefly foreland Mesozoic strata folded into anticlines separated by almost flat synclines. The folds are larger and more faulted towards the southeast (Fig. 20–5). Significantly, even the largest anticlines expose no rock older than the evaporite series, of Middle Triassic age.

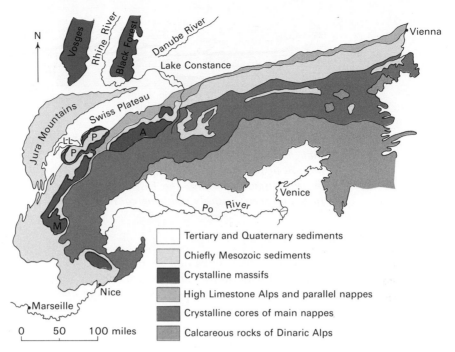

FIGURE 20–4   *Generalized map of the Alps. P, Prealps; M, Mont Blanc and Aiguilles Rouges massifs; A, Aar massif; LL, Lake Leman (Geneva). (After R. Staub, redrawn from L. W. Collet,* Structure of the Alps, *Edward Arnold and Co., 1927.)*

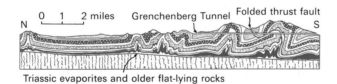

FIGURE 20–5   *Cross section of the Swiss Jura, as interpreted by A. Buxtorf, 1908. Note the essentially undisturbed Triassic and older rocks from which the overlying beds are considered to be sheared off and crumpled independently. (Redrawn from E. B. Bailey,* Tectonic Essays, *Clarendon Press, 1935.)*

Exposures nearby and in tunnels within the mountains suggest that this is because the younger strata were torn loose and folded independently of their basement. **Figures 20–5 and 20–6 show that the folds are disharmonic.** They do not involve the underlying basement rocks. The Jura lies farthest from the core of the Alps and is the smallest example of the horizontal movement of Alpine rocks, but even here several miles of movement is required to make the folds.

The 1908 interpretation shown in A. Buxtorf's cross section (Fig. 20–5) seems too simple: some Jura folds involve Miocene beds and the folding is therefore not older, yet correlative Miocene of the Swiss Plateau is almost undisturbed between the Jura and the main Alpine mass. If the crumpling was due to a push from the Alps, as the cross section implies, the plateau rocks should also have been folded, or, if they merely slid down hill, there should be a gap behind at the line

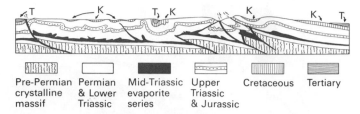

| Pre-Permian crystalline massif | Permian & Lower Triassic | Mid-Triassic evaporite series | Upper Triassic & Jurassic | Cretaceous | Tertiary |

FIGURE 20–6   *Cross section of the Swiss Jura as interpreted by D. Aubert, 1947. Note that although the younger rocks are still largely "unglued" from those below at the horizon of the Mid-Triassic evaporite, the disturbance has been brought about by thrust faulting within the basement rocks—the Pre-Permian metamorphic rocks and their passively overlying cover of Permian and Lower Triassic strata.*

from which they broke away—the "landslide scar." There is none, and furthermore the evaporite lies at a lower level near the Alps than in the Jura; the sliding would have been uphill.

Wells, drilled in some of the synclines, and gravity measurements disclosed great local thickening of the low-density evaporites beneath some of the folds. Some faults have not cut through to the surface, but have jammed the rigid basement rocks into the evaporites and squeezed and injected these plastic rocks upward. There is indeed a zone of "structural ungluing" between folded rocks and the rigid basement as Buxtorf thought, but the basement has also been involved in the shortening by concurrent thrust faulting (Fig. 20–6). As these thrust faults lie deep beneath the Swiss Plateau, its rocks were carried forward passively and undeformed. Recent studies and wells drilled in the Appalachians have shown that there, too, the surficial structures are disharmonic with the structures in more rigid rocks at depth—a relation that probably applies in all but the very simplest fold ranges.

The Swiss Plateau.—The Swiss Plateau (Fig. 20–4) is underlain by Tertiary sandstones and conglomerates derived from the Alps, as shown both by southward coarsening and by

FIGURE 20–7

Geologic map and section showing remnants of the great thrust sheets of the Prealps. The symbols are: 1, klippes of far-traveled Mesozoic rocks; 2, Jurassic; 3, Cretaceous; 4, chiefly Eocene; 5, chiefly Miocene; 6, thrust faults; S the Stanserhorn; B, the Buochserhorn. (Simplified from E. B. Bailey, Tectonic Essays, *Clarendon Press, Oxford, 1935. The section is schematic and not from Bailey.)*

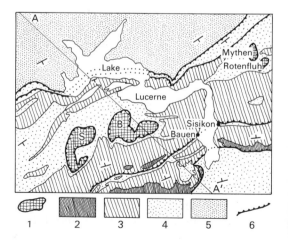

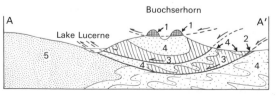

pebbles whose source can be identified. Though broadly synclinal, the rocks are little disturbed up to the Alpine border, where they are abruptly overridden and mangled by great thrust sheets of older rocks.

The Prealps.—Between the Plateau and the main Alpine chain are the Prealps, ranging from about 3500 to 6500 feet in height, and separated from the main range by a line of saddles in the connecting spurs. They expose chiefly Mesozoic rocks, overthrust onto the Tertiary of the Swiss Plateau (Figs. 20–7 and 20–8). Deep erosion has removed much of a formerly continuous thrust sheet and left the Prealps as remnants isolated in a broad expanse of younger rocks. Such remnants of thrust masses, isolated by erosion, are **klippes** (German; *Klippen,* cliffs). They were first recognized in the Alps, but abound in many other folded chains.

Figure 20–7 shows how this complex geology is interpreted. At the south end of Lake Lucerne Eocene rocks dip beneath a thrust carrying Jurassic, Cretaceous, and Eocene rocks; these, in turn, are overlain at Sisikon and Bauen by a higher thrust sheet of Cre-taceous. On this rests the highest sheet of all, the Triassic rocks of the Stanserhorn, Buoch-serhorn, Mythen, and Rothenfluh. All these strata are dated by fossils; their sequence can only be explained by thrust faulting.

The high Limestone Alps and the crystalline massifs.—It is beyond the scope of this book to detail the manifold complexities of Alpine geology. One feature, though, a plunging structure, will be described as illustrating a general method of structural interpretation.

The lower thrust sheets beneath the klip-pes of the Prealps continue southeastward into the High Limestone Alps, as shown diagrammatically in Figure 20–9. Here they lie superposed in sheets dragged out so far from anticlinal folds as to lie nearly flat. Swiss geologists call such thrust sheets **nappes** (French) or **Decken** (German).

The Aiguilles Rouges massif consists of granite and metamorphic rocks, as does the Mont Blanc massif just to the south. Distorted plant fossils show that at least a part of these metamorphic rocks is of Carboniferous age. The overlying Permian and Triassic conglomerates contain pebbles of these meta-

FIGURE 20–8   *Sketch of the Mythen klippe. The steep peaks of white Mesozoic limestone rest on Eocene shale. (After L. W. Collet,* Structure of the Alps, *Edward Arnold and Co., 1927.)*

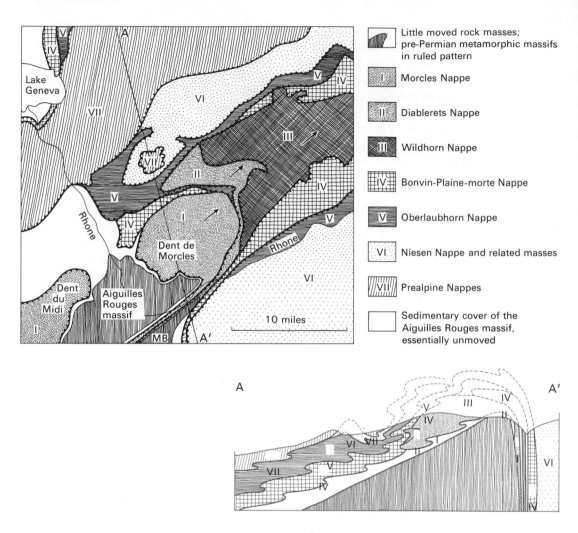

FIGURE 20–9   *Map and schematic cross section of the northeast end of the Aiguilles Rouges massif, near the Rhone Valley, southeast of Lake Leman. Unpatterned and lower dark pattern indicate the little-moved rock masses; pre-Permian metamorphic massifs are dark. I, Dent de Morcles Nappe; II, Diablerets Nappe; III, Wildhorn Nappe; IV, Bonvin-Plain Morte Nappe; V, Oberlaubhorn Nappe; VI, Niesen and related nappes; VII, Prealpine nappes. MB is the extreme end of the Mont Blanc massif. Note how the Morcles Nappe begins in the tightly squeezed area between the Mont Blanc and Aiguilles Rouges massifs. Arrows indicate plunge of fold and associated structures. The cross section is highly schematic and the topographic relief greatly exaggerated for clarity, but the relations of the several nappes are essentially correct as to age and superposition. (Greatly modified from E. B. Bailey,* Tectonic Essays, *Clarendon Press, 1935.)*

morphic rocks and must have been deposited close to where we now find them, or else both basement and the unconformably overlying beds have been thrust forward together.

The clue to the structure lies in the Rhone Valley at the northeast end of the Aiguilles Rouges massif, where the sedimentary rocks of the south side of the massif can be followed northeast, north, and northwest as a strongly sheared-out isoclinal fold, the Morcles Nappe, draped at a low angle over the much sheared Permian and Triassic strata overlying the crystalline basement. All the rocks are highly sheared parallel to their contacts, and the folds and minor structures all plunge to the northeast. It is clear that the Morcles Nappe was squeezed out of the narrow syncline between the Aiguilles Rouges and Mont Blanc massifs and strewn out northwestward. If the plunges are projected upward to the southwest, the folded mass of the Dent du Midi, across the Rhone Valley, is seen to be part of the Morcles Nappe separated by the erosional canyon of the Rhone. Northeastward, the plunges allow several higher nappes to be seen superposed on the Morcles; traced northwestward they dip beneath the even higher thrust sheets of the

Prealps. We find that the Morcles Nappe came from south of the Aiguilles Rouges massif and the successively higher nappes came from successively farther south. This relation is general in the Alps and also in most other fold chains—each successively higher thrust sheet came from nearer the hinterland than its predecessors.

Swiss geologists think that the crystalline massifs moved only a few miles during the folding, whereas the Morcles Nappe has been torn loose and overfolded northward for many miles. It can be followed northward for more than ten miles, before it disappears beneath sheets below the Prealps—proof of extensive horizontal movement. What, then, are we to think when several of the overlying nappes reappear from beneath the Prealps twenty miles farther north, where they rest in fault contact on the Tertiary of the plateau northeast of Lake Geneva! The only conclusion possible is that these superficial strata have been displaced for scores of miles.

Northeastward from the area of Figure 20–9 the fold plunges reverse and the structures begin to rise: first the Diablerets Nappe from beneath the Wildhorn, then the Morcles Nappe and finally crystalline rocks of the

FIGURE 20–10   *Block diagram, modified from P. Arbenz, showing how downwarped segments of the anticlinal structure represented by the Aiguilles Rouges and Aar crystalline massifs preserve a succession of thrust sheets (nappes I, II, III, IV) that have been eroded away on the axial culminations both to the northeast and to the southwest. Such "axial depressions" are what enable the Alpine geologists to determine the mutual relations of the nappes and to project the structures along the trend of the range. In this way the superposed nappes can be projected both beneath the surface and into the air, thereby enabling us to visualize the rock masses as they were before erosion.*

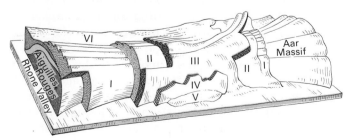

Aar massif, very like those of the Aiguilles Rouges. Between the two massifs is a sag in a northeast-trending ridge of crystalline rock; it is the plunge of the successively overlying units toward this sag that reveals their sequence unambiguously. Figure 20–10 illustrates the principle.

No single nappe extends the length of the Alps, though several have been traced for several scores of miles. The alternating axial depressions and culminations along the trends of the folded structures permit correlations of nappes for long distances. The architecture of the range can confidently be projected to surprising depths and reconstructed to great heights which erosion has long since reduced.

One strongly overfolded crystalline core after another is found south of the Aar massif, all the way to the southern border of the range, each separated from the next by much squeezed schists, some of which have yielded Mesozoic or Tertiary fossils. The spacial arrangement of the nappes demands tremendous shortening of the outer crust—a shortening that cannot be accurately measured but two Swiss geologists, Albert Heim and J. Cadisch, have independently estimated from their carefully worked out cross sections that a sedimentary region originally at least 400 miles wide has been piled together in a mountain range only about 100 miles wide. The superficial part of the crust beneath northern Italy must lie scores, if not, indeed, several hundred, of miles closer to the Swiss Plateau than it did in Eocene time.

The evidence is not only geometric; facies contrasts of the nappes also demand great shortening. For example, Arnold Heim mapped the Cretaceous rocks of eastern Switzerland and found the relations summarized in the simplified cross section of Figure 20–11. Drag folds showed that both nappes moved northward with respect to the rocks beneath, as the facies differences also disclose. Had the nappes always lain north of the Aar massif, and the upper one north of the lower

—their present relation—we would have the unlikely facies arrangement shown in the middle of Figure 20–11. Obviously, the arrangement shown in the bottom is much the more probable, and it also conforms to the testimony of the drag folds.

Flysch and Molasse.—We mentioned in Chapter 17 that the peculiar stratigraphic association of turbidite, shale, and normal sandstone known as *flysch* is common in many folded ranges, especially in the youngest strata involved in the folding. This is especially well illustrated in the Alps and Carpathians, where the flysch beds have become known as premonitory strata, indicating proximity to the geosyncline of the internal geanticline—the hinterland—from which the major sedimentary contribution is derived. We have already mentioned that most mountain chains of the folded type are "second generation"—their sediments derived from highlands in their hinterlands. As the geosyncline closes by lateral compression, the source area approaches the depositional basin and flysch deposits become common. They are widespread in the Coast Ranges of western America, from Alaska south, but are not as conspicuous in the Appalachian System, except in the Ouachita (Oklahoma) and Marathon (Texas) regions, and there is some question of whether these are actually continuations of the Appalachians rising from beneath younger rocks.

After the main folding episode, the geosyncline became segmented into basins, and the former drainage was disrupted—an ideal environment for terrestrial deposition, both fluvial and lacustrine. Thus, immediately after folding, coarse-grained clastic rocks containing terrestrial fossils are generally deposited; Swiss geologists have given the name **molasse** to this facies. Flysch and molasse deposits are common in fold ranges, but are by no means invariably present. They record the gradual closing of a depositional basin by the advance of the hinterland and coarsening of

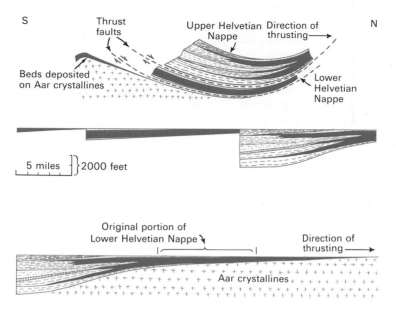

FIGURE 20–11 *Hypothetical reconstructions of the original sedimentary relations of the thrust sheets and unmoved sedimentary cover of the Aar massif, in eastern Switzerland. Top: The present relations; Middle: the relations that would have existed had the lower thrust sheet always been north of the massif and the higher sheet still farther north; Bottom: the former relations had both sheets been thrust over the massif from the south, the higher from farther south than the lower. Clearly this is the more probable reconstruction of the original relations. (After Arnold Heim.)*

FIGURE 20–12 *Idealized reconstruction of the structure of the Alps, neglecting erosion. (After Emile Argand, 1916.)*

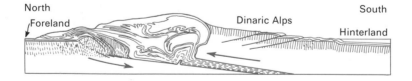

the sediment derived from it, followed by rapid filling of the foreland basins and piedmont slopes by sediments eroded from the new-born mountains. Thus flysch and molasse deposits are of considerable value in reading geologic history.

Summary of alpine structure.—Although the few examples cited can only hint at the almost incredibly complex structure of the Alps, they suffice to demonstrate that here, as in the Appalachians, prodigious horizontal forces, like the jaws of a great vise, have shoved together the upper part of the crust (Fig. 20–12.) During the process many rocks have been dynamically metamorphosed—a single rock mass may display all transitions between almost unaltered shale and highly metamorphosed schist. Granitic rocks caught in the deformation have been granulated and partly or wholly recrystallized into gneiss, with all transitional stages apparent. These are significant observations, for, as we saw in Chapter 18, geometric patterns like those in the towering Alps are common in the metamorphic rocks of the deeply eroded Precambrian shield areas.

Like the Alps and Appalachians, many other ranges also consist of long chains of folds, thrust faults, and cores of metamorphic and plutonic rocks so closely related as to indicate a genetic association of all. Plutons and metamorphic rocks are by no means invariably present in folded ranges but they so commonly are that a related origin seems implied.

The substructure of the fold mountains

The shortening of the shallower crustal layers so well shown in the fold mountains must have been accompanied by deformation in the deeper crust as well. Despite the disharmonic folding and shearing off of upper layers from lower, as in the Jura and the Morcles Nappe, the metamorphic facies exposed in many ranges could only have been formed at great depths and under pressure of several tens of kilometers of load; the deformation extended nearly or quite through the crust, even though different levels reacted differently. We have clear evidence in the isostatic anomalies (Chapter 10) and seismic data (Chapter 19) that many fold mountains are underlain by thick roots—those of the Sierra and Alps are more than 60 kilometers deep—nearly twice the normal crustal thickness. We might think the size of these roots a measure of the compression of the crust as a whole, except that many folded mountains have no excessive roots (the southern Rockies have a crustal thickness about like that of the great plains to the east) and some, like the northern Rockies, have thinner crusts than the adjacent plains. Furthermore, even so great a root as is present beneath the Alps, is not nearly adequate to account for all the crustal matter if the shortening is as great—300

miles—as the geometry of the structures indicated to Heim and Cadisch. We will return to this problem later in the chapter; here we can only comment that although fold mountains across the earth resemble each other, the deeper crust beneath them has by no means reacted to the mountain-making forces everywhere the same.

VOLCANIC MOUNTAINS

Many volcanic ranges, like the island arcs of the Pacific, Caribbean, and South Atlantic, and the Hawaiian chain, are largely submarine; they are treated in a later section. There are fewer continental than oceanic volcanic ranges; the only one of consequence in the United States is the Cascade Range of Washington and Oregon, which trends almost meridionally for about 500 miles. Huge glacier-clad volcanic cones such as Mounts Rainier, Hood, and Shasta crown the range. Between them lie innumerable smaller cones and lava fields. Beneath these young volcanoes is a platform of older, folded, and deeply eroded volcanic rocks, mostly derived from central volcanoes. Near Mount Hood they rest on gently tilted to highly folded plateau lavas—part of the great Columbia Plateau flood basalt. Farther north, near Yakima, groups of younger volcanoes trend directly across geosynclinal rocks that have been folded, and are currently folding (Chapter 8). Clearly the trend of this range is nearly or quite independent of the crustal structures on which it is built; it must be determined by deep-seated faults or a broad magmatic alignment in the upper mantle. There are few such volcanic ranges on the continents; most volcanic cones are isolated, like Kenya and Kilimanjaro in Africa, Ararat in Asia Minor, and Demavend in Iran, but the island arcs of eastern Asia and the Caribbean are typical volcanic mountains; so are parts of the Andes and Carpathians.

FAULT-BLOCK MOUNTAINS

In most of Nevada, western Utah, and large parts of Oregon, Idaho, Arizona, New Mexico, western Texas, eastern California, and northern Mexico, isolated mountain ranges rise above the desert plains and basins. Comparable features dominate the so-called "Rift Valley" areas of Israel, eastern Sudan, Ethiopia, Kenya, Uganda, and Tanzania. In all these areas geologic mapping has shown that the mountains are separated from the intervening valleys and lowlands by normal faults of great displacement, as with the Tobin Range, Nevada, described in Chapter 8.

These **fault-block mountains** differ from the fold mountains in having no necessary association with geosynclinal sedimentation; they were formed from crustal segments of widely differing histories. Some have indeed involved geosynclinal rocks, but the facies trends of the strata are wholly independent of the fault trends, and in some, an old geosyncline had been previously folded and deeply eroded long before the faulting to which the present mountains are due. Many of the fault-block mountains of East Africa are composed of thin or thick piles of late Tertiary lava, resting with great unconformity on a Precambrian terrain that had been, so far as the preserved record is concerned, virtually undisturbed for hundreds of millions of years.

Some of the fault-block mountains of the western states, like the Teton Range of Wyoming, are similar, but the Sierra Nevada is composed largely of folded Mesozoic strata and plutons, with small patches of Tertiary volcanics resting in great unconformity on its crest and western slope; Steens Mountain, Oregon (Fig. 20–13), consists entirely of gently tilted Tertiary lavas and tuffs; the Wasatch Range of Utah includes Precambrian strata and thick geosynclinal Paleozoic and Mesozoic rocks that have been greatly deformed and injected by plutons in early Tertiary time; the Little Hatchet Mountains of southern New Mexico are made up chiefly of geosynclinal Lower Cretaceous sedimentary rocks with some Tertiary volcanics; some of the ranges in southern Nevada expose more than 8000 feet of volcanic rocks, with no basement visible. Obviously this variation in rocks and geologic history sets the fault-block mountains apart from the fold mountains such as the Alps and Appalachians, which, for long distances along their trends, have had very similar sedimentational and structural histories.

Some fault-block mountains of the Rift Valley areas of East Africa have faults along one side only and are tilted like trap doors, with a steep scarp on the side overlooking the fault and a gentle slope on the other. Examples are the Aberdare Range of Kenya and the tilted block whose downthrown side contains Lake Tanganyika, in Tanzania. The Sierra Nevada and Teton Ranges of the United States are similar. In places whole series of such "trap-door" blocks all face in the

FIGURE 20–13   *Cross section of a relatively uneroded fault-block mountain range, Steens Mountain, Oregon. Note that the right-hand fault is somewhat older than the middle one, and is overlapped by unfaulted gravel; the middle fault cuts the gravel, so is younger. All three faults, however, are relatively young, for their scarps have not been eroded back far from them. The marked bed indicates the interpretation of the actual displacement.*

same direction, as in the block-faulted part of Ethiopia and near Lake Manyara, Tanzania in Africa, and north central Nevada in the United States. Other blocks have faults on both sides, either uplifted as a horst like the Ruwenzori (Mountains of the Moon) Range of Uganda and Steens Mountain, Oregon, or dropped into a graben as in some of the Rift Valleys of Africa. Many of the bounding faults die out gradually along strike, others end against transverse faults; some ranges are bounded by a single fault for many miles, others by zones of faults, each in turn dying out in the uplifted block and being replaced by another fault in echelon arrangement. The normal faults of all these ranges tell of extension of the crust—the precise opposite of the compression recorded by the fold mountains.

The greatest mountain ranges on earth, the submarine ranges of the mid-ocean ridges are also fault-block mountains; we discuss their origin after the next section.

UPWARPED MOUNTAINS

Some mountains are not readily classed as either fold mountains, volcanic mountains, or fault-block mountains. The Adirondacks, the Labrador highlands, the Black Hills, and many other mountain masses are examples. All are composed chiefly of ancient metamorphic rocks like those found in the deeply eroded parts of many fold mountains. But these mountains are not elongated parallel to their bedrock structures as are most folded ranges, but trend independently of them. Though some faults border the Adirondacks, they seem negligibly small and incapable of accounting for the relief of the range. These mountains seem to be recently uplifted parts of the Precambrian Shield. Long ago their rocks underwent deformation into typical fold mountains, but as shown by the even truncation of these ancient folds by the overlapping Cambrian strata, the fold mountains

had been reduced to a nearly level surface before the incursion of the Cambrian sea. The uplift of the present mountains is due to upwarping of a mass once covered with a flat sedimentary blanket of nongeosynclinal thickness. The upwarping came long after the folding and was independent of it.

Similar upwarping long after folding and deep erosion has gone on in the Appalachians, the Rockies, the Scandinavian and Caledonian mountains, and in many other ranges, but these warps are different because they are so obviously governed in trend by the bedrock structures. The mechanism of uplift of the mountains here considered must differ greatly from that controlling rejuvenation of these younger folded ranges. It can hardly have been caused by lateral compression, and it differs from the mechanism that formed the fault-block mountains in not involving notable crustal extension.

MOUNTAINS BENEATH THE SEA

The gross topography and extent of the island arcs and mid-ocean ridges and rises have been described in Chapter 16. Here we consider their similarities and contrasts with the mountains of the continents.

The island arcs are volcanic chains, largely composed of basaltic and andesitic lavas, with some plutons. Beneath several the crust is intermediate between normal oceanic and continental thicknesses, and seismic velocities in the upper mantle are significantly lower than usual. The western Aleutians are chiefly basaltic and andesitic, with some dioritic and gabbroic plutons, but toward the east the plutons become more siliceous and, in the continuation of the chain on the Alaskan Peninsula, very large siliceous volcanic and plutonic bodies are present. Japan, too, has many quartz-bearing intrusive and extrusive rocks. Heat flow of the arcs seems about normal except in areas of active volcanism, but in the associated ocean deeps the flow is exceptionally low—doubtless because of insulation by thick accumulations of Recent sediments. Some arcs lie on the transition between continental and oceanic crusts but others, like the Mariana arc, are bordered by oceanic crust on both sides (Chapter 19). The mid-ocean ridges are obviously very much faulted longitudinally, with steep scarps bounding flatter terraces on either side of the main ridges; commonly a central graben divides the highest ridges (Fig. 20–14). They differ in scale from most continental ranges in being as wide as 1000 miles for many thousands of miles along their trends; the Cordillera of western North America, the Iranian-Afghan ranges and parts of the Himalaya are the only continental ranges approaching this width. They differ also in being roughly symmetrical (Fig. 20–14), in contrast to the marked asymmetry (Fig. 20–12) of nearly all continental ranges. Although some geologists have compared the mid-ocean ridges with the Red Sea rift and the African Rift Valleys the analogy is not close—the graben (fault troughs) so often found axially in the mid-ocean ridges lies between high ranges. Only locally do the African grabens separate highlands; most of these fault troughs lie between flat plates of regional extent.

The largest strike-slip faults thus far recognized on the continents—the Great Glen Fault in Scotland (displacement 104 kilometers), the Alpine Fault in New Zealand (displacement 480 kilometers) and the San Andreas Fault in California (whose displacement has been variously estimated by different students between 60 and 640 kilometers)—all trend at narrow angles to the grain of the basement structures. But the mid-ocean ridges are cut by many and very large strike-slip faults, nearly at right angles to their trend, and similar large strike-slip faults—nearly normal to the coast—cut the floor of the northeast Pacific, where no ridge exists (Fig. 20–15). Many of these transverse faults have far larger displacements than any on the continents: the Mendocino Fracture Zone off California (Figs. 20–15, 20–16) offsets magnetic and topographic patterns in the ocean floor by 1185 kilometers, and some of the great strike-slip faults near the equator (Fig. 20–17) have offset the Mid-Atlantic Ridge by comparable distances, thereby accommodating the great swerve of the Atlantic between Africa and Brazil by a series of chiefly left-lateral offsets.

Heat flow is normal or lower in many parts of the mid-ocean ridges, but near the axis, where the seismic activity is also localized, it is somewhat higher, especially near volcanic areas. The axial zone is also one of anomalously low seismic speed in the upper mantle, attributed to higher than normal temperatures caused by the higher heat flow.

Basalt, and lesser amounts of peridotite, serpentine, and gabbro have been dredged from the Mid-Atlantic Ridge. St. Paul's Rocks, which rise from the Ridge, expose highly sheared dunite. Iceland, also on the Ridge, is chiefly composed of flood basalt and rhyolite, but its southeastern plateau is cut

FIGURE 20–14   *Cross section of the Mid-Atlantic Ridge at 30° N. Vertical exaggeration, 40:1. Note the central graben zone and the rough symmetry. Atlantis seamount is an extinct volcano. The belt of seismic activity is confined to the central zone. (After C. L. Drake,* Philosophical Transactions of the Royal Society, *1958.)*

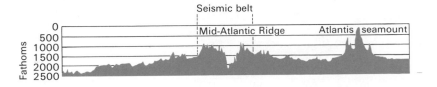

by several granitic plutons of Pliocene age and younger. Flood basalts seem to be associated with the Ridge in much of the North Atlantic but not elsewhere; like the island arcs, the ridges are not petrologically uniform along their trend, as might have been expected from their continuity and amazingly persistent form.

The oceanic rises, of which the best studied is the East Pacific Rise, are lower and much less faulted longitudinally than the ridges; volcanoes do not appear to be more abundant on them than elsewhere on the ocean floor. The East Pacific Rise has several nar-row linear belts of exceptional heat flow that have been attributed to dike intrusions into the ocean floor, but most of the rise has normal or even subnormal heat flow.

SUMMARY OF MOUNTAIN STRUCTURES

The fold mountains have formed on the sites of geosynclines; their strata are far thicker than those of the continental plates. Some of them have deep roots; others do not. Many contain plutons and high-grade metamorphic

FIGURE 20–15 *The oceanic ridges and rises and the fracture zones of large displacement. 1: Mendocino Fracture Zone; 2: Pioneer Fracture Zone; 3: Murray Fracture Zone; 4: Molokai Fracture Zone; 5: Clarion Fracture Zone; 6: Clipperton Fracture Zone; 7: Galapagos Fracture Zone; 8: Easter Island Fracture Zone; 9: Mid-Indian Ridge; 10: Kerguelen-Gaussberg Ridge; 11: Melanesian Rise; 12: Pacific-Antarctic Ridge; 13: East Pacific Rise; 14: Galapagos Rise; 15: Chile Rise; 16: Scotia Rise; 17: Mid-Atlantic Ridge; 18: Atlantic-Indian Ridge; 19: Carlsberg Ridge; 20: Walfisch Ridge. (Modified from H. W. Menard,* Philosophical Transactions of the Royal Society, *v. 258, 1965.)*

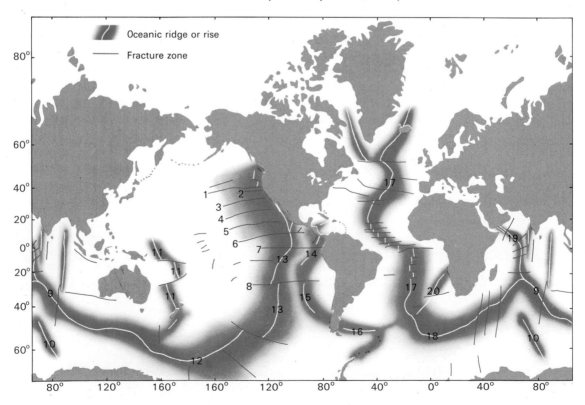

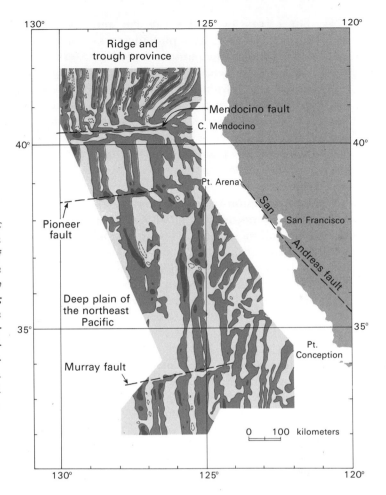

FIGURE 20–16

Magnetic anomalies in the Pacific sea floor off California. The dark brown shades indicate areas of positive anomalies; that is, areas in which the magnetic field is notably stronger than the regional average; the pale brown areas are those in which the magnetic field is weaker than the regional average. The origin of the anomaly pattern is discussed on page 529. (After R. G. Mason and A. D. Raff, Geological Society of America Bulletin, 1961.)

FIGURE 20–17   *The offsets in the Mid-Atlantic Ridge between the bulges of Africa and South America. R: Romanche Trench, offset about 500 kilometers; C: Chain Fracture Zone, offset about 300 kilometers; V: Vema Fracture Zone, offset about 300 kilometers. Central graben zone of the Ridge is left blank. (After B. C. Heezen and Marie Tharp, Philosophical Transactions of the Royal Society, v. 258, 1965.)*

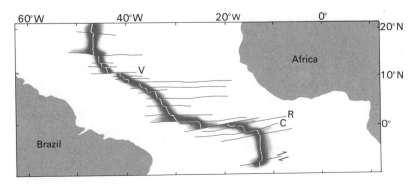

rocks, but others, even of great age and deeply eroded, do not. Most plutonic rocks are associated with fold mountains but many plutons also invade plateaus and continental plates at sites not obviously related to folding. The internal structures of many fold mountains demand great shortening in the exposed part of the crust, and their facies variations indicate that successive thrust sheets had their roots in successively more remote zones.

Volcanic ranges on the continents are few and apparently not associated with particular sedimentation patterns. The principal volcanic ranges are the island arcs that border much of the north and west shores of the Pacific, and bound the eastern Caribbean. Some of these rise from the critical zone in which the crust changes from oceanic to continental but some arcs lie wholly within the ocean basin.

The principal fault-block mountains of the earth are the great mid-oceanic ridges; indeed it has been suggested that the fault-block mountain areas of the continents—the Basin and Range province of western America and the Rift Valley province of east Africa—lie on subcontinental extensions of the oceanic rifts. The connection, if any, is, obscure, as their fault patterns differ conspicuously. The fault-block mountains of land and sea floor together cover a considerably larger area than the fold mountains, and since the faults are chiefly normal, they represent an extension of the earth's crust that may equal or exceed the shortening indicated in the fold mountains. The crust beneath the Basin and Range province is exceptionally thin, the heat flow high, and the upper mantle abnormally inelastic; under the oceanic ridges, although heat flow and seismic speeds resemble those of the Basin and Range province, the crustal thickness is greater than is normal for the oceans, and, in fact, no velocity as high as 8.2 kilometers per second—a representative value of compressional seismic

waves beneath the M Discontinuity—has been found beneath the central zone; the crust seems to blend into the mantle gradually, rather than being separated by sharp discontinuity (Fig. 19–21). Both continental and oceanic fault-block ranges are locally accompanied by basaltic and more siliceous volcanics, but the association is not invariable with either.

THE HISTORY OF FOLDED BELTS

When a geosynclinal prism is folded, faulted, and crowded together, by whatever process, isostasy demands that the base of the mass must sink. (Figs. 10–11, 10–15). The crust may be strong enough to sustain small masses but not large loads of regional extent. The sial composing the outer crust has an average density of about 2.7; the sima beneath is somewhat more dense. The material of the mantle must be still denser or isostasy could not prevail. Seismic data suggest a range between 3.0 and 3.3 for the density just below the M Discontinuity. Let us take the higher of these figures. If a crustal segment is thickened by folding, the bottom of the crust must sink into the mantle just as a ship settles deeper when a load is put aboard. If the increase in thickness were 5000 feet, the sinking would be enough to displace an equal mass of mantle: 2.7×5000 feet $\div 3.3$, or more than 4000 feet. (Part of the adjustment might, of course, take place by flowage within the crust rather than beneath it, but the principle is the same: the total mass per unit area above some "level of compensation" in the mantle must remain the same.)

With a thickening of 5000 feet, then, the surface of the ground would be only about 1000 feet higher than it was originally. This statement cannot be taken too literally, of course, but the principle is surely valid, for it accords with, and in part explains, the long persistence of uplift along most folded ranges.

Mountain uplift

For simplicity, we have neglected details of sedimentation in the Appalachian and Alpine geosynclines, but in both of them deposition was interrupted by uplift many times; folds grew high enough to be eroded more than once during the geosynclinal phase of these ranges and are recorded by many angular unconformities. The common coarse clastic deposits of the outer, more gently folded parts of these ranges, and the presence in them of pebbles identifiable as derived from originally deeply buried rocks also attest to these premonitory folds.

In some mountain ranges, such as the Sierra Nevada, the folding has thickened both sial and sima, as is shown by comparison of gravity and heat-flow measurements; elsewhere, as in the southern Rocky Mountains, the heat flow is so high as to require a thickened sial, but the fact that the crust is no thicker under the mountains than under the plains to the east shows that the sima was not comparably thickened; the crust beneath the plains is obviously composed of much denser, less siliceous and less radioactive material than that of the mountains. This relation must also be true of the northern Rockies, whose crust is even thinner than that of the plains.

Thickening of the sial leads to high relief and subsequent erosion. That some of the rise is prompt is shown in the Alps by the very coarse Miocene and Pliocene conglomerates of the Swiss plateau that lap against and are overridden by complexly deformed Miocene and older rocks of the mountains proper. The scattered fault blocks of Triassic conglomerate and sandstone in the Appalachian piedmont also testify to high relief soon after the late Paleozoic folding of that range. Some, however, of the range uplift came long after the folding. The present relief of the Appalachians, and of most pre-Tertiary ranges, is due to the upbowing of the deformed and deeply eroded rocks in late Tertiary time, as is shown by unconformities.

The Appalachian summit descends southward and passes beneath the Cretaceous strata of the Gulf Coastal Plain, which lies on a nearly featureless surface eroded across the folded Paleozoic strata. Figure 20–3 shows the basal contact of the Cretaceous to pass in a smooth curve directly across the edges of the steeply dipping Paleozoic rocks—there are no irregularities recording the differing resistances of the several strata to erosion, such as we see in the Appalachian mountain topography—the pre-Cretaceous surface was a flat plain. As far northeast as New Jersey the Cretaceous rocks of the coastal plain rest in strong unconformity upon the steeply dipping rocks of the Piedmont, which is structurally part of the Appalachians; there can have been but slight relief in the present Appalachian country in Cretaceous time, yet the present mountains attain a relief of 6700 feet, measured from the top of Mount Mitchell to the Coastal Plain. This relief must then be due to upwarping long after the Cretaceous beds were deposited.

Other evidence of long-delayed uplift of many ranges lies in the surfaces of low relief eroded across highly disturbed rocks of the summit uplands (Fig. 12–39). Such surfaces can rarely be dated, as they lack overlying fossiliferous rocks—though one in the Sierra Nevada has been dated radiometrically from an overlying lava flow—yet the reduction of a structurally disturbed landscape to a flat surface requires long erosion. Most mountain streams have high gradients in their source areas but in some mountains where flat uplands have been carved across complexly folded rocks the streams move sluggishly across the uplands and then plunge in foaming torrents down canyons far below. The contrast in gradient strongly suggests that the summit upland was carved by streams of low gradient such as could have existed only if the area was much nearer sea level than it now is. The uplift was far later than the fold-ing, for a long time was needed to erode the original relief to a smooth plain.

In summary: the dominant tendency dur-ing the geosynclinal phase of mountain his-tory was toward sinking, sporadically inter-rupted by local or general episodes of uplift. Growing modern folds (Chapter 8) and the relief of geologically young ranges testify to dominant uplift concurrent with folding. The history inferred from the Cretaceous un-conformity across the Appalachian folds and the flat summit uplands of many ranges is one of uplift interrupted by long stillstands.

Causes of uplift

Seismic and gravitational data show that the sial is thicker beneath folded mountains than elsewhere and that the sima is also thicker beneath some of them. The isostatic relations during erosion are the converse of those prevailing during sedimentation or crustal compression. Erosion lessens the load; as we saw, a load of sial a mile thick would raise the surface less than 1000 feet; the ero-sion of a mile of sial would only lower it the same amount. As most valley walls are con-cave upward, stream erosion normally re-moves more than half the volume between stream level and summit before lowering di-vides greatly. Accordingly, the altitude of the mountain peaks may actually increase be-cause of erosion and isostatic uplift, even though the average elevation of the moun-tainous region is reduced (Fig. 20–18). Iso-static uplift might thus account for many of the high flat summit areas, but in view of the quick response to glacial loading and unload-ing (Chapter 13), it is difficult to understand the long stillstand that preceded uplift while the low-gradient summit upland was being carved. Much remains to be learned before these paradoxes are understood.

FIGURE 20–18

How summit level may increase owing to iso-static uplift, even though the average level of the surface is being lowered by erosion. A: As-sumed summit and average level of mountain block at close of folding. B: Assumed topog-raphy after considerable erosion but with no isostatic response to the unloading from the block of the volumes marked V. Average level is the average altitude of the block but we arbi-trarily retain the same summit level as in A. C: Relations after isostatic uplift of the block, dis-sected as in B. Average level is higher than in B by 2.7 ÷ 3.3 times the difference between average level and summit level in part B. (See text for assumptions underlying choice of this fraction.)

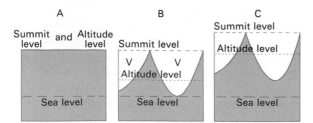

THE MOUNTAIN ROOT

So far, we have considered the thickened sial beneath the mountains as though it main-tained all its properties unchanged when it thickened. But it most assuredly does not: all rocks whose related structures show them to have been both deeply buried and de-formed in association with intrusive masses are metamorphosed. Mere burial beneath other rocks necessarily raises the temperature of the geosynclinal sediments by blanketing-in the earth's internal heat. Radioactivity, concentrated in the surficial layers of the earth (Chapter 19), is enriched in the geo-synclinal sediment and also contributes heat. This heating expands the geosynclinal prism, but because the heating is slow, it may be a long time before the surface of the column is raised by the expansion; the delayed ther-mal expansion may account for part of the long delayed uplift of many ranges.

There are also phase changes during metamorphism to consider. Under the high pressures of deep burial in the mountain substructure the minerals—under equilibrium during weathering and surface transport—become unstable and recrystallize into denser minerals. Such recrystallization may not keep pace with the increased load but await triggering by an increase in temperature. The shrinkage in volume brought about by converting less dense to more dense minerals at depth may account for long delayed stillstands during erosion of a mountain chain because the accumulation of the triggering heat must be a very slow process.

As we saw in Chapter 19, the normal heat loss to outer space could be supplied by the radioactivity of a layer of average granite only 13 kilometers thick. Geosynclinal sediments are chiefly derived from erosion of the outer crust, although there is some admixture of pyroclastic and volcanic flows; they therefore have about the same radioactivity as a mixture of the average exposed igneous rocks. A pile as thick as 40 or 50 kilometers, such as accumulated in the folding of many mountain ranges, might thus develop enough heat in its lower levels (whence conduction would be unable to remove it rapidly) to gradually heat up and partially melt, forming a mass of granitic magma. The abundance of migmatites in deeply eroded mountain chains suggests such refusion, as does the common occurrence of granitic plutons in many fold mountains. The plasticity developed by partial melting permits the root to yield and spread laterally, thereby thickening the sial alongside the range. Perhaps this process accounts for the high-standing plateaus and plains that border many large ranges—for example, the Himalayas and the Andes. But we have already noted that the thick crust of the High Plains alongside the Rockies cannot have developed in this way, for its density is higher than that of the mountains to the west.

By whatever means it is accomplished, whether by lateral flowage of sima and sial, by plutonic injection, by partial melting which separates a light mobile fraction of mantle or lower crust, leaving a denser residue behind, or by some other means, the history of mountain ranges and their hinterlands gives clear evidence that a crustal segment once standing high can later be drowned beneath the sea, and areas once submerged can be added permanently to the continent. Since isostasy generally prevails, such changes can only be due to lateral modifications of crustal density by shifting of sima and sial; the mass per unit area must remain virtually the same above some level of compensation within the mantle.

THE SHIELDS

Precambrian rocks are widely exposed on every continent: over most of northern and eastern Canada, Finland, Sweden, northeastern Siberia, India, much of Africa, western Australia, and eastern Brazil. These are the **Precambrian Shields.** At their borders most disappear beneath Cambrian or younger strata that cover an unconformity of relatively low relief.

Most shields stand but little above sea level, and the flat-lying sedimentary rocks that surround and partly overlie them suggest that they have remained low through most of Cambrian and later time. Yet, not all shield areas are low; the Adirondack and Labrador parts of the Canadian Shield, the Black Hills, the mountainous areas near Lake Baikal on the Siberian Shield, are all what we have called "upwarped" mountains. Great areas of Africa and of the Brazilian Shield expose Precambrian terrains at elevations of several thousand feet on broad plateaus—these are as high or higher than the Urals and Appalachians (which were folded near the end of the Paleozoic) or the Scottish Highlands (where the folding was mid-Paleozoic). But these are exceptional; most shield areas are low.

The structural patterns brought out by mapping strongly suggest that large parts of the shields are deeply eroded mountain chains whose original relief has been all but erased by long erosion. Figure 18–43 shows the geology of part of the Baltic shield; this map pattern is obviously similar to those depicted in Figures 20–3 and 20–12. The shields expose proportionately more granite and metamorphic rocks than the younger ranges. Migmatites, which are rare or absent near young plutons, abound in the shields; they make up about a quarter of Finnish outcrops. The proportion of intensely deformed metamorphic and plutonic rocks exposed is much higher in Paleozoic than in younger ranges; such rocks are virtually absent from late Tertiary or Quaternary ranges but are more and more abundant the older the range. Thus the contorted and metamorphosed rocks of the shields are such as we would expect to find at still deeper levels in a fold-mountain chain, exposed by erosion through still longer times (Fig. 18–47).

The generally low relief and structural stability of the shields—for it must be remembered that the shields are continuous with the basement of the generally flat-lying strata of the continental plates—may be due to long erosion combined with lateral spreading of former mountain roots. Despite the vast exposures of granitic and other siliceous rocks, the heat flow of the shields is much less than the average for the earth (Chapter 19); the only conclusion possible is that the widely exposed granite does not extend deep into the crust—we are looking at a structural level once far below the surface, and exposed only after isostatic uplifts and repeated erosions almost to sea level where further lowering is very slow. The shields may be further depressed by sedimentation, but most are stable. Why some parts have again risen to mountainous heights after long stillstand, as did the Black Hills and the Adirondacks, is a problem for which no satisfactory answer has yet been found—a problem still more baffling in the case of the widespread African shield.

OCEAN DEEPS AND THE BELTS OF NEGATIVE ANOMALIES

In Chapter 16 we pointed out the close association of most oceanic deeps with island arcs, and in Chapter 19 mentioned that the earthquake foci in these highly seismic regions are arranged close to a surface that intersects the ocean floor at the trench, and dips away from the ocean at about 40°. This suggests that the boundary between oceanic and continental crustal segments is a fault outlined by the foci (Fig. 19–15). Volcanoes are active in many island arcs on the concave sides of the deeps. These, then, are clearly areas of great crustal unrest, and the deeps must indeed be maintained by crustal forces now active. Several adjoin large islands (Mindanao, Cuba, Puerto Rico, Sumatra, Java) or even the continent of South America (Atacama Deep, Leeward Trough) and could hardly fail to be filled with sediment in a geologically short time unless the formative process was continuing. The deeps may be segments of the oceanic crust weighed down by overriding segments of the continental crust though the fact that the sediments are flat and undisturbed opposes this idea.

Between 1923 and 1932, before the development of shipboard gravimeters, the distinguished Dutch geodesist F. A. Vening-Meinesz made a most surprising discovery. He determined the value of gravity at many points at sea from a submarine, developing the information summarized in Figure 20–19. In Chapter 10 we noted that if the earth's surface were level and the crust and upper mantle homogeneous, the value of gravity at every point would depend solely on its latitude. The anomalies shown in Figure 20–19 were calculated (Chapter 10) by subtracting the theoretical value of gravity at

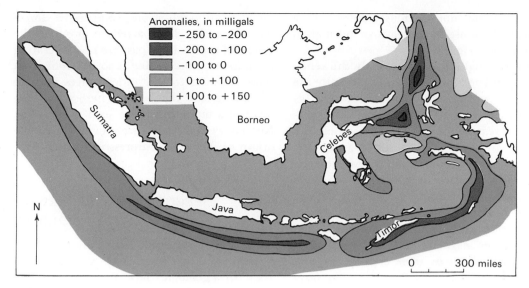

FIGURE 20–19

Map of Indonesia, showing regional gravity anomalies. (After F. A. Vening-Meinesz, 1934.)

FIGURE 20–20

Cross section of the Indonesian anomaly belt. Top: NW–SE section through southern Timor; Bottom: N–S section through eastern Java. Note that both negative troughs overlie topographic ridges, though one ridge is submarine. (After F. A. Vening-Meinesz, 1934.)

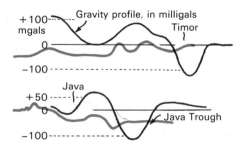

each station from the measured value after correction for the submerged depth of the submarine, the topography of land and sea floor for long distances, the density of sea water, and finally for "regional compensation" (equivalent to assuming that a very large crustal block centering at the station is in isostatic equilibrium with the remaining crust).

The calculation of these corrections is laborious and far beyond the scope of this book, but the results demonstrate a narrow belt of very strong negative anomalies extending nearly the full length of the outer arc of Indonesia. The anomalies are so great and so consistent that they can only mean that this narrow belt is underlain by rocks

much lighter than those at its sides. Because the belt is only 30 to 100 miles wide in most places, the light rocks must form a very deep septum to account for it. (The gravitational effect of the mass deficiency of course falls off with the square of the distance from the observation point).

The belt of negative anomalies, about 3000 miles long, generally lies close to the axis of the oceanic deep, though some sections lie on one side or the other, and others overlie a submarine ridge that divides the trough lengthwise. The ridge comes to the surface in the islands of Timor, Tanimber, Kei, and Ceram, but the negative strip continues. On either side of the narrow belt anomalies become positive over broad areas but these are not obviously linear—here dense rocks must be closer than normal to the surface (Fig. 20–20).

In short, light rocks are greatly thickened and extend to unusual depths beneath the negative strip, forming a narrow wedge between the denser rocks on either side.

Such great deviations from isostatic equilibrium are rare. Even in shield areas, presumably much stronger than the earthquake-prone volcanic arc of Indonesia, we have seen isostatic response to far smaller stresses. Vening-Meinesz pointed out that these facts can only be reconciled by assuming that the *rocks of the negative strip are being currently held down by some active force and thereby prevented from floating at the level appropriate to their density*. Were this negative strip like that in the Alps, we would expect to find mountains along it; clearly the active force is great and is systematically disposed throughout the length of the strip; it should be comparable to the forces that have folded and compressed the fold mountains. The islands along the belt are indeed composed of highly deformed rocks, and some are capped by tilted and uplifted coral reefs (Chapter 8). Do we have here a mountain chain in process of formation?

The analogies with older mountain chains are apparent, but not obviously close. Most geosynclines are filled with shallow-water deposits; the water depths in the Indonesian deeps are far greater than those at which most geosynclinal strata are inferred to have been deposited. On the other hand, the facies changes are such as to indicate that many of the island rocks were derived from areas now sunk to great depths; perhaps these vertical movements may also account for some of the extraordinary depths of basins. The location of the arc bordering a true oceanic basin, and supplied with sediments from Borneo, the site of the Java Sea, and perhaps from farther northwest, is also anomalous. The forelands of most mountain chains have been not oceanic but shelf seas. Conse-quently, although strong compressive forces like those that have acted to produce the ranges of the geologic past are now operating in Indonesia, the setting is so different from those we infer for the older ranges that we cannot be sure that we are here seeing the birth of a mountain range such as the Alps. Nor do we have any direct evidence of the origin of the great compressive forces.

SPECULATIONS REGARDING MOUNTAIN-BUILDING

Although, as the student will by now have recognized, every statement of a scientific "law" or a geologic "fact" necessarily carries within it an element of inference, the facts enumerated in this chapter are generally considered well established. The objectives of science include, however, not merely systematic description of natural phenomena, but also coordination of these data into broader generalizations and the subsuming from these of a comprehensive theory. We are still a long way from these objectives in our study of mountain-making. Even with scant data, however, speculations are useful in science, for they provoke tests that, when carried out, may negate, modify, or confirm some of the ideas proposed. New data have compelled the writers of this book to modify greatly some generalizations put forward in its previous editions on what then seemed sound grounds; it is certain that some of those here presented will also need future modification. Let us nevertheless review some of the "reasonable" speculations concerning the great enigma, mountain-making.

Theory of a shrinking earth

Many early geologists thought (and a few today agree) that the earth is shrinking and that mountains are made by the crust's adjusting to a smaller interior, crumpling as the skin of an apple crumples when the interior dries. The wrinkling was thought to be localized in the geosynclines where weak sediments are unusually thick. The temperature gradients were thought to prove a cooling and therefore a shrinking earth—highly plausible before the discovery of radioactivity.

Geologic objections are many. Perhaps the most potent is that areas of normal faulting —crustal stretching—are as widespread as the areas of compression. Furthermore, as shrinkage should shorten every great circle equally, either the geosynclines would have to be symmetrically distributed (as the mountains clearly are not) or there should be many mountains not derived from geosynclines. Another argument is from scale: as both crustal thickness and upper mantle elastic properties vary greatly from region to region, it seems most unlikely that the crust is uniform and rigid enough to transmit forces half way round the earth, concentrating nearly all the meridional shrinkage into the only significant east-west range, the Alpine-Himalayan-Indonesian trend, and all the latitudinal shrinkage of the southern hemisphere in the Andes and New Zealand. Finally, reasonable estimates of distribution of radioactivity in the earth make it doubtful that the earth is cooling at all. It may, indeed, be heating up, for computations of heat transfer show that even in three billion years the earth cannot have lost any appreciable heat by conduction from a depth greater than about 400 miles, a tenth of its radius.

Theory of continental drift

Probably every school boy who has studied a globe has independently discovered that if the Americas were pushed eastward they would almost fit the coasts of Africa and Europe. This rough fit is even more striking when we note the offset of the Mid-Atlantic Ridge to accord with the continental margins near the equator. About a century ago, Antonio Snider published a speculation that the Atlantic continents had once been joined and had since drifted apart. The idea seemed so bizarre to geologists of his day that it was ignored until about fifty years ago, when it was again independently suggested by the American geologist F. B. Taylor and the German meteorologist Alfred Wegener. If whole continents can move so far, the problem of mountain-building becomes incidental, for the forces involved in making even the greatest mountains are trivial compared to those needed to move continents.

Wegener assumed that the dense substratum upon which the continents are isostatically floating is so weak that it yields almost like a fluid to very small forces, two of which he recognized. The first is centrifugal: the continental masses stand higher than the oceans and so are farther from the earth's axis and subject to greater centrifugal force; this tends to drift them toward the equator. The second force is the tidal attraction of the sun and moon, which, as the earth rotates from west to east, tends always to drag the continents westward. (It must not be forgotten that the tidal forces act on the solid rock as well as on the seas and atmosphere.) Wegener thought that the Alpine-Himalayan chain was formed by collision of Eurasia with Africa and India in response to the first force and that the Andes and Rockies were piled up by friction as the Americas were dragged through the viscous substratum by the tidal forces. The drift, he thought, began in Mesozoic time. He did not explain why the first range is so far from the equator nor why the resistance of a fluid weak enough to permit drifting could suffice to cause crustal shortening in strong rocks for a thousand miles from the leading edge of a drifting continent.

Both of Wegener's postulated forces exist, but geophysicists have shown that they are millions of times too small for the task assigned. As this is so, one might wonder why drifting is seriously considered today. The fact is that many geologic phenomena are

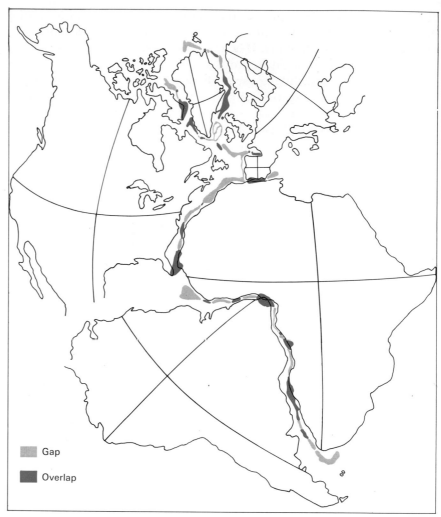

FIGURE 20–21   *The possible fit of all the Atlantic continents prior to drift. The test is of the 500-fathom subsea contour, which everywhere lies on the relatively steep continental slope. A present meridian and latitudinal circle is shown for each land mass. Between Ireland and Greenland, Rockall Bank has been included but Iceland has been ignored. Spain has been rotated to close the Bay of Biscay. Transverse Mercator projection. (From E. C. Bullard, J. Everett, and A. G. Smith,* Philosophical Transactions of the Royal Society, *v. 258, 1965.)*

well-established—continental glaciation for one—for which no adequate explanation has yet been offered; we therefore continue to examine all available evidence that seems to be explained readily by continental drift.

The British geophysicists Bullard, Everett, and Smith have tested the supposed fit of the Atlantic continents through a computer program in order to find the best fit possible of the continents at the 500 fathom subsea contour (Fig. 20–21).

The proposed fit is striking; the mean misfit is about 130 kilometers. The overlaps at Cape Hatteras and the Niger delta can read-

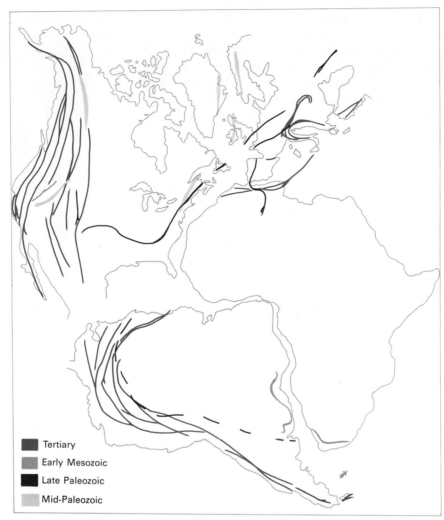

FIGURE 20–22   *Fold belts of various ages on the Atlantic continents in their pattern of best fit. (Many data from J. H. F. Umbgrove, 1947, and from later geologic maps.)*

ily be explained by post-Triassic sedimentation, but it should not be forgotten that in order to obtain this fit it has been necessary to ignore Iceland, Central America, Cuba, the Carribean, and much of Mexico. All except Iceland contain extensive areas of pre-Jurassic rocks. Spain, too, must be rotated to close the Bay of Biscay. As Bullard remarked, the question is raised of whether this fit is merely due to chance, like the resemblance of the map of Italy to a boot, or to a real drifting apart of formerly joined land masses.

An obvious approach in testing the proposed fit is to ascertain how the geologic features match when the continents are in their postulated original pattern. Figure 20–22 shows the trend lines of fold mountains of four broad groups, the first three of which are supposedly "pre-drift" features. It is obvious that the Mid-Paleozoic and Late Paleozoic trends across what is now the North Atlantic are in satisfactory alignment, though, of course, the abrupt curvatures of many younger ranges show that linearity is not a strong argument. We saw also in Chapter 17 that an Old Red Sandstone continent had been independently postulated on the site of the North Atlantic; its outlines are in full agreement with this reconstruction. Though the trend lines of the early Mesozoic ranges of the southern continents do not agree, it is noteworthy that closing the Atlantic would bring the African and South American ranges close together. The folds of the same age in the Falkland Islands, though more or less parallel to the continental ranges, would be not aligned with them but 500 miles away across the strike.

The present truncation of these fold lines by the ocean suggests, but does not prove, that they were formerly joined and have been parted by drift. The hazard in assuming this is shown by the fact that the Atlas and Pyrenees, both "post-drift" ranges, also

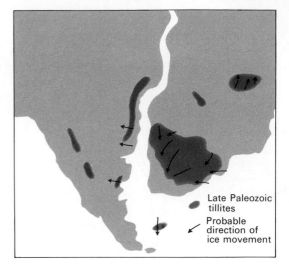

FIGURE 20–23
The relation of tillites and probable directions of movement of late Paleozoic glaciers in South America and Africa. The continents are in the positions of Figure 20–21. (Data from A. L. Du Toit.)

FIGURE 20–24   *Du Toit's assemblage of the continents prior to early Mesozoic time. Brown areas are those of late Paleozoic tillite, arrows indicate directions of ice flow. Cross is postulated position of the pole at the time of the glaciation. Heavy line is the axis of a late Paleozoic geosyncline. (Modified from A. L. Du Toit, 1937, and G. A. Doumani and W. E. Long, 1962.)*

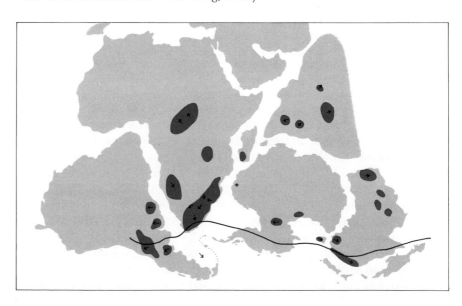

end at the shore, and though some have thought the Greater Antilles to be their American extensions, the pattern of gravity anomalies and island arcs prove that the Antilles structures curve southward through the nearly drowned arc of the Lesser Antilles to join the mountain ranges of Venezuela.

Stratigraphic similarities between South America and Africa are of interest: in both regions the oldest fossiliferous rocks are late Silurian or Devonian, containing fossil assemblages like those of the Falkland Islands, but differing from those of the northern hemisphere. In both regions similar land-laid beds intervene between these marine beds and late Paleozoic tillites (Fig. 20–23). Tillite of about the same age is found also in Antarctica, Australia, and India (Fig. 20–24). As Figure 20–23 shows, glaciers invaded South America from the East, the Falkland Islands from the north, Australia from the south; also an ice cap near 15°S in Africa left its northern moraines on the equator and its southern moraines near the Cape of Good Hope. A glacier in India centered in the Aravalli Mountains, north of Bombay in latitude 20°N. Characteristic rocks from these mountains are found in the tillite hundreds of miles to southeast and northwest. In all these localities the tillite is closely associated with fossils of two genera of fernlike plants, *Gangamopteris* and *Glossopteris,* found in the northern hemisphere only in France, Russia, northeastern Siberia, and India. The fossils show that the tillites are nearly, but not quite, contemporaneous. Du Toit, a South African geologist, noted that had the continents been assembled as shown in Figure 20–24, not only would the glaciated areas be in temperate or polar latitudes, but middle and late Paleozoic geosynclines of South America, Africa, and Australia would form a continuous line—the heavy line in that figure. Since Du Toit wrote, tillites of this episode have been discovered in Antarctica, strengthening his argument.

How, indeed, are we to account for con-tinental ice sheets in the present tropics unless the continents have moved? Mere shifting of the earth's axis, without moving the land masses relative to each other would not solve the problem; the tillites are now so placed that no possible position of the pole would avoid leaving one or another within 20° of the equator. Even the most favorable assemblage, that shown in Figure 20–24, places the Indian center not far from the 36th parallel—nearer the equator than any Pleistocene ice cap reached.

The *Glossopteris* flora, because it is abundant in the southern hemisphere and in India and rare elsewhere, has been considered strong evidence of a former closer grouping of the now scattered regions in which it is found. The name "Gondwanaland," from a rock group in India that contains the flora, has been given to the hypothetical continent, of which the assemblage in Figure 20–24 is only one of several proposed. Du Toit thought the American and European coals, of about the same age as the Gondwana glaciation, represent tropical peat swamps, whereas the *Glossopteris* coals formed in colder climates like those of the peat bogs of Ireland or Alaska. But if this were true, the French, Russian, and Siberian *Glossopteris* localities must have been in the tropics; climatic zoning of the plants is not an adequate explanation of their distribution.

In the last decade a new argument, from paleomagnetism, has seemed to favor continental drift. As we saw in Chapter 19, when the virtual magnetic poles for late Pleistocene and Recent rocks are plotted, their mean position is very near the geographic pole, as it should be under the dynamo theory of earth magnetism. Students of paleomagnetism thus believe that the position of the pole relative to a sampling station can be determined if a fairly thick section of strata is sampled so as to get an average of the magnetic field for a time long enough to average out the nondipole disturbances. If drift has gone on, each continent should

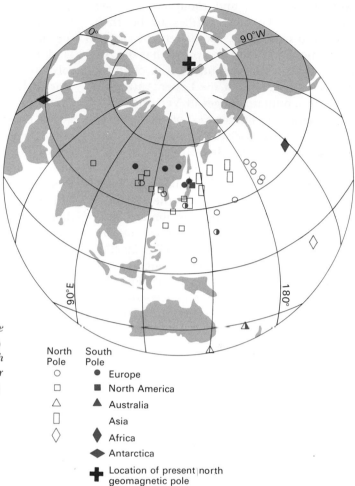

FIGURE 20–25
Virtual geomagnetic poles for the Carboniferous (275 to 355 m. y.) Schmidt equal-area projection with pole at 45°N and 135°E. (After R. R. Doell and Allan Cox, 1961.)

North Pole	South Pole	
○	●	Europe
□	■	North America
△	▲	Australia
▯		Asia
◇	◆	Africa
	◆	Antarctica
	✚	Location of present north geomagnetic pole

show virtual pole positions consistent among themselves but differing from the virtual pole positions derived from strata older than the beginning of drift from all the other continents. The virtual pole positions should also converge while drift went on and end with complete coincidence of virtual poles from all continents, as determined from Recent strata and lava flows.

Figure 20–25 presents the virtual pole positions for the Carboniferous strata from all the continents.

Obviously there is a wide scatter of the virtual poles from most of the continents. Samples from Europe yield virtual poles scattered roughly 45° in latitude and 85° in longitude; those from Australia and Africa show a practically random distribution, whereas the few Asian samples yield poles rather closely clustered. Despite the wide scatter of poles determined from several of the continents and the paucity of determinations from others, students of paleomagnetism have tried to trace the course of the poles as determined from Europe and North America through geologic time. Figure 20–26 shows two such deduced paths for each of these continents, from the late Precambrian to the present.

Whether or not the data plotted in Figure

20–25 are adequate to fix the geographic pole during the Carboniferous, they surely do indicate that the magnetic pole during that period was far from its present position. If the dynamo theory of magnetism is correct, the geographic pole must also have been different or else the continents have moved. Some geologists therefore hold that the dynamo theory is in error, or else that the circulation in the core which engenders the field is not always controlled in orientation by the rotation of the earth. Others consider it evidence that the continents have shifted from their original positions.

The earth's angular momentum is great; like a gyroscope it strongly resists change in its axis of rotation and astronomers do not believe that the polar axis has ever shifted more than a very small amount with respect to the body of the earth. If polar wandering has taken place, it must be by the shifting of the crust with respect to the deeper layers, in other words by drift. There are strong geophysical arguments against drift, as well as for it. Perhaps the strongest lies in the great

FIGURE 20–26
Polar wandering paths suggested for Europe and North America at different times. Dashed lines represent poles as determined from American data; solid lines, poles determined from European data. (After S. K. Runcorn, Philosophical Transactions of the Royal Society, *v. 258, 1965.)*

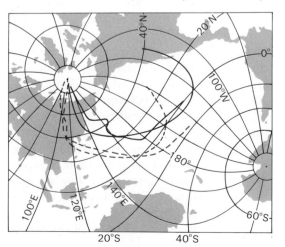

contrast in the differentiation of the upper mantle beneath the oceans with that beneath the continents, as shown by heat flow. It is difficult to see how the floor of the Atlantic —newly exposed by the westward drift of the Americas—should be so similar to that of the Pacific if the highly differentiated crust of the continent had formerly occupied the site. If drift has gone on, large thicknesses of the upper mantle must have moved along with the crust or there would now be great contrasts between the heat flow of various nonvolcanic continental segments.

Still another objection has been raised: on the average the deep-sea sediment beneath the Atlantic is twice as thick as that beneath the Pacific, yet if the drift theory is correct, the Atlantic sediment has been collecting only since the early Mesozoic, and that of the Pacific for many times as long.

The drift hypothesis thus has many appealing aspects, but can hardly, as yet, be said to have obtained the status of completely accepted theory. It has, however, focused attention on one of the most difficult problems of the earth: if the continents are indeed light masses floating on a denser substratum, how is it possible for an area once continental to become part of the ocean floor? The late Paleozoic glacial record of South Africa, Australia, the Falkland Islands, and the Argentine demands glacial flow from what is now the site of an ocean onto the land. The sedimentary record of the Appalachians, the western Alps, the continental shelf of the Atlantic States, and the monoclinal folding of the Greenland and west Indian flood basalts from land to deep-sea floor tell the same story: without question some large areas of former land have sunk to oceanic depths. By what mechanism?

DEEP SUBMERGENCE OF CONTINENTAL MARGINS. Sedimentational evidence shows that much of the west Alpine geosynclinal filling was derived from areas now sunk to depths of more than 2000 meters in the western Mediterranean—clearly by thinning of the crust in some manner. Seismic studies show a crust only about 12 kilometers thick but with elastic properties appropriate to a more than usually dense sima; prior to the Alpine orogeny the crust must have been both much thicker and much more sialic. At the west coast of India north of Bombay, the flows of the great Deccan flood basalts of late Cretaceous and Paleocene age, nearly horizontal for hundreds of miles to the east, abruptly bend into a steep monoclinal fold and descend to the deep ocean floor. Obviously liquid lava could not have retained a uniform thickness were this an original steep slope; the land area, with a less dense crust, must formerly have extended an unknown, but considerable, distance into what is now the Arabian Sea. A precisely analogous situation is presented in east Greenland, where the Tertiary flood basalts fold abruptly over a monoclinal axis and descend to the depths of the Atlantic. Here again the lower crust must have become thinned and denser.

The example best studied is that of the east coast of the United States where the American geophysicist W. M. Ewing and his colleagues have worked out the structure in detail. By explosion seismology they have traced the unconformity on which the Mesozoic and Tertiary rocks of the Coastal Plain overlie the ancient rocks of the Piedmont far out to sea, where it reaches depths of 17,000 feet beneath the edge of the continental shelf and 18,000 feet beneath the continental rise (Fig. 20–27). At least as far out as the continental slope this unconformity is continuous and the rocks beneath have the same elastic properties as those of the Piedmont. Clearly this was formerly land and its surface has since subsided in places to depths of more than 3 miles. The continental shelf is made up of Mesozoic and Tertiary sedimentary rock. We thus see that an area that had supplied sediment to the Appalachian geosyncline throughout the Paleozoic epoch has in Mesozoic times subsided to great depths—depths far greater than can be accounted for by isostatic response to the sedimentary load.

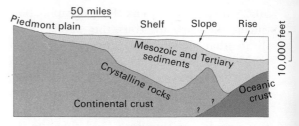

FIGURE 20–27
A cross section of the continental border off southern New Jersey. (Reprinted with permission from C. L. Drake, Continental Margins and Geosynclines, *v. 3 of* Physics and Chemistry of The Earth, *Copyright 1959, Pergamon Press.)*

How such changes in level can have come about is a major puzzle; the fact that they have, however, is indisputable. They give reason to doubt that drift is the only way to account for missing continental lands whose former existence is indicated by stratigraphic and facies features of the supposed fragments of Gondwanaland; some of these missing fragments may have sunk.

The convection theory

Any fluid heated from below tends to lose heat in two ways: by conduction and convection. In large masses conduction is ineffectively slow because the amount of heat transferred in a given time decreases as the square of the thickness of the mass through which it must be transmitted. We have already noted that in three billion years the earth cannot have lost any heat by conduction from depths greater than a tenth of its radius. The effectiveness of convection depends on the rate of convective overturn of the liquid (Fig. 20–28). Convection is favored by low viscosity, low conductivity, and large volume. Low conductivity and large volume insure large density differences between bottom and top of the fluid mass because of thermal expansion of the lower portion. A low viscosity favors overturn, allowing heat to be dissipated at the surface.

It may seem absurd to think of the mantle

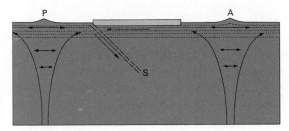

FIGURE 20–28

Scheme of convection with rising hot dikes under the Mid-Atlantic Ridge (A) and East Pacific Rise (P) and a sink under the island arcs and the Pacific Mountains (S). The shear surface is the one along which the deep-focus earthquakes of South America arise and is like that suggested beneath the Kurile Islands in Figure 19–16. The dotted horizontal lines are shear planes of continental drift in the Low Velocity Zone. (After Egon Orowan, 1964.)

of the earth as a liquid capable of convective overturn, for the speed of transverse seismic waves shows that under short-term stresses it behaves as a rigid solid as far down as the core boundary. Nevertheless, we know from the folded structures in the mountains and the contortion of many metamorphic rocks that, though never molten, these masses have been plastic and have flowed. And isostasy shows that over broad regions the mantle acts much like a dense liquid on which the lighter crust is floating. The viscosity of the Low Velocity Zone, computed from the rate of uplift of Scandinavia after unloading of the glacial ice, is very high, though data from Lake Bonneville suggest much lower values. Since the temperature increases downward the viscosity may be less nearer the core despite the tremendous pressure there. Even a content of radioactivity as little as that in meteorites might produce enough heat to make the mantle unstable, starting convective overturn.

Many variations of the convection theory have been advanced—perhaps two dozen in the last decade; a complete review and discussion would far exceed the space available here. Accordingly we review only one or two of the schemes that have been put forward, recognizing that all are highly speculative.

We noted that the mid-ocean ridges are marked by normal faulting, high seismic activity, somewhat higher heat flow along their axial regions, abnormally low seismic velocities, and the absence of a sharp M Discontinuity. These seismic properties are thought to be due to "softening" by the high heat flow and the ridges are considered in several convection schemes to be sites of upwelling mantle currents. H. H. Hess of Princeton University has suggested that the rising current consists of peridotite whose density, lower than that of the rest of the mantle, is due to heat and an enrichment in water derived from deeper in the mantle. As the rising column, with an estimated velocity of about one centimeter per year, rises near the surface and loses heat, the water reacts with part (estimated at 70 percent) of the olivine of the peridotite to form the less dense mineral, serpentine, thereby lowering the density of the rock. It is noteworthy that the oceanic layer away from the ridges has a remarkably uniform thickness: 4.7 kilometers ± .7 kilometer at more than 80 percent of the places where it has been measured. Though it has seismic properties comparable to those of basalt, Hess considers it more likely to be partially serpentinized peridotite (to which its seismic properties are also appropriate) because so uniform a thickness of basalt flows over nearly the whole ocean floor seems improbable. The uniform thickness he attributes to the fact that serpentinization cannot take place until the temperature falls below about 500°C, and the depth at which this temperature is reached (about 5 kilometers), fixes the thickness of the layer.

The serpentinized oceanic crust moves away from the ridge in both directions, carried on the back of deeper, unserpentinized but very hot peridotite, which also has lower-than-normal seismic velocities because of its high temperature. In this way the normal faulting and horizontal extension of the ridge at right angles to its length is brought about, with the development of the median graben characteristic of so much of the ridge length. Indeed, surveys in Iceland show that the country is being pulled apart at the rate of about 3.5 centimeters per year per kilometer of width, on the extension of the Mid-Atlantic graben zone. As the material moves away from the ridge at the rate of a few centimeters per year, both the partially serpentinized surficial layer and the hot peridotite below cool and thereby come to yield the seismic velocities normal to the oceanic segments.

The Atlantic continents, according to this scheme, thus move apart as new oceanic crust forms. Some proponents of this general scheme think the earth is expanding and that its diameter has doubled since the Cambrian, but there is no tangible evidence for such expansion. It seems best to apply Occam's dictum—avoid hypotheses not demanded by the evidence—and ignore this suggestion.

There seem to be enough areas of folding and compression at and near the continental borders to compensate for the expansion postulated at the mid-ocean ridges. Several advocates of this general scheme think that it is in these zones of compression that the convection current is descending (Figs. 20–28, 19–15). These include the belt of negative anomalies in Indonesia, which could only persist against the isostatic tendency to rise by being held down by actively descending currents. Similar belts in the West Indies and along the island arcs of the Pacific are also similarly interpreted. The alignment of earthquake foci along surfaces that dip toward a continent (Fig. 19–15) supports the idea that oceanic crust is being dragged down beneath the island arcs and to great depths, as indicated by the earthquakes beneath South America at depths as great as 700 kilometers.

Certainly there is great contrast between the Atlantic and Pacific coasts of North America. We have seen how the Piedmont rocks and their cover of Coastal Plain formations can be traced far offshore in the Atlantic; on the Pacific there seems to be complete decoupling of oceanic from continental crust.

Neither the great San Andreas fault of the continent nor the Mendocino Fracture Zone of the ocean floor can be traced across the boundary. Here, as in South America, the continent seems to be overriding the oceanic crust. These are both areas of young and growing mountains.

As the postulated currents descend, the oceanic sediment is skimmed off the ocean floor and crumpled against the continent, adding to it. The serpentinized peridotite beneath is heated up as it descends into the earth; it gives up its water as the serpentine reverts to olivine and the water so derived serves as a flux to facilitate melting of the adjacent rocks. The magma generated along the dipping shear zone between continental and oceanic crust rises to feed the volcanic chains of the island arcs or the continental crust above them.

This imaginative scheme fails to answer many questions. Although it may be postulated that the Americas are being transported "piggy-back" on currents diverging from the Mid-Atlantic Ridge and sinking under the western edge of these continents, it is difficult to find a place for the descending of the currents that are supposedly transporting Europe and Africa eastward from the Ridge. In fact, Africa is surrounded on three sides by the mid-oceanic ridge from which currents are postulated as flowing. Where do these converging currents descend? There does not appear to be any surface manifestation of descending currents either in Europe, the Mediterranean or northern Africa. It is also difficult to see how a continuous zone of upwelling such as the mid-oceanic ridges are supposed to represent can be so cleanly cut off by straight, unwavering transverse faults and translated laterally for hundreds of kilometers, as implied by the offsets of the Mid-Atlantic Ridge at so many places (Fig. 20–17). The scheme does not account for the preliminary formation of a geosyncline such as nearly all folded mountains are made from. Nor does it account for the fact that nearly all fold ranges were fed from their hinterlands—not from the foreland of the continental plate. No normal faults have been identified on the East Pacific Rise; there is no structural evidence that the crust is here being extended. On the other hand, the scheme does account for the central position of the ridge along the entire length of the Atlantic and for the absence of the huge volume of crustal material that once underlay the several hundred mile width of marine strata now piled into the Alps and Appalachians. It also accords with the fact that the oldest sediment thus far dredged from any ocean floor is Cretaceous, for of course this scheme envisages continual formation and elimination of ocean floors.

It also offers a rational explanation of the strange patterns of magnetic anomalies that have been found on the floor of the Pacific and Atlantic. For example, in the area shown in Figure 20–29, the magnetic anomalies measured at the sea surface—that is, the notable deviations from the regional average strength of the magnetic field—fall into linear patterns paralleling the axis of the Mid-Atlantic Ridge, to which they are symmetri-

cally arranged. As we noted in Chapter 19, the earth's magnetic field has reversed several times in the last four million years. If we assume that the belts of low magnetism correspond to the oceanic floor that cooled while the earth's field was reversed, and those of high strength to that cooling while the field

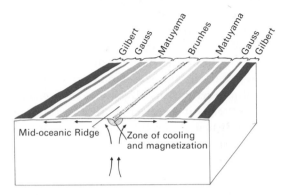

FIGURE 20–30
Showing how new spreading ocean floor that cooled through the Curie point during successive magnetic episodes of the past four million years might give the pattern of anomalies shown in Figure 20–29. (After Cox, Dalrymple, and Doell, 1967.)

FIGURE 20–29   *Magnetic anomalies in part of the North Atlantic (inset map). Note the symmetrical arrangement of the linear anomalies on either side of the ridge axis. Positive anomalies (in which the field strength is greater than the regional average) are dark brown; negative anomalies (in which the strength of the earth's field is less than the regional average), light brown. The bands are presumably produced by bands of rock with respectively normal and reversed magnetism. (After Allan Cox, G. B. Dalrymple, and R. R. Doell, 1967.)*

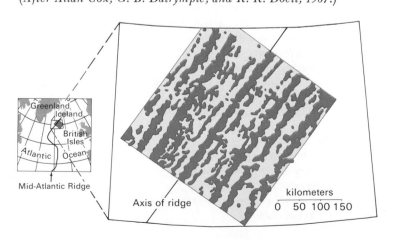

was normal, it is possible to interpret the pattern as shown in Figure 20–30. The successive anomaly belts record the sections of new ocean floor generated at the ridge during the several magnetic episodes enumerated on Figure 19–29. If this is the real explanation of the pattern, it indicates that a 300-kilometer width of ocean floor has been added during the last 4 m.y., implying a current speed in the convection cell of 3.75 centimeters per year. Were this rate constant, the widening of the Atlantic would have taken about 50 m.y.

We see that the convection hypothesis is consistent with many observable phenomena. Nevertheless it seems premature to consider it established. A careful analysis of hundreds of measurements by W. G. Langseth, Jr. and colleagues, of Columbia University, concludes that the heat flow from the Mid-Atlantic Ridge is only about 20 percent larger than from the basins in general; under assumptions most favorable to the convection hypothesis they computed that a current of only one centimeter a year—far less than that suggested by the magnetic pattern—would require a heat flow two or three times that measured. No convection could have taken place along the ridge in Cenozoic time without leaving a more pronounced heat pattern.

Clearly we need more information about the composition of the ocean floor. The abortive "Mohole" plan to drill through the ocean floor to the M Discontinuity must somehow be realized if we are ever to understand the fascinating puzzle confronting us: an earth more than three billion years old that is still endowed with energy literally to move mountains. The heat flow of the earth carries at least a thousand times the energy of all the earthquakes; is this the energy to make new sea floors as well as to move mountains?

Facts, concepts, terms

Mountains, plateaus
Fold mountains
Geosynclines, foreland, hinterland
Mountain structures
    Folds, asymmetric folds, overturned folds, thrust faults
    Crustal shortening, structural ungluing, klippes, nappes, massifs
    Use of fold plunge in deciphering structural history and geometry at depth
    Use of sedimentary facies in structural interpretation
    The substructure of fold mountains
    Mountain roots, metamorphism, migmatites, plutonic activity
Volcanic mountains
Fault block mountains
Upwarped mountains
    Dating of mountain uplift and of mountain folding
Mountains beneath the sea
    The strike-slip faults
    Heat flow beneath the sea
The shields
The belts of negative anomalies
Theory of a shrinking earth
Theory of continental drift
Theory of convection currents
Origin of ocean floors

Questions

1. In both the East and West Indies, volcanoes are arranged on an inner arc parallel to the arc of the ocean deeps and associated negative anomalies. The surface on which the deep-focus earthquakes occur slopes downward toward this inner arc (Fig. 19–15). What does this suggest as to the source of the magmas?

2. Many of the highest ridges of the Appalachians are synclinal in structure. In the light of Chapters 8, 9, and 12 can you offer a suggestion for the reasons?

3. What inferences can you make regarding the forces causing crustal deformation from such features as the San Andreas rift (Chap. 19)?

4. Many of the buildings of western England are roofed with slate whereas those near London are chiefly tiled. Can you draw from this any inferences as to the regional geology of England?

5. Many deep wells drilled in the search for oil have shown the existence of a long, rather narrow mass of granite beneath the Carboniferous strata of eastern Kansas and southeastern Nebraska. What features of the rocks brought up by the drill would enable you to decide whether this mass is unconformably buried by the sedimentary rocks or whether it invaded the sediments after they were deposited?

6. The Triassic rocks of the Atlantic slope of North America are commonly thought to have been formed under both topographic and climatic conditions that were closely similar to those of the present Great Basin. What features would you expect them to have from which such an origin was inferred?

7. In western Nevada a fossil-rich Permian limestone lies nearly horizontally across upturned slates beneath. A few fossils identifiable as Ordovician in age have been found in the slate. What history is recorded by these relationships?

8. What features would enable you to distinguish a sill of granitic rock (whose lower contact only is exposed) from a block of granite thrust over flat-lying sedimentary rocks?

9. How would you distinguish a klippe (an erosional remnant of a thrust sheet) from the erosional remnant of a resistant bed in an undeformed sedimentary series? Assume in both cases that the remnant is of Carboniferous rocks resting upon flat-lying Devonian.

10. What do you infer from the absence of a root beneath the Northern Rocky Mountains about the applicability of Airy isostasy to the region? From the presence of a root beneath the Alps?

Suggested readings

Bailey, E. B., *Tectonic Essays, Mainly Alpine*. Oxford: Clarendon Press, 1935.

Daly, R. A., *Architecture of the Earth*. New York: Appleton-Century, 1938.

Scientific American offprints

814. Robert L. Fisher and Roger Revelle, *The Trenches of the Pacific* (November 1955)

855. Don L. Anderson, *The Plastic Layer of The Earth's Mantle* (July 1962)

868. J. Tuzo Wilson, *Continental Drift* (April 1963)

chapter 21

Mineral
Resources

THE INDUSTRIAL REVOLUTION

Our world differs more from that of the Founding Fathers than theirs did from the world of Alexander the Great. In 1800, nearly four-fifths of all persons in Great Britain and Italy lived on farms, as did more than nine-tenths of those in the rest of Europe. Land transport was by wagons on roads hardly better than those Caesar used in Gaul; and Napoleon's crossing of the Alps was little less of a feat than Hannibal's, two thousand years before. Today a Zulu miner travels third-class to his labor compound in the Rand gold field in greater comfort than Louis XIV did in his state coach between Versailles and Paris. By our standards, the Zulu's lot is hard and his pay pitiably small; yet he is better clothed and fed than most of the people of George the Third's England. He is fortunate, indeed, when compared to a slave in the mines of Laurium, whose life expectancy beneath the Athenian lash was only four years, but whose labors produced the silver that sustained the Golden Age of Greece.

Most of us now reject the slave-holding philosophy of Plato and Pericles, but it is not primarily ethical principles that account for the differences between the ancient and modern worlds. Material goods are perhaps as unevenly distributed today as under most of the cultures of the past, but the standard of living of the Western World, at least, is higher.

The change began with two events of the eighteenth century. Neither attracted as much notice at the time as the intrigues of Bonnie Prince Charlie or the campaigns of Frederick the Great. But about 1730 a Shropshire Quaker, Abraham Darby, discovered how to use coke for smelting iron; and in 1768 James Watt invented the steam engine. These men made possible cheap iron, steel, mechanized power—and the industrial age. Without machinery, population would long since have outstripped food supply the world over, as Malthus predicted in 1798, and as indeed it has in China and India, where the Industrial Revolution is now underway, but as yet has only feeble roots.

Now, as always, agriculture is the basic industry. But a wholly agricultural economy imposes sharp limits on division of labor and the increased productivity that this allows. As transport improved, first with iron rails and then locomotives and steam-driven ships, a specialization formerly unknown made possible tremendous savings in labor. By 1830 a twelve-year-old girl operating a machine loom in a Lancashire mill could turn out 35 yards of calico daily—in a year, enough to clothe about 1200 persons.

This little girl's existence was doubtless as dismal as any Norman serf's, and even today the "better life for all" is an ideal that is still far from realization. Yet this very ideal would be pathetically ludicrous if there had been no Industrial Revolution. Even now the food supply of much of the world is less than that required for subsistence; it would be pitifully smaller if we were to revert to the economy of 1800.

These facts are commonplace and generally accepted. But what is not so widely understood is that all these changes in living standards ultimately depend upon the world's diminishing and nonreplenishable assets—its mineral resources.

THE MINERAL BASIS
OF CIVILIZATION

Throughout history mineral resources have played a greater role than is usually recognized. Today this role is second only to that of agriculture. The relationship between mineral wealth and national power even in ancient times, can be clearly traced, though most historians ignore it. The Greeks who turned back the Persian hosts at Marathon were armed with bronze swords and shields, while many of the enemy had only leathern shields and stone weapons; the Greek fleet at Salamis was built by the Athenian profits from the silver and lead mines of Laurium, discovered only a few years earlier. These profits also paid the mercenaries who fought Athens' battles in the Peloponnesian Wars, and with the exhaustion of the mines came the end of Athens as a military power. Philip burst from the wild Macedonian mountains, and his son, Alexander the Great, swept over the world, financed by the flush production of gold—roughly a billion dollars in modern equivalent—from the new mines on Mount Pangaeus. When Scipio drove the Carthaginians from Spain and won for Rome the gold, iron, copper, silver, and mercury of that peninsula, he sealed the fate of Carthage.

These are but a few examples from pre-industrial days. Today, mineral resources and national power and well-being are even more closely linked. Gold and silver could hire mercenaries and influence military campaigns, but useful goods could not be created from them; they merely gave control of the few goods then available to one group rather than another. They still possess this conventional value, but living standards and national power depend only incidentally on them. The greater part of the useful goods of the world depend on the mineral fuels and the industrial metals—iron, copper, aluminum, lead, and others. It was no accident that Britain was able to maintain the *Pax Britannica* through the nineteenth century; her industrial and military supremacy came from the happy fortune that her "tight little island" held a greater known mineral wealth per acre than any similar area in the world, together with a population intelligent and aggressive enough to exploit it.

At one time or another in the nineteenth century, Great Britain was the world's largest producer of iron, coal, lead, copper, and tin. From these came her machines, her mills, and the great cities founded on them. Before 1875 she had built more miles of railroad than any of the much larger Continental countries. Her flourishing internal markets and manufactured products, carried to all the world by the British merchant marine, brought her the greatest wealth any country in history had ever enjoyed. True, the cheap foodstuffs she received in return eventually ruined the island's agricultural economy, but her favorable trade balance enabled British capital to control Malayan tin, Spanish iron, and many of the mines and oil fields of Mexico, Chile, Iran, Australia, Burma, and the United States. These holdings saw her through one world war and maintained her credit through a second. When her flag followed her mining investments into South Africa and the Boers were defeated, she gained control of more than half the world's production of new gold, and ultimately of great deposits of copper, chromite, diamonds, asbestos, and manganese. Even the independence of South Africa has only diluted this control slightly; the African mineral holdings are among the most valuable sources of British capital even today.

Nowhere better than in the United States can be seen the cardinal significance of minerals to living standards and national power. Before 1840, manufacturing was inconsequential and only heavy subsidies and tariffs made it possible to compete with the advanced British industries. The small, scattered iron deposits along the eastern seaboard did, it is true, supply enough of the local demand to influence the British Parliament in 1750 to forbid their further exploitation; after independence there was slow growth, but as late as 1850 iron production was only about half a million tons annually. In 1855 the "Soo Canal" brought the rich Lake Superior iron deposits within economic reach of Pennsylvania coal; by 1860 iron production had trebled; by 1880 it had passed that of Great Britain.

It was the greater productivity of Northern industry, and the weight of armament, supplies, and equipment flowing over its superior railway net that were decisive in the Civil War. The Tredegar iron works at Richmond was the only one worth mentioning in the Confederacy, and it could not compete alone with the overwhelming output of the Pennsylvania furnaces.

Its huge internal market, prodigious endowment in all the minerals basic to manufacturing, and favorable agricultural heritage have all contributed to make the United States the most powerful country in the world at present. During the Battle of the Bulge in World War II, the Allies' troops hurled more metal at the Germans than was available in all the world in Napoleon's time. Cannon and tanks, as well as plowshares and tractors, are made of metals, and all are transported by mineral fuels.

SALIENT FEATURES OF MINERAL RESOURCES

That mineral resources are concentrated in relatively small areas, and that they are exhaustible and irreplaceable, are facts—facts of great social and political implication that are often overlooked by those not familiar with the mineral industry. Their effect on society is so profound that no citizen should fail to be aware of them, and of the geologic factors determining them.

Sporadic distribution

As we shall see in more detail later in this chapter, mineral deposits of all kinds are essentially "freaks of nature." An abnormal pituitary may make a man a giant, although his physiological processes are otherwise normal. Similarly, mineral deposits result from normal geologic processes, but under exceptional conditions. Only a few geologic environments favor the formation of mineral deposits.

These favored spots are by no means evenly distributed over the earth. Nearly nine-tenths of the world's nickel comes from less than a score of mines in the Sudbury district of Ontario. A single mine at Climax, Colorado, produces about as large a share of the world's molybdenum from an area of far less than one square mile. Nearly 30 percent of the copper produced in the United States since 1880 has come from an area of less than 4 square miles at Butte, Montana, an area that has supplied nearly 8 billion dollars worth of metals to the American economy. The Rand gold field of South Africa produces half the new gold of the world from an area about 50 miles long and 20 wide.

The mineral fuels are less localized, but they underlie only a trivial part of the continents. Less than 25 percent of Pennsylvania, a leading coal state, is underlain by coal. The East Texas oil field, the greatest thus far found in the United States, covers an area about 10 by 40 miles—a mere dot on the vast expanse of Texas—yet for several years it yielded about a quarter of the nation's oil. The most extensive oil field in the world is the El Nala anticline in Saudi Arabia. It is almost continuously productive for a length of 105 miles, but is only a few miles wide.

The economic implications of this unequal distribution of the mineral fuels are great. Modern chemistry may be able to make a rayon purse (perhaps even better than a silk one) out of a sow's ear, but only with the expenditure of energy. Today this means mineral fuels, or, less importantly, water power. The dreams of many countries of emulating the industrial development of the United States are foredoomed to failure because they lack adequate sources of cheap fuel. It is this fact that explains the tremendous interest of all nations in the prospect of the development of cheap atomic power. If such power could be obtained safely, the economics of many nations might come abreast of the United States. Some countries, such as the Scandinavian, have higher educational standards, or, like Argentina, a higher agricultural output per capita, but none is now so fortunate as the United States in the combination of high average educa-

tion (and hence a skilled population), great agricultural productivity, and a nearly balanced supply of mineral resources. But the supply of minerals is limited, and unlike agricultural products there is no second crop.

Exhaustibility

All mineral deposits are limited in extent; they represent unusual associations of geologic factors that have permitted their concentration. Once the valuable materials are extracted by mining, all that is left are holes in the ground. This is the fate of all mines, even of the greatest.

It is true that the mines of Almaden, Spain, have yielded mercury since the days of the Carthaginians and still hold the richest known reserves of this metal, but these deposits are unique. The mines of Cornwall—the "Cassiterides," or Tin Islands—supplied tin to the Phoenicians and provided varying amounts of this metal throughout the years until about 50 years ago. In the nineteenth century they led the world in production, but now the mines are worked out, and the Cornish miners have dispersed throughout the world, and spread their traditional mining lore far from Britain. The world's greatest single oil well, the Cerro Azul No. 4, in the Tampico Field, Mexico, yielded nearly sixty million barrels of petroleum in a few years, then suddenly gave forth only salt water. Neither the old Cornish tin mines nor the Cerro Azul will ever yield a new crop.

The still fertile Valley of the Nile has been the granary of the Mediterranean through most of recorded history, and huge areas in China and India have been farmed nearly or quite as long. The forests of Norway that built the Viking ships still produce lumber. But the mines of Freiberg, where Werner's Mining Academy flourished, and where even now a mining school survives, have long been abandoned. Belgium and Wales, with their cheap coal and metallurgical traditions, are still centers of smelting, but nearly all the metal mines on which their industries were founded have been exhausted for generations. Potosi, which supplied tons of silver to the viceroyalty of Peru, the fabulous Comstock Lode of Nevada, and the copper deposits of Michigan are not quite dead, but they are pale shadows of their former greatness. *There is no second crop of minerals!* And, lest the meaning—economic, political, and social—of this statement be overlooked, let it be noted: More metal has been mined since 1930 than in all preceding history.

It seems inevitable that a generation hence the world supply of readily available minerals will be so depleted that what remains can be won only by a greatly increased expenditure of energy. We are now in the period of the greatest exploitation of mineral resources in the long sweep of history. That we will be able to maintain our present standard of living is by no means a foregone conclusion; unless tremendous technological improvements can be made, the inevitable increase in the amount of energy required to win a pound of iron, a gallon of oil, or a ton of coal must be reflected in a lower standard of living. Such is the inevitable result of the localization of mineral resources in the earth's crust. Only technological developments of a revolutionary nature (such as indeed appear to be happening in the use of nuclear fuels) can postpone such an outcome for more than a very few years.

What the exhaustibility of mineral resources means socially can be seen in the long roll of Western "ghost towns," in which a few families now live where thousands lived before. More dramatically, it is seen in the "distressed" coal-mining towns of England and Appalachia, where, although the mines are not, strictly speaking, exhausted, the higher costs of deeper mining, of pumping ground water from greater depths, and of longer hauls from coal face to portal, have weakened their competitive position in world trade. Unemployment, wage cuts, and lower living standards have followed. Only drastic technologic changes can keep costs down.

Although geologic conditions make it inevitable that mineral procurement must in the future be more expensive *in terms of energy,* it does not necessarily follow that all industrial *costs* need rise. Many times in the past, technological improvements have made it feasible to rework a deposit that had been thoroughly exploited by an outmoded method. Alaskan gold dredges now operate at a profit on placer deposits that contain only a few cents' worth of gold per cubic yard—deposits that to the sourdough working with his sluice box were exhausted. Similarly, most of the world's copper is taken today from deposits that were impossible to exploit by methods in use seventy years ago. But there are limits to the development of low-grade deposits, and it is important to realize that these technological limitations, as well as the sporadic distribution and exhaustibility of mineral resources, place upon the mineral industries restrictions that differ *in kind* from those affecting most other economic activities.

Cycles of mineral production

The mineral industry, like others, constantly fluctuates, but follows discernible long-term trends. Newly discovered deposits and new technologies may increase prosperity for a while, but eventually the higher costs of deep mining and exhaustion of the deposits bring harder times. An American economic geologist, D. F. Hewett, has analyzed the history of the mineral industry in many countries, and has found a surprisingly consistent sequence of stages. Briefly put, these are as follows:

1. Period of exploration and discovery: many small mines and a few large deposits recognized; boom towns; many independent and competing organizations.

2. Period of amalgamation and consolidation: few new discoveries; small mines worked out; larger mines more efficient than the smaller had been; many smelters competing for ore with the better financed ones winning out.

3. Period of industrial integration: lower costs, higher living standards, rapid increase in internal and external markets and wealth; approaching height of commercial power.

4. Period of rapid depletion of cheap domestic raw materials: higher costs of mining and recovering from depleted deposits; more power required per unit of production; bitter commercial rivalry for raw materials; trade balance unfavorable; gradual loss of trade to foreign competitors.

5. Period of decreasing domestic and foreign trade: higher costs of manufacture because of necessity of importing raw materials; declining commercial power and living standards; increasing competition for cheap foreign materials, often leading to international friction and war.

Hewett did not maintain, of course, that there have been no deviations from this pattern nor that all phases are inevitable, but the sequence has been well enough followed in the past to merit serious attention. Broadly speaking, stage 1 is represented at present by Rhodesia; stage 2 by Canada; early stage 3 by the USSR and South Africa; late stage 3 and early stage 4 by the United States (note our heavy investments in petroleum in the Caribbean and Near East; in copper in Chile and Zambia; in iron in Brazil, Venezuela, and Cuba) ; stage 4 by Germany; and stage 5 by Great Britain, which passed through the first four stages during the eighteenth and nineteenth centuries. These stages in the evolution of the mining industry (stages 1 through 4), without corollary industrial development, may be recognized even in countries like Bolivia or Malaya, where lack of fuel or other sources of power prevents any significant manufacturing.

THE ECONOMIC IMPORTANCE OF MINERAL RESOURCES

Although mineral resources account directly for less than 4 percent of the total national product in the United States, they play a crucial role in industry, for all heavy manufacturing depends on them. Our industrial might depends upon them absolutely. Nearly two-thirds—in some years nearly three-fourths—of the value of mineral production of the United States is supplied by the energy sources; the **mineral fuels**—petroleum, gas, and coal. We are doubtless witnessing the technologic evolution of still other mineral fuels, the so-called nuclear fuels based on the radioactive elements uranium and thorium and the artificial elements made from them. Mineral resources other than fuels include the **metalliferous deposits,** the source of our metals; and the **nonmetallic deposits,** such as building stone, cement rock, clay, sand, and gravel. From 1940 to 1965 the total annual value of mineral products in the United States has ranged between 6 and $21\frac{1}{2}$ billion dollars.

The mineral fuels

The mineral fuels are the most important mineral resources. They are essential for heat and power and for metal refining, and are also the source of many useful chemicals and of nitrogen fertilizers. They are especially important to the geological profession, for the search for oil is the principal work of about half of all geologists.

The Industrial Revolution was based on coal, and coal is still a basic fuel, though petroleum has largely replaced it in the field of transport, and natural gas has made such inroads in power plants and metallurgy as to grow from furnishing only about 12 percent of the energy consumption of the country in 1940 to furnishing 37 percent in 1965. Since during the same time, the total energy

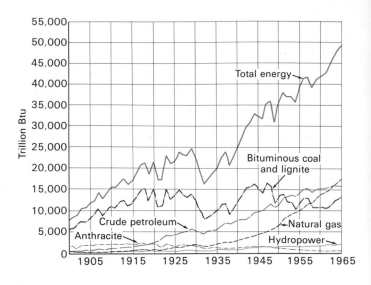

FIGURE 21–1
*Production of mineral energy re-
sources and energy from hydropower in the United States, 1900–
1965. (From U.S. Bureau of Mines
Yearbook, 1965.)*

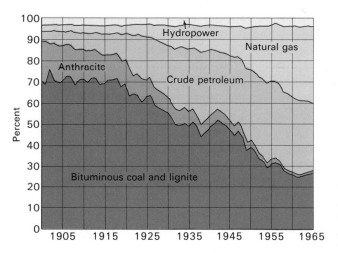

FIGURE 21–2
*Percentage of total production, in
British Thermal Units equivalent,
of mineral and hydropower energy
sources in the continental United
States, 1900–1965. (From U.S. Bureau of Mines Mineral Yearbook,
1965.)*

consumption has nearly doubled, the natural
gas industry has grown by a factor of 6 (Figs.
21–1, 21–2). As a result, coal which supplied
about half the total energy requirements of
the United States in 1940 supplied only
about 27 percent in 1965; in fact, the tonnage
mined has fallen off slightly since the end of
World War II, worsening the already depressed economy of Appalachia. It is likely,
though, that the increasing demand for electric generating plants will again turn upward
the trend of coal consumption.

World production of coal in 1963 was

2⅔ billion tons, mostly in Europe and the
United States, though India, South Africa,
and Japan all mined locally significant
amounts. At United States prices, the value
of this tonnage would be nearly 12 billion
dollars. World production of petroleum that
year was more than 9½ billion barrels, almost exactly twice what it had been a decade
before. Most of this came from the United
States (29 percent), Venezuela, the USSR,
and the region of the Persian Gulf. Its value
at United States prices was nearly 68 billion
dollars, more than five times that of the coal.

Table 21–1 **Distinctive features of coal of various ranks**

Kind of coal	*Physical appearance*	*Characteristics*
Lignite	Brown to brownish black	Poorly to moderately consolidated; weathers rapidly; plant residues apparent.
Subbituminous coal	Black; dull or waxy luster	Weathers easily; plant residues faintly shown.
Bituminous coal	Black; dense; brittle	Does not weather easily; plant structures visible with microscope; burns with short blue flame.
Anthracite coal	Black; hard; usually with glassy luster	Very hard and brittle; burns with almost no smoke.

COAL. Coal is a brownish-black to black combustible rock (see Chapter 3). It forms beds that range from a fraction of an inch to many feet in thickness, interbedded with shale, sandstone, and other sedimentary rocks (Fig. 21–3). A single sequence of strata may include several coal beds: in West Virginia 117 different beds have been named. They are distributed through several thousand feet of strata, which, taken together, are called the **coal measures.** Coal-bearing strata include many alternations of marine and non-marine beds. The coal beds are in the nonmarine parts of the section and are of nonmarine origin. They are composed chiefly of flattened, compressed, and somewhat altered remains of land-dwelling plants: wood, bark, roots (some still in the position of growth), leaves, spores, and seeds.

Coal rank.—Coals appear to have been formed chiefly from plant residues that accumulated in swamps. There is a continuous series from brown peat, obviously made up of slightly modified plant residues, to a hard, black, glistening type of coal that contains no recognizable plant remains. The principal members of this series are **peat, lignite, subbituminous coal, bituminous coal,** and **anthracite coal.** The more obvious features of all except peat, which is not considered a coal, are shown in Table 21–1.

FIGURE 21–3
Coal beds on Lignite Creek, Yukon region, Alaska. (Photo by C. A. Hickcox, U.S. Geological Survey.)

When coal is heated in the absence of air, it gives off water vapor and hydrocarbon gases. These are called the volatile matter. The woody and other plant components in peat are complex compounds of carbon, oxygen, and hydrogen. In the air they oxidize and rot away, yielding chiefly carbon dioxide and water, but if air is excluded by geologic burial, they slowly alter into many solid products, as well as some gases. Among the solid products is finely divided black elemental carbon, a substance whose presence distinguishes coal from peat. The higher the proportion of elemental ("fixed") carbon

Table 21–2 **Estimated total potential coal resources of the world,* in billions (10⁹) of short tons**

Continent	Known on the basis of existing mapping and exploration	Probable additional in unmapped and un-explored areas	Total potential resources
Asia †	7000 ‡	4000	11,000 §
North America	1720	2880	4600
Europe	620	210	830
Africa	80	160	240
Oceania	60	70	130
South and Central America	20	10	30
Total	9500 ‡	7330	16,830 §

SOURCE: Data from Paul Averitt, U.S. Geological Survey.

* Original resources in the ground in beds 12 inches thick or more and generally less than 4000 feet below the surface, but includes small amounts between 4000 and 6000 feet.

† Includes European U.S.S.R.

‡ Includes about 6500 billion short tons in the U.S.S.R.

§ Includes about 9500 billion short tons in the U.S.S.R.

FIGURE 21–4   *Coal resources of the United States remaining to be mined, 1965. Estimate is based on material between the surface and a depth of 6000 feet; anthracite and bituminous coal in beds 14 inches or more thick; subbituminous and lignite in beds 2½ feet or more thick. (Data from Paul Averitt, U.S. Geological Survey.)*

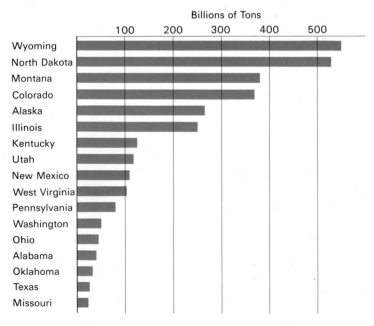

and the lower that of volatile matter, the higher the rank of the coal in the series from peat to anthracite. Clay and sand washed into the swamp while the coal accumulated remain as ash when the coal is burned. This lessens the heating value and increases waste, and thus detracts from coal value.

Most bituminous and anthracite coals are of Carboniferous age. Such coals are abundant in Europe and eastern North America. Most high-rank coal in Europe lies in a belt extending from Britain across Belgium. Luxembourg, and Germany into southern U.S.S.R. This is the industrial heart of Europe.

Coal reserves.—Coal is so abundant (Table 21–2) that generally only the thicker, more accessible, and higher-rank deposits are now being mined. An estimate of coal reserves means little unless the limits of thickness, depth (for it is expensive to mine deep underground) , and quality of coal are stated. We will not enter into the details but present in Figure 21–4, a careful estimate prepared by Paul Averitt, U.S. Geological Survey. This estimate includes all anthracite and bituminous beds 14 inches or more thick and all subbituminous and lignite beds 2½ or more feet thick, remaining in the ground to a depth of 6000 feet. Much of the coal of Montana, North Dakota, and Alaska is lignite; most of that in Wyoming and Washington and some in Colorado is subbituminous; of the rest nearly all is bituminous except for small tonnages of anthracite in Pennsylvania, Colorado, Alaska, and West Virginia (Fig. 21–5) . As seen in Figure 21–5, coal-bearing rocks underlie 14 percent of the land area of this part of the United States; the total tonnage is between a fifth and a sixth of the world total.

OIL AND GAS. Earth oil (petroleum) and natural gas are found in similar environments and usually together. Commercial ac-

cumulations exist only in special geologic conditions and are almost, though not entirely, limited to sedimentary rocks. Producing areas are known as "pools," although the oil and gas, like ground water, generally fills pore spaces in rocks, rather than open caverns.

There are four requisites for the formation of a commercial oil pool: (1) a source rock, (2) a permeable reservoir rock which will yield the oil rapidly enough to make drilling worthwhile, (3) an impermeable cap rock, and (4) a favorable structure, which allows the cap rock to retain the oil below ground. We will defer the discussion of the source rock until we have dealt briefly with each of the other requisites.

The essential feature of a **reservoir rock** is the presence of connected pores or cavities through which a liquid can move. *Permeability* (Chapter 14) is thus its prime characteristic, though *porosity*—that is, the storage capacity—of a volume of rock is obviously also significant. Most reservoir rocks are sandstones, though some are limestones or dolomites, either granular, with interstitial pore spaces, or jointed and cavernous. Shattered brittle rocks such as chert and basalt,

FIGURE 21–5
The coal fields of the United States. (After Bituminous Coal Institute, 1948.)

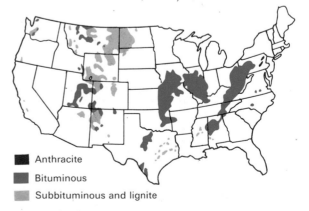

■ Anthracite
■ Bituminous
■ Subbituminous and lignite

FIGURE 21–6

Structures favorable to the commercial accumulation of oil and gas. A: Anticlinal fold, with reservoir sand underlain by shale (possible source rock) and overlain by shale (cap rock). Note the reservoir sand capped by asphalt at the outcrop, making a second trap for oil. B: Salt dome with oil at crest and on flanks. C: Trap in sandstone, formed where unconformity is overlain by shale. D: Porous limestone reef reservoir, in impermeable limestone and shale. E: Fractured schist reservoir beneath domed shale.

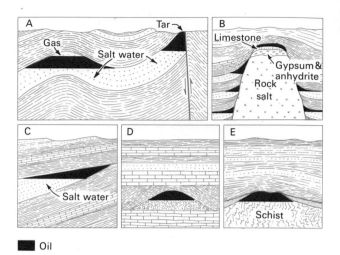

and very rarely even granite and schist, are productive reservoirs in a few fields. Extremely fine-grained sandstones, many formerly nonproductive because of low permeability, have recently been made highly productive: methods have been developed to shatter them underground by fluid pressure and to fill the newly formed crevices with coarse sand through which oil can drain to the wells.

A **cap rock** must be virtually impermeable to oil and gas. Most are shale, but nonporous sandstone seals some reservoirs; others are sealed by asphalt left near the surface where oil has escaped and its lighter components have evaporated—such spots are **oil seeps,** in Spanish countries, **breas.** Many commercial oil accumulations have been found by drilling beneath them.

Oil and gas fill pores in rocks much more rarely than water, and their accumulation in commercial quantities requires **favorable structure.** Because water fills most spaces below the water table, and because oil is lighter than water and hence floats on it, the favorable structures are generally high in the reservoir rock, directly beneath a cap rock seal. Since gas is lighter than oil it ordinarily rises to the top, although, under high pressures at depth much dissolves in the oil and is re-

leased only when the pressure is decreased. Some favorable structures are diagrammed in Figure 21–6.

Most oil fields occupy the crests of elongate **anticlinal folds,** often, but incorrectly, called domes (Figs. 21–6,A, 21–7). The Salt Creek Dome, Wyoming; the Kettleman Hills North Dome, California; the tremendous anticline called El Nala, in Saudi Arabia, apparently the longest continuous oil field in the world; the prolific field of Bahrein Island in the Persian Gulf are examples. Less common are the *salt dome fields,* which lie above or beside plugs of massive salt that have been injected from beneath, tilting the strata (Fig. 21–6,B). These abound along the Texas and Louisiana coast of the Gulf of Mexico, both on and offshore; the famous Spindletop Field, one of the first found, is representative. Similar accumulations have been found along the Caucasus and in the Carpathian foothills of Rumania. Finally, there are the **stratigraphic traps** (Fig. 21–6,C), with the reservoir capped, generally unconformably, by an overlying blanket of impermeable sediment. The greatest of all American oil fields, East Texas, is a stratigraphic trap on a gently dipping sandstone bed whose former outcrop is covered by younger strata. The great Leduc oil field of Alberta lies in the porous parts

FIGURE 21–7
Anticline with oil well sited on its crest. East Los Angeles, California, 1931. (Photo by M. N. Bramlette, U.S. Geological Survey.)

of a fossil coral reef, buried beneath impermeable strata (Fig. 21–6,D). The small but interesting Edison Field, California, has as its reservoir rock a fractured mass of schist, into which the oil must have seeped from sedimentary rocks that buried an old schist hill (Fig. 21–6,E).

Some traps, like the immense Hugoton gas field of Kansas and Oklahoma, contain gas, but no oil.

Source rocks of petroleum.—The conclusions about reservoir rock, cap rock, and favorable structure are well-established geological generalizations inductively based on repeated observations. Oil is found in permeable rocks confined by virtually nonpermeable ones, and in structural positions determined by hydraulic laws. But the sources of earth oil are matters of less certain inference. Some very important conclusions seem well established, but much more needs to be known. Most, but not quite all, geologists think that *petroleum originates exclusively in sediments.* Nearly all oil pools are in sedimentary rocks. The rare exceptions, such as the Edi-

son Field just mentioned, could have received their oil by migration from adjoining oil-bearing sandstones. Most pools are separated from the nearest igneous or metamorphic rock by thousands of feet of barren sedimentary rocks which contain no traces of oil.

Many oil fields, too, are in or near thick accumulations of marine or deltaic sediments that include cubic miles of shales that generally contain several percent—exceptionally as much as 80 percent—of organic matter, chiefly compounds of carbon originating from the bodies of former plants or animals. These organic shales were probably derived from marine ooze, for modern oozes have yielded similar compounds.

The original synthesis of carbon dioxide and water to form the organic compounds must have been by plants, perhaps largely by the very abundant diatoms. The organic compounds of carbon, hydrogen, and oxygen thus produced may then have been repeatedly worked over in the digestive tracts of many kinds of animals in the sea or on its floor, before final burial.

The bodies of dead animals also contribute. Even after burial, the organic residues in the ooze are further altered by bacteria, with partial elimination of oxygen. Some oozes probably accumulated in stagnant basins too poor in oxygen to permit bacterial transformation of the hydrogen-carbon residues into water and carbon dioxide again. Many geologists think that most oil is formed in this way, for many oil fields are associated with strata whose character suggests such an environment. Yet the transformation of organic matter into liquid oil is still poorly understood. It must have taken place under a cover of younger strata, and the pressure and rise of temperature resulting from burial apparently were essential factors.

The tentative prehistory of petroleum just outlined is based on much geological and chemical research. Three additional generalizations seem justified, though not all are universally accepted. First, little free oil has been found in areas containing only fresh-water sedimentary rocks, despite the vast quantities of "oil shale" (which contains no free oil, but from which liquid oil can be distilled) in the Eocene lake beds of Utah, Colorado, and Wyoming. Second, oil and coal are not the liquid and solid products, respectively, of the alteration of peat, even though both oil and coal are found in the same sedimentary sequences (but at different levels) in the mid-continent region of the United States. Third, the oil-forming process seems to be very slow, as no oil has been found in modern sediments, though similar compounds have been extracted from them. The hope, expressed by some chemists, that earth oil may now be forming at approximately the present rate of consumption seems quite unjustified geologically.

Oil map of the world.—Because of the economic importance of oil, a knowledge of petroleum geology is essential for the formulation of intelligent domestic and foreign policies. Where is oil now being produced? What reserves are still in the ground? Where may additional supplies be found in the future?

First, we may mark off on a map the areas where only igneous and metamorphic rocks crop out, calling these impossible or wholly unimportant because of the absence of marine organic sedimentary rocks. We can add to them, as unfavorable, the areas where only thin or nonmarine sedimentary rocks overlie the crystallines (Fig. 21–8). Then we may outline as favorable the areas where oil is being produced, and add those areas where thick marine strata have yielded evidences of oil, such as seeps. Finally, we may distinguish an intermediate, or possible, group of areas, which contain thick marine strata but no positive indications of petroleum.

Although such a map is valuable it leaves many questions unanswered. Which areas have produced the most oil? Which have the most left? Up to 1948 the United States had produced more than half of the world's oil, but by 1957 it was producing less than 47 percent, and in 1965 only 29 percent. And what

FIGURE 21–8   *Oil map of the world, based on the estimated probability of finding oil in each region. (After Arabian-American Oil Company, Middle East Oil Developments, 1948.)*

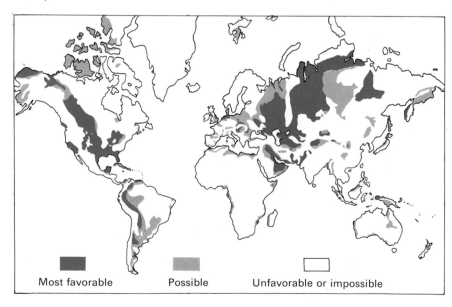

Most favorable   Possible   Unfavorable or impossible

about proved reserves? The United States still has much oil—proved reserves at the end of 1964 were nearly 39 billion barrels and probable reserves were several times that figure. But the proved reserves of the Middle East—Iraq, Kuwait, Bahrein, and Saudi Arabia—were more than five times as great. Those of Venezuela and other nearby parts of South America were considerably more than half as large, and it seems reasonable, in view of the later development of the oil industries in these areas, to conclude that their ultimate reserves are far greater than those of North America. There seem clearly to be two great petroliferous provinces on the earth: the region around the Persian Gulf and the region bordering the Caribbean— Venezuela, eastern Mexico, and the Gulf Coast of the United States. The fields of Iran, Saudi Arabia, and Kuwait are intrinsically so rich, and are being managed so much more efficiently than were those of the United States in the early days of wasteful competition, that their value is almost unimaginably great. Never in human history have there been such prizes of concentrated wealth. Even in 1957, early in their development, more than 3½ million barrels flowed daily from a few hundred wells. Compare this with America's hundred of thousands of wells, with an average production of less than 13 barrels a day in 1964 and consider the vast wealth that has come from them. Clearly, a crucial spot in the history of the next generation will be the Middle East and its vast treasury of oil.

No inventory of potential oil provinces would be complete without mention of the continental shelves. These submerged extensions of the continents are repositories of huge volumes of sedimentary rocks, most of them undoubtedly marine. Though the technological difficulties of both exploration and exploitation of these underwater reserves are tremendous, they were already in 1964 producing nearly 50 million barrels of oil a year off the coasts of California, Texas, and Lou-

isiana. Later-developed, and at the time less productive, reservoirs off Alaska and in the North Sea will surely add greatly to the world's supplies; with improved technology we may look forward to vast additions from the subsea sources.

OIL FINDING.   The first earth oil put to human use oozed from oil seeps. Noah's Ark, like the present native boats of the Near East, may have been calked with asphalt from a Mesopotamian seepage. The first well successfully drilled for oil (in Pennsylvania, 1859), was sunk beside a seepage, as were many successful wells later. Most wells beside seepages have been small producers, but Cerro Azul No. 4, perhaps the greatest single producer in history, was an exception. This well, near Tampico, Mexico, "blew in" on February 10, 1916, for 260,000 barrels a day, the column of oil rising 598 feet into the air. The well produced almost 60 million barrels of oil before suddenly yielding only salt water. It was drilled in limestone and apparently penetrated a real pool of oil and gas floating on salt water in interconnected caverns.

Seepages are obvious clues to oil, but their absence does not deter exploration. By 1883, random drilling in Pennsylvania and West Virginia had shown that many of the productive wells were grouped along anticlinal crests. Noting this, I. C. White advocated the anticlinal theory of accumulation and outlined the physical reasons for it. The theory came to be generally accepted as a guide to exploration. Between 1900 and 1918 most oil companies built up geological staffs and gradually came to rely, in exploration, not on random drilling, but on systematic geologic search for anticlines and similar favorable structures. By 1928 most anticlines observable from surface geology in the United States had been drilled and hundreds of oil fields had been discovered.

But the surface beds in many areas conceal the structures in older ones that lie unconformably beneath them. Nor can they, of course, give clues to underlying stratigraphic traps—a reservoir type generally overlooked until the early 1930's. Systematic exploration demanded some means of determining geologic structure at depth.

Geophysical methods.—The first geophysical method applied was the **gravity survey.** A few huge salt plugs (Fig. 21–6,B) along the Texas coast had yielded much oil from their flanks or crests. As salt is lighter than most other rocks, measurements of gravity over the flat coastal country should reveal similar buried plugs by their smaller gravitational attraction. Systematic surveys during the 1920's did, in fact, reveal many such anomalously low values of gravity, and by 1930 the coast of Texas and Louisiana was dotted with salt dome oil fields thus found. Gravity methods, however, are less useful in other regions because of smaller contrasts in rock densities and the difficulties introduced by rough local topography. Gravity surveys are mainly useful in searching for salt domes in flat country.

Explosion seismology, introduced about 1924, has proved more widely applicable than gravity studies. Of the several methods, "reflection shooting" has been most successful; the travel times of the seismic waves from small explosions are recorded on small portable seismographs, permitting the identification of various strata by their differing elastic properties, and by comparing travel times to different points, to deduce the structure of the buried strata.

This method has found many favorable structures not apparent on the surface. For example, the Louden field, in Illinois, was so accurately located by seismic work that the oil company was able to lease in advance of drilling nearly all of the 20,000 acres that have since been proved productive. This is a major field with an ultimate recovery estimated at about 200 million barrels. Similarly many fields in Texas and some hidden by the alluvium of the Central Valley of California have been discovered by use of the seismograph.

Subsurface methods.—By the late twenties, so many wells had been drilled in and near oil fields that the geology of the surrounding area at depth could often be determined almost independently of the surface rocks. This is obviously extremely important where unconformities, lensing of beds, or facies changes are present. The major problem is that of correlating beds between wells. If this can be done, favorable structures may be further explored and unfavorable ones avoided.

Three principal methods, lithologic, paleontologic, and electrical, are employed in correlation. **Lithologic correlations** are based on study of well cuttings or cores from the drill holes. An illustration showing such correlation in the Yates Field in Texas is given in Figure 21–9.

Where the rocks are not so readily distinguished as the anhydrite and red shale of the Yates Field, **paleontologic methods** are sometimes applicable. As any of the larger fossils that may be present are generally ground to bits in drilling, the principal paleontological materials are microfossils, chiefly Foraminifera (Fig. 17–27). These tiny fossils are extremely abundant in many strata and are small enough to escape being ground up. Some fossil zones—strata characterized by particular species of fossils—only 10 or 20 feet thick can be distinguished by their microfossils and readily traced from one oil field to another nearby, even though they may change from sand to shale in this distance. Hundreds of micropaleontologists are now working in the oil industry to make correlations by means of these fossils.

Many methods of correlation by physical properties have been tried. Of these the most widely used is the **electric log.** Electrodes lowered into an uncased well measure differences in electrical characteristics of the beds penetrated. These characteristics vary mark-

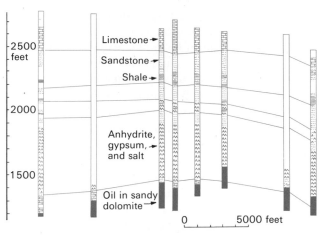

FIGURE 21–9

SW–NE section across the Yates oil field, western Texas, showing correlations from well to well. (After G. C. Gester and H. J. Hawley, Structure of Typical American Oil Fields. *American Association of Petroleum Geologists, 1929.)*

edly because of differences in the composition of the rocks, in their porosity, and in the kind of fluid—oil, salt water, or fresh water—that occupies the pores. Figure 21–10 illustrates the structure of a flat anticline in

FIGURE 21–10

SW–NE sections across Odem dome, southern Texas, showing correlations (dashed lines) from electric logs. The irregular lines to the right of the well-location lines record the resistance of the rocks to an electric current; the lines to the left measure the amount of natural current produced by the rocks themselves. These lines effectively mark the positions of the three sandstone strata shown by the dark brown pattern at the right. (After Society of Exploration Geophysicists, Geophysical Case Histories, *1949.)*

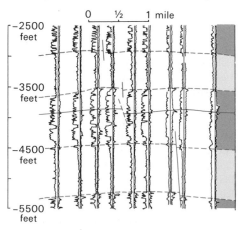

Texas as worked out from electric logs. The results confirmed the structure as inferred from an earlier seismic survey.

Summary of methods of oil exploration.— This brief review of some of the many technical and scientific approaches to oil exploration shows that, although the presence of oil in a particular place at a particular depth cannot be foretold by either geological or geophysical methods in advance of drilling, the search is not a blind one. Oil is localized, in response to definite physical laws, in structures and stratigraphic traps that are geologically determinable. The problem of finding it is a geological one, and the solution depends on the application of many principles of geophysics, physics, petrography, paleontology, and chemistry. Systematic and economical exploitation of fields already found, and the cutting down of waste involved in random drilling, have resulted from such efforts; hence all the large oil companies find it profitable to maintain elaborate geological departments.

ORE DEPOSITS

Ore deposits are rock masses from which metals are obtained commercially. Every ore body has been formed by the selective concentration of one or more elements in which the rock is greatly enriched as compared with the average of the earth's crust. How great this enrichment must be can be realized from the fact that more than 99 percent of the earth's crust is made up of only ten elements (Chapter 2, Table 2–1, and Appendix IV, Table IV–3). Of these ten, aluminum, iron, and magnesium are industrial metals, and yet only a tiny fraction of the total volume of each of these three is concentrated in deposits rich enough to constitute a mineable deposit. Most other industrial metals—copper, zinc, lead, tin, and others—are found in only minute amounts in the earth's crust (Table 21–3).

The abundance of an element in the average igneous rock is called the **clarke** of the element (in honor of the American geochemist F. W. Clarke). In any ore the concentration of the ore element must obviously be higher than the clarke of the element; this concentration is the **clarke of concentration** of the ore body. Thus an aluminum ore of low grade (about 25 percent metal) has a clarke of concentration of 3, for it contains 3 times as high a concentration as the average igneous rock. Similarly, an iron ore with 50 percent Fe has a clarke of concentration of 10, a copper ore of 1 percent Cu a clarke of concentration of more than 100. Most gold mines operate on less than $\frac{1}{3}$ ounce Au per ton, a clarke of concentration of 20,000. The clarke of concentration is a measure of the enrichment of the element over that of the average rock; for many metals this must necessarily be extremely high in order for the metal to be economically mined. It is thus a rough measure of the element's value. High clarkes of concentration must reflect either very unusual geologic conditions or the carrying of ordinary geologic processes to unusual perfection. We shall see examples of both aberrations.

Few ore bodies contain native elements; most are rock bodies containing minerals in which the valuable metal is combined with other elements (Table 21–4). If this combination is such that the useful metal may be economically extracted, the deposit is an **ore.** The valuable minerals that contain the metallic element are **ore minerals.** Separation of the ore minerals from their worthless associates—the **gangue minerals**—and the extraction of the valuable metals from the ore minerals is **metallurgy.**

The definition of ore is purely economic: it is rock that can be worked commercially for extraction of a useful metal. There is no stipulation as to the exact percentage of the metal in the ore—only that it be enough to extract at a profit. A particular rock may pass from subore to ore with increased metal

Table 21–3 **Abundance (clarkes) of some useful metals in the average igneous rock**

Element	Weight percentage	Element	Weight percentage
Aluminum	8.13	Cobalt	0.0023
Iron	5.0	Lead	0.0016
Magnesium	2.09	Tungsten	0.0015
Titanium	0.44	Uranium	0.0004
Manganese	0.1	Antimony	0.0001
Chromium	0.02	Mercury	0.00001
Vanadium	0.015	Silver	0.00001
Nickel	0.008	Gold	0.0000005
Copper	0.007	Platinum	0.0000005
Zinc	0.005	Radium	0.0000000013
Tin	0.004		

Table 21–4 **The common ore minerals**

Metal	Mineral	Elements contained	Percentage of metal in ore mineral	Chemical composition
Gold	Native gold	Gold	50 to 100 (alloyed with silver)	Au and Ag
Silver	Native silver	Silver	100	Ag
	Argentite	Silver, sulfur	87.1	Ag_2S
Copper	Native copper	Copper	100	Cu
	Chalcopyrite	Copper, iron, sulfur	34.6	$CuFeS_2$
	Chalcocite	Copper, sulfur	79.8	Cu_2S
	Enargite	Copper, arsenic, sulfur	48.3	$3Cu_2S \cdot As_2S_5$
Lead	Galena	Lead, sulfur	86.6	PbS
Zinc	Sphalerite	Zinc, sulfur	67	ZnS
	Franklinite	Zinc, iron, oxygen, manganese	About 12	$(Fe,Mn,Zn)O \cdot (Fe,Mn)_2O_3$
Iron	Hematite	Iron, oxygen	70	Fe_2O_3
	Magnetite	Iron, oxygen	72.4	$FeO \cdot Fe_2O_3$
Aluminum	Bauxite (actually a mixture of several minerals)	Aluminum, oxygen, hydrogen	35 to 40	$Al_2O_3, 2H_2O$ (varies)

prices (as happened to many mercury deposits during both world wars), with improved metallurgical techniques (as with many deposits of copper, zinc, and lead when the "flotation process" of separating ore minerals from gangue and from each other was developed), or with subsidies (as did the very low-grade Rhineland iron deposits under the Nazi "self-sufficiency" program). Conversely, a price decline or higher mining and metallurgical costs has often changed a valuable ore into worthless rock.

Among the many factors that determine whether a particular material is ore are:

1. The size, shape, and depth of the deposit. (All these greatly affect the cost of mining.)

2. The amenability of the ore to metallurgical treatment. (Fine-grained mineral aggregates may need to be ground very fine for clean separation from the gangue minerals; this grinding may be more costly than direct smelting of the ore.)

3. The distance to metallurgical centers or to market. (The exploitation of Brazilian iron ores, though they are richer than the Lake Superior ores, has lagged because of distance from fields of coking coal.)

There are many dramatic examples of the influence of these factors on mining. The great copper mine at Bingham Canyon, Utah, can today mine ore containing as little as 0.70 percent (14 pounds of copper to the ton), yet fifty years ago masses of pure copper weighing several tons were occasionally found in the Michigan mines but were not ore because they could not be effectively blasted and it cost too much to chisel them out. A generation ago rock containing 50 percent iron could not be mined on the Minnesota "Iron Ranges" because blast furnaces were designed to use only higher-grade ores; but with the exhaustion of the high-grade ores, furnace practices were changed so that these lower-grade materials can be used. At Birmingham, Alabama, the happy combina-

Table 21–5 **Types of mineral deposits**

Type	Manner of formation	Representative deposits
Magmatic segregation	By settling of early formed minerals to the floor of a magma chamber during consolidation.	Layers of magnetite, chromite, and platinum-rich pyroxenite in the Bushveldt lopolith, South Africa.
	By settling of late-crystallizing but dense metalliferous parts of the magma, which either crystallize in the interstices of older silicate minerals, or are injected along faults and fissures of the wall rocks.	Copper-nickel deposits of Norway and most of those of the Sudbury district, Canada. Injected bodies of magnetite in Sweden (greatest in Europe) and in New York.
	By direct magmatic crystallization.	Diamond deposits of South Africa (nonplacer).
Contact-metamorphic	By replacement of the wall rocks of an intrusive by minerals whose components were derived from the magma.	Magnetite deposits of Iron Springs, Utah; some copper deposits of Morenci, Arizona.
Hydrothermal (deposits from hot, watery solutions)	By filling fissures in and replacing both wall rocks and the consolidated outer part of a pluton by minerals whose components were derived from a cooling magma. These differ from contact-metamorphic deposits in having fewer silicate minerals and more obvious fissure control.	Copper deposits of Butte, Montana, and Bingham, Utah; lead deposits of Idaho and Missouri; zinc deposits of Missouri, Oklahoma, and Kansas; silver deposits of the Comstock Lode, Nevada; gold of the Mother Lode, California, Cripple Creek, Colorado, and Lead, South Dakota.
Sedimentary	By evaporation of saline waters, leading to successive precipitation of valuable salts.	Salt and potash deposits of Stassfurt, Germany, and of Saskatchewan, Canada, New Mexico, Utah, Michigan, Ohio, and New York.
	By deposition of rocks unusually rich in particular elements.	Iron deposits of Lorraine, France, Birmingham, Alabama, and some in Minnesota and Labrador.
	By deposition of rocks in which the detrital grains of valuable minerals are concentrated because of superior hardness or density.	Placer gold deposits of Australia, California, Siberia, Nome, Alaska, probably of the Rand, South Africa; titanium of Travancore, India, and Australia; diamond placers of Southwest Africa.
Residual	By weathering, which causes leaching out of valueless minerals, thereby concentrating valuable materials originally of too low grade into workable deposits.	Iron ores of Cuba, Bilbao, Spain, some of those of Michigan and Minnesota; barite deposits of Missouri.
	By concentration from weathering together with further leaching and enrichment of the valuable mineral itself.	Bauxite (aluminum) ores of Arkansas, France, Hungary, Jamaica, and British Guiana.

tion of abundant local coal and limestone flux for use in the metallurgy permits the mining of ores with as little as 35 percent iron. Such material would be useless rock, not ore, in Montana or California.

ORE FORMATION. *Processes of concentration.*—The processes that concentrate minerals into economic deposits are both mechanical and chemical, acting alone or in combination. These processes are those we have already noted: weathering, solution, transportation, and sedimentation at the surface; metamorphism, volcanism, and flow of solutions below the surface. Ore bodies are rocks, and at one place or another nearly every rock-forming process has produced a valuable mineral deposit. This is indicated in Table 21–5, a brief tabulation of a few geologic types of mineral deposits, to which many others could be added. These few are selected because they are economically important and illustrate different ways in which particular elements have been selectively concentrated to many times their normal proportions.

Magmatic segregations.—As we noted in Chapter 18, many large floored intrusive bodies show a density stratification—a more-or-less regular banding with the dense, early crystallizing minerals near the base. In the Palisade sill the mineral so concentrated by sinking was olivine, of no economic value. But in some places, economic minerals have accumulated in similar ways to form ore deposits. Among these are the chromite and platinum ores of the Bushveld, South Africa and the chromite of the Stillwater region, Montana. A representative specimen of such segregated chromite, in Alaska, is illustrated in Figure 21–11.

Floored intrusions of a variety of gabbro called norite, with concentrations of nickel sulfides and copper sulfides near their bases, are found in localities as widely scattered as Norway, Canada, and South Africa. The great Norwegian geologist J. H. L. Vogt pointed out in 1893 that the bulk composition of these intrusives resembles that of smelter charges of sulfide ores—that is, a small percentage of sulfide and a large preponderance of silicates of aluminum, magnesium, iron, and calcium. When such a sulfide ore is smelted, the molten sulfides (the matte) sink to the bottom of the crucible, while the slag of silicates rises to the top. Vogt suggested that the same mechanism might have operated in nature to produce the observed concentrations.

FIGURE 21–11
Banded chromite, Seldovia district, Alaska. (Photo by P. W. Guild, U.S. Geological Survey.)

FIGURE 21–12
The Sudbury lopolith, Ontario, Canada. (After A. P. Coleman and E. S. Moore, 1929.)

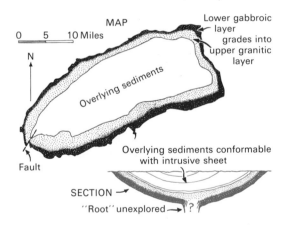

Among such deposits are the greatest nickel deposits of the world, those of Sudbury, Ontario, which occur along the base of the lopolith shown in Figure 21–12. Here nickel sulfides are commonly molded against the silicate minerals, which possess their own crystal forms. This suggests strongly that the sulfides remained molten after the silicates had crystallized and that they accommodated themselves to the intergrain spaces between the silicate minerals. Certain details of the Sudbury deposits suggest that the final distribution of some of the sulfides may have been affected not only by gravity but by other factors as well—perhaps some have been dissolved and remobilized by solutions from a younger granitic intrusion. But the settling process is generally considered the most important step in the formation of the ore.

Contact-metamorphic deposits.—In Chapters 3 and 18, it was pointed out that the wall rocks of some intrusives contain quite different minerals than the same rocks do at a distance. In many places features such as bedding and even fossils are still identifiable in beds of limestone right up to an intrusive contact, although the limestone near the contact may have been completely transformed to garnet, pyroxene, amphibole, and epidote. Such mineral changes in an already-existing rock at plutonic contacts prove that material has been transferred from magma to wall rock during the cooling of the intrusive. If the new minerals were merely concentrated from the limestone itself by solution and removal of the other constituents, the volume must have shrunk. Locally such shrinkage has been demonstrated but most contact zones show no volume change; minor details of bedding and delicate fossil structures are faithfully preserved in the new mineral phases.

Clearly, new material must have been added to the wall rock, and carbon dioxide and other substances removed in order to change the carbonates to silicates without volume change. Supporting this interpretation is the observation that gases escaping through fissures at Vesuvius and Katmai have deposited iron-rich minerals such as magnetite and hematite on the fissure walls.

Only atoms or gases and relatively dilute solutions of low viscosity could so intimately permeate the wall rocks as to bring about their transformation without disturbing the finer textural features of the rock; it is equally evident that part of the former material of the rock must have been removed in the same solutions. The replacement of calcite by garnet or pyroxene has taken place volume for volume, the unused atoms from the disintegrating calcite being removed at the same moment that the garnet crystals were being built in the space formerly occupied by the calcite. This volume-for-volume replacement is one of the most widespread phenomena of geology. It takes place not only at intrusive contacts, but in many other environments where circulating ground water or other fluids can transfer material. The contact-metamorphic deposits are distinctive, however, because of the high-temperature minerals they contain.

Contact-metamorphic deposits yield many useful products: garnet, for sandpaper; corundum (Al_2O_3), for emery wheels and, as rubies and sapphires, for gem use; copper; zinc; iron; and lead. The iron deposits of Iron Springs, Utah, are representative (Fig. 21–13). These deposits are pod-shaped, having replaced a limestone, in places to its full thickness, but elsewhere only in part. The ore is a mixture of magnetite and hematite, with a little apatite and smaller amounts of garnet, pyroxene, and quartz. Of these min-

FIGURE 21–13
Contact-metamorphic iron deposit at Iron Springs, Utah. (After J. H. Mackin, Utah Geological Survey, 1947.)

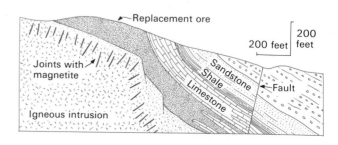

erals, only quartz is found in the unaltered limestone. The rest have been introduced from the magma, concurrently with the removal of calcium and carbon dioxide from the limestone.

Hydrothermal deposits.—Most ores of copper, lead, zinc, mercury, silver, and many of those of gold and tungsten are classed geologically as hydrothermal deposits; that is, they were formed by deposition from hot water solutions, as proved by the following facts.

1. Closely similar deposits have been seen to form in hot springs and fumaroles.

2. Many deposits are localized along faults and fissures that cut pre-existing rocks and therefore must have crystallized from fluids that penetrated cracks in the host rock.

3. The minerals of many of these ores are identical, though the deposit can be traced from one kind of wall rock into another. The ores must have formed in an environment independent of, and consequently later than, the diverse environments that prevailed during the formation of the different wall rocks.

4. Although the adjacent wall rocks often show drastic mineral changes, delicate structures inherited from the time of their own origin are preserved in them; hence the alterations must have been brought about by solutions so fluid that their passage did not mechanically disturb the rocks.

5. The well-developed crystal faces found on many of the minerals imply growth from solution, for such faces can readily be produced in this way in the laboratory and can be seen to form from solutions in nature.

That the solutions inferred from these features were of magmatic origin cannot always be proved, but is strongly implied by:

1. The close association of most of the deposits with intrusive masses.

2. The clustering of deposits about particular intrusives.

3. The especial abundance of these deposits near the upper parts of plutons.

4. The identity of the minerals in some of these deposits and their wall rocks with those that have been seen to form in volcanic areas; and also the identity of some of the minerals with minerals found in contact-metamorphic deposits. As there is between these extremes an essentially unbroken chain of deposits of intermediate characteristics, it seems probable that they, like the extreme varieties, are of magmatic origin.

Among the minerals that have been seen to form within fumaroles, geysers, and hot springs are magnetite, galena, sphalerite, and cinnabar (HgS, the principal source of mercury). In a few places, such as the sulfur mines of Sicily and the mercury deposit at Sulphur Bank, California, economic mineral deposits are directly associated with hot springs, and their valuable minerals were obviously deposited by the ascending hot waters. The similarities of both ore minerals and wall-rock alteration of these deposits to those of other deposits where hot springs are not now active are so close that most geologists agree that the latter—the so-called hydrothermal deposits—have been formed from magmatic solutions. Along the walls of these metallic deposits, just as along the walls of modern hot springs, the rocks have been altered to clay minerals, chlorite, and other hydrous minerals, doubtless by the action of the long-vanished hot solutions.

Paradoxically, one of the strongest evidences that hydrothermal deposits are of magmatic origin, and not formed from circulating ground water merely set in motion by magmatic heat, lies in the fact that many igneous bodies are *not* accompanied by such deposits, though other igneous masses that cut identical wall rocks nearby have great suites of them. Both plutons should have activated ground-water circulation, but only one has ore deposits associated with it. A characteristic of ore deposits is their habit of being grouped into clusters around certain igneous bodies. For example, nearly all the great copper deposits of Arizona and Utah are associated with or lie within intrusives that are very similar in composition, although other intrusive bodies in the same re-

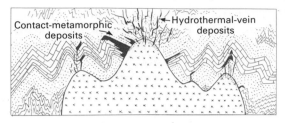

FIGURE 21–14

Concentration of ore deposits in and near the apexes of a large pluton. (After B. S. Butler and G. F. Loughlin, 1913.)

gion, comparable in size, surrounding rocks, and structural setting have no associated copper ores. This strongly suggests that the parental magma of some intrusives was richer in copper than that of others. Just as we are unable to explain the association of nickel and copper with many norites, we are completely at a loss to explain this pristine enrichment of a particular magma in a few other elements. But the association is so well established as to leave little doubt that most of the metal was derived from the magma and not from the wall rocks.

Hydrothermal deposits are not associated with all parts of intrusive bodies. Where erosion has been deep enough to disclose the form of the pluton, the ore deposits appear to be grouped about the higher parts—the apexes or "cupolas." A few deposits lie in deep sags of the roof or along its steeper walls. Further, in plutons so deeply eroded as to destroy all remnants of the roof, ore bodies are rare. These relations suggest that the ore-depositing solutions were hot-water residues from crystallization of the magma, and that they were concentrated in the higher parts by the upward convergence of the walls as they escaped toward the surface during magmatic crystallization (Fig. 21–14).

Form and relations of hydrothermal ore bodies.—The commonest form of hydrothermal ore body is the **vein.** Unlike the cylindrical veins of animals and plants, mineral veins are generally tabular—hundreds or even thousands of times as long and wide as they are thick. They may lie at any angle from vertical to horizontal; they pinch and swell, branch and swerve. Many occupy faults, as shown by offsets of geologic contacts across them. Some follow dikes or bedding planes and still others occupy joints. The so-called "true fissure veins" are veins that differ sharply in mineral content and structure from their wall rocks and generally break away from them cleanly. These are so common in some districts that many of the mining laws of the United States are based on the fallacious assumption that all ore deposits are *"true fissure veins."* Many veins whose geologic relations indicate that they formed at depths of only a few hundred feet are filled with quartz, calcite, and other carbonate minerals, plus a little feldspar, sulfides, and perhaps native gold. These minerals are arranged in bands (Fig. 21–15), in definite sequence from the walls toward the center of the vein. Unfilled cavities, lined with well-formed crystals, testify to the fact—already clear from the crustlike arrangement of the minerals—that the vein partly fills a formerly open channel, and that its minerals were deposited as crusts on the walls by the passing solutions. These are called crustified veins.

Other veins are not sharply separable from their walls; their vein matter blends into the walls. Microscopic study shows that the vein

FIGURE 21–15

A section across a banded vein.

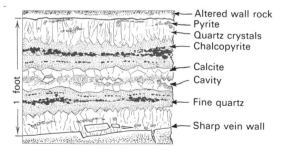

FIGURE 21–16 *Part of a crustified quartz vein from Grass Valley, California. (Photo by W. D. Johnston, Jr., U.S. Geological Survey.)*

matter has replaced the wall rock without disturbing it, just as in the contact-metamorphic deposits. These are replacement veins. Parts of a vein may show evidence of replacement, while other parts have features pointing to mineral growth in open spaces.

Lodes are unusually thick veins or groups of veins. Some lodes are scores or even hundreds of feet thick. Clearly the walls of an opening so wide would have collapsed from the weight of the overlying rock. Yet such features as chunks of wall rock lying along the lower side of a dipping vein and the crustified arrangement of well-formed crystals in the vein (Fig. 21–16) prove that open spaces existed. Careful study of many large veins and lodes shows that the quartz deposited early from the hydrothermal solutions has been broken and recemented with later quartz, often in several generations. This evidence of repeated rupture suggests that the fault occupied by the vein or lode was recurrently active for a long time, and repeatedly formed an avenue of escape for the hot solutions. Movement along an irregular fault would necessarily bring bends into contact and leave openings between (Fig. 21–17). Renewed faulting after such spaces were

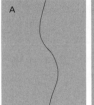

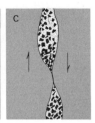

FIGURE 21–17

Vein deposits along an irregular fault. A: Fracture before movement. B: Ore filling cavities after first movement. C: Renewed movement and fracturing of old ore and emplacement of new.

filled would produce new openings to be filled in their turn, and so on—in this way a lode could be made far thicker than would have been possible in any cavity filled by a single generation of vein-stuff.

Disseminated deposits.—Other hydrothermal deposits are very irregularly shaped. Notable among these are the great so-called "porphyry copper" deposits, such as those of Bingham, Utah; Ely, Nevada; Morenci, Arizona; and Chuquicamata, Chile, the greatest copper deposit in the world. Most ore in these districts is disseminated along small fissures in porphyritic intrusive rocks, which it impregnates and replaces with copper and iron sulfides. The rock surrounding and within the ore body is generally highly altered to clay and fine-grained mica, with a little epidote and chlorite, and is so intimately veined with sulfides and quartz that it is hard to find an unveined piece as big as a tennis ball in a mass comprising many thousand cubic yards.

What shattered these great rock masses in such an intimate way as to permit this thorough impregnation is a mystery. Because many deposits occupy the higher parts of plutons, the shattering has been attributed to the upward streaming of volatiles as the intrusive mass slowly congealed, but this is only a conjecture. Another possibility is that the fracturing has been caused by wide fluctuations in the hydraulic pressure of the magma as various vents to the surface became open or closed during the congealing of the pluton. But such variations in internal pressure must be common to nearly all intrusives, whereas the minute fracturing of the porphyry bodies seems to be limited to the mineralized portions.

A different kind of disseminated deposit is exemplified by the lead ores of southeastern Missouri and the zinc-lead deposits of the "Tri-State District" (Oklahoma, Missouri, and Kansas). These lie along irregular and indefinite "runs" in limestone (Fig. 21–18). The ores are sulfides that replace the carbonate wall rocks, and although the pattern of the ore bodies shows some control by faults and other fractures, there are no well-marked veins. The sulfides are accompanied by dolomite and calcite, mostly well crystallized. These minerals were apparently introduced in solutions that permeated the entire rock but deposited their ores selectively in certain beds and along certain trends or channels called runs—perhaps because of some obscure variations in permeability or chemical composition.

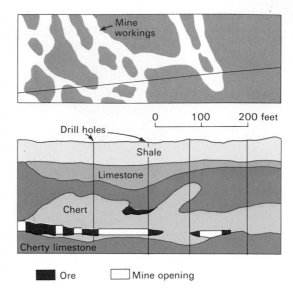

FIGURE 21–18
Map (top) *and section* (bottom) *showing the irregular distribution of ore and silicification of limestone in a Missouri zinc mine.*

SUMMARY.   The hydrothermal deposits consist of rocks that are, on the one extreme almost indistinguishable from contact-metamorphic deposits, and, on the other almost identical with hot-springs deposits.

Observations at fumaroles and hot springs show that the minerals so formed change with the temperature—as temperature falls, the earlier-formed minerals become unstable and are dissolved, and new minerals form. Although we have nowhere found within a single district a complete series of ore deposits filling the range from hot-spring to contact-metamorphic rocks, parts and gradations of such a series are apparent in many parts of the world. Study of many such partial series has made possible the tentative arrangement of ore deposits in a reasonably systematic sequence. Probably this sequence reflects the changes in composition, temperature, and pressure of magmatic solutions as they pass through and react with the minerals of different rocks, and as they cool on approaching the surface. Where conditions favorable to the deposition of one or more ore minerals have been fairly constant, and the volume of solution has been large, ore bodies have resulted. Where conditions changed too rapidly, or the volume of solution was too small, no ore was formed, though small quantities of minerals identical with those of ore bodies were deposited. "Gold is where you find it" —but it has been proved many times that there are often identifiable geologic factors that have controlled its deposition; factors that enable us to find new ore bodies or hidden extensions of those already known.

Sedimentary deposits

Many economic deposits have been concentrated by sedimentation. Among those already discussed are the clay used in ceramics and cement; limestone for building stone, mortar, or cement; dolomite, rock salt, gypsum and potassium salts. The total value of these deposits is very large; in the United States about twice as great each year as that of all metals mined. The value of each depends primarily on the kind and amount of impurities in the sedimentary rock, on the cost of mining or quarrying, and on the distance to market.

Some sedimentary strata, many of wide extent, consist of metallic ores. Among these are the iron ores of Alabama, Newfoundland, and northeastern France, and some of those of England. The ore beds in the Birmingham district of Alabama are of Silurian age, as shown by the associated fossils. Similar deposits of the same age are widespread in the Appalachians from New York southward, but the only large mines in them are near Birmingham, where the iron-rich beds are thickest—in some places as much as 20 feet. The ore beds are generally sharply separated from the adjoining beds of sandstone and shale, but in places they grade into sandstone. In these ores, hematite cements the rock and also coats and replaces some of the fossils. Some sand grains and pebbles, also, have rounded coatings of hematite. These show, by the abrasion of the hematite-covered surfaces, that the iron mineral was formed before the agitation of the grains was stopped by their burial. Many of the hematite granules are flattened in such a way as to suggest that they were soft and were squeezed during the consolidation of the rock. Fossils composed of calcite found with them are undeformed. These facts convince most students of these deposits that the present hematite granules were formerly soft jellylike aggregates of iron rust on the sea floor. The iron oxide was deposited in the sea on nuclei of clastic grains. It was presumably a hydrous oxide, from which the water was driven by heat and pressure after the rock was buried. These deposits are relatively low in iron, and are workable only because (1) they are slightly calcareous, and the calcite acts as a flux in the blast furnace, and (2) they are close to large sources of coking coal.

The present seas apparently contain no such concentrations of iron-rich sediments as must presumably have been present during the deposition of the Birmingham ores, although some iron is now being precipitated on the sea floor. We know from analyses of river waters that iron is leached from the rocks in great quantities; it is less abundant in the sea than in river water. The Silurian deposit is thought to have formed under exceptional conditions during which iron was carried to the sea in great abundance. In other words, it resulted from an unusual concentration in time and place, but from a normal geologic process.

PLACER DEPOSITS.   We saw in Chapter 4 that during normal weathering the feldspars and other silicate minerals tend to decompose to clays that are so fine grained and so weakly coherent as to break up with the slightest transportation. Quartz, however, is normally quite stable, and hence is concentrated in the stream beds of a granitic region, where it makes up most of the sand, even though it constitutes only 10 or 20 percent of the bed-rock. Minerals such as magnetite, chromite, diamond, gold, and cassiterite (SnO_2), the chief source of tin, are also chemically stable in most climatic environments, and since they are heavier than quartz, tend to fall to the bottom of a stream or to accumulate on the riffles of a sluice while quartz of the same grain size is carried on. Where streams from regions that supply such minerals reach the sea, the heavy minerals are further concentrated by the waves. This is the origin of the "black sands" of the Oregon Coast (chromite), of the raised beaches of Nome, Alaska (gold), of the monazite (thorium) sands of the Malabar Coast of India, of the ilmenite (titanium) sands of Florida, and of the diamond beaches of Southwest Africa. In all these localities, minerals that form only very minor parts of the inland rocks have been concentrated because of their density and their resistance to weathering and abrasion.

MINERAL EXPLORATION

Exploration for economic deposits of the sedimentary rocks is based primarily on accurate geologic mapping and careful sampling in systematic ways. But prospecting for disseminated or vein deposits is a much more difficult and complex task. The first step, and one that has been rather completely carried out by the prospectors of a generation ago, even in the most remote parts of the world, is the "panning" of stream gravels in search for placers or for characteristic mineral assemblages known to be commonly associated with valuable minerals. Thus a particular variety of garnet is common in the diamond pipes of South Africa; a systematic search for this resistant (and much more abundant mineral) is the first step in searching for additional diamond-bearing volcanic vents. Every iron-mining area has been throughly tested by magnetic surveys for possible extensions. Detailed gravity surveys have located chromite bodies in the serpentines of Cuba and chromite-bearing "black sands" in Oregon.

The search for disseminated ores now involves not only geologic mapping in search of favorable environments (as judged by similarities with known mineral occurrences), but considerable chemical investigations. Highly sensitive chemical tests enable the identification and quantitative determination of many valuable elements in such dilution as a few parts per billion in rocks (0.000,000,00x percent). Stream gravels are sampled in the promising areas, and followed if encouraging values are found. Where the stream values fall off, the outcrop from which the metal came is probably on one side or the other of the valley; the soils are then sampled in the same way. In this manner very large deposits of gold have recently been found in Nevada and of zinc and lead in New Brunswick. Once the outcrop of the ore body has been found, very detailed mapping is done to identify, if possible, the geologic controls, whether faults, fissures, schistose partings, bedding surfaces, or igneous contact. Every ore body is geologically controlled; the problem is to identify and extrapolate these controls so as to facilitate recovery of the ore.

With the depletion of our richest and most readily found ore deposits, it is inevitable that still more extensive geologic studies, and perhaps the devising of still more subtle tools, will be needed to supply the ever-expanding industrial needs of the world.

Facts, concepts, terms

Dependency of industry on minerals; sporadic distribution of mineral resources; exhaustibility of mineral resources

Mineral fuels

The sequence of coal alteration

    Peat to anthracite

Economic factors in coal mining

    Quality; thickness and structure of beds; over-burden; ground-water conditions; marketing conditions

Requisites for the concentration of petroleum

    Reservoir rock; cap rock; source rocks; favorable structure

Structure of oil fields

    Anticlines; salt domes; stratigraphic traps

Oil provinces

Geophysical exploration

    Gravity surveys; seismic prospecting

Subsurface geology

    Correlation by foraminifera; by lithology; by electrical properties

Ore deposits

Definition of ore

Ore minerals; gangue minerals

Factors in exploitation of a mineral deposit

    Size; shape; depth; grade of ore; amenability to cheap metallurgical processes; distance to market; price

Mechanical processes of ore concentration

    Weathering; solution; transportation; sedimentation

Chemical processes of concentration

    Magmatic segregation; metamorphic transfer; deposition from hot waters

Mineral exploration

Questions

1. Why did Holland and Denmark, which suffered greatly during World War II, oppose the suggestion to abolish the commercial production of coal from the Ruhr area in Germany despite their fear of renewed German aggression?

2. Why, in view of the great mineral endowment of the United States, did Congress authorize "stock-piling" of certain minerals as a defense measure?

3. From the description of placer deposits, explain how they can be used as guides to ore in bedrock. Why does a prospector carry a "pan"?

4. In view of the nonreplenishable nature of mineral deposits, what are the advantages and disadvantages of a tariff on minerals?

5. Although a "fault trap" was not described in the text, draw a cross section of an oil field which is a fault trap in a gently dipping sequence of sediments.

6. Why do the oil fields of the Persian Gulf region have fewer wells per square mile than those of East Texas? Does this reflect geologic or other conditions?

7. Determination of the depth of relatively recent unconsolidated river-deposited sediments in the estuary of the Congo River is important for the solution of the problem of submarine canyons (Chap. 16). What methods now routine in oil finding might be used to determine this depth at enough points to give the form of the bedrock surface? Which method would be quickest?

8. Sandstones used for making glass must consist of almost pure quartz. How is such purity attained by natural processes?

9. Why are placer deposits usually the first to be discovered in a gold-mining region?

10. Pyrite is common in many deposits of copper, lead, zinc, and gold. Why is a conspicuously brown-stained outcrop often a guide to a buried ore deposit?

Suggested readings

American Geographical Society, *World Atlas of Petroleum*. New York, 1950.

Bituminous Coal Institute, *Bituminous Coal Facts and Figures*. Washington, D.C., 1948.

Flawn, Peter T., *Mineral Resources*. Chicago: Rand McNally, 1967.

Lovering, T. S., *Minerals in World Affairs*. New York: Prentice-Hall, 1943.

Rickard, T. A., *Man and Metals*. New York: McGraw-Hill, 1932.

U.S. Geological Survey and Bureau of Mines, *The Mineral Resources of the United States*. Washington, D.C.: Public Affairs Press, 1948.

chapter

Speculations

about the origin
of the earth and of life

Since the earliest writings and doubtless long before, man has speculated about the relations of the earth to the cosmos. Volumes would be needed merely to enumerate the schemes and fancies proposed, but prior to the Renaissance none—even the few that were descriptively correct—can be thought of as in any way scientific. Not until the seventeenth century, when Newton, building on the fundamental work of Galileo and Kepler, discovered the Law of Gravitation, was the first tool essential to a scientific approach forged. Today, though the great advances in all the sciences enable us to place closer and closer limitations on the possibilities, questions about the origin and early history of the earth and of the evolution of its atmosphere, its oceans, and its life remain among the most uncertain—as well as most fascinating—of earth problems. A book such as this can touch only in broad outline upon the kind of reasoning employed, list some of the results attained, and outline a few of the speculations favored by modern studies; a full discussion would demand far more background in the supporting sciences than is appropriate to the level of our work.

THE EARTH'S PLACE
IN THE SOLAR SYSTEM

If we are to speculate about the origin of the earth, restricting our thinking to the scientifically plausible, we shall need to know something of the contributions of the sister science, astronomy, to this problem.

Pythagoras, born on Samos but widely traveled in Egypt and the founder of a most advanced school of philosophy in what is now southern Italy, taught as early as the sixth century B.C. that the earth is a sphere. His disciples, Philolaus and Aristarchus recognized that earth and other planets revolve about the sun, but were unable to prove it with their crude instruments. Copernicus nevertheless refers to Philolaus as having anticipated his own results by more than 2000 years. These men were far ahead of their time; their work was ignored by the more celebrated Aristotle (384–322 B.C.) whose erroneous dogmatism dominated the thought of the western world for many centuries. To Aristotle and his followers, the earth was the center of the Universe, around which the sun and all the stars of the heavens revolve each day, the moon a little more slowly than the rest.

The brilliant Polish cleric Copernicus (1473–1543) had only crude observational facilities and no telescopes, but by years of patient observations was able to show how much more logical is the converse idea that the earth revolves around the sun. Tycho Brahe (1546–1601), astronomer to the court of Denmark, using sextants as long as 30 feet, charted the wanderings of the moon and planets for many years. From the occasional retrograde motion of some of the planets when viewed against the background of the "fixed stars" (Fig. 22–1), he was able to deduce that these had orbits outside the earth's. Brahe left his observational data to a young

German mathematician Johannes Kepler (1571–1630), who after years of patient study, succeeded in reducing the mass of observational data to a precise mathematical model.

Kepler's was an amazing empirical achievement, summarized in what have since been referred to as Kepler's Laws:

1. *All planets, including the earth, move in elliptical orbits, with the sun at one focus of the ellipse.*

2. *A line drawn between sun and planet sweeps out equal areas in the plane of the orbit in equal periods of time* (Fig. 22–2). This law states that any planet travels fastest when nearest the sun and slowest when farthest away; in Figure 22–2 it travels the longer distance A-B in the same time as the shorter distance C-D.

3. *The square of the time,* T, *of a planet's revolution about the sun is proportional to the cube of its average distance,* D, *from the sun.* In other words, the greater the planet's average distance from the sun, the longer it takes to make a revolution, but the ratio of T^2 to D^3 is the same for every planet.

FIGURE 22–1
Diagram illustrating how any planet whose orbit is external to that of the earth will at times appear to have a retrograde motion.

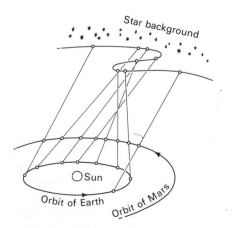

FIGURE 22–2
Illustration of Kepler's first two laws. The first law states that a planet moves in an ellipse about the sun with the sun at one focus. The second law states that a line drawn from the planet to the sun sweeps out equal areas in the plane of the orbit during equal periods of time. Area SAB is equal to area SCD. It is clear that the planet must move faster along the curve AB (when it is close to the sun) than it does from C to D (when it is farthest away).

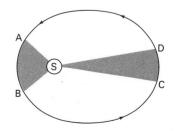

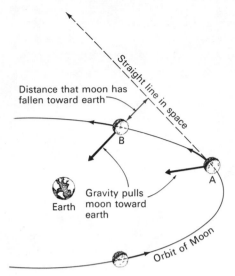

FIGURE 22–3
Showing how gravitational force causes the moon to fall toward the earth from the position it would have if its inertia could maintain its travel in a straight line.

Kepler's Laws, together with the brilliant work of Galileo (1564–1642) on the acceleration of gravity, furnished the background for Isaac Newton's epoch-making deduction of the Universal Law of Gravitation (Chapter 5). The moon follows an elliptical path about the earth, and the earth an elliptical path about the sun because, although the inertia of each tends to keep it moving in a straight line along a path tangential to its orbit, gravitational attraction tends to make each fall toward its principal (Fig. 22–3).

TELESCOPES AND SPECTROSCOPES

At the same time that the dynamics of the solar system were becoming better understood, a great new astronomical tool was developed. A Dutch spectacle maker, Hans Lippershey, about 1608, accidentally discovered that two lenses, one magnifying, the other reducing, when properly spaced and aligned, magnify distant objects. Galileo, learning of this, but never having seen the Lippershey invention, proceeded to develop his own telescope. His first (1609) magnified only three diameters, but he later produced better lenses and attained a magnification of 33 diameters. One of the first objects he examined was the moon, seeing, for the first time, its magnificent craters (Fig. 22–4). He found that the Milky Way is a great disc-shaped mass of stars "so numerous as to be almost beyond belief." He noted the spots on the sun, and following their motion, discovered that the sun is rotating. He discovered 4 of Jupiter's 12 satellites, and noted the "bulges" on Saturn. He followed the phases of Venus, comparable to the changes from full to dark moon so familiar to all. Copernicus' sun-centered solar system was therefore no longer merely the simpler way to explain the planetary motions, it became a demonstrated fact, confirmed also by the fact that Jupiter's moons revolve around Jupiter and not around the earth.

But man does not easily relinquish the self-flattering doctrine that he stands at the center of a universe created for his benefit alone. Though a devout churchman, Galileo was summoned before the Inquisition and forced to retract publicly his support of the Copernican system as being contrary to the accepted interpretation of the Bible. He continued privately in his convictions—"but it does move," he is said to have quietly observed after his public recantation of an orbiting earth. His works were placed on the Index of Prohibited Books, where they remained for nearly 200 years. The University of Salamanca was still teaching that the earth is central to the Universe in 1828. Galileo was in house arrest for the last eight years of his life, but though denied his telescope, he was permitted to continue his work on dynamics, a fundamental contribution underlying Newton's magnificent synthesis. He died the year Newton was born.

For the next two centuries the Galilean telescope, with variations and improvements, was the main tool of astronomers and great steps were made in the understanding of celestial mechanics. Planets previously unknown were discovered in positions deduced from the gravitational disturbances of the orbits of known planets, the belt of asteroids between Mars and Jupiter was recognized, and many other discoveries made.

The next fundamental forward step in astronomy was the application of **spectrography** to the study of the stars and planets. Newton had discovered that a wedge-shaped prism of glass splits sunlight into the component colors of the rainbow and spreads them out in a broad band that he named the **spectrum.** A rainbow is caused, Newton showed, by refraction and reflection of light from falling raindrops; different parts of the spectrum reflecting at slightly differing angles. The classical experiment of high school physics in which sunlight is passed through a triangular glass prism and bent (refracted) into its component colors is another example (Fig. 22–5). Light travels slower through glass than through air, and violet light, with shorter wavelength, is more delayed than red, with longer; in fact, with sensitive thermometers it is possible to prove that waves invisible to the human eye are still less refracted than the red—these **infrared** waves carry most of the heat in the sun's radiation. With the aid of photographic materials it can similarly be shown that waves of shorter wavelength than those of violet light—the **ultraviolet** waves are also part of the sun's radiation. But before much could be done with studies of the solar spectrum, two discoveries remained to be made.

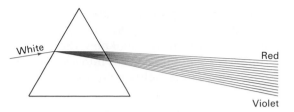

FIGURE 22–5

A diagram of a glass prism showing how it refracts the light to form a spectrum.

Fraunhofer lines

A Bavarian optician-turned-physicist, Joseph von Fraunhofer, while testing some optical glass, found (1814) that the spectrum of sunlight contains sharply defined black lines—in other words, no light comes through the prism at certain definite wavelengths. The sunlight reflected from the moon also contains lines at precisely the same places in the spectrum. Nearly fifty years later the German chemist R. W. Bunsen, and his colleague, the physicist G. R. Kirchoff, showed that all gases at low pressure, when heated to incandescence, produce characteristic bright spectral lines—**emission spectra**—each specific for a particular gas. Some of the gases they tested yielded bright emission spectral lines that coincide precisely with some of the dark lines Fraunhofer had found. Further experiments showed that white light passed through a cooler gas yields black spectral lines—an **absorption spectrum** —at precisely the same wavelengths as the emission spectrum of the same gas heated to incandescence. This shows that the Fraunhofer lines in the solar spectrum are caused by absorption of certain wavelengths by gases in the outer atmosphere of the sun, or

FIGURE 22–4   *The moon, at nearly full phase. The dark plains (maria), probably floods of basalt lava, contrast with the highly cratered uplands (terrae). The bright crater with radiating light-colored rays in the left center is Copernicus, about 55 miles in diameter. (Photo by Mount Wilson Observatory.)*

by the earth's atmosphere. Each element has its own spectral lines by which its presence can be identified. We all know that if we drop some common table salt into a gas flame it gives off a strong yellow light; incandescent sodium gives strong emission spectral lines in the yellow part of the visible spectrum. Other elements radiate at different wavelengths, each writing its own definite signature in spectral lines. Kirchoff and Bunsen discovered the hitherto unknown elements rubidium and lithium by their characteristic spectra, and helium was identified in the atmosphere of the sun before it was identified in our own. By their spectra we can identify elements in stars light years away, if we can focus the light upon a sufficiently sensitive **spectroscope.** For this the glass prism does not suffice.

A great step forward was the invention, in 1878, of the **diffraction spectroscope,** by R. W. Wood, an American physicist, who devised a method of scratching almost incredibly fine parallel lines on a polished metal surface curved in such a way that it produces not only an enormously magnified spectrum, but one in which lines of all wavelengths are equally in focus. This instrument permits recognition of any element by its characteristic spectral signature. Molecules and ions can also be identified.

The light emitted when an element is heated to incandescence—its emission spectrum—is caused by an abrupt jump of electrons in its orbital shells from one energy level to another (Chapter 2). The wavelengths that each element radiates are unique because the different charge on the nucleus of each different element requires a different input of energy to bring about the electron jumps. If white light is passed through cooler material containing a particular element, energy is absorbed and the electrons execute the reverse jump, producing the same characteristic signature but in dark absorption spectra—Fraunhofer lines.

Spectroscopes attached to the great reflecting telescopes enable us to photograph the sun or other incandescent objects in the light of a single spectral line. Displacements of characteristic spectral lines toward slightly shorter wavelengths (the Doppler effect) permit us to determine that certain stars are approaching us—the solar system is traveling toward the constellation Hercules at many miles a second. On the other hand, the spectral shifts toward longer wavelengths in the vast majority of stars and galaxies (assemblages of millions of stars like our Milky Way) indicate that they are retreating at speeds that increase with their distance from us. The universe seems to be expanding in all directions. We will not further discuss these matters as they are far afield from the study of geology.

Within our field of interest, though, and of vital importance in trying to understand the origin of the earth and its later evolution, is the fact that the spectrograph enables us to make realistic appraisals of the chemical composition of the sun, of the distant stars, and of the atmospheres of such of the planets as have them. The estimates of the chemical compositions of the distant stars are not wild guesses but very respectable approximations. Yet, prior to landing by the astronauts, we know virtually nothing of the composition of the moon, for it shines only by light reflected from the sun and the earth. Nor have we yet found a way to obtain the signatures of elements buried in the earth's core and mantle.

Radio telescopes and stellar distances

Versatile as are optical telescopes and spectroscopes, they make use of only a part of the electromagnetic spectrum (Fig. 22–6). Most wavelengths in the sun's radiation are shielded from our instruments by the earth's upper atmosphere and by its magnetic field —a happy circumstance for us because exposure to radiation of certain wavelengths is very harmful to life, and lethal if long continued.

But radio waves of certain restricted frequencies can penetrate the atmosphere, and, though radio astronomy is in its infancy, it has already found that the vast dust clouds in parts of the sky, although opaque to the telescope, are transparent to radio waves emitted by hydrogen atoms. The radio signals have enabled radio astronomers to chart the "arms" of the Milky Way and prove that we live about a third of the way from the center of a spiral nebula in one of its arms, as the telescopic astronomers had long suspected.

What an immensity of space we know! The light of the North Star that we see tonight began its journey (traveling at a speed of 186,-282 miles per second) about the time of Columbus; that from one of the nearest galaxies comparable to our own Milky Way, the great spiral nebula in Andromeda, started on its way far back in Precambrian time, for the nebula is 2 billion light years distant. The demonstration of the immensity of space and of the duration of geologic time has wholly replaced the framework in which man considered the earth and his place in the cosmos less than 300 years ago. Concepts which then seemed ridiculous or even vicious heresies are demonstrated facts. Far from being at the center of the universe, man occupies a small planet in orbit about an average sized star in a galaxy of millions of stars, a galaxy that is itself only one of millions within the range of our greatest telescopes. How many yet unknown galaxies and solar systems lie beyond? How many of the stars are accompanied by planets? How many of such planets are habitable? And of the habitable planets, has life developed upon them, and what stage of evolution has it reached? Consideration of the Law of Faunal Assemblages (Chapter 7), and of the vast and changing parade of life on this planet barely touched on in Appendix V should suffice to show that life elsewhere exactly comparable to our own is so improbable as to be virtually impossible. Evolution on earth has been controlled by a vast succession of environmental changes so incredibly complex that precise parallelism of the course of evolution on any other planet with our own seems out of the question. Yet, of course, life may indeed exist and may have evolved into organisms as uniquely adapted to their ecological niches, and perhaps to some of ours as well, as is the life on our planet.

FIGURE 22–6

The electromagnetic spectrum. The portion available to optical telescopes is shown enlarged. The diffraction spectrograph can cover the range between ultraviolet and microwaves. Radio astronomy makes use of the range shown by shading in the microwave–radio wave area.

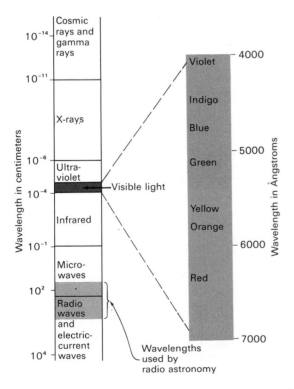

ORIGIN OF THE STARS

Despite these fascinating vistas into space and time, we are still far from an understanding of the origin of stars of which our sun is one. The origin of the ·planets is an even greater puzzle, although it is surely connected with that of the sun. Figure 22–7 summarizes present knowledge of the distribution of the principal elements in the stars and dark clouds of outer space, in the earth's crust, the ocean, the atmosphere, and in a living organism. The striking chemical difference between the earth and the cosmos is at once apparent: the universe as a whole is composed almost entirely of the two lightest elements, hydrogen and helium. To be sure, nearly all elements known on earth have also been detected in the turbulent atmosphere of the sun, but the most abundant elements of the earth's crust make up almost infinitesimal parts of the sun and other stars. Hydrogen and helium are the overwhelmingly dominant components of stars, diffuse neb-

ulae, and of the huge clouds of cold gas and dust that form the dark nebulae.

Most scientists who have investigated the problem think that hydrogen is the primary building block from which all other elements are ultimately formed. Its transformation into helium by a complex process, first suggested by Hans Bethe of Cornell University in 1938, was thought responsible for the sun's energy. This conversion begins at a temperature of about 10 million degrees; in simplified form 4 hydrogen atoms (with 4 electrons) combine to form 1 helium atom (only 2 electrons), and with the release of an enormous amount of energy. The mass of the two missing electrons is converted to energy; this thermonuclear reaction which heats the stars is of the same general nature as that occurring in the hydrogen (fusion) bomb. In hotter stars, whose temperatures are thousands or even millions of times greater than the sun's, more complex thermonuclear reactions produce heavier and heavier elements, in abundances that decrease, though not at

FIGURE 22–7   *The distribution of the principal elements in the stars and dark clouds of outer space, in the earth's crust, in the ocean, in the atmosphere, and in a living organism.*

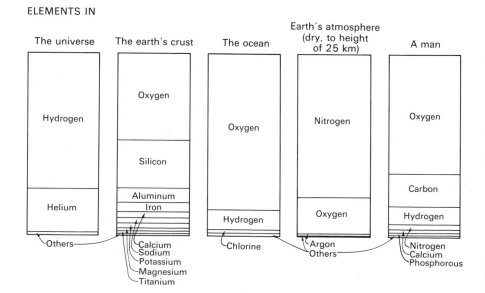

regular rates, with increase in atomic number.

Theoretical physicists think that during the evolution of extremely large stars the reactions may become so intense that the star explodes, forming an extraordinarily bright **nova,** and scattering its debris as clouds of dust and gas for tremendous distances. Several novas are recorded in history, though, of course, the actual explosions occurred millions of years ago, not within human history. The light of the explosions is just now reaching our eyes. Generally, the intensely bright novas die down rapidly in brilliance, some to complete extinction, within a few months. In the ejected clouds, though hydrogen and helium overwhelmingly predominate, there are small amounts of the heavier products of thermonuclear reactions, which took place in the star before and during the time it became a nova. Widely dispersed in space, the particles of the cloud soon (on an astronomical scale) cool and form a dark cloud.

Of course, no one knows how a new star is formed, but a presently popular theory among astronomers and physicists is that the cold dark clouds in outer space, derived from nova eruptions, are slowly driven into more compact masses by light pressure from the galaxies that surround them. With increase in density, their own gravitational attraction tends further to condense them. Since these dust clouds are by no means of uniform density throughout, but are highly turbulent, their contraction would not be by simple centripetal motion of all particles composing the cloud; chance aggregations of higher density would disturb, by their attractions, the paths of nearby dust particles, just as the attractions of the outer planets disturbed the orbit of Saturn, enabling Uranus to be discovered, and later Neptune and Pluto. The contraction would thus not lead to a simple spherical aggregation of the whole cloud about its center of gravity but to a disc-shaped agglomeration rotating in the plane of the disc. The shape would approximate the shape of nearly all the bright galaxies, including our own, and of the only planetary system we know. All parts of the collapsing cloud would indeed swing about their common center of gravity, but in a disc-shaped spiral, thin compared to its diameter.

As the cloud shrinks, it heats up and if the mass is sufficient, it eventually reaches a high enough temperature for thermonuclear reactions to begin and the mass becomes luminous—a star is born. In some cases more than one mass of the cloud is large enough to become a star; there are many double stars in our galaxy.

ORIGIN OF THE EARTH

The currently most popular hypothesis of the origin of the earth is a direct outgrowth of the theory of star formation just outlined. As the dust cloud from which the sun was formed began to contract, certain scattered accumulations of matter grew at the expense of the more rarified material between them. These, if massive enough, might themselves develop into stars, but if their mass were insufficient to create the temperatures needed for nuclear reactions, and at the same time they were moving in orbits about a star, they would become **protoplanets,** composed largely of hydrogen and helium gas and dust, but also containing solid bodies (meteorites and planetesimals) of the heavier elements.

In our solar system the first of the protoplanets to aggregate would naturally be Pluto, the most distant from the sun and therefore the coolest. The next possible stable accumulation of gas, dust, and meteorites to become a protoplanet would have to be far enough away from Pluto for its accumulating materials to resist the attraction of Pluto and remain a separate body; similarly with each of the planets that formed in succession sunward from Pluto to Mercury. Tidal attractions of these planets undoubtedly disrupted innumerable smaller masses that failed to reach sufficient size to withstand them; almost certainly the asteroids were formed in this way.

Because of random collisions with the innumerable dust particles, meteorites, and larger solid objects that the protoplanets were gathering to themselves, their originally elongated elliptical orbits became nearer and nearer to circular, though not quite attaining circularity. This is one of the most striking properties of the planetary orbits, and one of obvious importance to the existence of life, for it assures that variations in solar radiation received during a year are only moderate, and accordingly the surface temperatures of the planets vary only moderately.

The evolution of the protoplanets would be greatly affected by their masses, which determine their gravitational attraction, and by their distances from the sun, which determine the solar radiation they receive. The very massive Jupiter, far enough away so that it is cold and its gases not in extremely rapid motion, has been able to retain a large part of its original components. It is most like the sun in composition, chiefly hydrogen and helium, with small amounts of all other elements. The inner planets, so much nearer the sun, are subject to far higher solar radiation and possess far less mass. The gravitational attraction of the primitive earth was

relatively so slight that the **solar wind**—the emanations of ions and photons shooting outward from the sun—swept away all the gas on and around the primitive earth, leaving virtually nothing but solid planetesimals to aggregate into our planet.

This conclusion is supported, in fact practically demonstrated, by a comparison of the abundances of the inert gases on the earth to their abundances in the sun and other stars, as revealed by spectroscopic measurements of stellar radiation. The lightest of the inert gases, helium, we disregard, because, like hydrogen, it is still escaping from the earth's atmosphere at the present time, and its abundance in the atmosphere is simply due to radioactive disintegration of thorium and uranium and the release by erosion of much that is so produced.

But the heavier inert gases, neon, argon, krypton and xenon are not now being lost to outer space—their present terrestrial ratios record their presence at the time the earth was formed (except for argon, much of which is radiogenic). Careful studies by Harrison Brown, an American geochemist, have shown that all these inert gases are far less abundant (compared with silicon) on the earth than they are in the sun, and that the lighter of them are more impoverished than the heavier, in direct order. If, in accord with the theory outlined above, the earth

Table 22–1 **Estimates of maximum and minimum ratios of rare gases to silicon on earth; their solar ratios to silicon and the fractionation factors**

Gas	Atomic weight	Estimated terrestrial ratio to silicon (atoms per 10,000 atoms of silicon)		Cosmic ratio to silicon	Fractionation factor	
		max	*min*		*max*	*min*
Neon	20.2	8.1×10^{-10}	1.1×10^{-10}	37,000.	$10^{10.5}$	$10^{9.7}$
Argon	39.9	2.5×10^{-7}	5.5×10^{-8}	1000.	$10^{8.8}$	$10^{8.1}$
Krypton	83.8	4.4×10^{-11}	6.0×10^{-12}	0.87	$10^{7.2}$	$10^{6.3}$
Xenon	131.3	3.6×10^{-12}	4.9×10^{-13}	0.015	$10^{6.8}$	$10^{5.7}$

SOURCE: Data from Harrison Brown, 1952.

NOTE: Fractionation factors are solar abundances compared with that of silicon divided respectively by the maximum and minimum estimated terrestrial abundance ratios.

was originally composed of planetesimals of "average" solar composition, it has lost through diffusion and impact by the solar wind a truly stupendous mass of both hydrogen and helium, a mass many times that of the earth remaining. In addition, huge volumes of all the other light gases have also escaped; what remains is only a minute fraction of their original abundance. The "fractionation factor" of the inert gases, that is, the abundance of the element (compared with that of silicon) in the sun divided by the terrestrial ratio to silicon is shown in Table 22–1 and also in graphic form in Figure 22–8.

As the table shows, these noble gases—so called because they never form compounds in nature and are always in the gaseous state —have been stripped away from the earth or protoearth, apparently by the solar wind, in roughly inverse ratio to their atomic weights, the lighter elements being more depleted than the heavier. If water, nitrogen, oxygen and carbon dioxide had been in gaseous form at the same time, they should

FIGURE 22–8
Fractionation factors for the noble gases. Note that this is a logarithmic scale; maximum fractionation above, minimum below, based upon minimum and maximum estimates of abundances on earth.

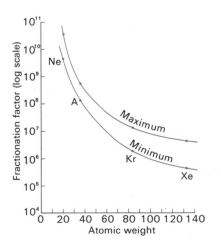

Table 22–2 **Fractionation factors expected for present atmospheric components had they been present as gases throughout earth history**

Molecule	Molecular Weight	Expected fractionation factor
H_2O	18.02	between 1×10^{10} and 1×10^{11}
N_2	28.02	between 6×10^8 and 3×10^9
O_2	32.	between 3×10^8 and 1.5×10^9
CO_2	44.01	between 5×10^7 and 2.5×10^8

have had fractionation factors, dependent on their molecular weights, listed in Table 22–2.

Instead of having been swept away in roughly inverse proportion to their atomic weights, as were the noble gases, the present major components of the atmosphere and ocean are in proportions that show no consistent dependence on their atomic or molecular weights. They could not, then, have been present as gases at the time the noble gases were being swept away by the solar wind. This is shown by the fact that water is more than ten million times as abundant as one would expect had it been present as water vapor throughout the time of depletion by the solar wind. Nitrogen is more than 3600 times as abundant, and oxygen, despite the fact that huge amounts have been consumed by weathering during the long course of geologic time, is still present *in the atmosphere alone* (ignoring that locked up in the sedimentary rocks as iron rust) in 340 times the abundance that would be expected had it always been gaseous. Carbon dioxide is more than 4000 times as abundant as the maximum expected.

Clearly, then, these components of our present atmosphere were not in the atmosphere at the time of the great solar wind; they must have been combined, the oxygen and water perhaps as hydrous silicates, the nitrogen as nitrides or nitrates, the carbon dioxide as carbonates, or dissociated, with the carbon in carbides and graphite. *At the time of the solar wind's sweeping away of the noble gases, the earth had no atmos-*

phere, nor was water vapor available for condensation to form the seas. Both the atmosphere and the oceans have formed from emanations from the interior of the solid earth, as we will discuss from several other viewpoints later in this chapter.

The hypothetical mechanism of planetary formation just outlined gives a partial explanation for the differences in density and mass of the planets shown in Table 22–3: the inner planets are all far denser than the sun, presumably because the solar wind has stripped them of nearly all the gas originally present in their protoplanets and perhaps even of other nongaseous but lighter weight particles. The anomalously low density of Saturn and the anomalously high density of Neptune are not explained. The least satisfactory item of all, however, is the great discrepancy in density between moon and earth far greater than can be explained by the differences in self-compression caused by their differences in mass. Certainly the moon cannot contain iron in anything near the earth's proportion. Sir George Darwin a half century or more ago tried to explain this by assuming that the moon was thrown off by the young earth in rapid rotation, leaving the Pacific Basin as the scar whence it was torn away. But there are strong physical and geological arguments against this simple explanation. Here is a puzzle that the astronauts may help to solve when they bring back samples of the moon's rocks.

However uncertain the processes involved in forming the solar system, the systematic differences between the inner and outer planets must have some significance. These are tabulated in Table 22–3 and illustrated in Figure 22–9.

The theory of origin of the planetary system just outlined requires many amendments in order to account, not merely for unexplained irregularities such as those mentioned, but for many others also. This theory is merely one, and currently perhaps the most popular, of a long series of proposed cosmogonies, none wholly satisfactory. Because of their historic interest, and because current theories borrow from both of them, two older schemes are briefly mentioned, though both have been discredited as seemingly fatal objections have confronted them.

The **Nebular Hypothesis** was proposed by the German philosopher Immanuel Kant in 1775, and was worked out in considerable detail by the French mathematical astronomer Pierre Laplace about forty years later. They postulated a slowly revolving dust cloud, which, as it shrank because of gravitational attraction, speeded up its rotation, just as a skater spins faster when he pulls his arms toward his body. The centrifugal force thus developed was so great that rings comparable to the rings of Saturn were successively left behind as the mass shrank. The material of each of these rings was thought to aggregate into a planet; the residual mass, the sun, became heated by infalling material and self-compression and became incandescent. Two objections to the hypothesis were early pointed out: (1) the thin rings of gas would dissipate into space by light pressure, or at least not aggregate into single planets any more than have Saturn's rings and the asteroids; (2) the sun should be spinning very much faster than it is, instead of loafing along at a spin rate that contributes only about 2 percent of the total angular momentum of the system. For these reasons, although the hypothesis was popular for nearly a century, it has now been abandoned.

The **Planetesimal Hypothesis** was first suggested by Georges Buffon, a French astronomer, in 1749, but it was mainly developed between about 1900 and 1925 by T. C. Chamberlin, geologist, and F. R. Moulton, astronomer, of the University of Chicago, and later by Harold Jeffreys, geophysicist, and James Jeans, astronomer, of Cambridge University. They assumed a near-collision of the sun and another large body, perhaps another sun. The close approach created enormous tides in the sun and wrenched from it a long sausage-shaped filament of matter which broke up into separate bodies that whirled about the sun in a spiral. They suggested that the ejected matter quickly cooled into solid fragments ranging in size from dust particles to large **planetesimals.** The larger planetesimals gradually swept up the smaller with their greater gravitational pull. The pock-marked surface of the moon (which has neither air nor water to erode away its scars of impact) was considered evidence of such a process (Fig. 22–4). The growing planets would at first be small cold bodies unable to hold water or an atmosphere, but as they grew some could retain volatiles and form atmospheres and oceans, and gravitational compaction might heat even a relatively small body to the point where volcanism could begin.

Later analysis has indicated that the likelihood such a "grazing" passage of two stars could produce ejection of a filament without causing mutual destruction is remote. Again, problems of angular momentum between the sun and major planets are a major difficulty. Most modern guesses about planetary origin have, however, retained the idea of planetesimals and "cold" accumulation of the planets, as first suggested in this hypothesis.

FIGURE 22–9

Diagrammatic representation of the sun and planets. Right: *according to size;* Left: *according to distance from the sun.*

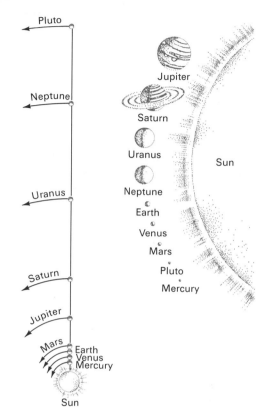

Table 22–3 **Some members of the solar system**

Body	Mean diameter, in miles	Mean distance, in miles	Mass (Earth = 1)	Density (Water = 1)	Period of rotation
Sun	864,000	0	331,950	1.4	25 days
Mercury	2900	35,960,000	0.05	6.1	88 days
Venus	7600	67,200,000	0.81	5.06	(?)
Earth	7913	93,000,000	1.0	5.52	23 h 56 m
Moon	2160	93,000,000	0.012	3.34	27 d 32 m
Mars	4200	141,600,000	0.11	4.12	24 h 36 m
Jupiter	86,800	483,300,000	318.4	1.35	9 h 50 m
Saturn	71,500	886,200,000	95.3	0.71	10 h 02 m
Uranus	29,400	1,783,000,000	14.5	1.56	10 h 45 m
Neptune	28,000	2,794,000,000	17.2	2.29	15 h 48 m
Pluto	6000?	3,670,000,000	0.8?	(?)	6 days(?)

Origin of the earth's core

According to almost all current hypotheses of planetary origin, the earth accumulated as a relatively cold body. This idea is strongly supported by the fact that the temperature of the surficial layers has never been high enough to volatilize all the water, carbon dioxide, nitrogen, sulfur, and chlorine (to which we can add several other elements, including the volatile metal, mercury). All of these are much more abundant on the earth than they are in the sun; had the earth been wholly molten, all of them, even including mercury, with an atomic weight of 80, should be less abundant, as we saw xenon, with almost as heavy an atom, to be. Had the earth ever been hot enough to melt throughout, it is difficult to see how it could have avoided developing a much more uniform crust than it has, for layered intrusives, well stratified by gravitative differentiation, should have crystallized throughout the mantle. As we saw in Chapter 19, the earth's mantle is solid to depths of 2900 kilometers, but is so poor a conductor of heat that even in four billion years no heat can have escaped from depths less than half that great. Had the mantle been molten throughout, it would still be molten in its deeper levels. Still another argument for an earth that has never been molten throughout is that if it had been, the clarkes of concentration of the ore minerals should not be so variable from place to place as they are: with a well-mixed molten globe there should be quite as many and as valuable copper deposits in Kansas or Brazil, proportional to area, as there are in Chile, Zambia, and Arizona, but obviously there are not. For all these and many other reasons, it seems highly improbable that the molten earth postulated by Buffon and Lord Rayleigh (Chapter 7) ever existed.

How, then, could the earth have developed a liquid core, in which are concentrated nickel, iron, and silicon to the amount of more than 32 percent of the whole mass of the earth? This is indeed a puzzle. Some geophysicists think that the core is still growing. Iron melts at considerably lower temperatures than the high-pressure modifications of olivine, pyroxene, and garnet—the supposedly dominant constituents of the mantle—so even though the mantle as a whole is solid, it may contain interstitial films of molten metals. These films, owing to their greater density, are continually working their way downward as tidal stresses distort the mantle. In this way, the core may still be growing. Such an increasing concentration of mass toward the earth's center should increase the speed of rotation, thus counteracting the tendency of the tides to slow it down.

Other students take a less uniformitarian view. They point out that since the earth was born it has lost much radioactive material by decay to stable isotopes. For example, four billion years ago it contained more than ten times as much U^{235} and nearly twice as much U^{238} as it now does and there were probably several radioactive elements of much shorter half-life also evolving heat. Thus the mantle might have heated up to a point where it was molten, even though the crust was not; the iron sank to the bottom in an almost catastrophically short time, and the convection that accompanied the cooling of the mantle produced a gigantic overturn which dragged all the sialic crust to one side of the globe, producing what we now know as the land hemisphere, whereas the other hemisphere, from which the crust had been skimmed during the great convective overturn, became the broad ocean basin of the Pacific. As we noted above, this highly imaginative hypothesis seems quite inconsistent with the present-day existence of a mantle nearly 2900 kilometers thick and virtually solid throughout. From what we now know of heat conduction through the rocks, a mantle once molten to this depth, even 4 billion years ago, would still be molten in much more than its lower half.

Whatever the true history may have been, at the time the earth had completed the accumulation of the great bulk of its matter —the end of its astronomic and beginning of its geologic history—it had no atmosphere, no ocean, no sedimentary rocks. Its surface was doubtless littered by large and small fragments of meteorites, as much of the moon's surface probably is today. All of the present atmosphere and ocean were sweated out from within by volcanic processes, and all of the sedimentary rocks that today cover so much of the continents were produced, in part by pyroclastic eruptions, but mainly by weathering, erosion, and sedimentation after ocean and atmosphere had formed. This last conclusion—long assumed by geochemists, as we saw in Chapter 17—seems strongly supported by the arguments that follow.

THE ORIGIN OF THE OCEAN

If the earth was indeed born with neither an atmosphere nor an ocean, as seems strongly indicated by the fractionation factors of the noble gases as compared with those of the present constituents of air and sea, they must have developed from the interior of the earth. An American geologist, W. W. Rubey, has advanced strong evidence that both atmosphere and ocean were derived from volcanic emanations during the course of earth history; they could not have been derived as was, say, the sodium in the ocean, by simply eroding the "average igneous rock" (Chapter 17).

Rubey first assumed arbitrarily that weathering and erosion can go on in the absence of water and carbon dioxide. He then computed the volume of water and carbon dioxide that would have been freed from the "average igneous rock" during the erosion that supplied all the sedimentary rocks of the earth's crust. He found that even if one selects the highest estimate of the volume of sedimentary rocks that has been made, and

thus the greatest volume of igneous rocks from which to derive them, such volatile substances as water, carbon dioxide, nitrogen, chlorine, and sulfur are present in the earth's atmosphere and oceans in far greater quantities than could possibly have been freed from the earth's crust in this way. His assumption was of course an impossible one: without water and carbon dioxide the complex weathering reactions that produce the clays and release the metallic ions when feldspars are decomposed could not go on. So there had to be an ocean and an atmosphere before any weathering could take place. The impossible assumption, however, is valuable as focusing attention on the problem posed by the composition and the existence of a very large ocean and atmosphere at present, though both were almost surely absent from the early earth.

We pointed out in Chapter 17 that data on both the abundance and the average composition of the sedimentary rocks are weak and that present estimates of the volume of igneous rock eroded to produce them may be in error by a factor of five. Despite this serious deficiency in our knowledge, it has for several decades been clear that whichever volume of igneous rocks (within these limits) one chooses as the source of the sedimentary rocks, the volatile substances, water, carbon dioxide, chlorine, nitrogen, and sulfur, are far more abundant in the atmosphere and oceans alone (not counting those quantities locked up in the sedimentary rocks) than could have been supplied simply by erosion of this volume of igneous rocks. The discrepancy is truly prodigious, as we shall see. Two semi-independent estimates have been made of the amount of these "excess volatiles" (Table 22–4).

Poldervaart used many of Rubey's data, but made separate computations; he did not specifically compute the excess volatiles, but as the table shows, except for his estimate of carbon dioxide (nearly two and a half times Rubey's), he was in close agreement. Should

Table 22–4 **Estimated quantities (in units of 10^{14} metric tons. One metric ton = 10^6 grams) of volatile substances now at or near the earth's surface, together with the amounts of these substances that have been supplied by weathering of the average igneous rock**

Volatile substances	Source *	H_2O	Total C as CO_2	Cl	N	S
Present in the atmosphere, in surface and ground water, and in organisms	R	14,600	1.5	276	39	13
	P	14,430	2	310	40	15
Buried in ancient sedimentary rocks	R	2,100	920	30	4	15
	P	2,010	2,280	30	5	15
Totals	R	16,700	921	306	43	28
	P	16,440	2,282	340	45	30
Supplied by weathering of average igneous rock (maximum estimate)	R	130	11	5	0.6	6
Difference, that is, the "excess volatiles" unaccounted for by rock weathering	R	16,600	910	300	42	22

* R: estimated by W. W. Rubey, 1951; P: estimated by A. Poldervaart, 1955.

Poldervaart's higher estimate for carbon dioxide prove the better one, it serves only further to strengthen an argument of Rubey's, that the ocean was not present, either as water or steam, during the earliest Precambrian, but developed gradually throughout earth history.

The argument is broadly as follows: if all the "excess volatiles"—those which could not have been derived from erosion of preexisting igneous rocks—were in gaseous form, that is, in an atmosphere at high temperature, or even in an ocean-atmosphere association at temperatures such as exist today, the fluid or fluids would be (1) under very high pressure, and (2) very strongly acidic. If all were in the atmosphere, the atmospheric pressure at the earth's surface would have been somewhere between 200 and 500 times that of the present. At such concentrations, the strongly acidic solutions would rapidly corrode any igneous rock or meteorite with which they came in contact. All the bases, major and minor—aluminum, calcium, magnesium, potassium, sodium, iron, and any others—would be taken into solution. For reasons we will review later, in discussing the primitive atmosphere, there

was little if any free oxygen in either ocean or atmosphere. For these reasons, therefore, it is a gross oversimplification (but one which on analysis proves immaterial) to assume that the materials carried to the sea in these primitive times were in the same proportions as those found today in streams draining areas underlain by igneous rocks. The relative amounts of the four main bases in such modern streams are, according to several careful estimates, as follows:

Ca	53
Mg	8
Na	25
K	14
	100 percent

In addition large quantities of aluminum and iron are now, and doubtless were in the past, carried to the sea in solution, along with many other elements. Nevertheless, it is clear that the first mineral that would be precipitated in abundance from the primitive ocean would be calcite. Only when this happened would the vast quantities of carbon dioxide in the postulated atmosphere-ocean system begin to diminish.

Over the past three billion years, evolution has unquestionably modified the tolerance of various organisms to changes in salinity, availability and concentration of carbon dioxide, nitrogen, sulfur, and many other chemicals, but within the span of the paleontologic record—from the beginning of the Cambrian onward—these modifications seem to have been very small. Few forms of life can exist under pressures of carbon dioxide more than a few times that of the present atmosphere (0.03 percent of one atmosphere). Certain mosses can live under pressures of as much as one atmosphere of carbon dioxide, and we may, for the purpose of this discussion, follow Rubey in assuming that life could begin when the pressure of carbon dioxide fell to this level.

If we accept this value as fixing the time of origin of plant life (and hence the beginning of photosynthesis), to which virtually all present atmospheric oxygen is due (Fig. 22–10), the sea water at that time would still be slightly acidic, the salinity would be twice that of the present ocean, and the amount of bases weathered in order to bring about these conditions would be fully as much as the most generous estimates of rock weathered throughout all geologic time. All this at a time when more than half the carbon dioxide postulated as present in the primitive atmosphere was either still there or dissolved in the ocean! Under this artificial assumption of a massive primitive atmosphere, prodigious quantities of limestone would have had to be deposited before the carbon dioxide pressure could have fallen to one atmosphere; the early Precambrian of every continent should be rich in limestone and dolomite.

But no such tremendous deposits of carbonates characterize the early Precambrian; on the average the earliest Precambrian of each continent contains about the same proportion of limestone to other sedimentary strata as the rest of the geologic column— perhaps slightly less rather than more than average. This artificial hypothesis also requires the solution of more sodium (from the same minerals that supplied the calcium) —even before the beginning of life—than can reasonably be inferred for all of geologic time. The conclusion seems inescapable that the primitive ocean could not have contained all, or even a very large proportion, of the "excess volatiles" now present in the atmosphere, ocean, and outer crust. Of course it would have been amazing to find the ocean and atmosphere fully developed early in the earth's history, when as we have discussed, the earth was almost surely born without either. There are other, wholly independent arguments, tending to show the gradual formation of the ocean through geologic time.

Gradual accumulation of the ocean

Let us assume for the moment, not only the uniform action of physical and chemical laws during geologic time, but also that other conditions were relatively uniform; that is, that only a small fraction of the excess volatiles were ever present in the atmosphere at any one time, as is true today. In other words, that all the volatiles have been added slowly from the earth's interior through geologic time. If, for example, the pressure of carbon dioxide in the atmosphere never exceeded one atmosphere, carbonates could begin to precipitate when the atmosphere and ocean contained less than 10 percent of the total excess volatiles. The total atmospheric pressure, instead of being hundreds of times as great as at present, would have been only 10 percent higher, the salinity of the sea about that of the present, and its acidity only slightly higher, according to Rubey's computations.

On this hypothesis, life could perhaps evolve in the very early Precambrian (Fig. 7–1) without an earlier deposition of vast thicknesses of limestone upon the sea floor. If, at this time, not enough free oxygen had yet accumulated to oxidize hydrogen sulfide, Rubey estimated that not more than 6 percent of his total excess volatiles could have been present in this early atmosphere and ocean; the volume of the ocean would have been far smaller than at present. Further arguments also favor a slow growth of the ocean throughout geologic time.

The balance between the positive and negative ions in sea water is very delicate. As Rubey pointed out, a decrease of only 1 percent of sodium in the sea would produce a very highly acidic solution, certainly fatal to many, if not most, organisms. Similarly with carbon dioxide, whose relations to the other components must lie within very narrow limits indeed to avoid fatal consequences on a massive scale to both flora and fauna. Despite the erroneous ideas of Cuvier (Chapter 7), the stratigraphic record contains no evidence whatever of such wholesale massive extinctions. If we assume, then, that the ocean has grown slowly throughout geologic time, we must find a mechanism whereby water and carbon dioxide—and, when examined in detail, other excess volatiles as well—are simultaneously added to the atmosphere and the ocean in closely consistent ratios.

Today carbon dioxide is being added to the atmosphere and ocean in three ways: (1) by rock weathering, (2) by decay and by artificial combustion of carbon-bearing materials, and (3) by emanations from volcanoes and hot springs. If we ignore the last two, we find that the loss of carbon dioxide by deposition is far greater than the gain from weathering. Sedimentary rocks, on weathering, furnish roughly equivalent amounts of calcium and carbon dioxide on the average, but the weathering of igneous rocks uses up vast quantities of carbon dioxide in balancing the calcium released (See Table 22–4 and Chapter 4). Rough calculations by several workers indicate that the amount of carbon dioxide removed from the ocean to maintain this balance would, *in only a few hundred thousand years,* render the ocean so strongly alkaline—the abun-

dance of OH^- ions in sea water would rise so high—that brucite (a rare mineral of the composition $Mg(OH)_2$) would be the first stable precipitate from sea water, rather than calcite. In earlier geologic times it would take only a very brief time, geologically speaking, for this condition to arise unless another source of carbon dioxide can be found, for, of course, combustion was trivial before the beginning of the industrial age, and in the earliest Precambrian, before the development of abundant plant life, even decay must have been a trivial source of carbon dioxide.

Now the fact is that there are no brucite-bearing strata known anywhere in the geologic column from the earliest Precambrian to the Recent; we must conclude that the ratio of carbon dioxide to water has not strayed far from its present value at any time in recognizable geologic history; there are neither massive biologic extinctions nor brucite deposits to record such deviations. We are driven to seek another source; it is clearly the third source in the preceding paragraph: volcanic emanations. This was suggested as long ago as 1894 by the distinguished Swedish geologist A. G. Högbom, and has been widely accepted ever since. Let us look into the possibilities.

Similarities of magmatic gases and "excess volatiles"

Rubey gathered analyses of the composition of gases from volcanoes, igneous rocks, and hot springs and has compared them. His data relative to the major components are summarized in Table 22–5.

Obviously there is no one-to-one correspondence between the various analyses in this table, and more recent data from Kilauea are even more divergent; nevertheless, when all the modifying factors, such as dilution from varying sources, organic activity, reworking of sedimentary rocks, and many others, are considered, the similarity is close enough to make it probable that the excess volatiles have indeed been released by igneous activity within the earth, and have reached the surface either directly in lava (already shown to be inadequate as the sole source), by fumarolic activity, or via ground water from hot springs. Furthermore, the volcanic release must have been at rates nearly uniform throughout geologic time so as not unduly to have affected the fauna and flora, as drastic changes in the supply of carbon dioxide and other components surely would have. Additions to atmosphere and ocean by emanations from the earth's interior seems clearly demonstrated; that it was at a roughly uniform rate is strongly suggested by the absence of stratigraphic brucite and of mass extinctions of organisms. It is unfortunate that geologic mapping is not yet sufficient to give a more quantitative picture, but all we do know of ancient and more recent strata seems to fit this model.

ORIGIN OF THE ATMOSPHERE

Thus, "excess volatiles" seem to have been added to atmosphere and ocean from volcanic exhalations at roughly constant rates throughout geologic time. Among them, of course, is the dominant component of the atmosphere, nitrogen (78.03 percent), the important minor constituent, carbon dioxide (0.03 percent), and variable amounts of water vapor. The question remains as to the source or sources of the other constituents: oxygen (20.99 percent), argon (0.94 percent) and helium, neon, krypton, xenon, and hydrogen, which together make up only 0.01 percent. Whence did these arise?

The abundance of oxygen is the most striking aspect of the atmosphere because it is not, like nitrogen, a component of volcanic emanations. Furthermore, many processes are operating to consume it: oxidation of metals at the earth's surface, respiration of animals, combustion of carbon compounds. A small amount is being released in the high atmosphere by the dissociation of water by solar radiation. Because of its low density and the high temperatures prevailing in the upper atmosphere, most of the hydrogen produced in this way escapes into space. Much of the oxygen so produced remains in the upper atmosphere in the form of ozone (O_3) molecules whose absorption of some of the most lethal waves in the sun's spectrum is extremely important to life. But some of the oxygen is carried by the turbulence of the atmosphere down to the earth's surface. Although this amount is trivial compared to that now produced by photosynthesis, it has been of prime importance in the early history of the earth, for prior to the evolution of photosynthetic plants it is the only logical source of the oxygen necessary for the beginning of life. By far the greatest source of oxygen today—and it must be continually produced to make up for the vast quantities consumed—is photosynthesis by

Table 22–5 **Composition of gases from volcanoes, igneous rocks, and hot springs, and of "excess volatiles" in the atmosphere, hydrosphere, and sedimentary rocks**

Gas	Kilauea and Mauna Loa	Basalt and Diabase	Obsidian, Andesite, and Granite	Fumaroles, Steam Wells, and Geysers	Excess Volatiles
H$_2$O	57.8	69.1	85.6	99.4	92.8
Total C as CO$_2$	23.5	16.8	5.7	0.33	5.1
S$_2$	12.6	3.3	0.7	0.03	0.13
N$_2$	5.7	2.6	1.7	0.05	0.24

SOURCE: Median analyses of major components, calculated to weight percent, after W. W. Rubey, 1951.

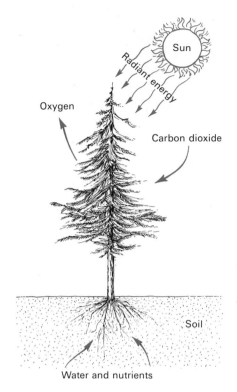

FIGURE 22–10
Photosynthesis releases oxygen to the air, and removes carbon dioxide.

plants. In this process green plants utilize the sun's radiation to decompose carbon dioxide and water, thus building hydrocarbons into their structures and releasing oxygen to the air (Fig. 22–10).

Helium is a rare constituent of the earth's upper atmosphere. The small quantity present is slowly escaping through the atmosphere, to which it has been supplied mainly by radioactive disintegration of uranium and thorium in rocks subsequently eroded (Chapter 7). Possibly some helium and the other noble gases are also released from rocks at depth by magmatic activity and escape among the volcanic emanations. A small amount of hydrogen has also been detected in the gases given off during volcanic eruptions.

THE ORIGIN OF LIFE

The classical philosophers of Miletus (600 B.C.) and the Neoplatonists, such as St. Augustine, of the early Christian era, thought that life is an inherent property of all matter, and that the germs of life are present everywhere throughout the Universe—a concept held by many philosophers to this day. During the Middle Ages grotesque creatures were fancied as living on the other planets and even on the sun. With the growth of biologic sciences, and especially since the work of Pasteur, it became obvious that this simplistic view cannot be true. Special conditions, varying from one life group to another, are necessary for reproduction and growth, and under many conditions no life at all is possible. The turbulent atmosphere of the sun, for example, is composed wholly of ions, electrons, and atoms; no organized life can exist there. Similarly, as Professor Wald of Harvard University has shown, carbon, hydrogen, and oxygen are essential to life (silicon cannot substitute for carbon, despite its many similar chemical qualities) and unless all these are available no life even remotely resembling that on earth is possible. Yet although the environment controls the possibilities of life, life itself also modifies the environment, in some places very drastically.

Obviously, the environmental conditions under which life arose on the earth depended on the earth's earlier history. Almost from the first, it may be assumed, volcanoes were active on the primitive earth, just as they still are on the much smaller moon, but most of the volatiles they released were swept away by the solar wind. As the solar radiation diminished, however, some volatiles, among which water and carbon dioxide presumably predominated as they do today, were retained in sufficient quantity to act as a partial solar shield, and an atmosphere such as we know began to form. The physical and chemical processes that went on during the further evolution of the atmosphere have been penetratingly studied by the American geophysi- cists L. V. Berkner and L. C. Marshall, upon whose work the following condensed account is largely based.

Water vapor in the atmosphere, as we noted above, is subject to dissociation into its constituent oxygen and hydrogen by in- tense solar radiation in the upper atmos- phere. The mass of the earth does not suffice to retain the hydrogen so formed, but some of the oxygen released is eventually carried to the ground by the turbulence of the air and in rains. The amount of oxygen accumu- lated in this way, however, is small and most would be quickly used up in oxidizing many of the minerals of the exposed rocks. Oxygen generation would also be self-controlled at a low level, because molecular oxygen (O_2) absorbs the same wavelengths that control the dissociation of water vapor. After the ac- cumulation of as little as 0.1 percent of the present atmospheric content of O_2, the oxy- gen-releasing dissociation of water vapor would be almost halted.

At such low oxygen concentrations, Berk- ner and Marshall conclude that much of the O_2 would disintegrate under ultraviolet radi- ation into atomic O and ozone (O_3), both of which are far more active chemically than molecular oxygen, O_2. Thus even though the oxygen content would remain extremely low, the atmosphere would be oxidizing; there- fore the abundant "red-beds" of the Precam- brian are not necessarily evidence of an oxy- gen-rich atmosphere, as has commonly been thought. In fact, Berkner, Marshall, and other students think that the lowest forms of organisms—and therefore the presumably earliest ones to evolve—could have been poi- soned by the small amount of oxygen in the primitive atmosphere. An independent evi- dence of an oxygen-poor atmosphere is the association of uraninite in the middle Pre- cambrian, metamorphosed, placer deposits of the Rand gold field of South Africa. Uran- inite is readily disintegrated in an oxygen- rich environment. No placer uraninites are known from rocks younger than Late Pre- cambrian.

The early atmosphere was thus primarily one of nitrogen and carbon dioxide, though the content of water vapor would continually increase after the atmosphere became dense enough to permit liquid water to accumu- late in the primitive lakes and seas.

In order for life to form, three chemical re- quirements must be met: (1) hydrocarbons must be present, (2) no free hydrogen may be present, and (3) water must be available. Under present conditions, virtually all the hydrocarbons on earth are formed by living organisms, chiefly by photosynthesis. A few bacteria, themselves composed of hydrocar- bons, can convert carbon dioxide directly into organic compounds by oxidizing sulfur, iron, or nitrogen. But, before bacteria, how did the hydrocarbon necessary for the begin- ning of life become available? Carbides of metals, particularly of iron, nickel, and co- balt, are common in meteorites, although very rare on earth. The primitive earth must have contained at least some of them. When these carbides react with water, they form hydrocarbons of inorganic origin. Methane (CH_4) is an important constituent in the at- mospheres of Jupiter, Saturn, and Neptune, where it is almost certainly of inorganic ori- gin. The primitive earth should have lost most of any original atmospheric content of methane, but some might remain enclosed in the solid accumulations not swept out by the solar wind during the early evolution of the planet. So at least some hydrocarbons of nonbiogenic origin may have been available early in earth history.

We have repeatedly cited the availability of water from volcanic processes; what about the third essential, the absence of free hydro- gen? Except for the small amount in the up- per atmosphere, escaping to space after radia- tive dissociation of H_2O, the earth could re- tain only a little free hydrogen after its early degassing. What it did produce was quickly combined with other volcanic products, forming ammonia, water, hydrogen sulfide, and hydrochloric acid.

Accordingly, the earth fairly early in its evolution possessed the chemical properties suitable for life. How did life's complex associations of molecules with the property of reproduction arise? The small amounts of oxygen were available to oxidize the simpler organic compounds into such more complex substances as alcohols, aldehydes, and other constituents. No one, of course, knows the details of the process. Experimentally, electric discharges through organic compounds of very primitive type have yielded amino acids, compounds that in nature are found only in organisms. Perhaps lightning strokes formed some similar compounds in the early seas or in water-saturated earth.

According to the Russian biochemist A. Oparin and his astronomer colleague V. Fesenkov, who have devoted much effort to the study of the preconditions of life, as long as the hydrocarbons in solution were of low molecular weight they would be highly diffused, but when, by chance, large molecules, analogous to a virus, were formed, they would tend to aggregate. If modern proteins are dispersed in a suitable medium, and those of different composition mixed in equal amounts, one variety always coagulates into larger aggregations than the other; it grows by absorbing part of the material making up the other. But this process cannot continue indefinitely. Eventually the large aggregations split into fragments, additional growth of which depends on availability of additional coagulants in the solutions present. We see, in the growth of one variety of protein accumulation at the expense of the other, a kind of natural selection. The larger bodies that grow and split leave their fragments in competition for whatever salts are useful for growth; here again is an opportunity for natural selection to operate. Eventually a complex developed with the capacity to select just the right constituents from the watery solution to enable it to grow and split into fragments that themselves had the power of regeneration. Thus the process of fermentation began and plant life had come into being. The time required for this evolution may have been many hundred million years. If the earth is indeed about 4500 m.y. old, as radiometric studies suggest, it may have required all the time intervening between then and about 3100 m.y. ago, when the oldest fossil algae and bacteria yet found were incorporated in the rocks of the Fig Tree Series of Swaziland; an interval of 1400 m.y., more than twice as long as all the time since the beginning of the Cambrian!

Blue green algae were among the earliest organisms. The basis for their recognition is, of course, not the identification of specific algal cells in these oldest known fossiliferous rocks, but the preservation at many levels from the early Precambrian on, of cabbage-shaped, or corrugated, brain-shaped structures of calcite, dolomite, or silica, similar to the structures built by present-day algal colonies.

One of the problems that confronted early life was the very high incidence of ultraviolet light in the long period before the oxygen content of the atmosphere sufficed to produce the ozone screen in the upper atmosphere that now protects us from most of these nearly lethal rays. Even now a day at the seashore can convince one of the intensity of these rays; at a time when the oxygen content of the air was only 0.1 percent of that today the rays would have been lethal to any organism that was fully exposed to them.

It seems likely, then, that the earliest organisms formed in damp places in the soil, or on the sea floor at depths great enough to screen out most of the ultraviolet rays. The modern blue-green algae are photosynthesizers, but in some families the mechanism seems highly diffuse and more primitive than in most plants. Perhaps these are inherited from the earliest development of this mechanism.

With the beginning of photosynthesis, the amount of oxygen increased slowly over several hundred million years as the plants gradually evolved more and more efficient mechanisms. Berkner and Marshall estimated that it was not until about the beginning of the Cambrian that the atmosphere contained as much as 1 percent of its present oxygen content; others place the date a few hundred million years earlier. It was not until photosynthesis developed that animal evolution could begin. Professor Cloud, of UCLA, has pointed out that photosynthetic plants provide sources of local enrichment of oxygen supply, so that animal life might arise in isolated areas of increased oxygen supply long before the atmosphere and oceans had accumulated enough oxygen to support life over wide areas. Possibly the many local and diversified environments offered as sites for natural selection may account for the wide diversity of life in the earliest Cambrian faunas. These contain representatives of nearly all phyla (Appendix V), implying a long evolutionary history. Because of this, many paleontologists think that Berkner and Marshall should have put the time at which free oxygen adequate for migratory life was widely available considerably earlier than the beginning of the Cambrian.

With the flourishing of vegetation, the content of oxygen continued to increase, ozone formed a screen in the upper atmosphere, reducing the amount of ultraviolet rays reaching the ground surface, and migration of both plants and animals was made possible. Some have thought that the heavy external armor of so many early organisms—even the earliest fish of Silurian time—was a protective mechanism against ultraviolet radiation. Certainly the bryozoa of today are far less massive than the early ones, and no fish of today are truly armored.

Thus, as life evolved, it not only adjusted to the environment but it also modified the environment fundamentally. "The present is indeed the key to the past," but only in the sense that we have confidence that the same physical laws held in the distant past as do today—surely the oceans of today are far larger than those of the distant past and the composition of the atmosphere is different from that of the early Precambrian.

Facts, concepts, terms

Earth-centered versus sun-centered solar system
Kepler's laws; Newton's law of gravitation
Galileo's telescope
The spectroscope
    Emission spectra versus absorption spectra
Origin of the stars
    Thermonuclear reactions in the stars
Origin of the earth and the solar system
    Nebular hypothesis
    Planetesimal hypothesis
Development of a "protoearth"
    Solid or liquid
    Retention or escape of gases
Solar wind, and its effects
Sources of ocean water
"Excess volatiles"
Magmatic gases compared with "excess volatiles"
Calcite versus brucite

Gradual accumulation of the oceans
Origin of the oceans through igneous activity
Source of gases in the atmosphere
    Fate of gases on the protoearth
    Fractionation factor for the early gases
    "Noble gases" on earth and sun compared
Source of water, carbon dioxide, and nitrogen gas
Source of oxygen
Origin of life
    Environmental conditions on a protoearth
    Chemical requirements for life
        Presence of water and hydrocarbons
        Absence of noxious gases
    Effects of the solar wind
    Role of oxygen
        Before photosynthesis; after life was established
    Role of carbon dioxide
    Coagulation and growth of dispersed large organic molecules
    Bacteria and algae
    Photosynthesis
    Armored fishes and solar radiation

Questions

1. In terms of the ocean's ultimate origin, what is wrong with the statement that "the water of the oceans comes from the rivers"?

2. Explain why sea water is salty. Why does the atmosphere contain little or no hydrogen, but a chemical analysis of sea water shows about 11 percent, by weight, of this element?

3. What is meant by "excess volatiles"? Excess over what? How does this jibe with the statement that the protoearth lost its volatiles to the solar wind?

4. What is the most abundant element in the universe? How do we know this?

5. Refer to Figure 22–7.
    a) Explain why there is more oxygen in the ocean than the atmosphere. Is this free oxygen?
    b) Where is the phosphorous concentrated in a man? The calcium?
    c) Why is helium recorded in only the first column?
    d) What changes would you make in column 4 to approximate an early Precambrian atmosphere?

6. Suppose the sun's light were suddenly turned off, as we turn off an electric light. How long would it be before we knew about it?

7. Granting that we had a space ship that could go to a planet in Andromeda, and that you are an astronaut, why would it be impossible for you to tell us what was there?

8. Permafrost is found on earth in the polar regions, and pictures taken during the 1965 flyby of Mars suggest the possibility that permafrost composed of both water ice and carbon dioxide ice may be present on that planet. Why do we not have carbon dioxide permafrost on earth?

9. What kind of weathering would you expect to have occurred on the primitive protoearth and what would be the chief agents (or processes) that produced it?

10. Armored fish of the early Paleozoic lived in shallow water and along mud flats. Why might they be better adapted to the risks of their environment than they would be if they lived in similar waters of today? Consider both physical and biological risks.

Suggested readings

Brancazio, P. J., and A. G. W. Cameron, eds., *The Origin and Evolution of Atmospheres and Oceans.* New York: John Wiley and Sons, 1964.

Fanning, A. E., *Planets, Stars and Galaxies,* revised by Menzel, D. H. New York: Dover Publications, 1966.

Faul, Henry, *Ages of Rocks, Planets, and Stars.* New York: McGraw-Hill, 1966. Kuiper, G. P., ed., *The Atmospheres of the Earth and Planets,* 2nd Ed. Chicago: University of Chicago Press, 1952.

Oparin, A., and V. Fesenkov, *Life in the Universe.* New York: Twayne Publishers, 1961.

Seaborg, G. T., and E. G. Valens, *Elements of the Universe.* New York: E. P. Dutton, 1965.

Symposium on the Evolution of the Earth's Atmosphere. Proceedings of the National Academy of Sciences, v. 53, No. 6, p. 1169–1226, 1965.

Scientific American offprints

210. William A. Fowler, *The Origin of the Elements* (September 1956)

250. Gart Westerhout, *The Radio Galaxy* (August 1959)

253. John H. Reynolds, *The Age of the Elements in the Solar System* (November 1960)

833. Harold C. Urey, *The Origin of the Earth* (October 1952)

Appendixes

Maps and mapping

Maps are the shorthand summary used by the student of the earth in presenting his data and observations. The earth's crust is complex. The intricate patterns of land and water, the forms of hills and valleys, the labyrinths that men have dug in mining are all so complicated in form that a true picture of them cannot be given by words alone. A map, however, condenses in intelligible form the findings regarding them.

Map scales

A blueprint of a machine part or a dress pattern may be thought of as a map. Most of these are **full-scale** maps. An inch on such a map represents an inch on the object it portrays.

Few geographic and geologic maps, however, are full size. Most of them are drawings to scale. In such **reduced-scale** maps, an inch on the map may correspond to 10 inches, 1000 inches, 1,000,000 inches, or whatever unit of reduction the map maker deems desirable to show the features he wishes to portray. If he decides to reduce the length of objects on the map to 1/10 of their true length on the ground, he plots on a "1/10 scale." The fraction is the ratio of reduction and simply means that 1 inch on the map equals 10 inches on the ground. Many of the newer maps of the *Topographic Atlas of the United States* prepared by the United States Geological Survey are drawn on a scale of 1/24,-000—1 inch on the map corresponds with 24,000 inches, or 2000 feet, on the ground.

Limitations of maps

On a full-scale drawing, it is possible to show, for example, the head of a nail 1/10 inch across in full size. If the nail were to be correctly represented on a 1/200 scale, however, it would have to be drawn as only 1/200 of 1/10, or 1/2,000, of an inch across. Such a point is too small to be visible. Thus, if nails are to be shown at all on the 1/200 scale, they must be shown diagrammatically. Their positions might be indicated, but their size would have to be greatly exaggerated if they are to be seen. This limitation of reduced-scale maps must be constantly kept in mind by the map user.

All maps are generalizations, drawn to perform a particular service. All represent selections of data chosen to serve the particular purpose, and these data are often exaggerated in relation to other features. A navigator's chart emphasizes the features useful to navigation—for example, shoals and shallow rocks are emphasized more than deep-water features of similar size; a good road map stresses highway junctions and, in doing so, may distort the distances between them.

The maps of Seattle Harbor shown in Figure I-1 illustrate one effect of map scale. Details such as the docks in Elliott Bay can be shown only on the larger scale map.

Whatever the scale, limitations in drawing and printing make it almost impossible for maps to be accurate to more than 1/100 inch in the location of points. It is difficult to make a legible pencil mark less than 1/100

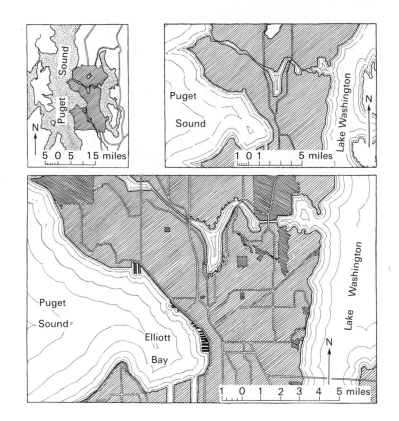

FIGURE I–1

Maps of Seattle harbor on different scales. Note that the smaller scale maps show much less detail, though all contain about the same number of lines per square inch. (After maps of the U.S. Geological Survey and of the Chamber of Commerce of Seattle.)

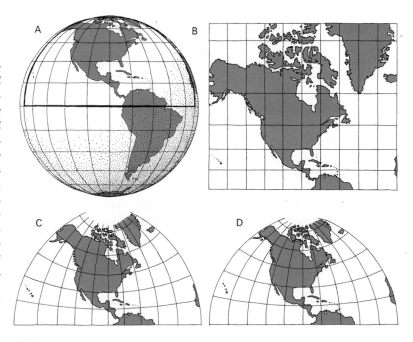

FIGURE I–2

The part of the world outlined in A is reproduced in three common map projections: B, the Mercator; C, the stereographic; and D, the polyconic. By comparing the size and shape of the longitude and latitude grid, it can be seen that each kind of projection distorts the earth's surface to a varying degree. This distortion is an unavoidable result of transferring a curved surface to a flat one.

inch wide. The scale of a map of the United States that could be printed on this page would be about 1/25,000,000; on it, separate points less than 8 miles apart could not be shown without distortion. A thin line representing the Mississippi River on such a map would scale at least 4 miles in width.

Maps of the earth—the summaries of geographical knowledge—have still another limitation: they must depict, on a flat surface, the curved surface of the earth. It is impossible to do this without distorting the distances between points or the angles between intersecting lines. Most maps are compromises between these evils. Some of the distortions that result from various methods of plotting are shown in Figure I-2.

Topographic maps

The maps described thus far may be called **planimetric maps;** they show the relative positions of points but do not indicate their elevations above or below sea level. The **relief** of an area is the difference in altitude between the highest and lowest points within it. Although, by skillful shading, a so-called **relief map** can give an impression of the relative steepness of the slopes in an area, such a map cannot be used to determine accurately the actual differences in elevation. It is impossible to read height accurately from such a map.

To meet this difficulty, geodesists have devised **topographic maps,** which are designed to show the elevations as well as the positions of points. They portray the three-dimensional form of the land surface—its **topography.**

A topographic map depicts a three-dimensional surface—one having length, breadth, and varying height above a reference plane or **datum** (usually mean sea level)—on a two-dimensional piece of paper. On such a map, lines called **contours** are drawn to portray the intersections of the ground surface with a series of horizontal planes at definite intervals above (or below) the datum plane (Fig. I-3).

There are many different methods of making topographic maps and their actual making is a quite complex process. To illustrate the principles, we have chosen the "Plane Table Method," a method still widely used in making geologic maps even though most topographic maps are now made from aerial photographs.

The first step in the preparation of a topographic map by any method is to acquire both **horizontal** and **vertical control** for the measurements. To attain this double control, we first establish the position of a point on the earth's surface (*a*) by its latitude and longitude and (*b*) by its altitude with respect to sea level. The more points determined, the better our control. If we knew the elevation, latitude, and longitude of many points on the surface, we could construct the map; the decision of how many we must determine for a given area depends on the scale and contour interval of the map, and the relief of the area.

Once the horizontal and vertical control (position and elevation) of one point, and the direction of the north-south line through it have been established, we can quickly determine many other points by a process called **triangulation.**

The first step in triangulation is the selection and measurement of a **base line.** The base line is a straight line from the point for which we have established control to another point. Each end of the base line is marked by a stake holding a flag (Fig. I-4), or by some other suitable marker, and the distance between them is measured carefully with a steel tape.

The accuracy of the whole map depends on the base line; therefore, as a check, the measurement is generally repeated. After the base line has been measured, it must also be carefully plotted on the plane table sheet

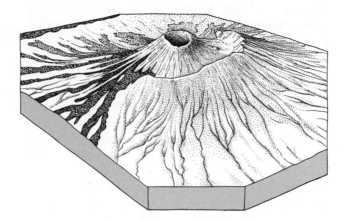

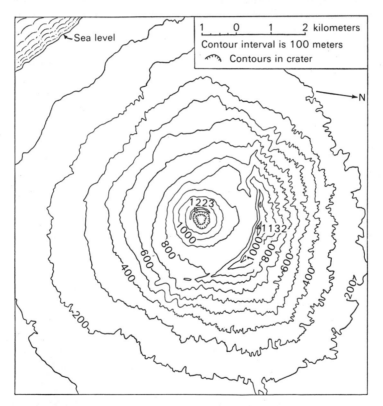

FIGURE I–3   *Relief model and topographic (contour) map of the volcano Vesuvius. (After Il Vesuvio sheet, Instituto Geografico Militaire.)*

(paper on which the map is to be constructed) in accordance with the reduced scale chosen for the map. Actually, the plotted length of the base line determines the scale, for if there are errors either in its measurement or in its plotting, they will be carried throughout the map.

Once the base line has been plotted, a **plane table** (essentially a drawing board mounted on a tripod) is set up over one end of the base line. Then the edge of an **alidade** (a telescope with a ruler as its base) is placed along the line drawn on the plane table sheet to represent the base line (Fig. I-4). The plane table, carrying the alidade, is rotated until the telescope points directly at the flag on the other end of the base line, and then clamped firmly in position. It is now correctly oriented, since the base line on the ground and the plotted base line on the plane table sheet have exactly the same trend (azimuth) in relation to true north.

With the table still clamped in this position, the telescope is pointed successively to-

ward each of several other flags, such as A, B, C in Figure I-4, or other marked points that are visible, and lines are drawn along the edge of the alidade to indicate the directions of these lines of sight. The plane table is then taken to the other end of the base line, oriented in the same manner by sighting back to the first flag, and the process of sighting upon and drawing lines toward each point visible from this location is repeated. The point of intersection of the two lines of sight toward an object, one line of sight having been drawn from the first end of the base line and the other from the second end, marks the true position of that object on the reduced-scale map (Fig. I-4). This point and the two ends of the base line form the apexes of a triangle. The new point can then be used, just as if it were one end of the base line, to determine the position of additional points, extending the system of triangles (triangulation net) within a given area.

A surveyor's transit or theodolite can be used in triangulation instead of a plane table

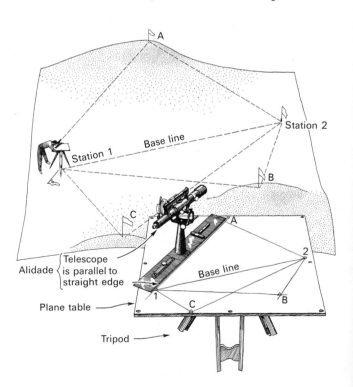

FIGURE I–4
Mapping with plane table and alidade.

and alidade. With a transit, the horizontal angle from the base line to the point to be determined is carefully measured at each end of the base line. Knowing the two angles, and having measured one side (the base line) of the triangle, we can compute the position of the apex of the triangle by trigonometry and plot it on the map.

Vertical control is established in the same way, and can be done at the same time as the horizontal triangulation. We establish the elevation of one end of our base line from some point of known elevation. Then, with the elevation of one point in our triangulation system established, we can readily compute the elevation of a second station. We have already determined the distance between the two stations by triangulation. The only other measurement we need for the computation is the vertical angle between the horizon and the line of sight to the station. The alidade is equipped with a vertical arc (Fig. I-4) for making this measurement. Thus, the vertical control is extended throughout the triangulation net, and the elevations of many points are determined.

By these and other auxiliary techniques (not described here) for obtaining horizontal and vertical control, we locate enough additional points to allow the topographer to sketch the contours in their proper relation to the ground surface as determined by the positions and elevations of the many points thus located and plotted. The map that results from this procedure is, we repeat, a generalization. Many factors other than the already mentioned base-line determinations affect its accuracy—for example, the number and spacing of the control points, trees that obscure the ground forms, the skill of the topographer, and the amount of time he has at his disposal for study of the shape of the land surface. Topographical engineers rate a map as excellent if, on testing it, they find not more than 10 percent of the elevations in error by an amount more than half of the contour interval.

Recently, great strides have been made in preparing topographic maps from photographs taken from airplanes. This saves much time formerly spent in surveying on the ground. The basic principles are, nonetheless, the same as those employed in making maps on the ground and, for the basic horizontal and vertical control, a preliminary ground survey is still necessary.

Good topographic maps are available for relatively few parts of the land surface of the earth. Less than half the area of the United States has been mapped on a scale that permits drawing contours with intervals as small as one hundred feet. Poland and several of the "backward Balkans" have much better map coverage. For large parts of the earth's surface, we have only crude maps.

Hydrographic maps

Hydrographic maps are topographic maps of the sea floor. They not only depict the shorelines of the water bodies but, by soundings (measurements of depth made by vessels at sea), they also show something of the topography of the bottom.

In the construction of maps of the sea floor, soundings were formerly made by measuring the length of a rope or wire paid out until it reached bottom. As a measurement in the deep part of the ocean would require several hours, it is not surprising that relatively few such soundings were made, except at shallow depth near the coasts.

Since World War I sonic sounding has superseded measurement of depth by wire or rope. In sonic sounding the time required for a sound signal to travel from a ship to the sea bottom and rebound is measured, and the depth is then calculated from the speed of sound in sea water. This method has been refined in the past decade by the development of the **precision profiler,** which sends out a very sharply focused sound wave so that a very narrow area on the sea floor is involved in the reflection. The sound intensity is enough to penetrate the sediments on the sea floor to considerable depths so that sub-bottom rock structures also can be recorded under favorable conditions. By sonic sounding it is now an easy matter for a ship to chart a continuous record of the depths traversed while it is under way. The position of the ship is determined to within a distance of a few hundred feet by radio signals from shore stations.

Although sonic sounding has greatly increased our knowledge of the ocean floor, the vastness of the sea, the lack of interest of many navigators in obtaining detailed information of this kind from little-traveled sea lanes, and the cost of operating a vessel for surveying purposes alone, still conspire to prevent more than a mere sampling of the topography of the ocean floor.

The hydrographer, compared with the topographer, is severely handicapped, for he is unable to see the sea bottom and therefore cannot choose the most suitable points to use for control in mapping. A series of points of equal depth can be connected by a contour line in several ways, but obviously only one such contour line represents the actual form of the sea floor. On land the topographer can see the topographic forms and sketch between his points accordingly; the hydrographer must get additional control or else make an interpretation which will probably be inaccurate in minor details, and may be seriously inaccurate.

Identification of minerals

The laboratory techniques in most common use today for the identification of minerals are noted here.

Petrographic analysis

Petrographic analysis is the most frequently used method for the precise identification of both minerals and rocks. A small piece of the substance to be identified is ground with abrasives on a revolving plate until it is 0.03 millimeters (about 0.001 inch) thick—much thinner than a sheet of paper. It is then mounted between thin glass slides. This **thin section** can then be examined under the petrographic microscope. In a thin section most minerals are transparent, or nearly so, and the optical properties which distinguish different minerals can be readily measured.

An alternative petrographic method is to crush the mineral to powder, place the powder in a drop of liquid of known optical properties on a glass slide, cover with a thin glass plate, and examine the fragments immersed in the liquid under the petrographic microscope.

X-ray analysis

As explained in Chapter 2, it is possible by means of X-rays to work out the internal structure of a mineral—the geometric arrangement of the ions or atoms within it. Since the internal structure is the most distinctive characteristic of a mineral, X-ray analysis is one of the most fundamental methods of mineral identification.

Chemical analysis

A chemical analysis, or even a qualitative chemical test for some particular element, will generally help to identify an unknown mineral, although even a complete chemical analysis may fail to establish the identity of some. Some distinct minerals, diamond and graphite for example, have identical chemical compositions and so cannot be distinguished chemically. Furthermore, most minerals are highly insoluble silicates, difficult to treat by standard chemical procedures which require dissolving the substance to be analyzed. Most minerals are also "solid solutions" whose compositions vary widely. For these reasons standard chemical procedures are little used in ordinary mineral identification, though they may be employed in special kinds of research on minerals.

As supplements to petrographic and other methods, however, a few special chemical techniques have proved useful in mineral identification. Many minerals that are too opaque to be readily identified by ordinary petrographic methods, can be identified by simple chemical tests made on the surface of the thin section or on a polished piece of the mineral while it is being examined under the microscope.

The spectroscope is widely used to detect elements that may be present in small amounts in a mineral. Its use requires that the mineral be heated in an arc until it vaporizes.

In the last twenty years many highly refined analytical methods have been developed for analysis of minerals and rocks:

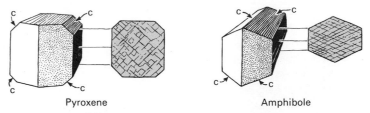

Pyroxene   Amphibole

FIGURE II–1   *The relation between crystal form and cleavage in pyroxene and amphibole. The cleavages parallel the crystal faces, C, and are shown in a sectional cut to the right of each crystal.*

emission spectroscopy, neutron-activation, X-ray fluorescence, and many others; these are beyond the scope of this book and are not further discussed.

Determination by physical properties

The common rock-forming minerals, and also many of the rarer minerals of economic value, can usually be identified without special instruments by a careful study of their physical properties. This method suffices for recognition of the minerals listed at the end of this appendix. The more important physical properties are given here.

CLEAVAGE.   Many minerals **cleave** (break) along *smooth planes* controlled by the internal structure of the crystal (Figs. II-1 and 2-8). Some minerals—mica, for example— have only one cleavage and can be split into countless thin flakes, all of which are parallel to one another; many minerals have two cleavages; others have three or more. Broken fragments of these minerals have characteristic shapes, which aid in identifying the mineral, because the number of cleavages and the angles between them are characteristic for a particular mineral.

FRACTURE.   Many minerals fracture irregularly instead of cleaving along smooth planes. Such rough fragments are less readily identified than cleavage fragments, but some minerals, of which quartz is an example, usually

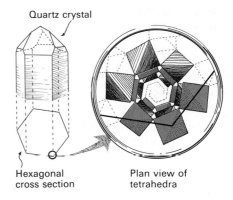

Quartz crystal

Hexagonal   Plan view of
cross section   tetrahedra

FIGURE II–2
The crystal form of quartz and its internal structure. The internal structure consists of silicon tetrahedra closely linked together because each oxygen atom serves as the corner for two tetrahedra. The linked tetrahedra lie in spirals around screw axes, producing a hexagonal basal pattern of the tetrahedra which is also reflected in the external shape of the crystal. In the enlarged plan view shown at the right *the linked tetrahedra are indicated for one screw axis. (Adapted from models by L. Pauling and by P. Niggli.)*

break with characteristic curved surfaces **(conchoidal fracture)**. Others have a splintery or **fibrous fracture** that helps to distinguish them.

FORM.   As mentioned previously, minerals tend to crystallize into definite, characteristically shaped crystals, bounded by smooth planes called **crystal faces.** When crystal faces are present, their shapes and interfacial angles are diagnostic (Figs. 2-2 and II-2), but many minerals occur in shapeless, granular forms, or in crystals so small that the crystal faces are not visible. In some minerals, crystal faces are parallel to cleavage surfaces; in others, they are not. For this reason, they should, of course, be carefully distinguished from cleavage surfaces. The distinction is not difficult if one remembers that crystal faces appear only on the outside of the crystal, whereas cleavage surfaces appear only on the broken or cracked fragments of a crystal.

COLOR. All specimens of some minerals, such as magnetite and galena, have a constant or uniform color; but others, such as quartz and calcite, are variable in color because of pigments that may be present as impurities. Even in minerals with constant intrinsic color, alteration of the surface through exposure to air and moisture may change the surface color. Nevertheless, the color of a freshly broken surface may be diagnostic, and even the color of the altered surface film aids in identifying some minerals.

STREAK. The color of the powdered mineral —which is called the **streak** because it is easily obtained as a "chalk mark" by rubbing the mineral against a piece of unglazed porcelain—is more constant and, for some minerals, more helpful in identification than the color of the mineral in a larger mass. The streak of a mineral may be similar to, or it may be entirely different from, the color of the mineral itself: silvery-gray galena gives a silvery-gray streak; but both the black and red varieties of hematite show a characteristic brownish-red streak that is very helpful in identifying the mineral.

LUSTER. The **luster** of a mineral refers to the way ordinary light is reflected from its surfaces. Metallic luster is like that of polished metals; vitreous luster is like that of glass; adamantine like that of diamond. Other self-explanatory terms used to describe luster are resinous, silky, pearly, and dull or earthy.

HARDNESS. The relative hardness of two different minerals can be determined by pushing a pointed corner of one firmly across the flat surface of the other. If the mineral with the point is harder, it will scratch or cut the other. Laboratory tests of the hardness of minerals are usually recorded in terms of a **scale of hardness** ranging from 1 to 10. Each number refers to the hardness of a specific mineral, ten of which, arranged in order of increasing hardness, constitute the scale.

1. talc	6. orthoclase
2. gypsum	7. quartz
3. calcite	8. topaz
4. fluorite	9. corundum
5. apatite	10. diamond

When specimens to make up this series are not available, it is convenient to know that the steel of a pocketknife is about $5\frac{1}{2}$ in this scale, a copper penny $3\frac{1}{2}$, and the thumbnail about $2\frac{1}{2}$.

SPECIFIC GRAVITY. The **specific gravity,** or density, of a mineral is given by the formula:

$$\text{Sp. Gr.} = \frac{\text{(wt. mineral in air)}}{\text{(wt. mineral in air)} - \text{(wt. mineral in water)}}$$

Specific gravity, therefore, is stated as a number indicating the ratio of the weight of the substance to that of an equal volume of water. Specific gravity is easily determined by an ordinary spring scale for large specimens or a sensitive microbalance for smaller ones. The specific gravity of different minerals varies greatly.

With a little practice, moderate differences in specific gravity can be detected from the "heft" of a moderate-sized specimen held in the hand. Quartz, with a specific gravity of

2.65, may be used as the standard of comparison. Gypsum (2.2 to 2.4) would then be called light; olivine (3.2 to 3.6) heavy; magnetite (5.0 to 5.2) very heavy.

OTHER PROPERTIES. Many other physical properties are useful in identifying minerals. Some minerals are attracted by a magnet, others are not; some conduct electricity better than others; some "fluoresce," or glow in various colors when ultraviolet light is played on them; some are characterized by fine striations, or "twinning lines," on certain cleavage surfaces; others have different striations —"growth striations"—on certain crystal faces. Minerals also differ in fusibility, in solubility, in their reactions to simple chemicals—such as bubbling when dilute hydrochloric acid is applied to them; and in many other ways, but the major physical properties listed above will suffice to identify the more common kinds.

List of minerals

The grouping of the minerals in the list that follows is not alphabetical but is based on similarities in chemical composition, physical properties, associations, or uses. The first group includes *common carbonates, sulfates, chlorides, and oxides.* These minerals are found mainly in the sedimentary rocks, though some of them (quartz and magnetite, for example) are abundant in many igneous and metamorphic rocks as well. The second group, *common rock-forming silicates,* includes chiefly minerals that crystallized in igneous and metamorphic rocks, but which may also be found as clastic particles in sedimentary rocks. Kaolinite, included in this group as a representative of the abundant clay minerals, is chiefly a weathering product. The third group, important *ore minerals,* are much less common, but are listed because of their importance as sources of valuable metals or other commercial materials.

In the tables those properties most useful in sight identification are italicized. Some minerals have more than one name; the less common names are given in parentheses. The chemical name and chemical formula follow the mineral name.

Common carbonates, sulfates, chlorides, and oxides

Mineral	Form	Cleavage	Hardness	Sp. Gr.	Other Properties
Calcite. Calcium carbonate, $CaCO_3$.	"Dog-tooth" or flat crystals showing excellent cleavages; granular, showing cleavages; also masses too fine grained to show cleavages distinctly.	*Three highly perfect cleavages at oblique angles,* yielding rhomb-shaped fragments (Fig. 2–4).	3	2.72	Commonly colorless, white, or yellow but may be any color owing to impurities. Transparent to opaque, transparent varieties showing *strong, double refraction* (e.g., 1 dot seen through calcite appears as 2). Vitreous to dull luster. *Effervesces readily in cold dilute hydrochloric acid.*
Dolomite. Calcium magnesium carbonate, $CaMg(CO_3)_2$.	*Rhomb-faced crystals showing good cleavage;* also in fine-grained masses.	*Three perfect cleavages at oblique angles, as in calcite.*	3.5–4	2.9	Variable in color, but commonly white. Transparent to translucent. Vitreous to pearly luster. *Powder will effervesce slowly in cold dilute hydrochloric acid, but coarse crystals will not.*
Gypsum. Hydrous calcium sulfate, $CaSO_4 \cdot 2H_2O$.	Tabular crystals, and cleavable, granular, fibrous, or earthy masses.	*One perfect cleavage, yielding thin, flexible folia;* 2 other much less perfect cleavages.	2	2.2–2.4	Colorless or white, but may be other colors when impure. Transparent to opaque. Luster vitreous to pearly or silky. Cleavage flakes flexible but *not elastic* like those of mica.
Halite. (Rock salt.) Sodium chloride, NaCl.	Cubic crystals (Fig. 2–7), in granular masses.	Excellent cubic cleavage (3 cleavages mutually at right angles).	2–2.5	2.1	*Colorless to white,* but of other colors when impure. The color may be unevenly distributed through the crystal. Transparent to translucent. Vitreous luster. *Salty taste.*
Opal. Hydrous silica, with 3% to 12% water, SiO_2nH_2O. Does not have a definite geometric internal structure, hence is a mineraloid, not a true mineral.	*Amorphous.* Commonly in veins or irregular masses showing a banded structure. May be earthy.	None; *conchoidal fracture.*	5.0–6.5	2.1–2.3	*Color highly variable, often in wavy or banded patterns.* Translucent or opaque. *Somewhat waxy luster.*
Chalcedony. (Cryptocrystalline quartz.) Silicon dioxide, SiO_2.	Crystals too fine to be visible; some are conspicuously banded, or in masses.	None; *conchoidal fracture.*	6–6.5	2.6	Color commonly white or light gray, but may be any color owing to impurities. Distinguished from opal by dull or clouded luster.
Quartz. (Rock crystal.) Silicon dioxide, SiO_2.	*Six-sided prismatic crystals,* terminated by 6-sided triangular faces; also massive (Fig. II–2).	None or very poor; *conchoidal fracture.*	7	2.65	Commonly *colorless* or white, but may be yellow, pink, amethyst, smoky-translucent brown, or even black. *Transparent* to opaque. *Vitreous* to greasy luster.

Common carbonates, sulfates, chlorides, and oxide—continued

Mineral	Form	Cleavage	Hardness	Sp. Gr.	Other Properties
Magnetite. A combination of ferric and ferrous oxides, Fe_3O_4.	Well-formed, 8-faced crystals, more commonly in compact aggregates, disseminated grains, or loose grains in sand.	None; conchoidal or uneven fractures; may show a rough parting resembling cleavage.	5.5–6.5	5.0–5.2	*Black.* Opaque. Metallic to submetallic luster. *Black streak. Strongly attracted by a magnet.* Magnetite is an important iron ore.
Hematite. Ferric iron oxide, Fe_2O_3.	Highly varied, compact, granular, fibrous, or earthy, micaceous; rarely in well-formed crystals.	None, but fibrous or micaceous specimens may show parting resembling cleavage; splintery to uneven fracture.	5–6.5	4.9–5.3	Steel-gray, reddish-brown, red, or iron-black in color. Metallic to earthy luster. *Characteristic brownish-red streak.* Hematite is the most important iron ore.
"Limonite." Microscopic study shows that the material called limonite is not a single mineral. Most "limonite" is a very finely crystalline variety of the mineral **Goethite** containing absorbed water. Hydrous ferric oxide with minor amounts of other elements, roughly $Fe_2O_3 \cdot H_2O$.	Compact or earthy masses; may show radially fibrous structure.	None; conchoidal or earthy fracture.	1–5.5	3.4–4.0	*Yellow,* brown, or black in color. Dull earthy luster, which distinguishes it from hematite. *Characteristic yellow-brown streak.* A common iron ore.
Ice. Hydrogen oxide, H_2O.	Irregular grains; lacelike flakes with hexagonal symmetry; massive.	None; conchoidal fracture.	1.5	0.9	Colorless, white or blue. Vitreous luster. *Melts at 0°C.,* so is liquid at room temperature. *Low specific gravity.*

Common rock-forming silicates

Mineral	Form	Cleavage	Hardness	Sp. Gr.	Other Properties
Potassium Feldspar. (Orthoclase, microcline, and sanidine.) Potassium aluminum silicate, $KAlSi_3O_8$.	Boxlike crystals (Fig. 2–2,B); massive.	One perfect and 1 good cleavage, making an angle of 90°.	6	2.5–2.6	Commonly *white,* gray, *pink,* or pale yellow; rarely colorless. Commonly opaque but may be transparent in volcanic rocks. Vitreous. Pearly luster on better cleavage. *Distinguished from plagioclase by absence of striations.*

Mineral	Form	Cleavage	Hardness	Specific gravity	Description
Plagioclase feldspar. (Soda-lime feldspars.) A solid solution group of sodium calcium aluminum silicates, NaAlSi_3O_8 to $CaAl_2Si_2O_8$.	In well-formed crystals and in cleavable or granular masses.	*Two good cleavages nearly at right angles (86°).* May be poor in some volcanic rocks.	6–6.5	2.6–2.7	Commonly *white or gray*, but may be other colors. Some gray varieties show a play of colors called *opalescence. Transparent in some* volcanic rocks. Vitreous to pearly luster. Distinguished from orthoclase by the presence on the *better cleavage surface of fine parallel lines or striations.*
Muscovite. (White mica; isinglass.) A complex potassium aluminum silicate, $KAl_3Si_3O_{10}(OH)_2$ approximately, but varying.	Thin, scalelike crystals and scaly, foliated aggregates.	*Perfect in one direction, yielding very thin, transparent, flexible scales.*	2–3	2.8–3.1	*Colorless,* but may be gray, green, or light brown in thick pieces. *Transparent to translucent.* Pearly to vitreous luster.
Biotite. (Black mica.) A complex silicate of potassium, iron, aluminum, and magnesium, variable in composition but approximately $K(Mg,Fe)_3 AlSi_3O_{10}(OH)_2$.	Thin, scalelike crystals, commonly 6 sided, and in scaly, foliated masses.	*Perfect in one direction, yielding thin, flexible scales.*	2.5–3	2.7–3.2	Black to dark brown. Translucent to opaque. Pearly to vitreous luster. White to greenish streak.
Pyroxene. A solid-solution group of silicates. Chiefly silicates of calcium, magnesium, and iron, with varying amounts of other elements. The commonest varieties are *augite* and *hypersthene.*	Commonly in short, 8-sided, prismatic crystals; *the angle between alternate faces nearly* 90°. Also as compact masses and disseminated grains.	*Two cleavages at nearly 90°* (Fig. II–1). Cleavage not always well developed; in some specimens, conchoidal or uneven fracture.	5–6	3.2–3.6	Commonly greenish to black in color. Vitreous to dull luster. Gray-green streak. Distinguished from amphibole by the *right-angle cleavage, 8-sided crystals,* and by the fact that most crystals are short and stout, rather than long, thin prisms, as in amphibole (Fig. II–1).
Amphibole. A group of complex, solid-solution silicates, chiefly of calcium, magnesium, iron, and aluminum. Similar to pyroxene in composition, but containing a little hydroxyl (OH⁻) ion. The commonest of the many varieties of amphibole is *hornblende.*	*Long, prismatic, 6-sided crystals;* also in fibrous or irregular masses of interlocking crystals and in disseminated grains.	*Two good cleavages meeting at angles of 56° and 124°* (Fig. II–1).	5–6	2.9–3.2	Color black to light green; or even colorless. Opaque. *Highly vitreous luster on cleavage surfaces.* Distinguished from pyroxene by the *difference in cleavage angle* and in crystal form. Amphibole also has much better cleavage and higher luster than pyroxene.

Common rock-forming silicates—continued

Mineral	Form	Cleavage	Hardness	Sp. Gr.	Other Properties
Olivine. Magnesium iron silicate, $(Fe,Mg)_2SiO_4$.	Commonly in small, *glassy* grains and granular aggregates.	So poor that it is rarely seen; *conchoidal fracture.*	6.5–7	3.2–3.6	*Various shades of green,* also yellowish; opalescent and brownish when slightly altered. *Transparent to translucent. Vitreous luster.* Resembles quartz in small fragments but has *characteristic greenish color,* unless altered.
Garnet. A group of solid solution silicates having variable proportions of different metallic elements. The most common variety contains calcium, iron, and aluminum, but garnets may contain many other elements.	Commonly in well-formed *equidimensional crystals* (Fig. 2-2,C) but also massive and granular.	*None; conchoidal or uneven fracture.*	6.5–7.5	3.4–4.3	Commonly *red, brown, or yellow,* but may be other colors. Translucent to opaque. *Resinous to vitreous luster.*
Sillimanite. (Fibrolite.) Aluminum silicate, Al_2SiO_5.	*In long slender crystals, or fibrous.*	Parallel to length, but rarely noticeable.	6–7	3.2	Gray, white, greenish-gray, or colorless *Slender prismatic crystals or in a felted mass of fibers.* Streak white or colorless.
Kyanite. (Disthene.) Aluminum silicate, Al_2SiO_5.	Long, *bladelike crystals.*	One perfect, and one poor cleavage, both parallel to length of crystals; and a crude parting across the crystals.	4–7	3.5–3.7	Colorless, white, or a *distinctive pale blue color.* Can be scratched by knife parallel to cleavage, but is harder than steel across cleavage.
Staurolite. Iron-aluminum silicate, $Fe(OH)_2(Al_2SiO_5)_2$.	*Stubby prismatic crystals,* and in cross-shaped twins.	Poor and inconspicuous.	7–7.5	3.7	Red-brown or yellowish-brown to brownish black. Generally in well-shaped crystals larger than the minerals of the matrix enclosing them.
Epidote. A complex group of calcium, iron, aluminum silicates, $Ca_2(Al,Fe)_3(SiO_4)_3(OH)$.	*Short, 6-sided crystals* or radiate crystal groups (Fig. 2-2,A) and in granular or compact masses.	One good cleavage; in some specimens, a second poorer cleavage at an angle of 115° with the first.	6–7	3.4	Characteristic *yellowish-green (pistachio green)* color. Vitreous luster.
Chlorite. A complex group of hydrous magnesium aluminum silicates containing iron and other elements in small amounts.	Commonly in *foliated or scaly masses;* may occur in tabular, 6-sided crystals resembling mica.	*One perfect cleavage,* yielding thin, flexible, but inelastic, scales.	1–2.5	2.6–3.0	*Grass-green to blackish-green color.* Translucent to opaque. Greenish streak. Vitreous luster. *Very easily disintegrated.*

Mineral	Form	Cleavage	Hardness	Sp. Gr.	Other Properties
Serpentine. A complex group of hydrous magnesium silicates, roughly $H_4Mg_3Si_2O_9$.	Foliated or fibrous, usually massive.	Commonly only one cleavage, but may be in prisms. Fracture usually conchoidal or splintery.	2.5–4	2.5–2.65	*Feels smooth,* or even *greasy.* Color *leek-green* to *blackish-green* but varying to brownish-red, yellow, etc. *Luster resinous to greasy.* Translucent to opaque. Streak white.
Talc. Hydrous magnesium silicate, $Mg_3(OH)_2Si_4O_{10}$.	In tiny *foliated scales* and soft compact masses.	*One perfect cleavage,* forming thin scales and shreds.	1	2.8	White or silvery white to apple green. *Very soft,* with a *greasy feel.* Pearly luster on cleavage surfaces.
Kaolinite. Hydrous aluminum silicate, $H_4Al_2Si_2O_9$. Representative of the 3 or 4 similar minerals common in clays.	Commonly in soft, compact, *earthy masses.*	Crystals always so small that cleavage is invisible without microscope.	1–2	2.2–2.6	White color, but may be stained by impurities. *Greasy feel. Adheres to the tongue,* and *becomes plastic when moistened.* "*Clay-like*" odor when breathed upon.

Important ore minerals (*See also the iron ores listed on p. 600*)

Mineral	Form	Cleavage	Hardness	Sp. Gr.	Other Properties
Galena. Lead sulfide, PbS.	Cubic crystals common, but mostly in coarse to fine granular masses.	*Perfect cubic cleavage* (three cleavages mutually at right angles).	2.5	7.3–7.6	*Silvery-gray color.* Metallic luster. Silvery-gray to grayish-black streak. Chief ore of lead.
Sphalerite. Zinc sulfide (nearly always containing a little iron), ZnS.	Crystals common, but chiefly in fine to coarse-granular masses.	*Six highly perfect cleavages at 60° to one another.*	3.5–4	3.9–4.2	Color ranges from white to black but is commonly *yellowish-brown. Translucent* to opaque. *Resinous* to *adamantine luster.* Streak white, pale yellow or brown. Most important ore of zinc.
Pyrite. ("Fool's gold.") Iron sulfide, FeS_2.	*Well-formed crystals,* commonly cubic, with striated faces (Fig. 2–2,D); also granular masses.	None; uneven fracture.	6–6.5	4.9–5.2	Pale *brassy-yellow color;* may tarnish brown. Opaque. Metallic luster. Greenish-black or brownish-black streak. Brittle. Not a source of iron, but used in the manufacture of sulfuric acid. Commonly associated with ores of several different metals.

Important ore minerals (*See also the iron ores listed on p. 600*)—continued

Mineral	Form	Cleavage	Hardness	Sp. Gr.	Other Properties
Chalcopyrite. Copper iron sulfide, $CuFeS_2$.	Compact or disseminated masses, rarely in wedge-shaped crystals.	None; uneven fracture.	3.5–4	4.1–4.3	Brassy to *golden-yellow. Tarnishes* to blue, purple, and reddish iridescent films. Greenish-black streak. Distinguished from pyrite by deeper yellow color and softness. A common copper ore.
Chalcocite. (Copper glance.) Cuprous sulfide, Cu_2S.	Massive, rarely in crystals of roughly hexagonal shape. May be tarnished and stained to blue and green.	Indistinct, rarely observed.	2.5–3	5.5–5.8	Blackish-gray to steel gray, commonly *tarnished to green or blue.* Dark gray streak. *Very heavy.* Metallic luster. An important ore of copper.
Copper. (Native copper.) An element, Cu.	*Twisted and distorted leaves and wirelike forms; flattened or rounded grains.*	None.	2.5–3	8.8–8.9	*Characteristic copper color,* but commonly stained green. Highly ductile and malleable. Excellent conductor of heat and electricity. *Very heavy.*
Gold. An element, Au.	Massive or in thin plates; also in flattened grains or scales; distinct crystals very rare.	None.	2.5–3	15.6–19.3	*Characteristic gold-yellow color and streak. Rarely in crystals. Extremely heavy.* Very malleable and ductile.
Silver. An element, Ag.	In flattened grains and scales; rarely in wirelike forms, or in irregular needle-like crystals.	None.	2.5–3	10–11	*Color and streak are silvery-white,* but may be tarnished gray or black. *Highly ductile and malleable. Very heavy.* Mirrorlike metallic luster on untarnished surfaces.
Cassiterite. Tin dioxide, SnO_2.	Well-formed, 4-sided prismatic crystals terminated by pyramids; 2 crystals may be intergrown to form knee-shaped twins; also as rounded pebbles in stream gravels.	None; curved to irregular fracture.	6–7	7	*Brown to black.* Adamantine luster. White to pale-yellow streak. Chief ore of tin.
Uraninite. (Pitchblende.) Uranium oxide, UO_2 to U_3O_8.	Regular 8-sided or cubic crystals; massive.	None; fracture uneven to conchoidal.	5–6	6.5–10	Color black to brownish-black. Luster submetallic, pitchlike, or dull. Chief mineral source of uranium, radium, etc.
Carnotite. Potassium uranyl vanadate, $K_2(UO_2)_2(VO_4)_2 \cdot 8H_2O$.	Earthy powder.	Not apparent.	Very soft	4.1 approx.	*Brilliant canary-yellow color.* An ore of vanadium and uranium.

Appendix

Identification of rocks

The classification of rocks given in this Appendix is a field classification based on features that can be seen without the aid of the petrographic microscope. Much more elaborate classifications have been built with the aid of this instrument and other laboratory techniques. Nearly all such classifications, however, have been made by expanding and adding varietal subdivisions to the major rock classes listed in the tables below. Therefore the field classification represents a broad framework into which more elaborate subdivisions can be fitted.

The field classification is based primarily upon the texture and mineral composition of the rock. Remember that rocks grade into one another, and hence some properties of an individual specimen you may be examining are likely to fall between those listed as typical of two major rock classes. To use the tables and lists below as guides in identifying an unknown rock specimen the student must be thoroughly familiar with the common rock-forming minerals listed in the Mineral Table of Appendix II. He must also have clearly in mind the basic distinctions between sedimentary, igneous, and metamorphic rocks and the general range of textures found in them. This fundamental information is given in Chapter 3. The common rock textures are here summarized in glossary form for easy reference.

Common textures of sedimentary rocks

Differences in *the nature of the constituent particles,* and in *how they are bound together* determine the texture of a sedimentary rock.

Clastic (Greek, "broken"). Composed of broken and worn fragments of pre-existing minerals, rock particles, or shells that have been cemented together. Further distinctions can be made on the *size* of the particles, and on the amount of *rounding* by wear of the individual fragments.

Organic. Composed of accumulations of organic debris (shells, plant remains, bones, etc.) in which the individual organic particles are so well preserved (not notably broken and worn) that organic features dominate the texture of the rock.

Crystalline. Composed of crystals precipitated from solution and therefore tightly interlocked by mutual interpenetration during growth. The rock owes its coherence to this interlocking of crystals, instead of to the presence of a cement as in the clastic and organic textures.

Common textures of igneous rocks

Differences in the *degree of crystallinity,* and in the *size of the crystals* determine the texture of an igneous rock. Both of these factors are controlled primarily by *rate of cooling,* though the chemical composition of the magma and its content of volatile materials play roles.

BASIC TEXTURES

Pyroclastic (Greek, "broken by fire"). Composed of slivers of volcanic glass, bits of frothy pumice, phenocrysts, and broken fragments of volcanic rock deposited together. The glass slivers and pumice may be largely altered to clay. Pyroclastic rocks are the products of volcanic explosions or of pyroclastic flows.

Glassy. Composed almost entirely of massive or streaky volcanic glass. Small phenocrysts of feldspar or other minerals may be scattered through the glass. The glass may be frothy, filled with minute bubbles, forming a *pumiceous glassy* texture.

Aphanitic (Greek, "invisible"). Composed chiefly of tiny crystals (less than 0.5 millimeter in diameter), with or without a glassy residue between the crystals. The crystals are mere specks, large enough to be seen but too small to identify without the aid of the microscope. Their presence gives the rock a stony or dull luster in contrast to the glassy (vitreous) luster of rocks with glassy texture. Most lava flows have aphanitic texture; in some, flow has aligned the tiny mineral grains, giving a streaky or flow-banded appearance.

Granular (Latin, "a grain"). Composed of crystals that are large enough to be seen and identified without the aid of lens or microscope. In different rocks the average size may vary from about 0.5 millimeter to more than 1 centimeter in diameter, but the common granular rocks such as granite have grains averaging from 3 to 5 millimeters in size.

MODIFYING TEXTURE

Porphyritic. Composed of two widely different sizes of minerals, giving a spotted appearance. Because porphyritic texture is most common in small intrusive bodies or in lavas, it has been attributed to a *change in the rate of cooling while the magma was crystallizing.* The inferred process is explained as follows: A large body of magma underground may cool to the temperature at which one or more minerals begin to crystallize. Because cooling is slow, the crystals of these minerals grow to considerable size. If, when the magma is perhaps half crystallized, a fissure opens in the roof of the chamber, some of the magma with its suspended crystals may escape to form a lava flow at the surface. The still-liquid portion of the magma quickly freezes at the surface of the ground and surrounds the large crystals, called *phenocrysts,* with a *groundmass* of aphanitic crystals. The phenocrysts were formed underground, the aphanitic groundmass at the surface. Such a lava has a *porphyritic aphanitic* texture. The adjective porphyritic is used to modify the prevailing texture of the groundmass. Rocks with *por-phyritic granular* texture—large crystals in a granular groundmass of finer grain—are common in intrusive bodies. *Porphyritic glassy* texture appears in some lava flows, and in the pumice fragments of pyroclastic rocks. Rarely, conditions other than a change in the rate of cooling may produce porphyritic rocks.

Common textures of metamorphic rock

Differences in the *orientation,* or alignment, of the crystals and in the *size* of the crystals determine the texture of a metamorphic rock. There are two general textural groups: *foliated textures* (Latin, "leafy"), in which platy or leaflike minerals such as mica or chlorite are nearly all aligned parallel to one another so that the rock splits readily along the well-oriented, nearly parallel cleavages of its constituent mineral particles, and *nonfoliated,* composed either of equidimensional minerals or of randomly oriented platy minerals, so that the rock breaks into angular particles.

BASIC TEXTURES

Gneissose (from Greek, "banded rock"). Coarsely foliated; individual folia are 1 millimeter or more, even several centimeters, thick. The folia may be straight, pancake-like, or wavy and crenulated. They commonly differ in composition; feldspars, for example, may alternate with dark minerals. Mineral grains are coarse, easily identified.

Schistose (Greek, "easily cleaved"). Finely foliated, forming thin parallel bands along which the rock splits readily. Individual minerals are distinctly visible. The minerals are mainly platy or rodlike—chiefly mica, chlorite, and amphibole. Equidimensional minerals like feldspar, garnet, and pyroxene may be present but are not abundant.

Slaty (from Old High German, "to split"). Very fine foliation, producing almost rigidly parallel planes of easy splitting due to the nearly perfect parallelism of microscopic and ultramicroscopic crystals of platy minerals, chiefly mica.

Granoblastic (Greek, "sprouting grains"). Unfoliated or only faintly foliated. Composed of mutually interpenetrating mineral grains that have crystallized simultaneously. Minerals are large enough to be easily identified without the microscope, and are chiefly equidimensional kinds such as feldspar, quartz, garnet, and pyroxene. Corresponds roughly to the granular texture of igneous rocks.

Hornfelsic (German, "hornlike rock"). Unfoliated. Mineral grains commonly microscopic or ultramicroscopic, though a few may be visible. Breaks into sharply angular pieces with curved fracture surfaces.

How to use the rock tables and lists

After carefully examining a specimen of rock, but before referring to the tables and lists in this Appendix, the student should ask himself the following three basic questions, and if in doubt about the answers, should refer back to the material in Chapter 3, Appendix II, and the glossary of textures just given.

1. What is the texture of the rock? (Glossary above)
2. Of what minerals is it composed? (Appendix II)
3. Is it an igneous, sedimentary, or metamorphic rock? (Chapter 3)

Once this basic information is worked out, turn to the appropriate rock table (Sedimentary, p. 608; Igneous, p. 612; Metamorphic, p. 615) and find the rock's name, then check against the description of the rock in the appropriate rock list.

Common sedimentary rocks

Conglomerate. Conglomerate is cemented gravel. Gravel is an unconsolidated deposit composed chiefly of rounded pebbles. The pebbles may be of any kind of rock or mineral and of all sizes. Most conglomerates, especially those deposited by streams, have much sand and other fine material filling the spaces between the pebbles. Some cleanly washed beach conglomerates contain little sand.

Breccia. Sedimentary breccias resemble conglomerate except that most of their fragments are angular instead of rounded. They commonly grade into conglomerates. Since their constituent fragments have been little worn, however, it is apparent that the components of breccia underwent relatively less transportation and wear before they were deposited. There are many kinds of breccias other than sedimentary breccias. Volcanic breccias, as well as sedimentary breccias, are described in this appendix; glacial breccias in Chapter 13; and fault breccias in Chapter 9.

Sandstone. Sandstone is cemented sand. Sand, by definition, consists of particles from 2 millimeters to 1/16 millimeter in diameter. Sandstones commonly grade into either shale or conglomerate. Three general varieties of sandstone are recognized:

Quartz sandstone is composed mainly of the mineral quartz. Most sand is chiefly quartz but contains small amounts of many other minerals and even small particles of rock.

Arkose is a feldspar-rich sandstone. It may contain nearly as many particles of partly weathered feldspar as of quartz, or even more. Most arkoses have been formed by the rapid erosion of coarse feldspar-rich rocks such as granites and gneisses, and the rapid deposition of this eroded debris before the feldspar has had time to weather completely into clay.

Graywacke is a cemented "dirty sand" containing clay and rock fragments in addition to quartz and feldspar. Many graywackes contain much pyroclastic debris in various stages of weathering and decomposition; others are crowded with bits of slate, greenstone, or other metamorphic rocks; and still others are rich in ferromagnesian minerals. All contain appreciable amounts of clay. Graywackes are commonly dark gray, dark green, or even black. Like arkose, they indicate rapid erosion and deposition without much chemical weathering.

Table III–1 **Sedimentary rocks**

CLASTIC SEDIMENTARY ROCKS			
Consolidated rock	*Chief mineral or rock components*	*Original unconsolidated debris*	*Diameter of fragments*
Conglomerate	Quartz, and rock fragments	Gravel (rounded pebbles)	More than 2 mm
Breccia	Rock fragments	Rubble (angular fragments)	
Sandstone	. . .	Sand	2 to $\frac{1}{16}$ mm
Quartz Sandstone	Quartz	Quartz-rich sand	
Arkose	Quartz and feldspar	Feldspar-rich sand	
Graywacke	Quartz, feldspar, clay, rock fragments, volcanic debris	"Dirty sand," with clay and rock fragments	
Shale	Clay minerals, quartz	Mud, clay, and silt	Less than $\frac{1}{16}$ mm
Clastic Limestone	Calcite	Broken and rounded shells and calcite grains	Variable

ORGANIC AND CHEMICAL SEDIMENTARY ROCKS			
Consolidated rock	*Chief mineral or rock components*	*Original nature of material*	*Chemical composition of dominant material*
Limestone	Calcite	Shells; chemical and organic precipitates	$CaCO_3$
Dolomite	Dolomite	Limestone, or unconsolidated calcareous ooze, altered by solutions	$CaMg(CO_3)_2$
Peat and Coal	Organic materials	Plant fragments	C, plus compounds of C, H, O
Chert	Opal, chalcedony	Siliceous shells and chemical precipitates	SiO_2 and SiO_2nH_2O
Evaporites, or Salt Deposits	Halite, gypsum, anhydrite	Evaporation residues from the ocean or saline lakes	Varied, chiefly NaCl and $CaSO_42H_2O$

Sand, the original material that is cemented into sandstone, accumulates in many different environments. Some sand is deposited by streams; some is heaped up in dunes by the wind; some is spread out by waves and currents along beaches or in the shallow water of the continental shelves; some is washed by turbidity currents down steep submarine slopes onto the deep sea floor.

Shale. Shale is hardened mud. Mud is a complex mixture of very small mineral particles less than 1/256 millimeter in diameter (chiefly clay), and coarser grains, called silt, from 1/256 to 1/16 millimeter in diameter.

Shale frequently contains small bits of organic matter.

The predominant minerals in shale are the hydrous aluminum silicates called clay minerals, but most shales also contain appreciable amounts of mica, quartz, and other minerals. Shale splits readily along closely spaced planes, parallel or nearly parallel to the stratification. Some rocks of similar grain size and composition show little layering and break into small angular blocks: these are more correctly called *mudstone;* when of appropriate grain size, *siltstone.*

Shales accumulate in many different environments. As the main load brought down to the sea by great rivers is mud and fine sand, it is not surprising that shale is the most abundant marine sedimentary rock. Mud deposited in deltas, on lake bottoms, and on plains along sluggish rivers may also harden into shale.

Many shales are black, some because they contain large amounts of carbon-rich organic matter in various stages of decomposition, some because of the precipitation of black iron sulfide (FeS_x) by sulfur bacteria. The iron sulfide may later crystallize into pyrite (FeS_2), forming small brass-colored crystals sprinkled through the rock. Many blue-green, dark gray, gray-green, or purplish-red mudstones owe their color to decomposed volcanic material.

Limestone. Limestone is composed almost entirely of calcium carbonate ($CaCO_3$), chiefly as the mineral calcite, though aragonite (which is also $CaCO_3$ but with a different crystalline form) may be plentiful.

Organic limestones are common rocks, and occur in great variety because of the many kinds of shells from which they are formed. Among the most common are: *coral limestone,* which contains a framework of coralline deposits but also includes the shells of many other animals, especially foraminifers, molluscs, and gastropods; *algal limestone,* made largely of deposits of calcite precipitated by algae and bacteria; *foraminiferal limestone,* composed chiefly of the tiny shells of foraminifera; *coquina,* composed mostly of the coarse shells of molluscs; and *chalk,* which consists largely of almost ultramicroscopic blades and spines from *coccoliths,* the tests of minute algae.

Clastic limestones are composed of broken and worn fragments of shells or of crystals of calcite. The white sands of the Florida Keys are made up largely of calcite grains worn from shells and organic limestones.

Chemically precipitated limestone is also forming today in shallow warm seas, in hot springs, and in saline lakes. The role of inorganic precipitation is, however, difficult to separate from that of biochemical and organic agents. Very fine-grained, flourlike, white *calcareous ooze* (calcareous means calcite-rich) is abundant in parts of the southwest Pacific and on the shallow Bahama Banks of the Atlantic. Some of this ooze consists of microscopic shells, but much of that in the Bahamas consists of tiny spines and crystals of aragonite and calcite, perhaps in part precipitated inorganically, or else precipitated from sea water as a result of the life processes of such microorganisms as algae and bacteria.

Limestone deposited from hot springs is coarsely crystalline, and commonly full of small irregular holes stained yellow or red by iron oxides. Such limestone is called *travertine.*

Limestones differ greatly in texture and color depending on the size of the shells or crystals composing them and the impurities they contain. Some black limestones are rich in hydrocarbons from the partially decayed bodies of organisms, as shown by the strong, fetid odor they give off when freshly broken. Most limestones, however, are light colored and contain many fossils.

Dolomite. Dolomite rock is composed chiefly of dolomite, the mineral of the same name. Dolomite resembles limestone, and also grades into it, by changes in the amount of calcite in the rock. Chemical and microscopic tests are generally necessary to determine the relative amounts of the minerals calcite and dolomite in the rock.

Most dolomite appears to result from alteration of limestone or its parental calcareous ooze by magnesia-bearing solutions. The alteration that formed most dolomite is thought to have taken place during slow deposition, by the action of the magnesium ions in sea water on calcareous ooze or other calcareous deposits. Some limestone, however, changed to dolomite long after it was deposited and consolidated.

Dolomite has rarely, perhaps never, been deposited directly as a precipitated sediment.

Fine-grained Siliceous Rocks. Rocks composed almost entirely of fine-grained silica are common, but they rarely form large masses. Many different kinds of siliceous (siliceous means silica-rich) sedimentary rocks have been described and named, but the most common is *chert*, a hard rock with grains so fine that a broken surface appears uniform and lustrous.

Chert nodules, many resembling a knobby potato in shape and size, are common in limestone and dolomite. Dark-colored chert nodules are often called *flint*. Chert also appears as distinct beds and as thin, wedgelike, discontinuous layers. Beds of chert are commonly associated with volcanic deposits.

The microscope shows that some cherts are made up largely of spines or lacelike shells of silica (opal) secreted by microscopic animals and plants. In other cherts, siliceous fossils are rare or absent, but siliceous shells may have been partly dissolved and reprecipitated as structureless silica during cementation. Abundant undissolved siliceous shells usually make the rock porous and light in weight. An example is *diatomite*, a white rock composed almost entirely of the siliceous shells of microscopic plants called diatoms.

Not all fine-grained siliceous rocks are of organic origin. Some are believed to have precipitated around silica-bearing submarine hot springs. Many have been formed by the replacement of wood, limestone, shale, or other materials by silica-bearing solutions. *Petrified wood* is a familiar example.

Peat and Coal. Peat and coal are not common sedimentary rocks but their economic importance justifies their mention here.

Peat is an aggregate of slightly decomposed plant remains. It can be seen in process of accumulation in swamps and shallow lakes in temperate climates and even spreading over steep hillsides in wet sub-arctic regions. Coal is the result of compression and more thorough decomposition of the plant material in ancient peat bogs which were buried under later sediments. Coals grade from *lignite,* which differs little from peat, through *bituminous* to *anthracite,* which may contain 90 percent or more of carbon. From evidence obtained in mines and by geologic mapping, we infer that the grade of the coal depends largely on the depth to which it has been buried (i.e., the pressure and heat to which it has been subjected). The nature of the original plant material may also affect the variety of coal.

Evaporites, or Salt Deposits. Evaporites vary greatly in mineral composition and texture. They are now being formed by the evaporation of land-locked masses of sea water, as at the Rann of Kutch in northwest India, and in saline lakes like Great Salt Lake. When sea water evaporates completely many different salts are precipitated from it, but *rock salt* (halite, NaCl) is the most abundant. In nature, however, calcium sulfate, which occurs both as a hydrated form, *rock gypsum* $(CaSO_4 2H_2O)$, and as the anhydrous mineral called *anhydrite* $(CaSO_4)$, is much more common than rock salt. Gypsum separates out early in the process of evaporation and will, therefore, accumulate in quantity from water bodies that are not saline enough to precipitate halite. Rock gypsum, accompanied by little or no rock salt, is abundant in the Paris Basin of France, in the Dakotas, and elsewhere. Thick beds of rock salt, accompanied by gypsum and anhydrite, are found in Utah, Texas, New Mexico, Saskatchewan, Germany, Iran, India and many other areas.

In a few places where relatively complete evaporation of sea water has occurred, deposits of potassium salts and other valuable, late-crystallizing minerals are found. Many rare and useful mineral products such as potash, salsoda, borax, nitrates, sodium sulfate, and epsom salts are recovered from salt deposits formed by the evaporation of ancient desert lakes. Commercial deposits of sulfur—presumably formed by reduction of sulfates by hydrocarbons—locally accompany evaporites.

Common igneous rocks

Volcanic Tuff. Volcanic tuff is a fine-grained pyroclastic deposit composed of fragments less than 4 millimeters in diameter. Most of the fragments are volcanic glass, either microscopic slivers called *shards* or frothy bits of *pumice*. Other common constituents are broken phenocrysts and fragments of solidified lava. Pieces of the basement rock on which the volcano rests may also be present.

Pumice and other kinds of glass fragments have been seen to form by the explosive disruption of sticky lava highly charged with gases. Evidently the gas pressure increases until it exceeds the containing pressure on the magma; then the pent-up gases separate into bubbles, causing the lava to expand tremendously and to froth. Upon breaking out to the surface, the froth disrupts further into a cloud of glass fragments and pumice which may be blown high into the air in a great volcanic explosion, or may froth forth more quietly and roll down the slope of the volcano as a *pyroclastic flow,* or "glowing avalanche."

The fragments from a volcanic explosion may be cemented together in the same way as the fragments of a sedimentary rock, forming an ordinary volcanic tuff. The component particles deposited by many pyroclastic flows, however, when viewed under the microscope, show flattening and collapse of the bits of frothy pumice and glass shards upon one another as if the rock had been welded—stuck together under its own weight while sticky and partly melted. Such *welded tuffs* are common products of rhyolitic and dacitic volcanoes. They are often confused with rhyolite and dacite lavas because of the close similarity of the welded fragmental matrix to the flow-banded aphanitic texture of lava flows.

Volcanic Breccia. Volcanic breccia is composed dominantly of fragments more than 4 millimeters in diameter. In general, fragments of lava are more abundant than in tuff; glass slivers and pumice may be scarce. *Scoria* (see p. 26) is abundant in some breccias. The scoria may form large angular blocks, streamlined bombs 1 to 6 inches long shaped into cigarlike or teardrop forms by flying through the air while still molten, or small bits of frothy lava less than an inch in diameter, called *lapilli.*

Some volcanic breccias are formed like the tuffs, but many are products of volcanic mudflows. Heavy rains falling on the steep slopes of a volcanic cone have been seen to set great avalanche-like slides of unconsolidated pyroclastic debris in motion. Other mudflows are formed by eruption clouds falling into rivers, or onto snowfields and glaciers, or by explosive eruptions through crater lakes. The water-soaked volcanic debris may travel for many miles down stream valleys.

Obsidian. Obsidian is natural glass, formed chiefly from magmas of rhyolitic, dacitic, or andesitic composition. It is lustrous and breaks with a curved fracture. Most obsidians are black because of sparsely disseminated grains of magnetite and ferromagnesian minerals, but they may be red or brown from the oxidation of iron by hot magmatic gases. Thin pieces of obsidian are almost transparent.

Obsidian forms lava flows and rounded domes above volcanic vents. It also is found as thin selvages along the edges of intrusions, and, rarely, makes small intrusive masses. Most intrusive obsidians have a dull, pitchlike luster, and are called *pitchstone.*

Pumice. Pumice is obsidian froth, characteristically light-gray to white and crowded with tiny bubbles. The bubbles are so numerous that pumice will float on water. Pumice is abundant as fragments in tuffs and breccias. It also may form distinct flows, or more commonly, it caps flows of obsidian or rhyolite, and grades downward into the unfrothed lava beneath.

Table III–2 **Igneous rocks**

TEXTURES	PREDOMINANT MINERALS			
	Feldspar and quartz	*Feldspar predominates (no quartz)*	*Ferromagnesian minerals and feldspar (no quartz)*	*Ferromagnesian minerals (no quartz or feldspar)*
PYROCLASTIC	**Volcanic tuff** (fragments up to 4 mm in diameter) **Volcanic Breccia** (fragments more than 4 mm in diameter)			Rocks of the texture and composition represented by this part of the table are rare.
GLASSY	**Obsidian** (if massive glass) **Pumice** (if a glass froth)		**Basalt Glass**	
APHANITIC (generally porphyritic-aphanitic)	**Rhyolite** and **Dacite**	**Andesite**	**Basalt**	
GRANULAR	**Granite** (potassium feldspar predominates) and **Granodiorite** (plagioclase feldspar predominates)	**Diorite**	**Gabbro** **Dolerite** or **Diabase** (if fine grained)	**Peridotite** (with both olivine and pyroxene) **Pyroxenite** (with pyroxene only) **Serpentine** (with altered olivine and pyroxene)

INCREASING GRAIN SIZE →

⟵ DECREASING SILICA CONTENT ⟶

Basalt Glass. Basalt glass is a jet-black natural glass formed by chilling of basaltic magma. Unlike obsidian, it is not noticeably transparent on thin edges. Basalt glass has never been found in large flows like those of obsidian; on this fact is based the inference that basalt magma crystallizes much more readily than rhyolite. Basalt glass forms thin crusts on the surfaces of lava flows, small fragments in volcanic breccia, and thin contact selvages in volcanic necks and dikes. Breccias of basalt glass form in abundance when basalt magma is extruded into water and quickly quenched. These may quickly alter to a yellow mineraloid called palagonite.

Rhyolite. Rhyolite has an aphanitic groundmass generally peppered with phenocrysts of quartz and potassium feldspar. The color of rhyolite ranges widely, but generally is white or light yellow, brown, or red. Most rhyolites are flow banded; that is, they show streaky irregular layers that were formed by the flowing of the sticky, almost congealed magma.

Dacite is like rhyolite except that plagioclase predominates instead of potassium feldspar. It bears the same relation to rhyolite that granodiorite does to granite (see below).

Rhyolite and dacite are found in lava flows and as small intrusions.

Andesite. Andesite is an aphanitic rock, generally porphyritic, that resembles dacite but contains no quartz. Plagioclase feldspar is the most common phenocryst, but pyroxene, amphibole, or biotite may appear. Most andesites are flow banded, though not so conspicuously as rhyolites. Andesites range from white to black, but most are dark gray or greenish gray.

Andesite is abundant as lava flows and as fragments in volcanic breccias, tuffs, and mudflows. Glacier-clad andesite volcanoes tower above mountain ranges such as the Andes (from which the name), the Cascades, and the Carpathians. Andesite also forms small intrusive masses.

Basalt. Basalt is a black to medium-gray aphanitic rock. Most basalts are nonporphyritic, but some contain phenocrysts of plagioclase and olivine.

Basalt is the world's most abundant lava and is very widespread, forming great lava plateaus that cover thousands of square miles in the northwestern United States, India, and elsewhere. It is the chief constituent of the isolated oceanic islands. Although it typically forms lava flows, basalt is also common in small intrusive masses.

Granite. Granite, characterized by a granular texture, has feldspar and quartz as its two most abundant minerals, and in consequence most granite is light colored. Biotite or hornblende, or both, are also present in most granite.

Technically, the term *granite* is reserved for those granular quartz-bearing igneous rocks that have potassium feldspar as the chief mineral. Those in which plagioclase predominates are called *granodiorite*. (Compare rhyolite and dacite above.) Granodiorite can usually be distinguished from granite by the fine striations that characterize one cleavage surface of plagioclase.

Geologic mapping shows that great quantities of granite and granodiorite are present in the earth's crust. They form large intrusive masses along the cores of many mountain ranges and in other areas where deep erosion has occurred, such as northeastern Canada, the Scandinavian region, and eastern Brazil. They are typical continental rocks; the Seychelles Islands of the Indian Ocean and Iceland are the only oceanic islands on which they occur in large masses.

Some granites are of metamorphic instead of igneous origin. (Chapters 3 and 18.)

Diorite. Diorite is a granular rock composed of plagioclase and lesser amounts of ferromagnesian minerals. The most common ferromagnesian minerals are hornblende, biotite, and pyroxene. In general, diorite masses are much smaller than those of granite or granodiorite.

Gabbro. Gabbro is a granular rock composed chiefly of plagioclase and pyroxene commonly with small amounts of other ferromagnesian minerals, especially olivine. If ferromagnesian minerals predominate over the plagioclase so that the rock is dark-colored, it is generally correct to call it gabbro, though the microscopic distinction from diorite rests on the composition of the plagioclase, a character not determinable with the unaided eye.

Gabbro is widely distributed in both large and small masses. Dikes and thin sills of fine-grained gabbro are especially common. In most of these small intrusions, the mineral grains are so small that they are barely recognizable without the aid of the microscope. Such gabbros, intermediate in grain size between basalt and normal gabbro, are called *dolerite*. (Some geologists prefer the name *diabase*.)

Peridotite, Pyroxenite, and Serpentine. Granular rocks composed almost entirely of ferromagnesian minerals and without feldspar are common in some areas. If the rock contains olivine as a conspicuous constituent, it is called *peridotite;* if it is made up almost wholly of pyroxenes, it is called *pyroxenite.*

Olivine is a very unstable mineral, easily altered to a mixture of greenish hydrous minerals. Some varieties of pyroxene also alter easily. These alterations probably occur soon after consolidation of the magma and are caused by the hot gases and solutions that escape from the crystallizing peridotite or perhaps from nearby granite or gabbro masses. Such altered peridotites and pyroxenites are called *serpentine*. Because serpentine is composed almost entirely of secondary minerals which did not solidify directly out of the magma, it is often classed as a metamorphic rock instead of an igneous rock. Nearly all plutonic igneous rocks, however, show some features that suggest alteration and "working over" by hot gases during the last stages of crystallization, although most are not modified as much as serpentine.

Serpentine forms sills, dikes, and other small intrusive masses.

Porphyry. This ancient term is used rather indefinitely. It may be applied to porphyritic-textured, fine-grained intrusive igneous rocks in which phenocrysts constitute 25 percent or more of the volume. The groundmass may be either coarse-grained, aphanitic, or fine-grained granular. The name of the rock whose composition and texture fit the groundmass part of the rock is usually prefixed to the word porphyry. Thus *diorite* porphyry has a fine-grained granular groundmass and contains abundant phenocrysts of plagioclase and perhaps some ferromagnesian mineral. Andesite porphyry is similar except that the groundmass is aphanitic.

The noun "porphyry," as distinguished from the adjective "porphyritic," should not be applied to porphyritic rocks with a coarse granular groundmass or to porphyritic lava containing abundant glass. The former should be called porphyritic diorite and the latter porphyritic andesite if they have the same composition as diorite and andesite.

Granite porphyry, granodiorite porphyry, and diorite porphyry form many dikes near granite and granodorite masses. Rhyolite porphyry, dacite porphyry, and andesite porphyry are common in volcanic plugs and other small intrusive masses.

Metamorphic rocks

Hornfels. Hard, unfoliated, very fine-grained rock which breaks into sharp angular pieces. In many hornfelses traces of original structures such as stratification, flow banding, or slaty cleavage can be seen, but the rock will not break along them. The mineral composition is highly variable, and grains are, in general, too small to be recognizable without a microscope.

Hornfels is formed by the partial or complete recrystallization, near an igneous intrusion, of such fine-grained rocks as shale, shaly limestone, slate, chlorite schist, tuff, and lavas.

Quartzite. Very hard, sugary-textured granoblastic rock, composed predominantly of interlocking quartz grains. Unlike most sandstones, quartzite breaks across the grains, not around them. Colors range from white through pale buff to pink, red, brown, and black, but most quartzite is light colored.

Quartzite is formed by the metamorphism of quartz sandstone. It is a widely distributed metamorphic rock.

Sandstone with a cement of silica (sedimentary "quartzite") is difficult to tell from metamorphic quartzite since both break across the grains. Distinction by use of the petrographic microscope is usually not difficult, for the cement can be readily distinguished from the original sand grains. Metamorphic quartzite can also be distinguished from silica-cemented sandstone by the rocks associated with it in the field, for true quartzite is associated with other metamorphic rocks, and sandstone with other sedimentary rocks.

Marble. Granoblastic, fine- to coarse-grained rock composed chiefly of calcite or dolomite or both. Many marbles show a streaky alteration of light and dark patches; others show brecciated structures healed by veinlets of calcite.

Marble is formed by the metamorphism of limestone and dolomite; if from dolomite, it commonly contains magnesium-bearing silicates such as pyroxene, amphibole, and serpentine.

Table III–3 **Metamorphic rocks**

Name	Texture	Commonly derived from	Chief minerals
UNFOLIATED OR FAINTLY FOLIATED			
Hornfels	Hornfelsic	Any fine-grained rock	Highly variable
Quartzite	Granoblastic, fine grained	Sandstone	Quartz
Marble	Granoblastic	Limestone, dolomite	Calcite, magnesium and calcium silicates
Tactite	Granoblastic, but coarse and variable	Limestone or dolomite plus magmatic emanations	Varied; chiefly silicates of iron, calcium, and magnesium, such as garnet, epidote, pyroxene, amphibole
Amphibolite	Granoblastic	Basalt, gabbro, tuff	Hornblende and plagioclase, minor garnet and quartz
Granulite	Granoblastic	Shale, graywacke, or igneous rocks	Feldspar, pyroxene, garnet, kyanite, and other silicates
FOLIATED			
Slate (and **Phyllite**)	Slaty	Shale, tuff	Mica, quartz
Chlorite schist	Schistose to slaty	Basalt, andesite, tuff	Chlorite, plagioclase, epidote
Mica schist	Schistose	Shale, tuff, rhyolite	Muscovite, quartz, biotite
Amphibole schist	Schistose	Basalt, andesite, gabbro, tuff	Amphibole, plagioclase
Gneiss	Gneissose	Granite, shale, diorite, mica schist, rhyolite, etc.	Feldspar, quartz, mica, amphibole, garnet, etc.
Migmatite	Coarsely banded, highly variable	Mixtures of igneous and metamorphic rocks	Feldspar, amphibole, quartz, biotite

Tactite. Granoblastic, but variable in texture, grain size, and mineral composition. Tactite is rich in silicates of calcium, iron, and magnesium—amphibole, pyroxene, garnet, and epidote. It occurs in many areas where limestone or dolomite has been invaded by granite or granodiorite. From this it is inferred that fluids escaping from the congealing magma have carried into the limestone large quantities of silica, iron, and other substances that combined with the calcite and dolomite to form new minerals. Ores of iron, copper, tungsten, and other metals may be associated with these rocks.

Amphibolite. Granoblastic, rocks consisting chiefly of plagioclase and amphibole. Garnet, quartz, and epidote may be present in small quantities. Amphibolites have been formed by the metamorphism of basalt, gabbro, and rocks of similar composition; some are derived from impure dolomite.

Granulite. Granoblastic-textured, medium- to coarse-grained rock consisting chiefly of feldspars, pyroxenes, and garnet, but commonly containing small amounts of many other minerals such as quartz, kyanite, and staurolite. Most show an indefinite streakiness or a faint foliation. The feldspar may show a fine mottling when viewed under a lens or microscope. Granulites are formed by the high-grade metamorphism of shale, graywacke, and many kinds of igneous rock.

Slate and Phyllite. Very fine-grained, exceptionally well-foliated rocks. Because of their excellent foliation, they split into thin sheets. Mineral grains are too small to be identified without the microscope or X-rays. Slate is dull on cleavage surfaces; phyllite is shiny and coarser grained, containing some mineral grains large enough to be identified by the eye. Slate and, to a lesser extent, phyllite, commonly show remnants of sedimentary features such as stratification, pebbles, and fossils.

Slate and phyllite are abundant. Most were formed by the metamorphism of shale, but others are derived from tuffs or other fine-grained rocks.

Chlorite Schist or Greenschist. Green, very fine-grained, schistose to slaty rock. Most are soft, greasy, and easily pulverized, composed of chlorite, plagioclase, and epidote—all except chlorite generally are in grains too small to identify. Remnants of original volcanic structures such as phenocrysts and scoria may be present.

Chlorite schists are common. They are often called *greenschist* or, if poorly foliated, *greenstone,* from the color of the chlorite. Most have formed by metamorphism of basalt or andesite and their corresponding tuffs, but some have been derived from dolomitic shale, gabbro, and other ferromagnesian rocks.

Mica Schist. Schistose rock composed chiefly of muscovite, quartz, and biotite in varying proportions; any one of these minerals may predominate. The most common varieties are rich in muscovite.

Mica schist is one of the most abundant metamorphic rocks. Like slate, most has been formed from shales and tuffs, although some derives from arkose, shaly sandstone, rhyolite, or other rocks. It represents more intense metamorphism than slate.

Amphibole Schist. Schistose rock, composed chiefly of amphibole and plagioclase, with varying amounts of garnet, quartz, or biotite. It is a common metamorphic derivative of basalt, gabbro, chlorite schist, and related rocks.

Gneiss. Coarse-grained gneissose rock with distinct layers or lenses of different minerals. Mineral composition is variable, but feldspar especially abundant. Other minerals common in gneiss are quartz, amphibole, garnet, and mica.

Gneisses are among the most plentiful metamorphic rocks. They may be derived from many different rocks—granite, granodiorite, shale, rhyolite, diorite, slate, and schist, among others.

Migmatite. Migmatites are highly complex rocks (see Chapter 18 and Fig. 18–42). In general, they are intimate small-scale mixtures of igneous and metamorphic rocks, characterized by a roughly banded or veined appearance. They are widespread, especially near large granite masses. Their mineral composition is complex and highly variable, but most contain abundant feldspar and quartz, and smaller amounts of biotite, and amphibole.

Appendix **IV**

Chemical Data

Table IV–1 **The atomic numbers, symbols, and names of the elements**

Atomic number	Symbol	Element	Atomic number	Symbol	Element
1	H	Hydrogen	37	Rb	Rubidium
2	He	Helium	38	Sr	Strontium
3	Li	Lithium	39	Y	Yttrium
4	Be	Beryllium	40	Zr	Zirconium
5	B	Boron	41	Nb	Niobium
6	C	Carbon	42	Mo	Molybdenum
7	N	Nitrogen	43	Tc	Technetium
8	O	Oxygen	44	Ru	Ruthenium
9	F	Fluorine	45	Rh	Rhodium
10	Ne	Neon	46	Pd	Palladium
11	Na	Sodium	47	Ag	Silver
12	Mg	Magnesium	48	Cd	Cadmium
13	Al	Aluminum	49	In	Indium
14	Si	Silicon	50	Sn	Tin
15	P	Phosphorus	51	Sb	Antimony
16	S	Sulfur	52	Te	Tellurium
17	Cl	Chlorine	53	I	Iodine
18	Ar	Argon	54	Xe	Xenon
19	K	Potassium	55	Cs	Cesium
20	Ca	Calcium	56	Ba	Barium
21	Sc	Scandium	57	La	Lanthanum
22	Ti	Titanium	58	Ce	Cerium
23	V	Vanadium	59	Pr	Praseodymium
24	Cr	Chromium	60	Nd	Neodymium
25	Mn	Manganese	61	Pm	Promethium
26	Fe	Iron	62	Sm	Samarium
27	Co	Cobalt	63	Eu	Europium
28	Ni	Nickel	64	Gd	Gadolinium
29	Cu	Copper	65	Tb	Terbium
30	Zn	Zinc	66	Dy	Dysprosium
31	Ga	Gallium	67	Ho	Holmium
32	Ge	Germanium	68	Er	Erbium
33	As	Arsenic	69	Tm	Thulium
34	Se	Selenium	70	Yb	Ytterbium
35	Br	Bromine	71	Lu	Lutetium
36	Kr	Krypton	72	Hf	Hafnium

*Table IV–1—***Continued**

Atomic number	Symbol	Element	Atomic number	Symbol	Element
73	Ta	Tantalum	88	Ra	Radium
74	W	Tungsten	89	Ac	Actinium
75	Re	Rhenium	90	Th	Thorium
76	Os	Osmium	91	Pa	Protactinium
77	Ir	Iridium	92	U	Uranium
78	Pt	Platinum	93	Np	Neptunium
79	Au	Gold	94	Pu	Plutonium
80	Hg	Mercury	95	Am	Americium
81	Tl	Thallium	96	Cm	Curium
82	Pb	Lead	97	Bk	Berkelium
83	Bi	Bismuth	98	Cf	Californium
84	Po	Polonium	99	E	Einsteinium
85	At	Astatine	100	Fm	Fermium
86	Rn	Radon	101	My	Mendellium
87	Fr	Francium	102	No	Nobelium

Table IV–2 **Chemical composition of the earth's crust, ocean, and atmosphere**

Element	Rocky crust (a)	Rocky crust (b)	Ocean	Atmosphere (dry air to height of 25 kilometers)
O	46.6%	43.8	85.79%	21.0%
Si	27.7	27.0	. . .	. . .
Al	8.1	10.0	. . .	. . .
Fe	5.0	5.9	. . .	. . .
Ca	3.6	5.1	. . .	. . .
Na	2.8	2.2	1.14	. . .
K	2.6	1.7	. . .	. . .
Mg	2.1	3.2	0.14	. . .
Ti	0.4	1.0	. . .	. . .
H	0.14		10.67	. . .
Cl	0.03		2.07	. . .
N	0.005		. . .	78.1
A	. . .		. . .	0.9
CO_2	. . .		. . .	0.03 (variable)

NOTES AND SOURCES:
(a) As estimated from composition of exposed rocks. (After B. Mason, 1952.)
(b) As estimated from seismic properties of the crust correlated with chemical compositions of rocks having similar elastic properties. (After L. C. Pakiser and R. Robinson, 1966.)

Table IV–3 **Averaged chemical compositions of igneous rocks and sedimentary rocks**

Constituent	Igneous rocks	Sedimentary rocks
SiO_2	59.14%	57.95%
TiO_2	1.05	0.57
Al_2O_3	15.34	13.39
Fe_2O_3	3.08	3.47
FeO	3.80	2.08
MgO	3.49	2.65
CaO	5.08	5.89
Na_2O	3.84	1.13
K_2O	3.13	2.86
H_2O	1.15	3.23
P_2O_5	0.30	0.13
CO_2	0.10	5.38
SO_3	. . .	0.54
BaO	0.06	. . .
C	. . .	0.66
Total	99.56	99.93

NOTES AND SOURCES: The compositions in the table above are based on 5159 analyses of igneous rocks compiled by F. W. Clarke, and on selected analyses of sedimentary rocks compiled by C. K. Leith and W. F. Mead. The sedimentary rocks have been weighted in the proportions of 82 percent shale, 12 percent sandstone and 6 percent limestone. The compositions are reported as *oxides*, which is the conventional system for reporting data on the composition of rocks and minerals.

Table IV–4 **Chemical composition of dissolved solids in river water and in the sea**

Ion	River water (weighted average)	Sea water
CO_3^{--}	35.15%	0.41 (HCO_3^-)%
SO_4^{--}	12.14	7.68
Cl^-	5.68	55.04
NO_3^-	0.90	. . .
Ca^{++}	20.39	1.15
Mg^{++}	3.41	3.69
Na^+	5.79	30.62
K^+	2.12	1.10
$(Fe, Al)_2O_3$	2.75	. . .
SiO_2	11.67	. . .
Sr^{++}, H_3BO_3, Br^-	. . .	0.31
Total	100.00	100.00

SOURCE: After F. W. Clarke.

Fossils

Life is virtually ubiquitous over the earth, from high in the air, where pollen and single-celled organisms have been carried by the winds, to the deepest sunless trenches of the oceans. As we noted in Chapter 7, the more ancient the strata, the less do the fossils contained in them resemble living forms; our contemporary organisms, like ourselves, are the modified survivors—the best adjusted to present environments—of an almost incredibly great number of species, most long vanished from the earth. The study of living organisms is the province of the biologist; the study of their mostly unsuccessful ancestors or former competitors is the occupation of many paleontologists. Anything but a most cursory treatment is far beyond the scope of this book, but we feel that at least a sample of the diverse life-forms of the past should be presented.

To the zoologist, fossils are invaluable as a record of the evolution of life; for the paleontological geologist, in addition to the evolutionary record, they furnish clues to past environments and through the correlation of strata by short-lived forms of life provide basic data for the history of the earth. The ecologic niche of an individual modern relative cannot alone be evidence that its fossil analogues occupied the same environment. For example, in the Early Eocene (London Clay), the Nipa palm (now living in the Indo-Malayan area) and the mollusk *Astarte* lived in association. Most of the other fossils in the London Clay are related to modern tropical forms as is the Nipa palm, but all of the living members of the genus *Astarte* are found only in cold water and nowhere within thousands of kilometers of the present habitat of the palm. Obviously the *Astarte* line has adapted to a very different environment today than this genus occupied in the early Eocene. Though an individual genus may thus modify its living habits, associations comprised of many genera are not likely to. Faunal and floral *groups,* then, offer trustworthy guides to habitats of the geologic past, though, of course, less trustworthy the more remote the past.

THE PLANT AND ANIMAL KINGDOMS

The two great divisions of life are the plant and animal kingdoms. Most plants, as noted in Chapter 22, are able to synthesize organic matter from simple inorganic substances in the presence of light; animals live only on organic matter so produced, or on each other. Other living things, such as the bacteria, differ from both plants and animals in neither performing photosynthesis nor integrating organic compounds from others. Instead, they are the main agents of decay, breaking down complex organic matter into water, carbon dioxide, and simple salts. Without them, life could not have persisted to the present, for all the carbon in the atmosphere would long since have been combined in organic matter. As we saw (Fig. 7–1), bacteria are known from very old rocks of the Lake Superior country, and, in fact, have been identified in rocks of the Fig Tree Series of Swaziland, South Africa, known to be more than three billion years old. They probably evolved along with the blue-green algae as the earliest organisms on earth.

The plant kingdom has existed for many million more years than the animal kingdom, but its fossil residues are much less resistant to geologic processes, and it is only in rocks of Silurian and younger age that plant fossils useful in correlation are recognizable. For this reason, we consider the animal kingdom first, as its fossils are generally more abundant and therefore more useful even in the younger rocks.

The animal kingdom

Since the time of the great Swedish naturalist Linnaeus (1707–1778), biologists have classified the organisms of both plant and animal kingdoms in a hierarchy of his devising. The basic unit in the Linnaean System is the species, which may be defined as a population whose members may differ widely among themselves—as, for example, the Great Dane and the Mexican Hairless dogs—but are connected, through intermediate varieties, into an interbreeding group. Species closely similar but not normally interbreeding, such as dogs, wolves, and coyotes, are grouped as a single genus.

In identifying an individual in this system, both the generic and specific names, in latinized form, are used: the domestic dog is *Canis familiaris,* the coyote *Canis latrans.* The generic name is always capitalized, the specific name never, even when it has been derived from a proper name. Both are invariably printed in italics, generally followed by the name of the individual who first described and defined the species.

The genera are in turn grouped with similar ones into families, the families into orders, etc. The hierarchy of the Linnaean System is as follows:

Kingdom
  Phylum
    Class
      Order
        Family
          Genus
            Species

As noted in Chapter 7, the history of life is a history of successions of species, some long-lived, some very short-lived, so that assemblages of the faunas and floras have continually changed through time by natural selection of those species best suited to a contemporary environment and elimination of those less fit. New species arose through successive mutations that tended better to fit a creature to its environment; deleterious mutations led to prompt elimination of the line in which they took place. Even without unfavorable mutations a species might be eliminated by the competition of a newly evolved, more efficient competitor or by its own inability to adjust to environmental changes clearly indicated in the geologic record. Thus random mutations and environmental changes have enabled natural selection not only to produce the remarkably divergent species of fossil and living organisms, but also to permit the adaptation of some form or other to almost every environment on or near the earth's surface, in every water body, and through much of the atmosphere.

ANIMAL FOSSILS

The Great Auk became extinct in 1844, the passenger pigeon soon after. The aurochs, Irish elk, mammoth, and mastodon, painted on many a cave wall by Pleistocene men, did not survive that epoch. The one-toed horse did not evolve until the Pleistocene, but his ancestry is well documented back to the Eocene, with characteristic intermediate forms at various spans of the Tertiary. The geologic time scale has been developed by intercomparisons of the fossil assemblages of known stratigraphic succession. Such intercomparisons show that the several classes of the animal kingdom are represented by fossils during the time intervals shown in Table V-1, though, of course, no single species survived even a small fraction of the time its class existed.

Though, as the table shows, many Classes have long pedigrees, it should not be overlooked that at the next lower rung of the Linnaean ladder, most of the Orders are far more limited in their time span. The orders Blastoidea, Cystoidea, Ophiocistoidea, and Heterostela among the Echinodermata, for example, are all limited to the Paleozoic; they have since been extinct. All of the Ammonoidea, among the stratigraphically most useful orders of the Cephalopoda because they swarmed in the seas of the late Paleozoic and Mesozoic, had died out by the end of the Cretaceous. Many other examples could be given. The earliest mammals are of Triassic age, the earliest birds of Jurassic, both descended from reptilian stock.

We cannot, of course, in a book of this size offer a systematic coverage of paleontology; all we can do is to offer a few examples of the kind of material that has been used in the compilation of the geologic time scale, and is still used as the primary basis of correlation of the stratified rocks.

Protozoa

Figure 17–27 illustrates a representative collection of Foraminifera from the ocean floor off Central America. Although Fora-

Table V–1 **Life spans of some classes of the animal kingdom**

Phylum	Class	Life Span
Protozoa (one-celled)	Foraminifera	Cambrian to Recent
	Radiolaria	Cambrian (Precambrian?) to Recent
Porifera (sponges)	several varieties	Cambrian to Recent
Coelenterata (corals and related forms)	Hydrozoa	Cambrian? to Recent
	Anthozoa	Ordovician to Recent
Brachiopoda (lamp-shells)	Inarticulata	Cambrian to Recent
	Articulata	Cambrian to Recent
Bryozoa ("moss-corals")	Phylactolaemata	Cretaceous to Recent
	Gymnolaemata	Ordovician to Recent
Annelida (worms)	several varieties	Precambrian to Recent
Arthropoda	Trilobita (trilobites)	Cambrian through Permian
	Crustacea (lobsters, crabs)	Cambrian to Recent
	Arachnida (spiders, scorpions)	Cambrian to Recent
	Insecta (insects)	Devonian to Recent
Molluska	Gastropoda (snails)	Cambrian to Recent
	Pelecypoda (clams)	Cambrian to Recent
	Cephalopoda (squids, nautilids)	Cambrian to Recent
Echinodermata (echinoids)	Pelmatozoa (sea lilies)	Cambrian to Recent
	Eleutherozoa (star fish)	Cambrian to Recent
Chordata	Graptolithina (graptolites)	Cambrian to Carboniferous
	Vertebrata (vertebrates)	Ordovician to Recent

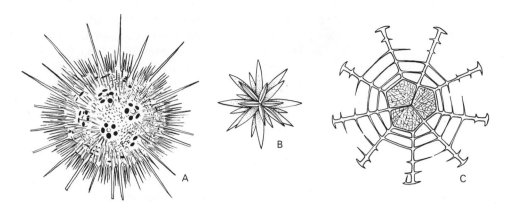

FIGURE V–1 *Some representative Radiolaria.* A: Haeckeliana (*Recent*). B: Zygacantha (*Recent*). C: Tetraphormis (*Cretaceous to Recent*). (*After A. S. Campbell, in* Treatise on Invertebrate Paleontology, *Part D, edited by R. C. Moore, Geological Society of America and University of Kansas Press, 1954.*)

minifera have been reported from rocks as old as Cambrian, their record is very limited until early in the Carboniferous. They abounded during Cretaceous time and fragments of their minute skeletons are common constituents of the widespread chalks that gave the name to the system. A genus of Foraminifera whose members were much larger, some several centimeters across, and coin-shaped, the *Nummulites,* was very prominent in the Eocene and Oligocene; the Pyramids of Egypt are faced with limestone mainly composed of their shells. In later Tertiary and Quaternary time these larger species disappeared, and few foraminifers of the living genera exceed a millimeter or two in length; many are much smaller. The Radiolaria, also minute unicellular organisms (Fig. V-1), have tests composed of silica rather than of calcium carbonate as foraminiferal shells are. They have been reported from the Precambrian rocks of Brittany but there is some question as to the correctness of the identification. Certainly they have persisted ever since the beginning of the Cambrian. The Radiolaria and the Foraminifera have been much studied during the past few decades, because their small size commonly enables them to escape being ground up during rotary drilling operations

(as are most larger fossils). Foraminifers especially have proved useful in subsurface correlations of strata from one oil well to another.

Porifera

The stratigraphically most useful class of the Porifera is the Archaeocyathidae (Fig. V-2) considered an independent phylum by some students; these conical creatures were confined to the Cambrian, and since they are readily recognized, serve as particularly valuable "guide fossils." Although sponges have been recognized in all later systems, most of them are so simple and so readily disintegrated that they are of little value stratigraphically.

Coelenterata

The Hydrozoa, represented today by such creatures as the sea anemone and jellyfish, are known by traces from the early Paleozoic, but are so sparse and generally poorly preserved that they are of little value below the Cenozoic. In the Cenozoic they are represented by ancestors of the living "staghorn" corals and by the Millepora, or stinging corals, which form colonies an inch or two

FIGURE V–2
Syringocnema, a Lower and Middle Cambrian archaeocyathid. (After V. J. Okulitch, in Treatise on Invertebrate Paleontology, *Part E, edited by R. C. Moore, Geological Society of America and University of Kansas Press, 1955)*

thick, and grow in wall-like patterns as minor constituents of living coral reefs.

Much more important as stratigraphic aids are the Anthozoa, or true corals. Of these, the subclass Tetracoralla, or horn corals, were very prominent from the Ordovician through the Paleozoic (Fig. V-3,A,B). Other members of this subclass formed chains, such as *Halysites* (Fig. V-3,C), or compact masses, such as *Favosites* (Fig. V-3,D); these were especially abundant in Silurian and Devonian time and became extinct at the close of the Paleozoic.

The subclass Hexacoralla arose during the Mesozoic and is now the dominant variety. These organisms have radial symmetry and are either colonial or solitary. The shallow-water colonial forms are confined to warm seas, but many solitary forms live in very deep and cold environments.

Brachiopoda

Brachiopods are solitary marine animals, commonly anchored by a stalk. The phylum is in decline, represented during the Cenozoic by less than a third of the number of genera that lived in the Ordovician. They are relatively small shelled creatures, generally about an inch or so across; the largest ever found was only about a foot wide. They are bivalves; in the Class Inarticulata, the valves are held together by muscles alone. The Class Articulata has toothed hinges as well as muscles for this service. One inarticulate brachiopod, *Lingula,* has survived from the Ordovician to the present day with little change in form—perhaps the longest lived

FIGURE V–3   A *and* B: Streptelasma trilobatum *Whiteaves, a Late Ordovician horn coral. (After R. J. Ross, Jr., U.S. Geological Survey, 1957.)* C: Halysites catenularius *Edwards and Haime, a Late Ordovician chain coral. (After R. G. Creadick, 1941, via H. W. Shimer and R. R. Schrock,* Index Fossils of North America, *M.I.T. Press, 1944.)* D: Favosites prolificus *Billings, a Late Ordovician compact coral. (After R. J. Ross, Jr., U.S. Geological Survey, 1957.)*

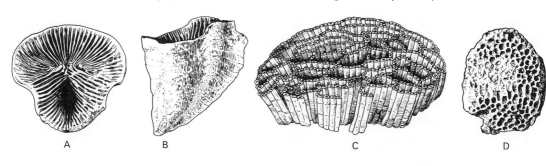

A   B   C   D

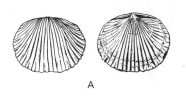

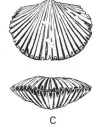

A   B   C

FIGURE V–4   A: Dinorthis occidentalis *Okulitch, Late Ordovician, Montana.* B: Lepidocyclus gigas *Wang, Late Ordovician, Montana.* C: Austinella whitfieldi *Winchell and Schuchert, Middle or Late Ordovician, Idaho.* (*Representative Ordovician brachiopods, after R. J. Ross, Jr., U.S. Geological Survey, 1957.*)

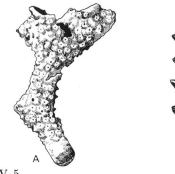

A   B

FIGURE V–5
A. Hallopora ramosa *d'Orbigny, from the Ordovician of Ohio.* (*After C. O. Dunbar,* Historical Geology, *John Wiley and Sons, 1960.*) B. Archimedes wortheni *Hall, a common bryozoan in the Mississippian of Missouri.* (*After H. W. Shimer and R. R. Shrock,* Index Fossils of North America, *M.I.T. Press, 1944.*)

genus known. Most inarticulate brachiopods have phosphatic shells, whereas all the articulate forms have calcareous shells. Figure V-4 illustrates some articulate species from the Late Ordovician of Montana and from the Middle or Late Ordovician of Idaho.

Bryozoa

Bryozoa are extremely small animals but they, like the corals, commonly grow into fantastically complex colonies attached to the sea floor. Many colonies are branching, others have leaf-like forms, but all are characterized by minute tubules and perforations in which the individual animals lived (Fig. V-5,A) . As they grow, some colonies change form, even so drastically that broken fragments of fossils, now known from perfect matching of the fractured ends to have belonged to a single colony, earlier had been mistakenly assigned not merely to different species but to different genera! The identification of most bryozoa is a matter for experts, but some readily recognized genera have proved very useful "guide fossils." For example, the genus *Archimedes,* so-called because of its resemblance to the Archimedes screw used for raising water in many primitive cultures, is a guide to the Mississippian of the midcontinental United States, though its range extends into the early Pennsylvanian of the western Cordillera (Fig. V-5,B) .

Annelida

Although annelid worms are known from both Precambrian strata and younger rocks, their soft parts are so poorly preserved that they are almost useless as stratigraphic guides. A few lived in protective calcareous tubes: thus *Serpula,* though a long lived genus, is useful in certain stratigraphic investigations. Its characteristic coiled tubes are practicable markers in the Cenozoic of California. Worm marking and trails formed in soft sediments are very common, and are similarly useful in some places, even though these rather vague markings are not demonstrably restricted to strata of one age.

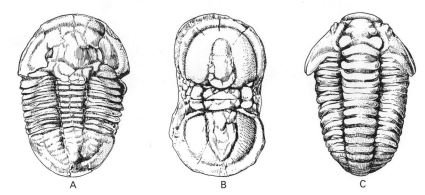

FIGURE V–6   A: Asaphiscus wheeleri *Meek*. B: Peronopsis interstrictus *White. Both are Middle Cambrian trilobites from the House Range, Utah. (After A. R. Palmer, U.S. Geological Survey, 1954.)* C: Flexicalymene retrorsa *Foerste, Lake Ordovician, Ohio. (After R. J. Ross, Jr., U.S. Geological Survey, 1967.)*

Arthropoda

The phylum Arthropoda contains, in the class Insecta alone, many times as many genera as all the other phyla together. But the most important stratigraphically are the Trilobita, a class that flourished in the Cambrian and Ordovician and then gradually lessened in abundance and finally died out in the Permian. Any fossil of this class is thus conclusive evidence of the Paleozoic age of the strata containing it; the genera are, of course, much more limited in range than the class as a whole and allow the rocognition of many restricted stratigraphic zones, especially in the early Paleozoic. The name refers to the three longitudinal lobes that all these creatures have, a characteristic immediately definitive of the class. A few representative specimens are illustrated in Figure V-6.

Despite their prodigious numbers, both of individuals and of species, insects have left few fossil records, though some are preserved with great clarity (Fig. V-7). Some Carboniferous cockroaches were as long as 10 centimeters. Because of their rarity, insect fossils are not as valuable as those of many other classes.

Much more useful as stratigraphic guides are the minute bivalved Ostracoda, which are crustacea, distantly related to the modern

FIGURE V–7
A fossil Plecia *from the Green River Shale, Eocene, Wyoming. (After W. H. Bradley, U.S. Geological Survey.)*

crabs. Like the Foraminifera and Radiolaria, many ostracods are small enough to escape destruction during well-drilling and thus are useful in oilfield correlations.

Although a few fossil spiders have been recognized, the most important arachnids,

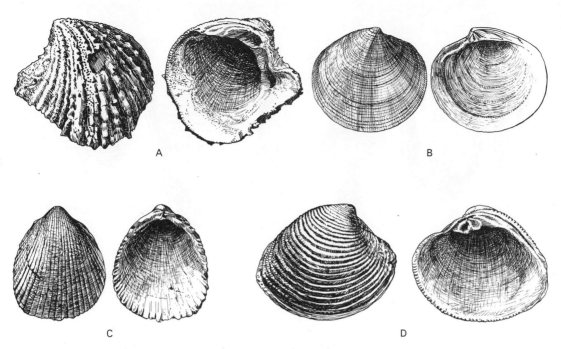

FIGURE V–8   *Some Miocene clams from Jamaica.* A: Echinochama antiqua. B: Codakia spinulosa. C: Cardium (Trachycardium) waylandi. D: Chione sawkinsi. (*After W. P. Woodring, U.S. Geological Survey, 1925.*)

stratigraphically, are the eurypterids, giant water scorpions, some as long as 2 meters. They flourished from Ordovician to Permian time, when their line died out.

Molluska

Among the most useful fossils are the mollusks: the gastropods (snails), pelecypods (clams), and cephalopods, all of which have flourished from the Cambrian to the present day, though many orders have had much shorter life spans. The Lamellibranchia (pelecypods) were not abundant until the late Paleozoic but are extremely useful in strata of that age and younger. Representative examples of some Miocene clams are illustrated in Figure V-8.

Gastropoda, the class to which the snails belong, were also not abundant until the Carboniferous, but their fossils, too, are both abundant in and useful for stratigraphic correlations of rocks of that and younger ages. Representatives of several varieties are illustrated in Figure V-9.

The Cephalopoda, represented by the present-day chambered nautilus of the Philippine Seas and by the more widespread octopus and squid, have been known in rocks of all ages from Cambrian on. The squid shell is internal and not well developed; the squid's only stratigraphically important fossil relatives are the belemnoids, which lived from the Mississippian to the Paleocene. Their fossil remains are the cigar-shaped internal shells, very dense and solid. They abound in the Cretaceous but are not good guide fossils because of their simplicity.

Far more important stratigraphically are extinct cephalopods that are related to the living nautilus: the rather similar Nautiloidea and the Ammonoidea. Both orders had

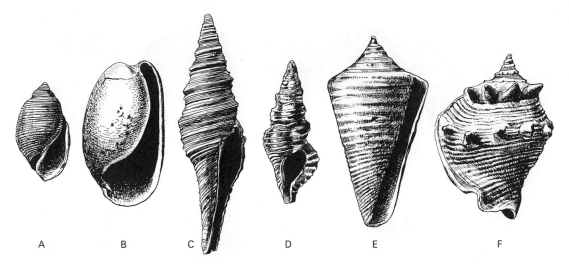

FIGURE V–9   *Some Miocene snails from Jamaica.* A: Acteon textilis. B: Bulla vendryesiana. C: Polystira barretti. D: Carinodrillia bocatoroensis. E: Conus (Leptoconus) planiliratus. F: Strombus bifrons. (*After W. P. Woodring, U.S. Geological Survey, 1928.*)

FIGURE V–10
A: *A nautiloid cephalopod, showing representative sutures.* (*After K. von Zittel, 1916.*) B: *An orthoceratid of the Ordovician.* (*After C. R. Knight.*) C: Plectoceras occidentale, *a loosely coiled Ordovician nautiloid.* (*After C. O. Dunbar,* Historical Geology, *John Wiley and Sons, 1960.*)

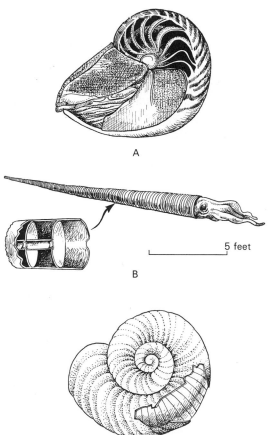

chambered shells. As the animal—and the shell—grew, he successively vacated the smaller inner chambers, leaving them filled only with air and thus enabling the organism to float. All the chambers were connected by a narrow tube, the siphuncle. The classification of the nautiloids depends largely on the location of the siphuncle and the pattern of the junctions (called sutures) of the partitions that formed living chambers with the wall of the outer shell. The nautiloids have been in existence since the Late Cambrian, but they are doubtless a dying class, represented now only by the single genus *Nautilus.* In the nautiloids the partitions between the successive living chambers are simply curved walls so that their sutures, too, are simple curves (Figure V-10,A). The early forms left mostly straight conical shells. Some forms from the Ordovician are as much as 5 meters long and 25 centimeters across the large end—they were doubtless the most formidable carnivores of their time (Fig. V-10,B). A few Ordovician nautiloids had loosely curved shells (Fig. V-10,C).

The Ammonoidea became differentiated from the nautiloids in Devonian time and died out at the end of the Cretaceous. They offer some of the most accurate stratigraphic correlations for the span of time in which they lived, as they were abundant, evolved rapidly, and their floating dead bodies were widely distributed by currents. They are differentiated from the nautiloids by more complex septa between the chambers; accordingly the sutures where the septa join the shell are more complex. Sutures of the goniatites, which lived in the late Paleozoic, are rather simple multiple curves (Fig. V-11,A), but in the later evolving ammonites they become complex, indeed (Fig. V-11,B).

Most of the ammonites were coiled rather tightly, but some were less tightly coiled, and others, though evidently coiled at immature stages, became nearly straight when adult. Examples are shown in Figure V-11,C,D, and E.

FIGURE V–11   A: *Representative goniatite sutures.* B: *representative ammonite sutures. The left-hand end of the patterns corresponds to the middle of the whorl; the sutures were symmetrical about this line.* C: Baculites thomi *Reeside.* D: Exiteloceras jenneyi *Whitfield.* E: Didymoceras nebrascence *Meek and Hayden. (C, D, and E are all Late Cretaceous species, courtesy of W. A. Cobban, U.S. Geological Survey.)*

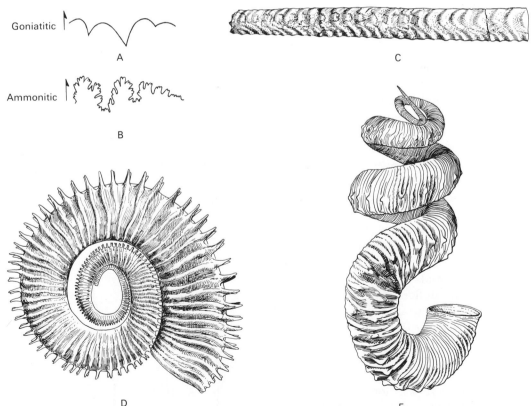

Goniatitic

A

Ammonitic

B

C

D

E

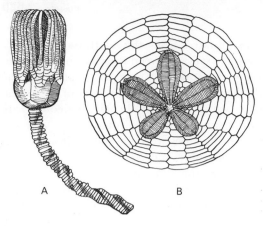

FIGURE V–12

A: *Platycrinites hemisphericus, a Mississippian crinoid.* (*After C. O. Dunbar,* Historical Geology, *John Wiley and Sons, 1960.*) B: *Dendraster eccentricus, a sea urchin living since the Pliocene.* (*After U. S. Grant and L. G. Hertlein,* Western American Cenozoic Echinoidea, *University of California Press, 1938.*)

Echinodermata

Echinoderms of both great classes, Pelmatozoa and Eleutherozoa, are found as fossils in rocks from the Cambrian to the present. The Pelmatozoa, represented by living sea lilies, are attached to the sea floor, some by stalks many feet high. Crinoids, another form of Pelmatozoa, were abundant in Paleozoic times. Many limestones contain so many segments of crinoid stalks as to be called crinoidal limestones. A representative Mississippian crinoid is illustrated in Figure V-12,A.

The Eleutherozoa, or mobile echinoids, occur as fossils in rocks from Cambrian to present, but were unimportant stratigraphically until the Mississippian. Since then starfishes and many other varieties have flourished. Echinoids of the kind represented by modern sand dollars have proven widely useful in Cenozoic stratigraphy. A Pliocene form is illustrated in Figure V-12,B.

Chordata

GRAPTOLITHINA. It was long thought that the earliest chordates were the primitive fish of the Ordovician, but in the late 1930's unusually well-preserved specimens of Graptolithina—a class hitherto assigned to a much more primitive evolutionary level—were recognized to be chordates. The earliest graptolithinas may be of Middle Cambrian age; by the late Cambrian they were widespread. The dendroids, an early form, resemble small ferns (Fig. V-13,A); their much more useful relatives, the graptolites, flourished from the Early Ordovician to the beginning of the Devonian, when they died out. Most graptolites have been flattened between the bedding surfaces of shales. They look like pencil marks (hence the name, from the Greek for "written rock"). Those few that have been found as three-dimensional fossils in limestone or chert permit something to be learned of their anatomy, including the fact that they had notochords, a characteristic feature of chordates.

Most graptolites were very small creatures, rarely more than a few centimeters long, though some as long as 50 centimeters have been found in Silurian strata. They are

FIGURE V–13

A: Dendrograptus fruticosus *Hall, Lower Ordovician, Quebec.* B: Tetragraptus fruticosus *Hall, Lower Ordovician, Quebec.* C: Dicranograptus ramosus longicaulis *Elles and Wood, Middle Ordovician, Scotland.* D: Monograptus turriculatus *Barrande, Lower Silurian, Bohemia.* E: Monograptus dubius *Suess, Upper Silurian, England.* (*After O. M. B. Bulman, in* Treatise on Invertebrate Paleontology, *Part V, edited by R. C. Moore, Geological Society of America and University of Kansas Press, 1955.*)

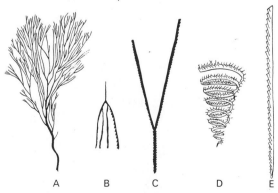

thought to have floated freely in the sea, supported by tiny air sacs, and because this facilitated wide distribution, they are unusually valuable for long distance correlations. A few examples are illustrated in Figure V-13,B,C,D, and E.

VERTEBRATA. We know no living descendants of the graptolites; it seems most unlikely that they are in any way connected with vertebrate evolution, despite their relatively advanced nervous systems. From what phylum, then, did the vertebrates evolve? Some students have thought, because amphibians resemble eurypterids in form, that an arachnid stem might be ancestral. Physiologically, however, the eurypterids differ fundamentally from even the most primitive vertebrates. Others have thought the worms might be ancestral to the vertebrates because some worms have principal nerves approaching the mammalian spinal cord in form, but here too there are fundamental physiological difficulties.

Perhaps the evolution of the vertebrates took place in an ecological setting different from that of any vertebrate fossil yet discovered. More likely our difficulties in tracing vertebrate ancestry are because evolution was by way of soft-bodied forms which were not preserved as fossils. At any rate, some authorities, notably Professor A. S. Romer of Harvard University, whose general ideas we are here following, think it likely that the vertebrates had an echinoid ancestry: our distant cousins the sea lilies are closer relatives than our other cousins, the scorpions and the worms of today!

Some bone fragments in the Ordovician of Colorado show that vertebrates existed then, but the earliest vertebrate fossils well-enough preserved for sound analysis are Late Silurian. These were small fish: jawless bottom-dwellers, mud-eaters with suckers rather than teeth, heavily armored (presumably against the giant carnivorous eurypterids of the time, but possibly as protection against lethal solar radiation). Because of their bony

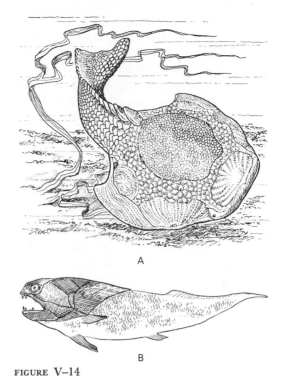

FIGURE V–14
A: *An ostracoderm,* Psammolepis. (*After Mark and Bystrow, courtesy of Alfred S. Romer, Harvard University.*) B: *A giant Late Devonian placoderm,* Dinichthys, *some of which attained a length of 30 feet.* (*After Obruchev, 1964, courtesy of Alfred S. Romer, Harvard University.*)

armor, these primitive fish are called ostracoderms, from the Greek word for "bone skinned" (Fig. V-14,A). Though differing tremendously in shape and in armor from any existing lamprey, they were physiologically so similar that they are considered ancestral both to the lamprey and to all higher vertebrates.

The kidney structures of the lampreys and all higher vertebrates suggest very strongly that they evolved from a freshwater ancestor, which may, at first, seem difficult to reconcile with the marine ancestry of all crinoids and of phyla from which vertebrates might have evolved. Because osmotic pressures through organic membranes must be balanced with those of the environment, the operation of the kidneys to separate excess salt from the blood stream is essential to life in a fresh-water environment. Though this function is most disadvantageous to marine life, all fish, even salt-water dwellers, retain kidneys that operate like our own; they have developed auxiliary organs to counter the kidney's activity. It seems most improbable that a marine organism without a freshwater ancestry would have developed both antithetic operations.

During the Devonian fishes multiplied and diversified so rapidly that the period is sometimes referred to as the Age of Fishes. Some abandoned their freshwater habitat and took to the sea. The first fishes with jaws evolved, and by the end of the period all four of the major groups of fish now known had been established:

(1) the Agnatha, represented by the ostracoderms and the modern lamprey;

(2) the Placodermi, the first jawed fishes, which had armored heads and grew to great size. These were undoubtedly the most ferocious carnivores of the Late Devonian but the line died out completely by the end of the Paleozoic (Fig. V-14,B).

(3) the Chondrichthyes, the ancestors of the modern sharks and other cartilagenous fish such as the rays and skates; and

(4) the Osteichthyes, or bony fish, ancestral to nearly all living vertebrates.

We can devote no space to the evolution of the first three of these groups; we pass directly to the bony fishes from which all other vertebrates and most modern fish have descended. And of the bony fishes, too, we will omit further discussion of the great group from which modern fish arose, and refer only to a second, very much smaller group, the fleshy-finned fishes—very unsuccessful as fishes, but rather important as the ancestors of the amphibians and of all land vertebrates, including ourselves.

Fleshy-finned fish.—The fleshy-finned fish divided, during the Devonian, into two groups: the lungfish and the lobe-finned fish. The

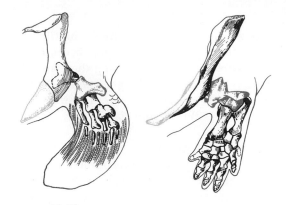

FIGURE V–15

A comparison between the fin of a Late Devonian lobe-finned fish, Eusthenopteron foordi, *and the limb of a primitive amphibian,* Euryops, *of late Paleozoic age. (After W. K. Gregory, via A. S. Romer,* The Vertebrate Story. *Copyright 1959 by The University of Chicago Press.)*

lungfish developed the ability to breathe air through a nostril in the top of its head. They were freshwater fish, and as the Devonian was a time of widespread deserts (Chapter 17), they adapted to a life of intermittent water-supply. When the stream or lake home dried up in summer, they could dig themselves holes in the muddy bottom, wrap themselves in mud, and survive by breathing air until the waters returned with the next rainy season. Like hibernating bears of cold countries they were wholly inactive while dormant. Descendants of the early lungfish, with much the same habits, live today in the upper Nile drainage, in Queensland, Australia, and in the Gran Chaco of Paraguay. Despite their partial adaptation to land life, their fins were never modified to permit walking; the land vertebrates were not derived from this subdivision of the fleshy-finned fish, but from their cousins, the lobe-finned fishes.

The lobe-finned fishes also developed lungs but at the same time they had a tremendous advantage over the ancestors of the surviving lungfish in that their lobe-like fins grew more sturdy and more muscular. They probably did not have any advantage as far as food-seeking or protection was concerned, but when the droughts came, they were able to move, awkwardly and slowly, no doubt, from one waterhole to another, adapting their diet, perhaps to the dormant lungfishes or possibly to primitive land plants. Their jaws did not become so specialized as those of the lungfish, whose diet of mollusks led them to develop shell-cracking modifications of their jaws. By the end of the Devonian, the lobe-finned fishes had been so modified that, somewhat like the modern salamander, they lived much of their lives on land: the Amphibia had evolved (Fig. V-15).

The ancestry of the primitive amphibians is unquestionable: the head bones, the armor over their heads and foreparts, their teeth and even their vestigial tails are closely similar to those of their ancestors, the lobe-finned fish.

Reptilia.—Although the amphibians were the first land vertebrates and thrived in the late Paleozoic, their modern amphibian descendants are few: the salamanders, frogs, toads, and a few others. They were succeeded by their much modified descendants, the reptiles, dominant in the Mesozoic—the Age of Reptiles.

Of course, no one really knows all the factors in what was doubtless a very complex story, but one obvious weakness in the life scheme of the amphibians is the necessity for them to deposit their eggs in water. Here both egg and young are vulnerable to attack by any number of animals. The reptiles developed the greatly advantageous attribute of laying eggs with shells, which could be hatched in the sand. Because the shelled eggs contain yolks adequate for nourishment of the embryo—as amphibian eggs do not—the young, when hatched, are further developed and hence less vulnerable to attack in infancy than amphibian young. Whatever the reason, the stratigraphic record is unmistakable: by the end of the Permian the Amphibia were all but eliminated and the rep-

tiles, in fantastic variety and modes of life, dominated the land. Soon after, they dominated the sea also, to which some groups returned.

The earliest of the "stem" reptiles, from which all others evolved, developed in the Pennsylvanian, when the amphibians were at their height. Like their direct ancestors, the amphibians, and their more remote ancestors, the bony fishes, they had solid skulls without lateral openings. But early in their history some descendants developed openings in the sides of the skull, facilitating the contraction of the jaw muscles. By the patterns and numbers of these lateral skull openings paleontologists have classified the reptiles and are able to trace the various lineages. We will not go into the details of the classification; all of the main branches of the reptiles were well established by the end of the Permian. Of these, one subclass developed toward mammalian characters and is ancestral to mammals; another toward the plesiosaurs and ichthyosaurs, which returned to the sea, and of which no living representative is known today; still another evolved along the line of the crocodiles. It was ancestral to dinosaurs, the "ruling reptiles" of the Mesozoic, which also died out at the end of that era, but are represented today by their cousins the birds and the mammals.

Every reader of this book will know how many kinds of dinosaurs looked, from museums, and cartoons and science fiction. We shall trace only the reptilian family tree that leads to the birds and mammals.

Birds.—Although, among the many diverging lines of "ruling reptiles" several took on the outward shape of running birds such as ostriches, and still other reptiles actually became fliers, none of these variants is ancestral to the birds we know. The birds sprang from the basic stock of the "ruling reptiles" and not from any variant bird-like forms otherwise recognized. Indeed, both the running and the flying bird-like reptiles were flourishing long after the earliest feathered birds (known from the Upper Jurassic) were well established.

Mammalian evolution

Early in the history of the "stem" reptiles, in the late Carboniferous, an aberrant branch arose with skull modifications and tooth arrangement that turned from the normal reptilian scheme toward that of the mammals. These carnivorous offshoots of the reptile line looked a lot like lizards, but were structurally quite distinct. Their Permian and Triassic descendants took more and more the ultimate form of mammals both in skull structure and in the arrangement of the limbs, which changed from the sprawling appendages of a lizard to upright supports growing under the body. Beasts of this kind dominated the late Permian and earliest Triassic, but then arose the "ruling reptiles"; by the end of the Triassic the mammal-like reptiles were extinct.

But they had left behind the first mammalian stem—animals that still laid eggs like their reptilian ancestors (and the living Australian platypus), but were in all other respects truly mammals. The placental mammals (whose young are attached to the mother's womb by a placenta) had probably arisen by the Late Jurassic, though the evidence is extremely slender: it must be based on similarities in such things as teeth and jawbones rather than on flesh and soft parts, which are not preserved. The creatures were tiny, many no bigger than mice, and carnivorous, probably subsisting mainly on insects and worms. Many, perhaps all, were tree-dwellers. They were far outnumbered by the marsupials, whose newborn young are carried in the mother's pouch.

It was not until the end of the Cretaceous, when the great reptiles died out, that the time came for the great mammalian expansion that made the Cenozoic the Age of Mammals. This expansion, with amazing speed, filled virtually every conceivable ecologic niche. Both marsupials and placental mammals took part in it, though eventually the placentals, with their great advantage in protection of the young, took the dominant place. By Eocene time porpoises and gigantic whales had occupied the seas, and flying mammals, the bats, were fully at home in the air. Our own line, the primates, retained its arboreal habitat well into the Tertiary, though by Miocene time a likely ancestor of man, *Proconsul*, whose remains have been found near Lake Victoria, had lost some of the stronger indicators of tree life.

PLANT FOSSILS

Of the many classifications of the plant kingdom, we regard the simplest as adequate to our purpose and present it in Table V-2.

Thallophyta

BACTERIA.   We have noted that the Fig Tree Series of Swaziland has yielded bacterial fossils more than 3 billion years old. Some much younger ones from the Lake Superior region are illustrated in Figure 7–1. While of great interest as throwing light on the antiquity of life on the earth, these organisms are too rarely preserved to be useful in correlations.

DIATOMACEAE.   Though these minute unicellular organisms enclosed in siliceous tests seem so simple that one would think they had evolved very early, their oldest fossils yet found are of Jurassic age. This flora is so diversified, however, as to suggest a much longer history. Possibly their ancestors did not secrete silica tests, or perhaps their tests have been dissolved from the older rocks, for although their tests are of silica, the silica is hydrated and is much more soluble than most forms of silica.

Table V–2 **Life spans of some members of the plant kingdom**

Division	Subdivision	Class	Life Span
Thallophyta (nonvascular plants)	Bacteria *		Precambrian to Recent
	Diatomacea *		Jurassic to Recent
	Algae (photosynthetic)		Precambrian to Recent
	Fungi (degenerate, non-photosynthetic)		Precambrian to Recent
Bryophyta (liverworts and mosses)			Silurian to Recent
Pteridophyta (spore-bearing vascular plants)			Silurian to Recent
	Psilophytales (Psylopsida)		Devonian
	Lycopodiales (Lycopsida)		Silurian to Recent
	Articulatales (Sphenopsida)		Devonian to Recent
	Filicales (Pteropsida)		Late Devonian to Recent
Spermophyta (seed-bearing plants)			Carboniferous to Recent
	Gymnospermae ("naked seeds")		Carboniferous to Recent
		Pteridospermae (seed-ferns)	Carboniferous to Jurassic
		Cycadales (cycads)	Triassic to Recent
		Bennettitales (cycad-like but with flowerlike shoots)	Triassic to Cretaceous
		Ginkgoales (ginkgoes and related forms)	Triassic to Recent
		Coniferales (pines, cypresses, and related forms)	Carboniferous to Recent
	Angiospermae (flowering plants, protected seeds)		Triassic to Recent
		Monocotyledonae (grasses, lilies, palms)	Triassic to Recent
		Dicotyledonae (beans, peas, most flowers)	Cretaceous to Recent

* In many classifications, these organisms are excluded from both animal and plant kingdoms, and along with a few other microorganisms set apart as Protista.

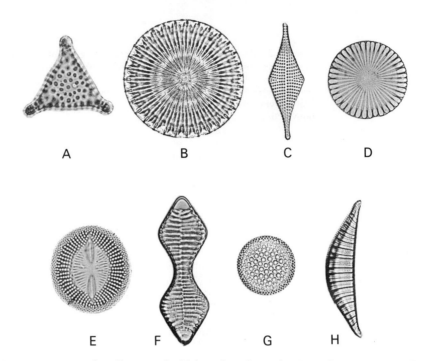

FIGURE V–16   *Some representative diatoms.* A: Trinacria aries *Witt, Late Cretaceous, California, marine.* B: Lepidodiscus elegans *Witt, Eocene, Russia, marine.* C: Raphoneis angularis *Lohman, Pliocene only, California, marine.* D: Melosira clavigera *Grunow, mid-Miocene to Lower Pliocene, California, marine.* E: Raphidodiscus marylandicus *Christian, middle Miocene only, very widespread, marine.* F: Rhabdonema valdelatum *Tempere and Brun, Miocene to Pleistocene, marine.* G: Coscinodiscus elegans *Greville, Eocene in Barbados, to Miocene in Cailifornia, marine.* H: Rhopalodia gibberula (*Ehrenberg*) *Miller, Pliocene to Recent, very widespread, commonly in hot springs.* (*Photos by K. E. Lohman, U.S. Geological Survey.*)

The Jurassic species were marine; the earliest terrestrial diatoms are of Miocene age. Within the last forty years, largely through the work of K. E. Lohman, of the U.S. Geological Survey, they have become extremely useful horizon markers in the Cretaceous and Tertiary of the Pacific States. Some representative specimens are illustrated in Figure V-16.

ALGAE.   As mentioned in Chapter 22, cabbage-shaped heads and columns formed by algae have been found in strata of all ages from far back in the Precambrian to the present. Although they have been successfully used in correlations on a gross scale,

FIGURE V–17
An algal reef from the Green River Shale, Eocene, Wyoming. A: *Top view.* B: *Sectional view.* (*After W. H. Bradley, U.S. Geological Survey.*)

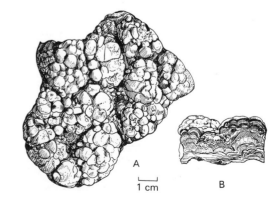

1 cm

FIGURE V–18 *Some microscopic planktonic organisms.* A: Braarudosphaera bigelowi, *a Paleocene coccolith.* B: Discoaster septemradiatus, *Middle Eocene.* C: Discoaster helianthus, *Paleocene. All are from California. (After A. O. Woodford, 1965. Specimens from M. N. Bramlette, University of California, San Diego.)*

they are not sufficiently differentiated to be particularly valuable. A representative Eocene freshwater algal colony is shown in Figure V-17.

Much more useful than the colonial algae are the minute discoasters and coccoliths, which are fragments of floating algae. Their small size—most are at the very limit of optical microscopes and must be studied by phase contrast or electron microscopes—permits a virtually worldwide distribution by marine currents; identical forms have been found in Eocene rocks from Iran, New Zealand, Britain, California, Japan, and Italy. Despite the difficulty of their study, they are rapidly becoming extremely useful guide fossils—the coccoliths for rocks of Jurassic and younger age, the discoasters for the Cenozoic. Representative specimens are illustrated in Figure V-18.

Bryophyta

The bryophytes include the existing liverworts and mosses, and though they have been found sporadically in rocks of Silurian and all later ages, they are of little use stratigraphically; their preservation is usually very poor.

Pteridophyta

PSILOPHYTALES. The oldest land plants were very simple ones perhaps ancestral to (or perhaps paralleling the ancestry of) the living

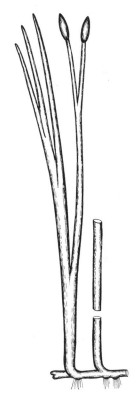

FIGURE V–19
One of the earliest land plants, Rhynia, *from the Old Red of Scotland. (After Kidston and Lang,* Transactions, *Royal Society of Edinburgh, v. 52, 1921–1922.)*

Psilotum. They are found in the Silurian of Australia and in the Middle Devonian of Germany, Scotland, and eastern Canada. These were extremely simple rush-like plants that rose vertically from a horizontal rhizome

(Fig. V-19). There were many representatives in the Upper Devonian, some with trunks 4 feet in diameter. Though it was once thought that all higher plants were derived from these simple plants, this is now seriously questioned. Other classes were probably developing at the same time.

LYCOPODIA. The living lycopsids (club mosses), though widely distributed over the earth, are few compared with their abundant varieties in the Devonian and Carboniferous, when they dominated the flora of the coal swamps. Two genera, especially, *Lepidodendron* and *Sigillaria*, grew to immense

FIGURE V–20   *Some lycopsids of the Carboniferous coal swamps.* A: Lepidodendron. (*After a drawing by Edward Valliamy, in* Plant Life Through the Ages, *by A. C. Seward, Cambridge University Press, 1932.*) B: Sigillaria. C: *the bark of* Lepidodendron, *showing leaf scars on the trunk.* (B *and* C *after C. O. Dunbar,* Historical Geology, *John Wiley and Sons, 1960.*)

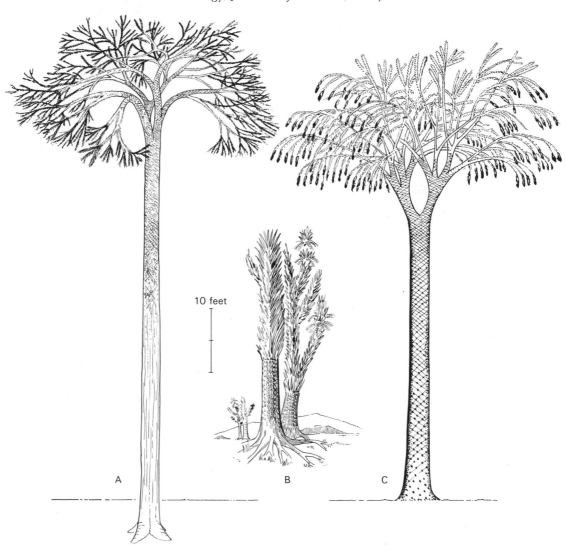

10 feet

A   B   C

heights of as much as 40 or 50 meters (Fig. V-20). The line became much reduced in Triassic and later time.

Articulatales.—The only living descendant of the once abundant trees of Carboniferous time belonging to this group is the common *Equisetum* or scouring rush, so-called because of the silica spicules on its jointed stems. The group was represented in the Carboniferous by great trees more than a foot in diameter, the most common being *Calamites* (Fig. V-21). Few forms survived the Triassic period.

FIGURE V–22
An Eocene fern from Yellowstone Park, Wyoming. (After Erling Dorf, Princeton University.)

FILICALES.   The Filicales include the ferns, the only division of the pteridophytes that is still prominent. They dominated the Late Devonian floras and produced tree-sized genera during the Carboniferous. An Eocene fern from one of the many fossil forests of Yellowstone Park is shown in Figure V-22.

Spermatophyta

GYMNOSPERMAE.   Of the seed-bearing plants, the gymnosperms, whose seeds are more or less exposed, have the longer lineage, but they are surely losing out to their cousins, the angiosperms, whose seeds are better protected.

Pteridospermae.—The seed ferns originated in the Late Devonian and became important components of the Carboniferous flora, especially in the Gondwanaland areas, characterized by *Glossopteris* and *Gangamopteris* as the dominant genera (Fig. V-23). This class died out by Jurassic time.

FIGURE V–21
One of the great contributors to the Carboniferous coal swamps, Calamites. *(Modified from Arthur Cronquist,* Introductory Botany, *Harper and Row, 1961.)*

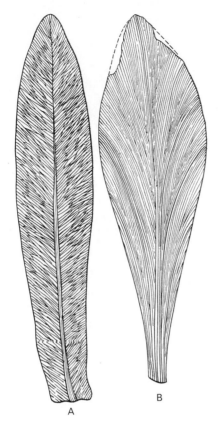

FIGURE V-23
Leaves of the seed ferns. A: Glossopteris. B: Gangamopteris. *Both are from the late Paleozoic Gondwanaland flora. (After E. A. N. Arber, 1905.)*

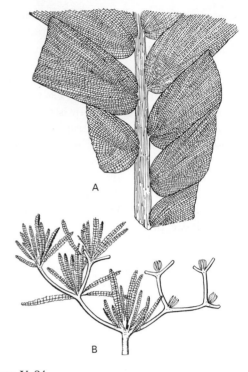

FIGURE V-24
A: *Fragment of a cycad leaf* (Sphenozamites rogersiana) *from the Triassic of Virginia. (After M. Fontaine, U.S. Geological Survey.)* B: *Restoration of* Wielandiella, *a Triassic cycad of Sweden. (After A. G. Nathorst, 1910.)*

Cycadales.—The cycads, now chiefly southern hemisphere inhabitants, became very widespread in the Triassic and are found as fossils from Siberia to Virginia. They dominated many Jurassic floras but are now much reduced. Figure V-24 represents some Triassic forms. Most living forms have stumpy pine-like trunks to which the leaves cling for many years; they have few branches and a crown of large leaves that reminds the layman of palms. The Bennettitales were very similar trees, but carried their seeds in exposed shoots resembling flowers.

Ginkgoales.—The ginkgoes arose in the Triassic and became very widespread, with many

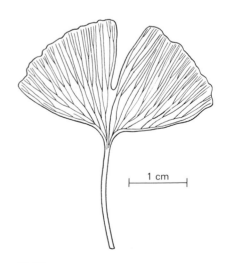

FIGURE V-25
A leaf of Ginkgo biloba, *the only surviving representative of the Ginkgoales. (After Erling Dorf, Princeton University.)*

genera, during the Cretaceous. Just one species survives and that, perhaps only because it is cultivated for its grace and foliage. A leaf of the modern genus, *Ginkgo biloba,* is shown in Figure V-25.

Coniferales.—The conifers rose in the Carboniferous and are there represented by one of the important trees of the coal forests, *Cordaites.* (Some paleobotanists classify Cordaites as a separate class, but all agree it was some kind of a proto-conifer). It is illustrated in Figure V-26. The great Eocene fossil forests of the Yellowstone Park have preserved trunks by the thousand and leaves by the million of conifers ancestral to the modern redwoods. Some trunks and a leaf fragment are illustrated in Figure V-27.

ANGIOSPERMAE. The angiosperms are so familiar that they require no illustration. Nonetheless, it seems worthwhile to illustrate a tremendous wealth of fossil trees, 27 successive layers of forests, some with trees estimated to be more than 1000 years old, each in turn buried beneath ash from a nearby volcano. Both the succession of forests and some representative fossil leaves are shown in Figures V-28 and V-29.

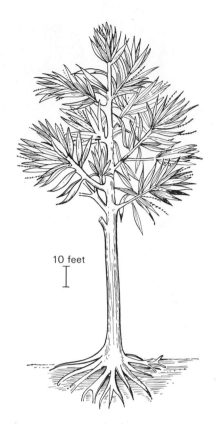

10 feet

FIGURE V–26
A Cordaites *from the Pennsylvanian. (After C. O. Dunbar,* Historical Geology, *John Wiley and Sons, 1960.)*

FIGURE V–27   *Petrified trunks and a leaf fragment from one of the petrified Eocene forests of Yellowstone Park. Many of the trees were ancestral to the living redwoods. (From Erling Dorf, Princeton University.)*

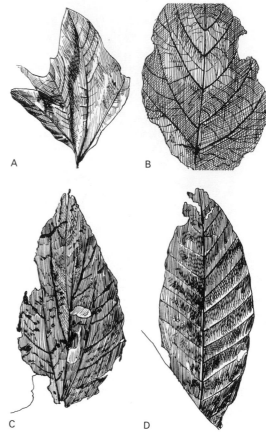

FIGURE V–28

A succession of fossil forests (Eocene) were buried beneath falls of volcanic ash. Lamar River canyon in northeastern Yellowstone Park. (After Erling Dorf, Princeton University.)

FIGURE V–29

Some leaves from the fossil forests of Yellowstone Park. A: Leaf of an extinct sycamore. B: Leaf of an extinct grape. C: Leaf of a tree related to the rare Chinese katsura tree. D: A meliosoma leaf, whose nearest living relatives are restricted to tropical and subtropical forests. (After Erling Dorf, Princeton University.)

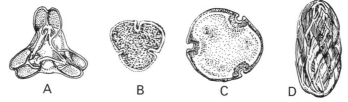

FIGURE V–30   *Some representative pollen grains, greatly enlarged. A: Oculopolis, Cretaceous of Tennessee, a plant with no close relatives living. B and C: Tilia pollenites, Tertiary of Kentucky, a relative of the living linden tree. D: Ephedra pollenites, Cretaceous of Kentucky, a relative of the living "Mormon tea." (After Robert Tschudy, U.S. Geological Survey.)*

One of the relatively recent developments of paleobotany is the growing emphasis on the use of pollen in correlation. The pollen of many plants is highly characteristic, and as the spore is both small and highly resistant chemically, it is commonly preserved when larger fossils such as leaves and invertebrates are destroyed. Pollen spores are therefore of increasing use and value in stratigraphy. A few representative specimens are illustrated in Figure V-30.

Index

*(Page references to important concepts and technical terms are given in **boldface** type.)*